Purchased
    Feb. 1967

Bill Ryder
530 Beacon St.
Boston, Mass.

Fundamentals of Optics

FUNDAMENTALS OF OPTICS

Francis A. Jenkins
Harvey E. White

PROFESSORS OF PHYSICS
UNIVERSITY OF CALIFORNIA

Third Edition

New York   Toronto   London

McGRAW-HILL BOOK COMPANY, INC.

1957

PREFACE

The chief objectives in preparing this new edition have been simplification and modernization. Experience on the part of the authors and of the many other users of the book over the last two decades has shown that many passages and mathematical derivations were overly cumbersome, thereby losing the emphasis they should have had. As an example of the steps taken to rectify this defect, the chapter on reflection has been entirely rewritten in simpler form and placed ahead of the more difficult aspects of polarized light. Furthermore, by expressing frequency and wavelength in circular measure, and by introducing the complex notation in a few places, it has been possible to abbreviate the derivations in wave theory to make room for new material.

In any branch of physics fashions change as they are influenced by the development of the field as a whole. Thus, in optics the notions of wave packet, line width, and coherence length are given more prominence because of their importance in quantum mechanics. For the same reason, our students now usually learn to deal with complex quantities at an earlier stage, and we have felt justified in giving some examples of how helpful these can be. Because of the increasing use of concentric optics, as well as graphical methods of ray tracing, these subjects have been introduced in the chapters on geometrical optics. The elegant relationships between geometrical optics and particle mechanics, as in the electron microscope and quadrupole lenses, could not be developed because of lack of space; the instructor may wish to supplement the text in this direction. The same may be true of the rather too brief treatments of some subjects where old principles have recently come into prominence, as in Čerenkov radiation, the echelle grating, and multilayer films.

A difficulty that must present itself to the authors of all textbooks at this level is that of avoiding the impression that the subject is a definitive, closed body of knowledge. If the student can be persuaded to read the original literature to any extent, this impression soon fades. To encourage such reading, we have inserted many references, to original papers as well as to books, throughout the text. An entirely new set of problems, representing a rather greater spread of difficulty than heretofore, is included.

It is not possible to mention all those who have assisted us by suggestions for improvement. Specific errors or omissions have been pointed out by L. W. Alvarez, W. A. Bowers, J. E. Mack, W. C. Price, R. S. Shankland, and J. M. Stone, while H. S. Coleman, J. W. Ellis, F. S. Harris, Jr., R. Kingslake, C. F. J. Overhage, and R. E. Worley have each contributed several valuable ideas. We wish to express our gratitude to all of these, as well as to T. L. Jenkins, who suggested the simplification of certain derivations and checked the answers to many of the problems.

FRANCIS A. JENKINS
HARVEY E. WHITE

CONTENTS

PART I

GEOMETRICAL OPTICS

CHAPTER 1

LIGHT RAYS

Optics, the study of light, is conveniently divided into three fields, each of which requires a markedly different method of theoretical treatment. These are (*a*) *geometrical optics*, which is treated by the method of light rays, (*b*) *physical optics*, which is concerned with the nature of light and involves primarily the theory of waves, and (*c*) *quantum optics*, which deals with the interaction of light with the atomic entities of matter and which for an exact treatment requires the methods of quantum mechanics. This book deals almost entirely with (*a*) and (*b*), although some of the salient features of (*c*) will be outlined in the last chapter. These fields might preferably be called macroscopic, microscopic, and atomic optics as giving a more specific indication of their domains of applicability. When it is a question of the behavior of light on a large scale, the representation by means of rays is almost always sufficient.

1.1. Concept of a Ray of Light. The distinction between geometrical and physical optics appears at once when we attempt by means of diaphragms to isolate a single ray of light. In Fig. 1*A* let *S* represent

(*a*)   (*b*)   (*c*)

Fig. 1*A*. Attempt to isolate a single ray of light.

a source of light of the smallest possible size, a so-called *point source*. Such a source is commonly realized by focusing the light from the white-hot positive pole of a carbon arc on a metal screen pierced with a small hole.* If another opaque screen *H* provided with a much larger hole is now interposed between *S* and a white observing screen *M* [Fig. 1*A*(*a*)], only the portion of the latter lying between the straight lines drawn from

---

* The concentrated-arc lamp to be described in Sec. 21.2 also furnishes a very convenient way of approximating a point source.

3

S will be appreciably illuminated. This observation forms the basis for saying that light is propagated in straight lines called *rays*, since it can be explained by assuming that only the rays not intercepted by H reach the observing screen. If the hole in H is made smaller, as in (*b*) of the figure, the illuminated region shrinks correspondingly, so that one might hope to isolate a single ray by making it vanishingly small. Experiment shows, however, that at a certain width of H (a few tenths of a millimeter) the bright spot begins to widen again. The result of making the hole exceedingly small is to cause the illumination, although it is very feeble, to spread over a considerable region of the screen [Fig. 1A (*c*)].

The failure of this attempt to isolate a ray is due to the process called *diffraction*, which also accounts for a slight lack of sharpness of the edge of the shadow when the hole is wider. Diffraction is a consequence of the wave character of light and will be fully discussed in the section on physical optics. It becomes important only when small-scale phenomena are being considered, as in the use of a fine hole or in the examination of the edge of the shadow with a magnifier. In most optical instruments, however, we deal with fairly wide beams of light and the effects of diffraction can usually be neglected. The concept of light rays is then a very useful one because *the rays show the direction of flow of energy* in the light beam.

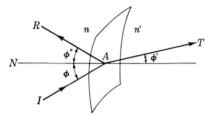

FIG. 1B. Reflection and refraction of a ray at a boundary.

1.2. Laws of Reflection and Refraction. These two laws were discovered experimentally long before their significance was understood, and together they form the basis of the whole of geometrical optics. They may be derived from certain general principles to be discussed later, but for the present we shall merely state them as experimental facts. When a ray of light strikes any boundary between two transparent substances in which the velocity of light is appreciably different, it is in general divided into a reflected ray and a refracted ray. In Fig. 1B let IA represent the incident ray, and let it make the angle ϕ with NA, the normal or perpendicular to the surface at A. ϕ is called the *angle of incidence* and the plane defined by IA and NA is called the *plane of incidence.*

The *law of reflection* may now be stated as follows:

The reflected ray lies in the plane of incidence, and the angle of reflection equals the angle of incidence.

That is, IA, NA, and AR are all in the same plane and

$$\phi'' = \phi \tag{1a}$$

The *law of refraction*, usually called Snell's law after its discoverer,[*] states that

The refracted ray lies in the plane of incidence, and the sine of the angle of refraction bears a constant ratio to the sine of the angle of incidence.

The second part of this law therefore requires that

$$\frac{\sin \phi}{\sin \phi'} = \text{const.} \tag{1b}$$

If on the left side of the boundary in Fig. 1B there exists a vacuum (or for practical purposes air), the value of the constant in Eq. 1b is called the *index of refraction n* of the medium on the right. By experimental measurements of the angles ϕ and ϕ' one can determine the values of n for various transparent substances. Then, in the refraction at a boundary between two such substances having indices of refraction n and n', Snell's law may be written in the symmetrical form

$$n \sin \phi = n' \sin \phi' \tag{1c}$$

Wherever it is feasible we shall use *unprimed* symbols to refer to the first medium and *primed* ones for the second. The ratio n'/n is often called the *relative index* of the second medium with respect to the first. The constant ratio of the sines in Eq. 1b equals this relative index. When the angle of incidence is fairly small, Eq. 1c shows that the angle of refraction will also be small. Under these circumstances a very good approximation is obtained by setting the sines equal to the angles themselves, so we obtain

$$\frac{\phi}{\phi'} = \frac{n'}{n} \qquad \text{FOR SMALL ANGLES} \tag{1d}$$

1.3. Graphical Construction for Refraction. A relatively simple method for tracing a ray of light across a boundary separating two optically transparent media is shown in Fig. 1C. Because the principles involved in this construction are easily extended to complicated optical systems, the method is useful in the preliminary design of many optical instruments.

After the line GH is drawn, representing the boundary separating the two media of index n and n', and the angle of incidence ϕ of the incident ray JA is selected, the construction proceeds as follows: At one side of

[*] Willebrord Snell (1591-1626) of the University of Leyden, Holland. He announced what is essentially this law in an unpublished paper in 1621. His geometrical construction required that the ratios of the cosecants of ϕ' and ϕ be constant. Descartes was the first to use the ratio of the sines, and the law is generally known as Descartes' law in France.

the drawing, and as reasonably close as possible, a line OR is drawn parallel to JA.   With a point of origin O, two circular arcs are drawn with their radii proportional to the two indices n and n', respectively.

Through the intersection point R a line is drawn parallel to NN', intersecting the arc n' at P.   The line OP is next drawn in, and parallel

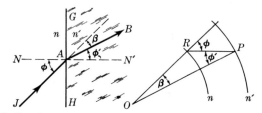

Fɪɢ. 1C. Graphical construction for refraction at a plane surface.

to it, through A, the refracted ray AB.   The angle β between the incident and refracted ray is called the *angle of deviation* and is given by

$$\beta = \phi - \phi' \tag{1e}$$

To prove that this construction follows the law of refraction, we apply the *law of sines* to the triangle ORP.

$$\frac{OR}{\sin \phi'} = \frac{OP}{\sin (\pi - \phi)}$$

Since $\sin (\pi - \phi) = \sin \phi$, $OR = n$, and $OP = n'$, substitution gives directly

$$\frac{n}{\sin \phi'} = \frac{n'}{\sin \phi} \tag{1f}$$

which is Snell's law (Eq. 1c).

1.4. Principle of Reversibility.   The symmetry of Eqs. 1a and 1c with respect to the primed and unprimed symbols shows at once that *if a reflected or refracted ray be reversed in direction, it will retrace its original path*.   For a given pair of media with indices n and n' any one value of ϕ is correlated with a corresponding value of ϕ'.   This will be equally true when the ray is reversed and ϕ' becomes the angle of incidence in the medium of index n'; the angle of refraction will then be ϕ.   Since the reversibility holds at each reflecting or refracting surface, it holds also for even the most complicated light paths.   This useful principle has more than a purely geometrical foundation, and it will be shown later that it follows from the application to wave motion of a corresponding principle in mechanics.

1.5. Optical Path.   In order to state a more general principle which will include both the law of reflection and that of refraction, it is convenient to have the definition of a quantity called the *optical path*. When light travels a distance d in a medium of refractive index n the optical path is the product nd. The physical interpretation of n, to be given later, shows that the optical path represents the distance in vacuum that the light would traverse in the same time that it goes the distance d in the medium. When there are several segments $d_1, d_2, \ldots$ of the light path in substances having different indices $n_1, n_2, \ldots$, the optical path is found as follows:

$$\text{Optical path} = [d] = n_1d_1 + n_2d_2 + \cdots = \sum_i n_id_i \qquad (1g)$$

For example, let L in Fig. $1D$ represent a lens of refractive index n' immersed in some liquid of index n. The optical path between two points Q and Q' on a ray becomes, in this case,

$$[d] = nd_1 + n'd_2 + nd_3$$

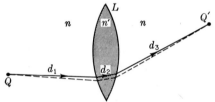

Here Q and Q' need not necessarily represent points on the object and image; they are merely *any* two chosen points on an actual ray.

FIG. $1D$. Illustrating the concept of optical path and Fermat's principle.

One may also define an optical path in a medium of continuously varying refractive index by replacing the summation by an integral. The paths of the rays are then curved, and the law of refraction loses its meaning. We shall now consider a principle which is applicable for any type of variation of n and hence contains within it the laws of reflection and refraction as well.

1.6. Fermat's* Principle. A correct and complete statement of this principle is seldom found in textbooks, because the tendency is to cite it in Fermat's original form, which was incomplete. Using the concept of optical path, the principle should read

The path taken by a light ray in going from one point to another through any set of media is such as to render its optical path equal, in the first approximation, to other paths closely adjacent to the actual one.

The "other paths" must be possible ones in the sense that they may only undergo deviations where there are reflecting or refracting surfaces. Now Fermat's principle will hold for a ray whose optical path is a *minimum*

---

* Pierre Fermat (1608–1665). French mathematician, ranked by some as the discoverer of differential calculus. The justification of his principle given by Fermat was that "nature is economical," but he was unaware of circumstances where exactly the reverse is true.

with respect to adjacent hypothetical paths. Fermat himself stated that the time required by the light to traverse the path is a minimum, and the optical path is a measure of this time. But there are plenty of cases in which the optical path is a *maximum,* or else neither a maximum nor a minimum but merely *stationary* (at a point of inflection) at the position of the true ray.

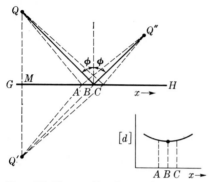

Consider the case of a ray of light that must first pass through a point Q, then, after reflection from a plane surface, pass through a second point Q'' (see Fig. 1E). To find the real path, we first drop a perpendicular to GH and extend it an equal distance on the other side to Q'. The straight line $Q'Q''$ is drawn in and from its intersection B the line QB. The real light path is therefore QBQ'' and, as can be seen from the sym-

FIG. 1E. Illustrating Fermat's principle as it applies to reflection at a plane surface.

metry relations in the diagram, obeys the *law of reflection.*

Consider now adjacent paths to points like A and C on the mirror surface close to B. Since a straight line is the shortest path between two points, both of the paths $Q'AQ''$ and $Q'CQ''$ are greater than $Q'BQ''$.

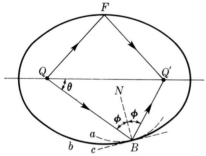

FIG. 1F. Illustrating Fermat's principle as it applies to an elliptical reflector.

FIG. 1G. Graphs of optical paths involving reflection, and illustrating conditions for (a) maximum; (b) stationary; and (c) minimum light paths. Fermat's principle.

By the above construction, and equivalent triangles, $QA = Q'A$, and $QC = Q'C$, so that $QAQ'' > QBQ''$ and $QCQ'' > QBQ''$. Therefore the real path QBQ'' is a minimum.

A graph of hypothetical paths close to the real path QBQ'', as shown in the lower right of the diagram, indicates the meaning of a minimum, and the flatness of the curve between A and C illustrates that *to a first approximation adjacent paths are equal to the real optical path.*

Consider finally the optical properties of an ellipsoidal reflector as shown in Fig. 1F. All rays emanating from a point source Q at one focus are reflected according to the law of reflection and come together at the other focus Q'. Furthermore all paths are equal in length. (It will be recalled that an ellipse can be drawn with a string of fixed length with its ends fastened at the foci.) Because all optical paths are equal, this is a stationary case as mentioned above. On the graph in Fig. 1$G(b)$ equal path lengths are represented by a straight horizontal line.

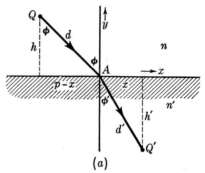

Some attention will here be devoted to other reflecting surfaces like (a) and (c) in Fig. 1F. If these surfaces are tangent to the ellipsoid at the point B, the line NB is normal to all three surfaces and QBQ' is a real path for all three. Adjacent paths from Q to points along these mirrors, however, will give a *minimum* condition for the real path to and from reflector c, and a *maximum* condition for the real path to and from reflector a (see Fig. 1G).

(a)

FIG. 1H. Geometry of a refracted ray used in illustrating Fermat's principle.

It is readily shown mathematically that both the laws of reflection and refraction follow Fermat's principle. Figure 1H, which represents the refraction of a ray at a plane surface, may be used to prove the law of refraction (Eq. 1c). The length of the optical path between a point Q in the upper medium of index n, and another point Q' in the lower medium of index n', passing through any point A on the surface, is

$$[d] = nd + n'd' \tag{1h}$$

where d and d' represent the distances QA and AQ', respectively.

Now if we let h and h' represent perpendicular distances to the surface and p the total length of the x axis intercepted by these perpendiculars, we can invoke the Pythagorean theorem concerning right triangles and write

$$d^2 = h^2 + (p - x)^2 \qquad d'^2 = h'^2 + x^2$$

When these values of d and d' are substituted in Eq. 1h, we obtain

$$[d] = n[h^2 + (p - x)^2]^{\frac{1}{2}} + n'(h'^2 + x^2)^{\frac{1}{2}} \tag{1i}$$

According to Fermat's principle $[d]$ must be a minimum or a maximum (or in general stationary) for the actual path. One method for finding a minimum or maximum for the optical path is to plot a graph of $[d]$ against x and find at what value of x a tangent to the curve is parallel to the x axis (see Fig. 1G). The mathematical means for doing the same thing is, first, to differentiate Eq. 1i with respect to the variable x, thus obtaining an equation for the slope of the graph, and, second, to set this resultant equation equal to zero, thus finding the value of x for which the slope of the curve is zero.

By differentiating Eq. 1i with respect to x and setting the result equal to zero, we obtain

$$\frac{d[d]}{dx} = \frac{\frac{1}{2}n}{[h^2 + (p - x)^2]^{\frac{1}{2}}} (-2p + 2x) + \frac{\frac{1}{2}n'}{(h'^2 + x^2)^{\frac{1}{2}}} (2x) = 0$$

This gives

$$n \frac{p - x}{[h^2 + (p - x)^2]^{\frac{1}{2}}} = n' \frac{x}{(h'^2 + x^2)^{\frac{1}{2}}}$$

or, more simply,

$$n \frac{p - x}{d} = n' \frac{x}{d'}$$

By reference to Fig. 1H it will be seen that the multipliers of n and n' are just the sines of the corresponding angles, so that we have now proved Eq. 1c, namely,

$$n \sin \phi = n' \sin \phi' \tag{1j}$$

A diagram for reflected light, similar to Fig. 1H, can be drawn and the same mathematics applied to prove the law of reflection.

1.7. Color Dispersion. It is well known to those who have studied elementary physics that refraction causes a separation of white light into its component colors. Thus, as is shown in Fig. 1I, the incident ray of white light gives rise to refracted rays of different colors (really a continuous *spectrum*) each of which has a different value of ϕ'. By Eq. 1c the value of n' must therefore vary with color. It is customary in the exact specification of indices of refraction to use the particular colors corresponding to certain dark lines in the spectrum of the sun. Tables of these so-called Fraunhofer* lines, which are designated by the letters A, B, C, . . . , starting at the extreme red end, are given later in Tables 21-II and 23-I. The ones most commonly used are those in Fig. 1I.

The angular divergence of rays F and C is a measure of the *dispersion* produced, and has been greatly exaggerated in the figure relative to the

---

* Joseph Fraunhofer (1787–1826). Son of a poor Bavarian glazier, Fraunhofer learned glass grinding, and entered the field of optics from the practical side. His rare experimental skill enabled him to produce much better spectra than those of his predecessors and led to his study of the solar lines with which his name is now associated. Fraunhofer was one of the first to produce diffraction gratings (Chap. 17).

average *deviation* of the spectrum, which is measured by the angle through which ray D is bent. To take a typical case of crown glass, the refractive indices as given in Table 23-I are

$$n_F = 1.53303 \qquad n_D = 1.52704 \qquad n_C = 1.52441$$

Now it is readily shown from Eq. 1d that for a given small angle ϕ the dispersion of the F and C rays ($\phi'_F - \phi'_C$) is proportional to

$$n_F - n_C = 0.00862$$

while the deviation of the D ray ($\phi - \phi'_D$) depends on $n_D - 1 = 0.52704$

FIG. 1I. Upon refraction white light is spread out into a spectrum. This is called dispersion.

FIG. 1J. A graph showing the variation of refractive index with color.

and is thus more than sixty times as great. The ratio of these two quantities varies greatly for different kinds of glass and is an important characteristic of any optical substance. It is called the *dispersive power* and is defined by the equation

$$\frac{1}{\nu} = \frac{n_F - n_C}{n_D - 1} \tag{1k}$$

The reciprocal of the dispersive power, designated by the Greek letter ν, lies between 30 and 60 for most optical glasses.

Figure 1J illustrates schematically the type of variation of n with color that is usually encountered for optical materials. The numerator of Eq. 1k, which is a measure of the dispersion, is determined by the difference in the index at two points near the ends of the spectrum. The denominator, which measures the average deviation, represents the magnitude in excess of unity of an intermediate index of refraction.

It is customary in most treatments of geometrical optics to neglect chromatic effects and assume, as we have in the next seven chapters, that the refractive index of each specific element of an optical instrument is that determined for yellow sodium D light.

PROBLEMS

1. A ray of light in air is incident on the polished surface of a piece of glass at an angle of 15°. What percentage error in the angle of refraction is made by assuming that the sines of angles in Snell's law can be replaced by the angles themselves? Assume $n' = 1.520$.

2. A ray of light in air is incident at an angle of 45° on glass of index 1.560. Find the angle of refraction (*a*) graphically, and (*b*) by calculation using Snell's law. (*c*) What is the angle of deviation?   *Ans.* (*a*) 27°.   (*b*) 26°57′.   (*c*) 18°3′.

3. A straight hollow pipe exactly 1 m long is closed at either end with quartz plates 10 mm thick. The pipe is evacuated, and the index of quartz is 1.460. (*a*) What is the optical path between the two outer quartz surfaces? (*b*) By how much is the optical path increased if the pipe is filled with a gas at 1 atm pressure if the index is 1.000250?

4. The points Q and Q' in Fig. 1H are at a distance $h = 10$ cm and $h' = 10$ cm, respectively, from the surface separating water of index $n = 1.333$ from glasss of index $n' = 1.500$. If the distance x is 4 cm, find the optical path [*d*] from Q to Q'.

Ans. 30.83 cm.

5. An approximate law of refraction was given by Kepler in the form $\phi = \phi'/(1 - k \sec \phi')$, where $k = (n' - 1)/n'$, n' being the relative index of refraction. Calculate the angle of incidence ϕ for glass of index $n' = 1.600$, if the angle of refraction $\phi' = 30°$, according to (*a*) Kepler's formula, and (*b*) Snell's law.

6. White light in air is incident at an angle of 80° on the polished surface of a piece of barium flint glass. If the refractive indices for red C light and blue F light are 1.5885 and 1.5982, respectively, what is the angular dispersion between these two colors?   *Ans.* 16.4′.

7. White light in air is incident at an angle of 89° on the smooth surface of a piece of crown glass. If the refractive indices for red C light and violet G′ light are 1.5088 and 1.5214, respectively, what is the angular dispersion between these two colors?

8. A solid glass sphere 4 cm in radius has an index 1.50. Draw a straight line from a point Q on the surface of this sphere through its center and to a point Q'' 6 cm beyond the sphere on the other side. Find by graphical construction, and measurement of paths, whether this path is a maximum or mininum.   *Ans.* Minimum.

9. Calculate the ν values for the two following pieces of glass: (*a*) crown glass, $n_C = 1.6205$, $n_D = 1.6231$, and $n_F = 1.6294$; (*b*) flint glass, $n_C = 1.7230$, $n_D = 1.7300$, and $n_F = 1.7478$.

10. Two plane mirrors are inclined to each other at an angle α. Applying the law of reflection, show that any ray whose plane of incidence is perpendicular to the line of intersection is deviated in the two reflections by an angle which is independent of the angle of incidence. Express this deviation in terms of α.   *Ans.* $\delta = 2(\pi - \alpha)$.

11. A ray of light is incident normally on a glass plate 2 cm thick and of refractive index 1.60. If the plate is turned through an angle of 45° about an axis perpendicular to the ray, what is the increase in optical path?

12. An ellipsoidal mirror has a major axis of 10 cm and a minor axis of 6 cm. The foci are 8 cm apart. If there is a point source of light at one focus Q, there are only two light rays that pass through the point Q'' at the center. Draw such a reflector, and graphically determine whether these two paths are maxima, minima, or stationary.

Ans. One maximum, one minimum.

13. A ray of light under water (index 1.333) arrives at the surface, making an angle of 40° with the normal. Using the graphical method, find the angle this ray makes with the normal after it is refracted into the air above ($n = 1.00$).

14. A solid glass sphere 6 cm in diameter has an index $n = 2.00$. Parallel rays of light 1 cm apart and all in a single plane are incident on this sphere with one of them traversing the center. Find by calculation the points where each of these rays crosses the central undeviated ray. *Ans.* 5.91 cm, 5.63 cm, and 4.73 cm from first vertex.

15. Show mathematically that the law of reflection follows from Fermat's principle.

CHAPTER 2

PLANE SURFACES

The behavior of a beam of light upon reflection or refraction at a plane surface is of basic importance in geometrical optics. Its study will reveal several of the features that will later have to be considered in the more difficult case of a curved surface. Plane surfaces often occur in nature, for example as the cleavage surfaces of crystals or as the surfaces of liquids. Artificial plane surfaces are used in optical instruments to bring about deviations or lateral displacements of rays as well as to break light into its colors. The most important devices of this type are prisms, but before taking up this case of two surfaces inclined to each other, we must examine rather thoroughly what happens at a single plane surface.

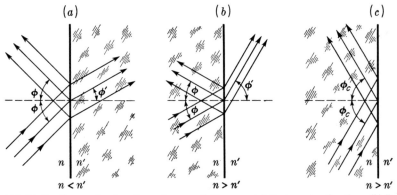

FIG. 2A. Reflection and refraction of a parallel beam: (a) External reflection; (b) Internal reflection at an angle smaller than the critical angle; (c) Total reflection at the critical angle.

2.1. Parallel Beam. In a beam or pencil of parallel light, each ray meets the surface traveling in the same direction. Therefore any one ray may be taken as representative of all the others. The parallel beam remains parallel after reflection or refraction at a plane surface, as is shown in Fig. 2A(a). Refraction causes a change in width of the beam which is easily seen to be in the ratio $\cos \phi'/\cos \phi$, whereas the reflected beam remains of the same width. This will prove to be important for intensity considerations (Sec. 25.2). There is also chromatic dispersion of the refracted beam but not of the reflected one.

Reflection at a surface where n increases, as in Fig. $2A(a)$, is called *external reflection*. It is also frequently termed *rare-to-dense* reflection because the relative magnitudes of n correspond roughly (though not exactly) to those of the actual densities of materials. In Fig. $2A(b)$ is shown a case of *internal reflection* or *dense-to-rare* reflection. In this particular case the refracted beam is narrow because ϕ' is close to 90°.

2.2. The Critical Angle and Total Reflection. We have already seen in Fig. $2A(a)$ that as light passes from one medium like air into another

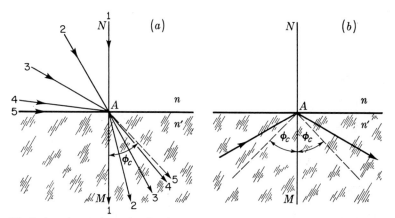

Fig. 2B. Refraction and total reflection. (a) The critical angle is the limiting angle of refraction. (b) Total reflection beyond the critical angle.

medium like glass or water the angle of refraction is always less than the angle of incidence. While a decrease in angle occurs for all angles of incidence, there exists a range of refracted angles for which no refracted light is possible. A diagram illustrating this principle is shown in Fig. $2B$, where for several angles of incidence, from 0 to 90°, the corresponding angles of refraction are shown from 0° to ϕ_c, respectively.

It will be seen that in the limiting case, where the incident rays approach an angle of 90° with the normal, the refracted rays approach a fixed angle ϕ_c beyond which no refracted light is possible. This particular angle ϕ_c, for which $\phi = 90°$, is called the *critical angle*. A formula for calculating the critical angle is obtained by substituting $\phi = 90°$, or $\sin \phi = 1$, in Snell's law (Eq. $1c$),

$$n \times 1 = n' \sin \phi_c$$

so that
$$\sin \phi_c = \frac{n}{n'} \tag{2a}$$

a quantity which is always less than unity. For a common crown glass of index 1.520 surrounded by air sin ϕ_c = 0.6579, and ϕ_c = 41°8′.

If we apply the principle of reversibility of light rays to Fig. 2B(a), all incident rays will lie within a cone subtending an angle of $2\phi_c$, while the corresponding refracted rays will lie within a cone of 180°. For angles of incidence greater than ϕ_c there can be no refracted light and every ray undergoes total reflection as shown in Fig. 2B(b).

The critical angle for the boundary separating two optical media is defined as the smallest angle of incidence, in the medium of greater index, for which light is totally reflected.

Total reflection is really total in the sense that no energy is lost upon reflection. In any device intended to utilize this property there will,

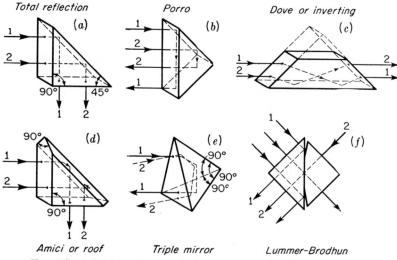

Fig. 2C. Reflecting prisms utilizing the principle of total reflection.

however, be small losses due to absorption in the medium and to reflections at the surfaces where the light enters and leaves the medium. The commonest device of this kind is the *total reflection prism*, which is a glass prism with two angles of 45° and one of 90°. As shown in Fig. 2C(a), the light usually enters perpendicular to one of the shorter faces, is totally reflected from the hypotenuse, and leaves at right angles to the other short face. This deviates the rays through a right angle. Such a prism may also be used in two other ways which are illustrated in (b) and (c) of the figure. The Dove prism (c) interchanges the two rays, and if the prism is rotated about the direction of the light, they rotate around each other with twice the angular velocity of the prism.

Many other forms of prisms which use total reflection have been devised for special purposes. Two common ones are illustrated in Fig. 2$C(d)$ and (e). The roof prism accomplishes the same purpose as the total reflection prism (a) except that it introduces an extra inversion. The triple mirror (e) is made by cutting off the corner of a cube by a plane which makes equal angles with the three faces intersecting at that corner. It has the useful property that any ray striking it will, after being internally reflected at each of the three faces, be sent back parallel to its original direction. The Lummer-Brodhun "cube" shown in (f) is used in photometry to compare the illumination of two surfaces, one of which is viewed by rays (2) coming directly through the circular region where the prisms are in contact, the other by rays (1) which are totally reflected in the area around this region.

FIG. 2D. Refraction in the prism of a Pulfrich refractometer.

Since, in the examples shown, the angles of incidence can be as small as 45°, it is essential that this shall exceed the critical angle in order that the reflection be total. Supposing the second medium to be air ($n' = 1$), this requirement sets a lower limit on the value of the index n of the prism. By Eq. 2a we must have

$$\frac{n'}{n} = \frac{1}{n} \geqq \sin 45°$$

so that $n \geqq \sqrt{2} = 1.414$. This condition always holds for glass and is even fulfilled for optical materials having low refractive indices such as lucite ($n = 1.49$) and fused quartz ($n = 1.46$).

The principle of most accurate *refractometers* (instruments for the determination of refractive index) is based on the measurement of the critical angle ϕ_c. In both the Pulfrich and Abbe types a convergent beam strikes the surface between the unknown sample, of index n, and a prism of known index n'. Now n' is greater than n, so the two must be interchanged in Eq. 2a. The beam is so oriented that some of its rays just graze the surface (Fig. 2D), so that one observes in the transmitted light a sharp boundary between light and dark. Measurement of the angle at which this boundary occurs allows one to compute the value of ϕ_c and hence of n. There are important precautions that must be observed if the results are to be at all accurate.*

* For a valuable description of this and other methods of determining indices of refraction see A. C. Hardy and F. H. Perrin, "Principles of Optics," 1st ed., pp. 359–364, McGraw-Hill Book Company, Inc., New York, 1932.

2.3. Reflection of Divergent Rays. When a divergent pencil of light is reflected at a plane surface, it remains divergent. All rays originating from a point Q (Fig. 2E) will after reflection appear to come from another point Q' symmetrically placed behind the mirror. The proof of this proposition follows at once from the application of the law of reflection (Eq. 1a), according to which all the angles labeled ϕ in the figure must be equal. Under these conditions the distances QA and AQ' along the line QAQ' drawn perpendicular to the surface must be equal: i.e.,

$$s' = s$$

The point Q' is said to be a *virtual image* of Q, since when the eye receives the reflected rays they appear to come from a source at Q' but do not

FIG. 2E. The reflection of a divergent pencil of light.

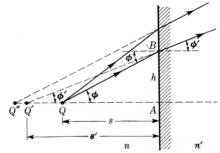

FIG. 2F. The refraction of a divergent pencil of light.

actually pass through Q' as would be the case if it were a *real image*. In order to produce a real image a surface other than a plane one is required.

2.4. Refraction of Divergent Rays. Referring to Fig. 2F, let us find the position of the point Q' where the lower refracted ray, when produced backward, crosses the perpendicular to the surface drawn through Q. Let $QA = s$, $Q'A = s'$, and $AB = h$. Then

$$h = s \tan \phi = s' \tan \phi' \tag{2b}$$

so that

$$s' = s \frac{\tan \phi}{\tan \phi'} = s \frac{\sin \phi \cos \phi'}{\sin \phi' \cos \phi}$$

Now according to the law of refraction (Eq. 1c) the ratio

$$\frac{\sin \phi}{\sin \phi'} = \frac{n'}{n} = \text{const.}$$

We therefore have

$$s' = s \frac{n'}{n} \frac{\cos \phi'}{\cos \phi} \tag{2c}$$

The ratio of the cosines is not constant. Instead, starting at the value unity for small ϕ, it increases slowly at first, then more rapidly. As a consequence the projected rays do not intersect at any single point such at Q'. Furthermore they do not all intersect at any other point in space.

2.5. Images Formed by Paraxial Rays. It is well known that when one looks at objects through the plane surface of a refracting medium, as for example in an aquarium, the objects are seen clearly. Actually one is seeing virtual images which are not in the true position of the objects. When one looks perpendicularly into water they appear closer to the surface in about the ratio $3:4$, which is the ratio n'/n, since $n' = 1$

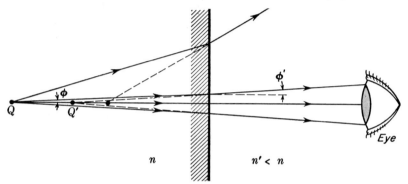

Fig. 2G. The image seen by refraction at a plane surface.

for air and $n = 1.33 \cong 4/3$ for water. This observation is readily understood when one considers that the rays entering the pupil of the eye will in this case make extremely small angles with the normal to the surface, as shown in Fig. 2G. Therefore both cosines in Eq. 2c are nearly equal to unity, and their ratio is even more nearly so. Hence, as long as the rays are restricted to ones that make very small angles with the normal to the refracting surface, a good virtual image is formed at the distance s' given by

$$s' = \frac{n'}{n} s \qquad \text{PARAXIAL RAYS} \qquad (2d)$$

Rays for which the angles are small enough so that we may set the cosines equal to unity, and the sines equal to the angles, are called paraxial rays.

2.6. Plane-parallel Plate. When a single ray traverses a glass plate with plane surfaces that are parallel to each other, it emerges parallel to its original direction but with a lateral displacement d which increases with the angle of incidence ϕ. Using the notation shown in Fig. 2H(a), we may apply the law of refraction and some simple trigonometry to show that the displacement is given by

$$d = t \sin \phi \left(1 - \frac{n}{n'} \frac{\cos \phi}{\cos \phi'} \right) \qquad (2e)$$

From 0° up to appreciably large angles, d is nearly proportional to ϕ, for as the ratio of the cosines becomes appreciably less than 1, causing the right-hand factor to increase, the sine factor drops below the angle itself in almost the same proportion.*

If we now consider a divergent beam to be incident on such a plate [Fig. 2H(b)] the different rays of the beam are not all incident at exactly the same angle ϕ, and therefore they undergo slightly different lateral

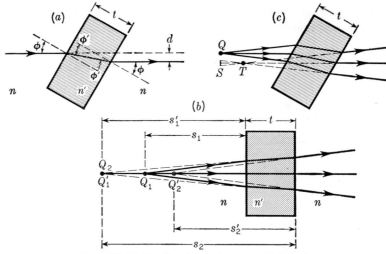

FIG. 2H. Refraction by a plane-parallel plate.

shifts.   For paraxial rays this yields a point image which is shifted toward the plate by a distance Q_1Q_2'.   By applying Eq. 2d successively for the two surfaces, and considering the image due to the first surface to be the object for the second, we find

$$Q_1Q_2' = t\left(1 - \frac{n}{n'}\right) \tag{2f}$$

When the plate is turned through an appreciable angle as in part (c) of Fig. 2H, the emergent beam becomes *astigmatic*, because the lateral displacements of the rays are such that their projections no longer pass even approximately through a point.   This leads, as in the case of a single surface, to the formation of two virtual focal lines T and S.   These two line images S and T are parallel and perpendicular, respectively, to the plane of incidence and are called *astigmatic images*.

2.7. Refraction by a Prism.   In a prism the two surfaces are inclined at some angle α so that the deviation produced by the first surface is not

* This principle is made use of in most of the moving-picture "film-editor" devices in common use today.

annulled by the second but is further increased. The chromatic dispersion (Sec. 1.7) is also increased, and this is usually the main function of a prism. First let us consider, however, the geometrical optics of the prism for light of a single color, i.e., for *monochromatic light* such as is obtained from a sodium arc.

The solid ray in Fig. 2I shows the path of a ray incident on the first surface at the angle ϕ_1.

Its refraction at the second surface, as well as at the first surface, obeys Snell's law, so that in terms of the angles shown

$$\frac{\sin \phi_1}{\sin \phi_1'} = \frac{n'}{n} = \frac{\sin \phi_2}{\sin \phi_2'} \qquad (2g)$$

FIG. 2I. The geometry associated with refraction by a prism.

The angle of deviation produced by the first surface is $\beta = \phi_1 - \phi_1'$, and that produced by the second surface is $\gamma = \phi_2 - \phi_2'$. The total angle of deviation δ between the incident and emergent rays is given by

$$\delta = \beta + \gamma \qquad (2h)$$

Since NN' and MN' are perpendicular to the two prism faces, α is also the angle at N'. From triangle ABN' and the exterior angle α, we obtain

$$\alpha = \phi_1' + \phi_2' \qquad (2i)$$

Combining the above equations, we obtain

$$\delta = \beta + \gamma = \phi_1 - \phi_1' + \phi_2 - \phi_2' = \phi_1 + \phi_2 - (\phi_1' + \phi_2')$$

or
$$\delta = \phi_1 + \phi_2 - \alpha \qquad (2j)$$

2.8. Minimum Deviation. When the total *angle of deviation* δ for any given prism is calculated by the use of the above equations, it is found to vary considerably with the angle of incidence. The angles thus calculated are in exact agreement with the experimental measurements. If, during the time a ray of light is refracted by a prism, the prism is rotated continuously in one direction about an axis (A in Fig. 2I) parallel to the refracting edge, the angle of deviation δ will be observed to decrease, reach a minimum, and then increase again as shown in Fig. 2J.

The smallest deviation angle is called the *angle of minimum deviation*, δ_m, and occurs at that particular angle of incidence where the refracted ray inside the prism makes equal angles with the two prism faces (see Fig. 2K). In this special case

$$\phi_1 = \phi_2 \qquad \phi_1' = \phi_2' \qquad \beta = \gamma \qquad (2k)$$

To prove these angles equal, assume ϕ_1 does not equal ϕ_2 when minimum deviation occurs. By the principle of the reversibility of light rays (see Sec. 1.4), there would be two different angles of incidence capable of giving minimum deviation. Since experimentally we find

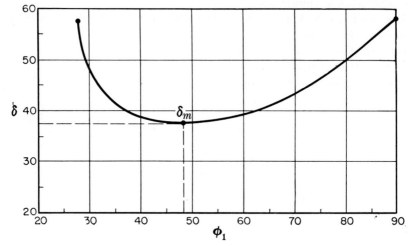

Fig. 2J. A graph of the deviation produced by a 60° glass prism of index $n' = 1.50$. At minimum deviation $\delta_m = 37.2°$, $\phi_1 = 48.6°$, and $\phi_1' = 30.0°$.

only one, there must be symmetry and the above equalities must hold.

In the triangle ABC in Fig. 2K the exterior angle δ_m equals the sum of the opposite interior angles $\beta + \gamma$. Similarly, for the triangle ABN', the exterior angle α equals the sum $\phi_1' + \phi_2'$.

Consequently

$$\alpha = 2\phi_1' \qquad \delta_m = 2\beta$$
$$\phi_1 = \phi_1' + \beta$$

Solving these three equations for ϕ_1' and ϕ_1,

$$\phi_1' = \tfrac{1}{2}\alpha \qquad \phi_1 = \tfrac{1}{2}(\alpha + \delta_m)$$

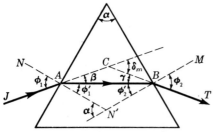

Fig. 2K. The geometry of a light ray traversing a prism at minimum deviation.

Since by Snell's law $n'/n = \sin \phi_1/\sin \phi_1'$,

$$\frac{n'}{n} = \frac{\sin \tfrac{1}{2}(\alpha + \delta_m)}{\sin \tfrac{1}{2}\alpha} \qquad (2l)$$

The most accurate measurements of refractive index are made by placing the sample in the form of a prism on the table of a spectrometer and measuring the angles α and δ_m, the latter for each color desired. When prisms are used in spectroscopes and spectrographs, they are always set as nearly as possible at minimum deviation because otherwise any slight divergence or convergence of the incident light would cause astigmatism in the image. A divergent pencil incident at any arbitrary angle on a prism yields two focal lines T and S similar to those shown in Fig. 2$H(c)$. Only at minimum deviation do they merge to form a true point image.

2.9. Thin Prisms. The equations for the prism become much simpler when the refracting angle α becomes small enough so that its sine, and also the sine of the angle of deviation δ, may be set equal to the angles themselves. Even at an angle of 0.1 rad, or 5.7°, the difference between

FIG. 2L. Thin prisms. (a) The displacement x, in centimeters, at a distance of 1 m, gives the power of the prism in diopters. (b) Risley prism of variable power. (c) Vector addition of prism deviations.

the angle and its sine is less than 0.2 per cent. For prisms having a refracting angle of only a few degrees, we may therefore simplify Eq. 2l by writing

$$n' = \frac{\sin \frac{1}{2}(\delta_m + \alpha)}{\sin \frac{1}{2}\alpha} = \frac{\delta_m + \alpha}{\alpha}$$

and
$$\delta = (n' - 1)\alpha \qquad \text{THIN PRISM IN AIR} \qquad (2m)$$

The subscript on δ has been dropped because such prisms are always used at or near minimum deviation, and n has been dropped because it will be assumed that the surrounding medium is air, $n = 1$.

It is customary to measure the *power* of a prism by the deflection of the ray in centimeters at a distance of 1 m, in which case the unit of power is called the *prism diopter*. A prism having a power of 1 prism diopter therefore displaces the ray on a screen 1 m away by 1 cm. In Fig. 2$L(a)$ the deflection on the screen is x cm and is numerically equal to the power of the prism. For small values of δ it will be seen that the power in prism diopters is essentially the angle of deviation δ measured in units of 0.01 rad, or 0.573°.

For the barium flint glass of Table 23-I, $n'_D = 1.59144$, and Eq. 2m shows that the refracting angle of a 1-diopter prism should be

$$\alpha = \frac{0.573}{0.59144} = 0.97°$$

2.10. Combinations of Thin Prisms. In measuring binocular accomodation, ophthalmologists make use of a combination of two thin prisms of equal power which can be rotated in opposite directions in their own plane [Fig. 2L(b)]. Such a device, known as the *Risley* or *Herschel prism*, is equivalent to a single prism of variable power. When the prisms are parallel the power is twice that of either one, while when they are opposed the power is zero. To find how the power and direction of deviation depend on the angle between the components, we use the fact that the deviations add vectorially. In Fig. 2L(c) it will be seen that the resultant deviation δ will in general be, from the law of cosines,

$$\delta = \sqrt{\delta_1{}^2 + \delta_2{}^2 + 2\delta_1\delta_2 \cos \beta} \tag{2n}$$

where β is the angle between the two prisms. To find the angle γ between the resultant deviation and that due to prism 1 alone (or, we may say, between the "equivalent" prism and prism 1) we have the relation

$$\tan \gamma = \frac{\delta_2 \sin \beta}{\delta_1 + \delta_2 \cos \beta} \tag{2o}$$

Since almost always $\delta_1 = \delta_2$, we may call the deviation by either component δ_i, and the equations simplify to

$$\delta = \sqrt{2\delta_i{}^2(1 + \cos \beta)} = \sqrt{4\delta_i{}^2 \cos^2 \frac{\beta}{2}} = 2\delta_i \cos \frac{\beta}{2} \tag{2p}$$

and

$$\tan \gamma = \frac{\sin \beta}{1 + \cos \beta} = \tan \frac{\beta}{2}$$

so that

$$\gamma = \frac{\beta}{2} \tag{2q}$$

2.11. Graphical Method of Ray Tracing. It is often desirable in the process of designing optical instruments to be able quickly to trace

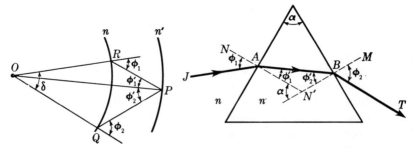

Fig. 2M. A graphical method for ray tracing through a prism.

rays of light through the system. When prism instruments are encountered, the principles presented below are found to be extremely useful. Consider first a 60° prism of index $n' = 1.50$ surrounded by air of index $n = 1.00$. After the prism has been drawn to scale as in Fig. 2M, and the angle of incidence ϕ_1 has been selected, the construction begins as in Fig. 1*C*.

Line *OR* is drawn parallel to *JA*, and, with an origin at *O*, the two circular arcs are drawn with radii proportional to *n* and *n'*. Line *RP* is drawn parallel to *NN'*, and *OP* is drawn to give the direction of the refracted ray *AB*. Carrying on from the point *P*, a line is drawn parallel to *MN'* to intersect the arc *n* at *Q*. The line *OQ* then gives the correct direction of the final refracted ray *BT*. In the construction diagram at the left the angle *RPQ* is equal to the prism angle α, and the angle *ROQ* is equal to the total angle of deviation δ.

2.12. Direct-vision Prisms. As an illustration of ray tracing through several prisms, consider the design of an important optical device known as a *direct-vision prism*. The primary function of such an instrument is to produce a visible spectrum the central color of which emerges from the prism parallel to the incident light. The simplest type of such a combination usually consists of a crown-glass prism of index *n'* and angle α' opposed to a flint-glass prism of index *n''* and angle α'', as shown in Fig. 2*N*.

The indices *n'* and *n''* chosen for the prisms are those for the central color of the spectrum, namely, for the sodium yellow D lines. Let us

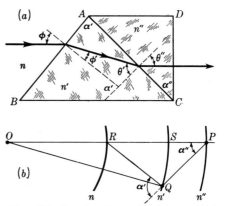

FIG. 2*N*. Graphical ray tracing applied to the design of a direct-vision prism.

assume that the angle α'' of the flint prism is selected and the construction proceeds with the light emerging perpendicular to the last surface and the angle α' of the crown prism as the unknown.

The flint prism is first drawn with its second face vertical. The horizontal line *OP* is next drawn, and, with a center at *O*, three arcs are drawn with radii proportional to *n*, *n'*, and *n''*. Through the intersection at *P* a line is drawn perpendicular to *AC* intersecting *n'* at *Q*. The line *RQ* is next drawn, and normal to it the side *AB* of the crown prism. All directions and angles are now known.

OR gives the direction of the incident ray, *OQ* the direction of the refracted ray inside the crown prism, *OP* the direction of the refracted ray inside the flint prism, and finally *OR* the direction of the emergent ray on the right. The angle α' of the crown prism is the supplement of angle *RQP*.

If more accurate determinations of angles are required, the construction diagram will be found useful in keeping track of the trigonometric calculations. If the dispersion of white light by the prism combination is desired, the indices n' and n'' for the red and violet light can be drawn in and new ray diagrams constructed proceeding now from left to right in Fig. 2N(b). These rays, however, will not emerge perpendicular to the last prism face.

The principles just outlined are readily extended to additional prism combinations like those shown in Fig. 20.* It should be noted that

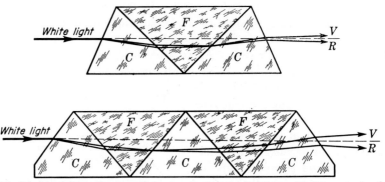

FIG. 20. Direct-vision prisms used for producing a spectrum with its central color in line with the incident white light.

the upper direct-vision prism in Fig. 20 is in principle two prisms of the type shown in Fig. 2N placed back to back.

PROBLEMS

1. A clear thick mineral oil ($n = 1.573$) is poured into a beaker to a depth of 6 cm. On top of this is poured a layer of alcohol ($n = 1.450$) 8 cm deep. (a) How far above or below its true position does a silver coin on the bottom of the beaker appear to an observer looking straight down? (b) What is the critical angle for the interface between the oil and alcohol, and from which side of the interface must the light approach?

2. Using Snell's law, derive Eq. 2e for the lateral displacement of a ray which is incident on a plane-parallel plate at an angle ϕ.

3. Calculate the lateral displacements of a ray of light incident on a parallel plate at the following angles: (a) 10°, (b) 20°, (c) 30°, (d) 40°, and (e) 50°. Assume a plate thickness of 2 cm and an index of 1.50. Plot a graph of ϕ against d, and draw a straight line tangent to the resultant curve at the origin.

4. Make a graph of the variation of the image distance s' with the angle of the incident rays (ϕ in Fig. 2F), using s' as the ordinate and ϕ as the abscissa. Take the object point to be situated in air 3.0 cm from a plane surface of glass of refractive index 1.573. *Ans.* Graph with $s' = 4.72$ cm at $\phi = 0°$, and 5.96 cm at $\phi = 45°$.

5. The refractive index of a liquid is measured with a Pulfrich refractometer in which the prism has an index of 1.625 and a refracting angle of 80° (see Fig. 2D). The boundary between light and dark field is found to make an angle of 27°20′ with the normal to the second face. Find the refractive index of the liquid.

* See E. J. Irons, *Am. J. Phys.*, **21**, 1, 1953.

6. A crown-glass prism with an angle of 60° has a refractive index of 1.62. If the prism is used at an angle of incidence $\phi_1 = 70°$, find the total angle of deviation δ by (a) the graphical method, and (b) calculation. (c) Calculate the angle of minimum deviation for this same prism. *Ans.* (a) 52.3°. (b) 52°18′. (c) 48°12′.

7. A 60° flint-glass prism has a refractive index of 1.75 for sodium yellow light. Graphically find (a) the angle of minimum deviation, and (b) the corresponding angle of incidence at the first surface. (c) Calculate answers for (a) and (b).

8. Two thin prisms are superimposed so that their deviations make an angle of 60° with each other. If the powers of the prisms are 6 prism diopters and 4 prism diopters, respectively, find (a) the resultant deviation in degrees, (b) the power of the resultant prism, and (c) the angle the resultant makes with the stronger of the two prisms.
Ans. (a) 4°59′. (b) 8.7 D. (c) 23°25′.

9. A 60° prism gives a minimum deviation angle of 39°20′. Find (a) the refractive index, and (b) the angle of incidence ϕ_1.

10. A 50° prism has a refractive index of 1.620. Graphically determine the angle of deviation for each of the following angles of incidence: (a) 35°, (b) 40°, (c) 45°, (d) 50°, (e) 60°, and (f) 70°. Plot a graph of δ vs. ϕ_1 (see Fig. 2J).
Ans. (a) 37.4°. (b) 36.5°. (c) 36.4°. (d) 36.9°. (e) 39.5°. (f) 44.0°.

11. Two thin prisms have powers of 8 D each. At what angles should they be superimposed to produce powers of (a) 3.0 D, (b) 5.8 D, and (c) 12.5 D, respectively?

12. Two facets of a diamond make an angle of 40° with each other. Find the angle of minimum deviation if $n = 2.42$. *Ans.* 71°43′.

13. A direct-vision prism is to be made of two elements like the one shown in Fig. 2N. The flint-glass prism of index 1.75 has an angle $\alpha'' = 45°$. Find the angle α' for the crown-glass prism if its refractive index is 1.55. Solve graphically.

14. Solve Prob. 13 by calculation using Snell's law. *Ans.* 66°54′.

15. A direct-vision prism is to be made of two elements like the one shown in Fig. 2N. If the crown-glass prism has an angle $\alpha' = 70°$ and a refractive index of 1.52, what must be (a) the angle α'', and (b) the refractive index of the flint prism? Solve graphically if the crown-glass prism is isosceles.

16. Prove that as long as the angles of incidence and refraction are small enough so that the angles may be substituted for their sines, i.e., for a thin prism not too far from normal incidence, the deviation is independent of the angle of incidence and equal to $(n - 1)\alpha$.

17. Show that, for any angle of incidence on a prism,

$$\frac{\sin \frac{1}{2}(\alpha + \delta)}{\sin \frac{1}{2}\alpha} = n' \frac{\cos \frac{1}{2}(\phi_1' - \phi_2')}{\cos \frac{1}{2}(\phi_1 - \phi_2)}$$

and that the right-hand side reduces to n' at minimum deviation.

CHAPTER 3

SPHERICAL SURFACES

Many common optical devices contain not only mirrors and prisms having flat polished surfaces but lenses having spherical surfaces with a wide range of curvatures. Such spherical surfaces in contrast with plane surfaces treated in the last chapter are capable of forming real images.

Cross-section diagrams of several standard forms of lenses are shown in Fig. 3A. The three *converging*, or *positive*, *lenses*, which are thicker at the center than at the edges, are shown as (a) *equiconvex*, (b) *plano-convex*, and (c) *positive meniscus*. The three *diverging*, or *negative*, *lenses*,

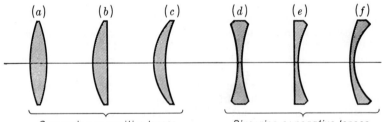

Converging or positive lenses   Diverging or negative lenses

Fig. 3A. Cross sections of common types of thin lenses.

which are thinner at the center, are (d) *equiconcave*, (e) *plano-concave*, and (f) *negative meniscus*. Such lenses are usually made of optical glass as free as possible from inhomogeneities, but occasionally other transparent materials like quartz, fluorite, rock salt, and plastics are used. Although we shall see that the spherical form for the surfaces may not be the ideal one in a particular instance, it gives reasonably good images and is much the easiest to grind and polish.

It is the purpose of this chapter to treat the behavior of refraction at a single spherical surface separating two media of different refractive indices, and then in the following chapters to show how the treatment can be extended to two or more surfaces in succession. These latter combinations form the basis for the treatment of thin lenses in Chap. 4, thick lenses in Chap. 5, and spherical mirrors in Chap. 6.

3.1. Focal Points and Focal Lengths. Characteristic diagrams showing the refraction of light by convex and concave spherical surfaces are given in Fig. 3*B*. Each ray in being refracted obeys Snell's law as given by Eq. 1*c*. The principal axis in each diagram is a straight line through the center of curvature *C*. The point *A* where the axis crosses the surface is called the *vertex*. In diagram (*a*) rays are shown diverging from a point source *F* on the axis in the first medium, and refracted into a

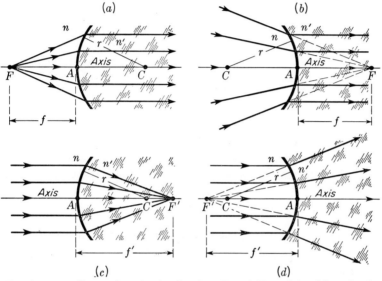

FIG. 3*B*. Diagrams illustrating the focal points *F* and *F'* and focal lengths *f* and *f'*, associated with a single spherical refracting surface of radius *r* separating two media of index *n* and *n'*.

beam everywhere parallel to the axis in the second medium. Diagram (*b*) shows a beam converging in the first medium toward the point *F*, and then refracted into a parallel beam in the second medium. *F* in each of these two cases is called the *primary focal point*, and the distance *f* is called the *primary focal length*.

In diagram (*c*) a parallel incident beam is refracted and brought to a focus at the point *F'*, and in diagram (*d*) a parallel incident beam is refracted to diverge as if it came from the point *F'*. *F'* in each case is called the *secondary focal point*, and the distance *f'* is called the *secondary focal length*.

Returning to diagrams (*a*) and (*b*) for reference, we now state that *the primary focal point F is an axial point having the property that any ray coming from it, or proceeding toward it, travels parallel to the axis after refraction.* Referring to diagrams (*c*) and (*d*), we make the similar statement that *the secondary focal point F' is an axial point having the property that any incident ray traveling parallel to the axis will, after refraction, proceed toward, or appear to come from, F'.*

A plane perpendicular to the axis and passing through either focal point is called a *focal plane.* The significance of a focal plane is illustrated for a convex surface in Fig. 3C. Parallel incident rays making an angle θ with the axis are brought to a focus in the focal plane at a point Q'. Note that Q' is in line with the undeviated ray through the center of curvature C and that this is the only ray that crosses the boundary at normal incidence.

Fig. 3C. Illustrating how parallel incident rays are brought to a focus at Q' in the secondary focal plane of a single spherical surface.

It is important to note in Fig. 3B that the primary focal length f for the convex surface [diagram (a)] is not equal to the secondary focal length f' of the same surface [diagram (c)]. It will be shown in Sec. 3.4 (see Eq. 3e) that the ratio of the focal lengths f'/f is equal to the ratio n'/n of the corresponding refractive indices.

$$\frac{f'}{f} = \frac{n'}{n} \tag{3a}$$

In optical diagrams it is common practice to show incident light rays traveling from left to right. A convex surface therefore is one in which the center of curvature C lies to the right of the vertex, while a concave surface is one in which C lies to the left of the vertex.

If we apply the principle of the reversibility of light rays to the diagrams in Fig. 3B, we should turn each diagram end-for-end. Diagram (a), for example, would then become a concave surface with converging properties, while diagram (b) would become a convex surface with diverging properties. Note that we would then have the incident rays in the more dense medium, i.e., the medium of greater refractive index.

3.2. Image Formation. A diagram illustrating image formation by a single refracting surface is given in Fig. 3D. It has been drawn for the case in which the first medium is air with an index $n = 1$ and the second medium is glass with an index $n' = 1.60$. The focal lengths f and f' therefore have the ratio 1:1.60 (see Eq. 3a). Experimentally it is observed that if the object is moved closer to the primary focal plane the image will be formed farther to the right away from F' and will be larger, i.e., magnified. If the object is moved to the left, farther away from F, the image will be found closer to F' and will be smaller in size.

All rays coming from the object point Q are shown brought to a focus at Q'. Rays from any other object point like M will also be brought to a focus at a corresponding image point like M'. This ideal condition never holds exactly for any actual case. Departures from it give rise to slight defects of the image known as *aberrations*. The elimination of aberrations is the major problem of geometrical optics and will be treated in detail in Chap. 9.

FIG. 3D. All rays leaving the object point Q, and passing through the refracting surface, are brought to a focus at the image point Q'.

FIG. 3E. All rays leaving the object point Q, and passing through the refracting surface, appear to be coming from the virtual image point Q'.

If the rays considered are restricted to *paraxial rays*, a good image is formed with *monochromatic light*. *Paraxial rays* are defined as *those rays which make very small angles with the axis and lie close to the axis throughout the distance from object to image* (see Sec. 2.5). The formulas given in this chapter are to be taken as applying to images formed only by paraxial rays.

3.3. Virtual Images. The image $M'Q'$ in Fig. 3D is a real image in the sense that if a flat screen is located at M' a sharply defined image of the object MQ will be formed on the screen. Not all images, however, can be formed on a screen, as is illustrated in Fig. 3E. Light rays from an object point Q are shown refracted by a concave spherical surface separating the two media of index $n = 1.0$ and $n' = 1.50$, respectively. The focal lengths have the ratio $1:1.50$.

Since the refracted rays are diverging, they will not come to a focus at any point. To an observer's eye located at the right, however, such rays will appear to be coming from the common point Q'. In other words, Q' is the image point corresponding to the object point Q. Similarly M' is the image point corresponding to the object point M. Since the refracted rays do not come from Q' but only appear to do so, no image can be formed on a screen placed at M'. For this reason such an image is said to be *virtual*.

3.4. Conjugate Points and Planes. The principle of the reversibility of light rays has the consequence that, if $Q'M'$ in Fig. 3D were an object, an image would be formed at QM. Hence, if any object is placed at the position previously occupied by its image, it will be imaged at the position previously occupied by the object. The object and image are thus interchangeable, or conjugate. Any pair of object and image points such as M and M' in Fig. 3D are called *conjugate points*, and planes through these points perpendicular to the axis are called *conjugate planes*.

If one is given the radius of curvature r of a spherical surface separating two media of index n and n', respectively, as well as the position of an object, there are three general methods that may be employed to determine the position and size of the image. One is by graphical methods, a second is by experiment, and the third is by calculation using the formula

$$\frac{n}{s} + \frac{n'}{s'} = \frac{n' - n}{r} \tag{3b}$$

In this equation s is the object distance and s' is the image distance. This equation, called the Gaussian formula for a single spherical surface, is derived in Sec. 3.10.

Example: The end of a solid glass rod of index 1.50 is ground and polished to a hemispherical surface of radius 1 cm. A small object is placed in air on the axis 4 cm to the left of the vertex. Find the position of the image. Assume $n = 1.00$ for air.

Solution: By direct substitution of the given quantities in Eq. 3b we obtain

$$\frac{1}{4} + \frac{1.50}{s'} = \frac{1.50 - 1.00}{1} \qquad \frac{1.50}{s'} = \frac{0.50}{1} - \frac{1}{4}$$

from which $s' = 6.0$ cm. One concludes, therefore, that a real image is formed in the glass rod 6 cm to the right of the vertex.

As an object M is brought closer to the primary focal point, Eq. 3b shows that the distance of the image from the vertex, AM', becomes steadily greater and that in the limit when the object reaches F the refracted rays are parallel and the image is formed at infinity. Then we have $s' = \infty$, and Eq. $3b$ becomes

$$\frac{n}{s} + \frac{n'}{\infty} = \frac{n' - n}{r}$$

Since this particular object distance is called the primary focal length f, we may write

$$\frac{n}{f} = \frac{n' - n}{r} \qquad (3c)$$

Similarly, if the object distance is made larger and eventually approaches infinity, the image distance diminishes and becomes equal to f' in the limit, $s = \infty$. Then

$$\frac{n}{\infty} + \frac{n'}{s'} = \frac{n' - n}{r}$$

or, since this value of s' represents the secondary focal length f',

$$\frac{n'}{f'} = \frac{n' - n}{r} \qquad (3d)$$

Equating the left-hand members of Eqs. $3c$ and $3d$, we obtain

$$\frac{n}{f} = \frac{n'}{f'} \qquad \text{or} \qquad \frac{n'}{n} = \frac{f'}{f} \qquad (3e)$$

When $(n' - n)/r$ in Eq. $3b$ is replaced by n/f or by n'/f' according to Eqs. $3c$ and $3d$, there results

$$\frac{n}{s} + \frac{n'}{s'} = \frac{n}{f} \qquad \text{or} \qquad \frac{n}{s} + \frac{n'}{s'} = \frac{n'}{f'} \qquad (3f)$$

Both these equations give the conjugate distances for a single spherical surface.

3.5. Convention of Signs.   The following set of sign conventions will be adhered to throughout the following chapters on geometrical optics, and it would be well to have them firmly in mind:

1. *All figures are drawn with the light traveling from left to right.*
2. *All object distances (s) are considered as positive when they are meas-ured to the left of the vertex, and negative when they are measured to the right.*
3. *All image distances (s') are positive when they are measured to the right of the vertex, and negative when to the left.*
4. *Both focal lengths are positive for a converging system, and negative for a diverging system.*

5. *Object and image dimensions are positive when measured upward from the axis and negative when measured downward.*

6. *All convex surfaces encountered are taken as having a positive radius, and all concave surfaces encountered are taken as having a negative radius.*

Example: A concave surface with a radius of 4 cm separates two media of refractive index $n = 1.00$ and $n' = 1.50$. An object is located in the first medium at a distance of 10 cm from the vertex. Find (*a*) the primary focal length, (*b*) the secondary focal length, and (*c*) the image distance.

Solution: To find (*a*), we use Eq. 3c directly to obtain

$$\frac{1.0}{f} = \frac{1.5 - 1.0}{-4} \qquad \text{or} \qquad f = \frac{-4.0}{0.5} = -8.0 \text{ cm}$$

To find (*b*), we use Eq. 3d directly and obtain

$$\frac{1.5}{f'} = \frac{1.5 - 1.0}{-4} \qquad \text{or} \qquad f' = \frac{-6.0}{0.5} = -12.0 \text{ cm}$$

Note that in this problem both focal lengths are negative and that the ratio f/f' is $1/1.5$ as required by Eq. 3a. The minus signs indicate a diverging system similar to Fig. 3E.

To find the answer to part (*c*), we use Eq. 3f and obtain, by direct substitution,

$$\frac{1.0}{10} + \frac{1.5}{s'} = \frac{1.0}{-8.0} \qquad \text{giving} \qquad s' = -6.66 \text{ cm}$$

The image is located 6.66 cm from the vertex A, and the minus sign shows it is to the left of A and therefore virtual as shown in Fig. 3E.

3.6. Graphical Constructions. The Parallel-ray Method. It would be well to point out here that, although the above formulas hold for all possible object and image distances, they apply only to images formed by paraxial rays. For such rays the refraction occurs at or very near the vertex of the spherical surface, so that the correct geometrical relations are obtained in graphical solutions by drawing all rays as though they were refracted at the plane through the vertex A and normal to the axis.

The parallel-ray method of construction is illustrated in Figs. 3F and 3G for convex and concave surfaces, respectively. Consider the light emitted from the highest point Q of the object in Fig. 3F. Of the rays emanating from this point in different directions the one, QT, traveling parallel to the axis, will by definition of the focal point be refracted to pass through F'. The ray QC passing through the center of curvature is undeviated because it crosses the boundary perpendicular to the surface.

These two rays are sufficient to locate the tip of the image at Q', and the rest of the image lies in the conjugate plane through this point. All other paraxial rays from Q, refracted by the surface, will also be brought to a focus Q'. As a check we note that the ray QS, which passes through the point F, will, by definition of the primary focal point, be refracted parallel to the axis and will cross the others at Q' as shown in the figure.

FIG. 3F. Parallel-ray method for graphically locating the image formed by a single spherical surface.

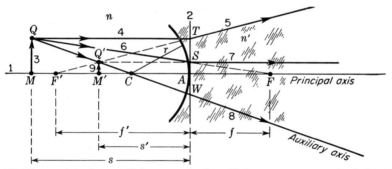

FIG. 3G. Illustrating the parallel-ray method applied to a concave spherical surface having diverging properties.

This method is called the *parallel-ray method*. The numbers 1, 2, 3, etc., indicate the order in which the lines are customarily drawn.

When the method just described is applied to a diverging system as shown in Fig. 3G, similar procedures are carried out. Ray QT, drawn parallel to the axis, is refracted as if it came from F'. Ray QS, directed toward F, is refracted parallel to the axis. Finally ray QW, passing through C, goes on undeviated. Extending all these refracted rays back to the left finds them intersecting at the common point Q'. $Q'M'$ is therefore the image of the object QM. Note that $Q'M'$ is not a real image since it cannot be formed on a screen.

In both these figures the medium to the right of the spherical surface has the greater index; i.e., we have made $n' > n$. If in Fig. 3F the medium on the left were to have the greater index, so that $n' < n$, the surface would have a diverging effect and each of the focal points F and F' would lie on the opposite side of the vertex from that shown, just as they do in Fig. 3G. Similarly, if we made $n' < n$ in Fig. 3G, the surface would have a converging effect and the focal points would lie as they do in Fig. 3F.

Since any ray through the center of curvature is undeviated and has all the properties of the principal axis it may be called an *auxiliary axis*.

3.7. Oblique-ray Methods. *Method* 1. In more complicated optical systems that are treated in the following chapters it is convenient to be able graphically to trace a ray across a spherical boundary for any given

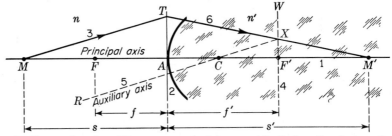

Fig. 3H. Illustrating the oblique-ray method for graphically locating images formed by a single spherical surface.

angle of incidence. The oblique-ray methods permit this to be done with considerable ease. In these constructions one is free to choose any two rays coming from a common object point and, after tracing them through the system, find where they finally intersect. This intersection is then the image point.

Let MT in Fig. 3H represent any ray incident on the surface from the left. Through the center of curvature C a dashed line RC is drawn, parallel to MT, and extended to the point where it crosses the secondary focal plane. The line TX is then drawn as the refracted ray and extended to the point where it crosses the axis at M'. Since the axis may here be considered as a second ray of light, M represents an axial object point and M' its conjugate image point.

The principle involved in this construction is the following: If MT and RA were parallel incident rays of light, they would, after refraction, and by the definition of focal planes, intersect the secondary focal plane WF' at X. Since RA is directed toward C, the refracted ray ACX remains undeviated from its original direction.

Method 2. This method is shown in Fig. 3I. After drawing the axis MM' and the arc representing the spherical surface with a center C, any line such as 1 is drawn to represent any oblique ray of light. Next, an auxiliary diagram is started by drawing XZ parallel to the axis.

With an origin at O, line intervals OK and OL are laid off proportional to n and n', respectively, and perpendiculars are drawn through K, L, and A. From here the construction proceeds in the order of the numbers 1, 2, 3, 4, 5, and 6. Line 2 is drawn through O parallel to line 1, line 4 is drawn through J parallel to line 3, and line 6 is drawn through T parallel to line 5.

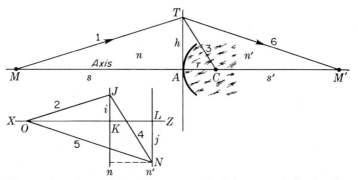

FIG. 3*I*. Illustrating the auxiliary-diagram method for graphically locating images formed by paraxial rays.

A proof for this construction is readily obtained by writing down proportionalities from three pairs of similar triangles in the two diagrams. These proportionalities are

$$\frac{h}{s} = \frac{i}{n} \qquad \frac{h}{s'} = \frac{j}{n'} \qquad \frac{h}{r} = \frac{i+j}{n'-n}$$

We now transpose n and n' to the left in all three equations.

$$\frac{hn}{s} = i \qquad \frac{hn'}{s'} = j \qquad \frac{h(n'-n)}{r} = i+j$$

We finally add the first two equations and for the right-hand side substitute the third equality.

$$\frac{hn}{s} + \frac{hn'}{s'} = i+j \qquad \text{and} \qquad \frac{n}{s} + \frac{n'}{s'} = \frac{n'-n}{r}$$

It should be noted that to employ method 1 the secondary focal length f' must be known or it must first be calculated from the known radius of curvature and the refractive indices n and n'. Method 2 can be applied without knowing either of the focal lengths.

3.8. Magnification. In any optical system the ratio between the transverse dimension of the final image and the corresponding dimension of the original object is called the lateral magnification. To determine the relative size of the image formed by a single spherical surface, reference is made to the geometry of Fig. 3F. Here the undeviated ray 5 forms two similar right triangles QMC and $Q'M'C$.

The theorem of the proportionality of corresponding sides requires that

$$\frac{M'Q'}{MQ} = \frac{CM'}{CM} \qquad \text{or} \qquad \frac{-y'}{y} = \frac{s'-r}{s+r}$$

We will now define y'/y as the lateral magnification m and obtain

$$m = \frac{y'}{y} = -\frac{s'-r}{s+r} \tag{3g}$$

If m is positive, the image will be virtual and erect, while if it is negative, the image is real and inverted.

3.9. Reduced Vergence. In the formulas for a single spherical refracting surface (Eqs. 3b to 3f), the distance s, s', r, f, and f' appear in the

Fig. 3J. Illustrating the refraction of light waves at a single spherical surface.

denominators. The reciprocals $1/s$, $1/s'$, $1/r$, $1/f$, and $1/f'$ actually represent curvatures of which s, s', r, f, and f' are the radii.

Reference to Fig. 3J will show that if we think of M in the left-hand diagram as a point source of waves their refraction by the spherical boundary causes them to converge toward the image point M'. In the right-hand diagram plane waves are refracted so as to converge toward the secondary focal point F'. Note that these curved lines representing the crests of light waves are everywhere perpendicular to the corresponding light rays that could have been drawn from object point to image point.

As the waves from M strike the vertex A, they have a radius s and a curvature $1/s$, and as they leave A converging toward M', they have a radius s' and a curvature $1/s'$. Similarly the incident waves arriving at A in the second diagram have an infinite radius ∞ and a curvature of $1/\infty$, or zero. At the vertex where they leave the surface the radius of the refracted waves is equal to f' and their curvature is equal to $1/f'$.

The Gaussian formulas may therefore be considered as involving the addition and subtraction of quantities proportional to the curvatures of spherical surfaces.   When these curvatures, rather than radii are used, the formulas become simpler in form and for some purposes more convenient.   We therefore introduce at this point the following quantities:

$$V = \frac{n}{s} \qquad V' = \frac{n'}{s'} \qquad K = \frac{1}{r} \qquad P = \frac{n}{f} \qquad P = \frac{n'}{f'} \qquad (3h)$$

The first two of these, V and V', are called *reduced vergences* because they are direct measures of the convergence and divergence of the object and image wave fronts, respectively.   For a divergent wave from the object s is positive, and so is the vergence V.   For a convergent wave, on the other hand, s is negative, and so is its vergence.   For a converging wave front toward the image V' is positive, and for a diverging wave front V' is negative.   Note that in each case the refractive index involved is that of the medium in which the wave front is located.

The third quantity K is the curvature of the refracting surface (reciprocal of its radius), while the fourth and fifth quantities are, according to Eq. 3e, equal and define the refracting *power*.   *When all distances are measured in meters, the reduced vergences V and V', the curvature K, and the power P are in units called diopters.*   We may think of V as the power of the object wave front just as it touches the refracting surface and V' as the power of the corresponding image wave front which is tangent to the refracting surface.   In these new terms, Eq. 3b becomes

$$V + V' = P \qquad (3i)$$

where $\qquad P = \dfrac{n' - n}{r} \qquad$ or $\qquad P = (n' - n)K \qquad (3j)$

Example: One end of a glass rod of refractive index 1.50 is ground and polished with a convex spherical surface of radius 10 cm.   An object is placed in the air on the axis 40 cm to the left of the vertex.   Find (*a*) the power of the surface, and (*b*) the position of the image.

Solution: To find the solution to (*a*), we make use of Eq. 3j, substitute the given distance in meters, and obtain

$$P = \frac{1.50 - 1.00}{0.10} = +5.0 \text{ D}$$

For the answer to part (*b*), we first use Eq. 3h to find the vergence V.

$$V = \frac{1.00}{0.40} = +2.5 \text{ D}$$

Direct substitution in Eq. 3i gives

$$2.5 + V' = 5 \qquad \text{from which} \qquad V' = +2.5 \text{ D}$$

To find the image distance, we have $V' = n'/s'$, so that

$$s' = \frac{n'}{V'} = \frac{1.50}{2.5} = 0.60 \text{ m}$$

or $$s' = 60 \text{ cm}$$

This answer should be verified by the student, using one of the graphical methods of construction drawn to a convenient scale.

3.10. Derivation of the Gaussian Formula. The basic equation 3*b* is of sufficient importance to warrant its derivation in some detail. While there are many ways of performing a derivation, a method involving oblique rays will be given here. In Fig. 3*K* an oblique ray from an

FIG. 3*K*. Geometry for the derivation of the paraxial formula used in locating images.

axial object point M is shown incident on the surface at an angle ϕ, and refracted at an angle ϕ'. The refracted ray crosses the axis at the image point M'. If the incident and refracted rays MT and TM' are paraxial, the angles ϕ and ϕ' will be small enough so that we may put the sines of the two angles equal to the angles themselves and for Snell's law write

$$\frac{\phi}{\phi'} = \frac{n'}{n} \tag{3k}$$

Since ϕ is an exterior angle of the triangle MTC and equals the sum of the opposite interior angles,

$$\phi = \alpha + \beta \tag{3l}$$

Similarly β is an exterior angle of the triangle TCM', so that $\beta = \phi' + \gamma$, and

$$\phi' = \beta - \gamma \tag{3m}$$

Substituting these values of ϕ and ϕ' in Eq. 3*k* and multiplying out, we obtain

$$n'\beta - n'\gamma = n\alpha + n\beta \qquad \text{or} \qquad n\alpha + n'\gamma = (n' - n)\beta$$

For paraxial rays α, β, and γ are very small angles, and we may set $\alpha = h/s$, $\beta = h/r$, and $\gamma = h/s'$. Substituting these values in the last equation, we obtain

$$n\frac{h}{s} + n'\frac{h}{s'} = (n' - n)\frac{h}{r}$$

By canceling h throughout we obtain the desired equation,

$$\frac{n}{s} + \frac{n'}{s'} = \frac{n' - n}{r} \tag{3n}$$

3.11. Nomography. The term nomograph is derived from the greek words *nomos*, meaning *law*, and *graphein*, meaning *to write*. In physics

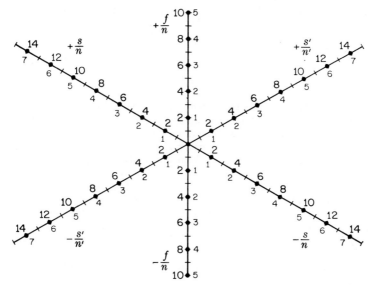

FIG. 3L. Nomograph for determining the object or image distance for a single spherical surface, or for a thin lens.

the term applies to certain graphical representations of physical laws, which are intended to simplify or speed up calculations. Figure 3L is a nomograph relating *object* and *image distances* as given by Eq. 3f, namely,

$$\frac{n}{s} + \frac{n'}{s'} = \frac{n}{f} \tag{3o}$$

Its simplicity and usefulness become apparent when it is seen that any straight line drawn across the figure will intersect the three lines at values related by the above equation.

Example: One end of a plastic rod of index 1.5 is ground and polished to a radius of +2.0 cm. If an object in air is located on the axis 12.0 cm from the vertex, what is the image distance?

Solution: By direct substitution, and by the use of Eq. 3*o*, we obtain

$$\frac{s}{n} = \frac{12}{1} = +12.0 \quad \text{and} \quad \frac{f}{n} = \frac{r}{n' - n} = \frac{2}{1.5 - 1} = +4.0$$

If the straight edge of a ruler is now placed on $s/n = +12.0$, and $f/n = +4.0$, it will intersect the third line at $s'/n' = +6.0$. Since $n' = 1.5$, s' is equal to 6×1.5, or $+9.0$ cm.

A little study of this nomograph will show that it applies to all object and image distances, real or virtual, and to all surfaces with positive or negative radii of curvature. Furthermore we shall find in Chap. 4 that it can be applied to all thin lenses by setting n and n' equal to unity. For thin lenses the three axes represent s, s', and f directly, and no calculations are necessary.

PROBLEMS

1. The left end of a long glass rod of index 1.60 is ground and polished to a convex spherical surface of radius 3.0 cm. A small object is located in the air and on the axis 10.0 cm from the vertex. Find (*a*) the primary and secondary focal lengths, (*b*) the power of the surface, (*c*) the image distance, and (*d*) the lateral magnification.

2. Solve Prob. 1 graphically. (*a*) Find the image distance by either of the oblique-ray methods. (*b*) Find the relative size of the image by the parallel-ray method.

Ans. (*a*) +16.0 cm. (*b*) −1.0.

3. The left end of a long plastic rod of index 1.56 is ground and polished to a convex spherical surface of radius 2.80 cm. An object 2.0 cm high is located in the air and on the axis 15.0 cm from the vertex. Find (*a*) the primary and secondary focal lengths, (*b*) the power of the surface, (*c*) the image distance, and (*d*) the size of the image.

4. Solve Prob. 3 graphically. (*a*) Find the image distance by either of the oblique-ray methods. (*b*) Find the size of the image by the parallel-ray method.

Ans. (*a*) +11.7 cm. (*b*) −1.0 cm.

5. The left end of a water trough has a transparent surface of radius −1.5 cm. A small object 3.0 cm high is located in air and on the axis 9.0 cm from the vertex. Find (*a*) the primary and secondary focal lengths, (*b*) the power of the surface, (*c*) the image distance, and (*d*) the size of the image. Assume water to have an index 1.333.

6. Solve Prob. 5 graphically. (*a*) Find the image distance by either of the oblique-ray methods. (*b*) Find the size of the image by the parallel-ray method.

Ans. (*a*) −4.0 cm. (*b*) +1.0 cm.

7. The left end of a long plastic rod of index 1.56 is ground and polished to a spherical surface of radius −2.80 cm. An object 2.0 cm high is located in the air and on the axis 15.0 cm from the vertex. Find (*a*) the primary and secondary focal lengths, (*b*) the power of the surface, (*c*) the image distance, and (*d*) the size of the image.

8. Solve Prob. 7 graphically. (*a*) Find the image distance by either of the oblique-ray methods. (*b*) Find the size of the image by the parallel-ray method.

Ans. (*a*) −5.85 cm. (*b*) +0.5 cm.

9. The left end of a long glass rod of index 1.666 is polished to a convex surface of radius 1.0 cm and then submerged in water ($n = 1.333$). A small object 3.0 cm high is located in the water and on the axis 12.0 cm from the vertex. Calculate (*a*) the primary and secondary focal lengths, (b) the power of the surface, (c) the image distance, and (d) the size of the image.

10. Solve Prob. 9 graphically. (a) Find the image distance by either of the oblique-ray methods. (b) Find the size of the image by the parallel-ray method.

Ans. (a) +7.5 cm. (b) −1.5 cm.

11. A glass rod 2.8 cm long and of index 1.6 has both ends polished to spherical surfaces with the following radii: r_1 = +2.4 cm, and r_2 = −2.4 cm. An object 2.0 cm high is located on the axis 8.0 cm from the first vertex. Find (a) the primary and secondary focal lengths for each of the surfaces, (b) the image distance for the first surface, (c) the object distance for the second surface, and (d) the final image distance from the second vertex.

12. Solve Prob. 11 graphically, after first calculating the answer to (a).

Ans. (a) +4.0 cm, +6.4 cm, +6.4 cm, +4.0 cm. (b) +12.8 cm. (c) −10.0 cm. (d) +2.45 cm.

13. A parallel beam of light enters a clear plastic bead 2.0 cm in diameter and index 1.40. At what point beyond the bead are these rays brought to a focus?

14. Solve Prob. 13 graphically by the method illustrated in Fig. 3*I*.

Ans. +0.75 cm.

15. A glass bead of index 1.60 and radius 2.0 cm is submerged in a clear liquid of index 1.40. If a parallel beam of light in the liquid is allowed to enter the bead, at what point beyond the far side will the light be brought to a focus?

16. Solve Prob. 15 graphically by the method illustrated in Fig. 3*I*. *Ans.* +6.0 cm.

17. A hollow glass cell is made of thin glass in the form of an equiconcave lens. The radii of the two surfaces are 2.0 cm, and the distance between the two vertices is 2.0 cm. When sealed airtight, this cell is submerged in water of index 1.333. Calculate (a) the focal lengths of each surface, and (b) the power of each surface.

18. A spherical surface with a radius of +2.5 cm is polished on the end of a glass rod of index 1.650. Find its power when placed in (a) air, (b) water of index 1.333, (c) oil of index 1.650, and (d) an organic liquid of index 1.820.

Ans. (a) +26.0 D. (b) +12.7 D. (c) 0 D. (d) −6.8 D.

CHAPTER 4

THIN LENSES

Diagrams of several standard forms of thin lenses are shown in Fig. 3*A* at the beginning of the last chapter. They are shown there as illustrations of the fact that most lenses have surfaces that are spherical in form. Some surfaces are convex, others are concave, and still others are plane. When light passes through any lens, refraction at each of its surfaces contributes to its image-forming properties according to the principles put forward in Chap. 3. Not only does each individual surface have its own primary and secondary focal points and planes, but the lens as a whole has its own pair of focal points and focal planes.

A thin lens may be defined as one whose thickness is considered small in comparison with the distances generally associated with its optical properties. Such distances are, for example, radii of curvature of the two spherical surfaces, primary and secondary focal lengths, and object and image distances.

4.1. Focal Points and Focal Lengths. Diagrams showing the refraction of light by an equiconvex lens and by an equiconcave lens are given in Fig. 4*A*. The axis in each case is a straight line through the geometrical center of the lens and perpendicular to the two faces at the points of intersection. For spherical lenses this line joins the centers of curvature of the two surfaces. *The primary focal point F is an axial point having the property that any ray coming from it, or proceeding toward it, travels parallel to the axis after refraction.*

Every thin lens in air has two focal points, one on each side of the lens and equidistant from the center. This may be seen by symmetry in the cases of equiconvex and equiconcave lenses, but it is also true for other forms provided the lenses may be regarded as thin. *The secondary focal point F' is an axial point having the property that any incident ray traveling parallel to the axis will, after refraction, proceed toward, or appear to come from, F'.* The two lower diagrams in Fig. 4*A* are given for the purpose of illustrating this definition. In analogy to the case of a single spherical surface (see Chap. 3), a plane perpendicular to the axis and passing through a focal point is called a *focal plane*. The significance of the focal plane is illustrated for a converging lens in Fig. 4*B*.

Parallel incident rays making an angle θ with the axis are brought to a focus at a point Q' in line with the chief ray. The chief ray in this case is defined as the ray which passes through the center of the lens.

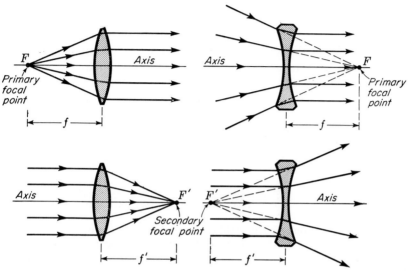

FIG. 4A. Ray diagrams illustrating the primary and secondary focal points F and F', and the corresponding focal lengths f and f', of thin lenses.

The distance between the center of a lens and either of its focal points is called its focal length. These distances, designated f and f', usually measured in centimeters or inches, have a positive sign for converging lenses and a negative sign for diverging lenses. It should be noted in Fig. 4A that the primary focal point F for a converging lens lies to the left of the lens, whereas for a diverging lens it lies to the right. For a lens with the same medium on both sides, we have, by the reversibility of light rays,

$$f = f'$$

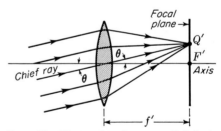

FIG. 4B. Illustrating how parallel incident rays are brought to a focus at the secondary focal plane of a thin lens.

Note carefully the difference between a thin lens in air where the focal lengths are equal and a single spherical surface where the two focal lengths have the ratio of the two refractive indices (see Eq. 3a).

4.2. Image Formation. When an object is placed on one side or the other of a converging lens, and beyond the focal plane, an image is formed on the opposite side (see Fig. 4C). If the object is moved closer to the primary focal plane, the image will be formed farther away from the secondary focal plane and will be larger, i.e., magnified.   If the object is moved farther away from F, the image will be formed closer to F' and will be smaller in size.

In Fig. 4C all the rays coming from an object point Q are shown as brought to a focus Q', and the rays from another point M are brought to a focus at M'.   Such ideal conditions and the formulas given in this chapter hold only for paraxial rays, i.e., rays close to and making small angles with the lens axis.

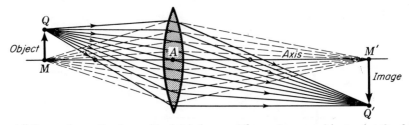

Fɪɢ. 4C. Image formation by an ideal thin lens.   All rays from an object point Q, which pass through the lens, are refracted to pass through the image point Q'.

4.3. Conjugate Points and Planes.   If the principle of the reversibility of light rays is applied to Fig. 4C, we observe that $Q'M'$ becomes the object and QM becomes its image.   The object and image are therefore *conjugate* just as they are for a single spherical surface (see Sec. 3.4).   Any pair of object and image points such as M and M' in Fig. 4C are called *conjugate points*, and planes through these points perpendicular to the axis are called *conjugate planes*.

If we know the focal length of a thin lens and the position of an object, there are three methods of determining the position of the image.   One is by graphical construction, the second is by experiment, and the third is by use of the lens formula.

$$\frac{1}{s} + \frac{1}{s'} = \frac{1}{f} \tag{4a}$$

Here s is the object distance, s' is the image distance, and f is the focal length, all measured to or from the center of the lens.   The lens equation (Eq. 4a), will be derived in Sec. 4.14.   We will now consider the graphical methods.

4.4. The Parallel-ray Method.   The parallel-ray method is illustrated in Fig. 4D.   Consider the light emitted from the extreme point Q on the object.   Of the rays emanating from this point in different directions the one QT, traveling parallel to the axis, will by definition of the focal point be refracted to pass through F'.   The ray QA, which goes through the lens center where the faces are parallel, is undeviated and meets the other ray at some point Q'. These two rays are sufficient to locate the tip of the image at Q', and the rest of the image lies in the conjugate plane through this point. All other rays from Q will also be brought to a focus at Q'. As a check, we note that the ray QF which passes through the primary focal point will by definition of F be refracted parallel to the axis and will cross the others at Q' as shown in the figure. The numbers 1, 2, 3, etc., in Fig. 4D indicate the order in which the lines are customarily drawn.

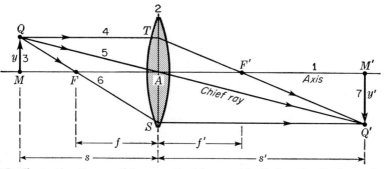

Fig. 4D. Illustrating the parallel-ray method for graphically locating the image formed by a thin lens.

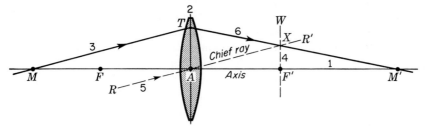

Fig. 4E. Illustrating the oblique-ray method for graphically locating the image formed by a thin lens.

4.5. The Oblique-ray Method. Let MT in Fig. 4E represent any ray incident on the lens from the left. It is refracted in the direction TX and crosses the axis at M'. The point X is located at the intersection between the secondary focal plane $F'W$ and the dashed line RR' drawn through the center of the lens parallel to MT.

The order in which each step of the construction is made is again indicated by the numbers 1, 2, 3, ... The principle involved in this method may be understood by reference to Fig. 4B. Parallel rays incident on the lens are always brought to a focus at the focal plane, the ray through the center being the only one undeviated. Therefore, if we actually have rays diverging from M, as in Fig. 4E, we may find the direction of any one of them after it passes through the lens by making it intersect the parallel line RR' through A in the focal plane. This construction locates X and the position of the image M'. Note that RR' is not an actual ray in this case and is treated as such only as a means of locating the point X.

4.6. Use of the Lens Formula. To illustrate the application of Eq. 4a to find the image position, we select an example in which all quantities occurring in the equation have a positive sign. Let an object be located 6 cm in front of a positive lens of focal length $+4$ cm. As a first step we transpose Eq. 4a by solving for s'.

$$s' = \frac{s \times f}{s - f} \qquad\qquad (4b)$$

Direct substitution of the given quantities in this equation gives

$$s' = \frac{(+6) \times (+4)}{(+6) - (+4)} \qquad \text{or} \qquad s' = +12.0 \text{ cm}$$

The image is formed 12 cm from the lens and is *real*, as it will always be when s' has a positive sign. In this instance it is inverted, corresponding to the diagram in Fig. 4C. These results can be readily checked by either of the two graphical methods presented above.

The sign conventions to be used for the thin-lens formulas are identical to those for a single spherical surface given on page 33.

4.7. Lateral Magnification. A simple formula for the image magnification produced by a single lens may be derived from the geometry of Fig. 4D. By construction it is seen that the right triangles QMA and $Q'M'A$ are similar. Corresponding sides are therefore proportional to each other, so that

$$\frac{M'Q'}{MQ} = \frac{AM'}{AM}$$

where AM' is the image distance s' and AM is the object distance s. Taking upward directions as positive, $y = MQ$, and $y' = -Q'M'$; so we have by direct substitution $y'/y = -s'/s$. The lateral magnification is therefore

$$m = \frac{y'}{y} = -\frac{s'}{s} \qquad\qquad (4c)$$

When s and s' are both positive, as in Fig. 4D, the negative sign of the magnification signifies an inverted image.

4.8. Virtual Images. The images formed by the converging lenses in Figs. 4C and 4D are real in that they can be made visible on a screen.

They are characterized by the fact that rays of light are actually brought to a focus in the plane of the image. A virtual image cannot be formed on a screen (see Sec. 2.3). The rays from a given point on the object do not actually come together at the corresponding point in the image; instead they must be projected backward to find this point. Virtual images are produced with converging lenses when the object is placed between the focal point and the lens, and by diverging lenses when the object is in any position. Examples of these cases are shown in Figs. 4F and 4G.

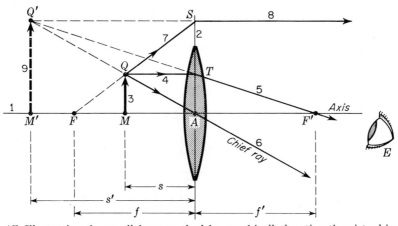

Fig. 4F. Illustrating the parallel-ray method for graphically locating the virtual image formed by a positive lens when the object is between the primary focal point and the lens.

Figure 4F shows the parallel-ray construction for the case where a positive lens is used as a magnifier, or reading glass. Rays emanating from Q are refracted by the lens but are not sufficiently deviated to come to a real focus. To the observer's eye at E these rays appear to be coming from a point Q' on the far side of the lens. This point represents a virtual image, because the rays do not actually pass through Q'; they only appear to come from there. Here the image is right side up and magnified. In the construction of this figure, ray QT parallel to the axis is refracted through F', while ray QA through the center of the lens is undeviated. These two rays when extended backward intersect at Q'. The third ray QS, traveling outward as though it came from F, actually misses the lens, but if the latter were larger, the ray would be refracted parallel to the axis, as shown. When projected backward, it also intersects the other projections at Q'.

Example: If an object is located 6 cm in front of a lens of focal length $+10$ cm, where will the image be formed?

Solution: By making direct substitutions in Eq. 4*b* we obtain

$$s' = \frac{(+6) \times (+10)}{(+6) - (+10)} = \frac{+60}{-4} = -15$$

The minus sign indicates that the image lies to the left of the lens. Such an image is always virtual. The magnification is obtained by the use of Eq. 4*c*,

$$m = -\frac{s'}{s} = -\frac{-15}{+6} = +2.5$$

The positive sign means that the image is erect.

In the case of the negative lens shown in Fig. 4*G* the image is virtual for all positions of the object, is always smaller than the object, and lies

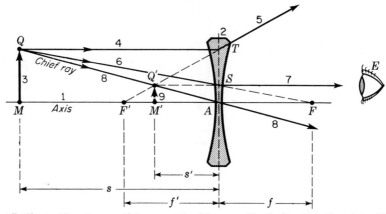

Fɪɢ. 4*G*. Illustrating the parallel-ray method for graphically locating the virtual image formed by a negative lens.

closer to the lens than the object. As is seen from the diagram, rays diverging from the object point Q are made more divergent by the lens. To the observer's eye at E these rays appear to be coming from the point Q' on the far side of but close to the lens. In applying the lens formula to a diverging lens it must be remembered that the focal length f is negative.

Example: An object is placed 12 cm in front of a diverging lens of focal length 6 cm. Find the image.

Solution: We substitute directly in Eq. 4*b*, to obtain

$$s' = \frac{(+12) \times (-6)}{(+12) - (-6)} = \frac{-72}{+18}$$

from which $s' = -4$ cm. For the image size Eq. 4c gives

$$m = -\frac{s'}{s} = -\frac{-4}{12} = +\frac{1}{3}$$

The image is therefore to the left of the lens, virtual, erect, and one-third the size of the object.

4.9. Lens Makers' Formula. If a lens is to be ground to some speci-fied focal length, the refractive index of the glass must be known. It is customary for manufacturers of optical glass to specify the refractive index for yellow sodium light, the D line. Supposing the index to be known, the radii of curvature must be so chosen as to satisfy the equation

$$\frac{1}{f} = (n - 1)\left(\frac{1}{r_1} - \frac{1}{r_2}\right) \tag{4d}$$

As the rays travel from left to right through a lens, *all convex surfaces encountered are taken as having a positive radius, and all concave surfaces encountered, a negative radius.* For an equiconvex lens like the one in Fig. 3A (a), r_1 for the first surface is positive and r_2 for the second surface negative. Substituting the value of $1/f$ from Eq. 4a, we may write

$$\frac{1}{s} + \frac{1}{s'} = (n - 1)\left(\frac{1}{r_1} - \frac{1}{r_2}\right) \tag{4e}$$

Example: A plano-convex lens having a focal length of 25 cm [Fig. 3A (b)] is to be made of glass of refractive index $n = 1.520$. Calculate the radius of curvature of the grinding and polishing tools that must be used to make this lens.

Solution: Since a plano-convex lens has one flat surface, the radius for that surface is infinite, and r_1 in Eq. 4d is replaced by ∞. The radius r_2 of the second surface is the unknown. Substitution of the known quantities in Eq. 4d gives

$$\frac{1}{25} = (1.520 - 1)\left(\frac{1}{\infty} - \frac{1}{r_2}\right)$$

Transposing and solving for r_2,

$$\frac{1}{25} = 0.520\left(0 - \frac{1}{r_2}\right) = -\frac{0.520}{r_2}$$

giving $\qquad r_2 = -(25 \times 0.520) = -13.0$ cm

If this lens is turned around, as in the figure, we will have $r_1 = +13.0$ cm and $r_2 = \infty$.

4.10. Thin-lens Combinations. The principles of image formation presented in the preceding sections of this chapter are readily extended to optical systems involving two or more thin lenses. Consider, for example, two converging lenses spaced some distance apart as shown in Fig. $4H$. Here an object Q_1M_1 is located at a given distance s in front of the first lens, and an image $Q_2'M_2'$ is formed some unknown distance s_2' from the second lens. We first apply the graphical methods to find this image distance and then show how to calculate it by the use of the thin-lens formula.

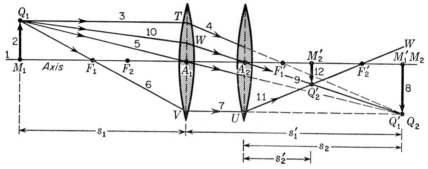

FIG. $4H$. Illustrating the parallel-ray method for graphically locating the final image formed by two thin lenses.

The first step in applying the graphical method is to disregard the presence of the second lens and find the image produced by the first one alone. In the diagram the parallel-ray method, as applied to the object point Q_1, locates a real and inverted image at Q_1'. Any two of the three incident rays 3, 5, and 6 are sufficient for this purpose. Once Q_1' is located, we know that all the rays leaving Q_1 will, upon refraction by the first lens, be directed toward Q_1'. Making use of this fact, we construct a fourth ray by drawing line 9 back from Q_1' through A_2 to W. Line 10 is then drawn in connecting W and Q_1.

The second step is to imagine the second lens in place and to make the following changes: Since ray 9 is seen to pass through the center of lens 2, it will emerge without deviation from its previous direction. Since ray 7 between the lenses is parallel to the axis, it will upon refraction by the second lens pass through its secondary focal point F_2'. The intersection of rays 9 and 11 locates the final image point Q_2'. Q_1 and Q_1' are conjugate points for the first lens, Q_2 and Q_2' are conjugate points for the second lens, while Q_1 and Q_2' are conjugate for the combination of lenses. When the image $Q_2'M_2'$ is drawn in, corresponding pairs of conjugate points on the axis are M_1 and M_1', M_2 and M_2', and M_1 and M_2'.

The oblique-ray method given in Fig. $4E$ is applied to the same two lenses in Fig. $4I$. A single ray is traced from the object point M to the final image point M_2'.   The lines are drawn in the order indicated.   The dotted line 6 is drawn through A_1 parallel to ray 4 to locate the point R_1'. The dotted line 9 is drawn through A_2 parallel to ray 7 to locate R_2'. This construction gives the same conjugate points along the axis.   Note that the axis itself is considered as the second light ray in locating the image point M_2'.

By way of comparison and as a check on the graphical solutions, we can assign specific values to the focal lengths of the lenses and apply the thin-lens formula to find the image.   Assume that the two lenses have

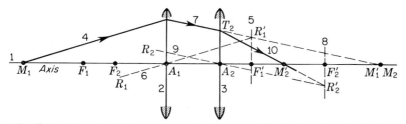

FIG. 4*I*. Illustrating the oblique-ray method for graphically locating the final image formed by two thin lenses.

focal lengths of $+3$ and $+4$ cm, respectively, that they are placed 2 cm apart, and that the object is located 4 cm in front of the first lens.

We begin the solution by applying Eq. 4*b* to the first lens alone.   The given quantities to be substituted are $s_1 = +4$ cm and $f_1 = +3$ cm.

$$s_1' = \frac{s_1 \times f_1}{s_1 - f_1} = \frac{(+4) \times (+3)}{(+4) - (+3)} = +12 \text{ cm}$$

The image formed by the first lens alone is, therefore, *real* and 12 cm to the right of A_1.   The image becomes the object for the second lens, and since it is only 10 cm from A_2, the object distance s_2 becomes -10 cm. The minus sign is necessary and results from the fact that the object distance is measured to the right of the lens.   We say that the image produced by the first lens becomes the object for the second lens.   Since the rays are converging toward the image of the first lens, the object for the second lens is virtual and its distance therefore has a negative value.   Applying the lens formula (Eq. 4*b*) to the second lens, we have $s_2 = -10$ cm and $f_2 = +4$ cm.

$$s_2' = \frac{(-10) \times (+4)}{(-10) - (+4)} = +2.86 \text{ cm}$$

The final image is 2.86 cm to the right of lens 2 and is *real*.

4.11. Object Space and Image Space.   For every position of the object there is a corresponding position for the image.   Since the image may be either real or virtual and may lie on either side of the lens, the *image space* extends from infinity in one direction to infinity in the other. But object and image points are conjugate; so the same argument holds for the *object space*. In view of their complete overlapping, one might wonder how it is that the distinction between object and image space is made. This is done by defining everything that pertains to the rays before they have passed through the refracting system as belonging to the object space and everything that pertains to them afterward as belonging to the image space. Referring to Fig. 4H, the object Q_1 and the rays Q_1T, Q_1A_1, and Q_1V are all in the object space for the first lens. Once these rays leave that lens, they are in the image space of the first lens, as is also the image Q'_1. This space is also the object space for the second lens. Once the rays leave the second lens, they and the image point Q'_2 are in the image space of the second lens.

4.12. The Power of a Thin Lens. The concept and measurement of lens power correspond to those used in the treatment of reduced vergence and the power of a single surface as given in Sec. 3.9. The power of a thin lens in diopters is given by the reciprocal of the focal length in meters.

$$P = \frac{1}{f} \qquad \text{Diopters} = \frac{1}{\text{focal length, m}} \qquad (4f)$$

For example, a lens with a focal length of $+50$ cm has a power of $1/0.50$ m $= +2$ D ($P = +2.0$ D), whereas one of -20 cm focal length has a power of $1/0.20$ m $= -5$ D ($P = -5.0$ D), etc. Converging lenses have a positive power, while diverging lenses have a negative power.

By making use of the lens makers' formula (Eq. 4d) we may write

$$P = (n - 1)\left(\frac{1}{r_1} - \frac{1}{r_2}\right) \qquad (4g)$$

where r_1 and r_2 are the two radii, measured in meters, and n is the refractive index of the glass.

Example: The radii of both surfaces of an equiconvex lens of index 1.60 are equal to 8 cm. Find its power.

Solution: The given quantities to be used in Eq. 4g are $n = 1.60$, $r_1 = 0.08$ m, and $r_2 = -0.08$ m (see Fig. 3A for the shape of an equiconvex lens).

$$P = (n - 1)\left(\frac{1}{r_1} - \frac{1}{r_2}\right) = (1.60 - 1)\left(\frac{1}{0.08} - \frac{1}{-0.08}\right)$$
$$P = 0.60\left(\frac{2}{0.08}\right) = +15.0 \text{ D}$$

Spectacle lenses are made to the nearest quarter of a diopter, thereby reducing the number of grinding and polishing tools required in the optical shops. Furthermore, the sides next to the eyes are always concave to permit free movement of the eyelashes and yet to keep as close to and as normal to the axis of the eye as possible. NOTE: it is important to insert a plus or minus sign in front of the number specifying lens power; thus, $P = +3.0$ D, $P = -4.5$ D, etc.

4.13. Thin Lenses in Contact. When two thin lenses are placed in contact as shown in Fig. 4J, the combination will act as a single lens with

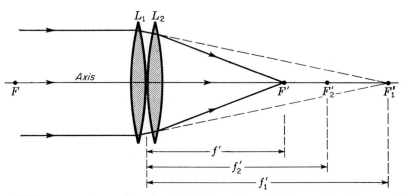

FIG. 4J. The power of a combination of thin lenses in contact is equal to the sum of the powers of the individual lenses.

two focal points symmetrically located at F and F' on opposite sides. Parallel incoming rays are shown refracted by the first lens toward its secondary focal point F'_1. Further refraction by the second lens brings the rays together at F'. This latter is defined as the secondary focal point of the combination, and its distance from the center is defined as the combination's secondary focal length f'.

If we now apply the simple lens formula (Eq. 4a) to the rays as they enter and leave the second lens L_2, we note that for the second lens alone f'_1 is the object distance (taken with a negative sign), f' is the image distance, and f'_2 is the focal length. Applying Eq. 4a, these substitutions for s, s', and f, respectively, give

$$\frac{1}{-f'_1} + \frac{1}{f'} = \frac{1}{f'_2} \qquad \text{or} \qquad \frac{1}{f'} = \frac{1}{f'_1} + \frac{1}{f'_2}$$

Having assumed the lenses are in air, the primary focal lengths are all equal to their respective secondary focal lengths, and we can drop all primes and write

$$\frac{1}{f} = \frac{1}{f_1} + \frac{1}{f_2} \tag{4h}$$

In words, *the reciprocal of the focal length of a thin-lens combination is equal to the sum of the reciprocals of the focal lengths of the individual lenses.* Since by Eq. 4f we can write $P_1 = 1/f_1$, $P_2 = 1/f_2$, and $P = 1/f$, we obtain for the power of the combination

$$P = P_1 + P_2 \tag{4i}$$

In general, *when thin lenses are placed in contact, the power of the combination is given by the sum of the powers of the individual lenses.*

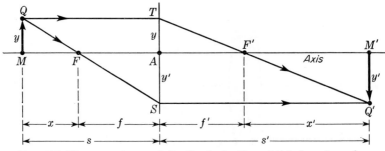

Fig. 4K. The geometry used for the derivation of thin-lens formulas.

4.14. Derivation of the Lens Formula. A derivation of Eq. 4a, the so-called "lens formula," is readily obtained from the geometry of Fig. 4D. The necessary features of the diagram are repeated in Fig. 4K, which shows only two rays leading from the object of height y to the image of height y'. Let s and s' represent the object and image distances from the lens center and x and x' their respective distances from the focal points F and F'.

From similar triangles $Q'TS$ and $F'TA$ the proportionality between corresponding sides gives

$$\frac{y - y'}{s'} = \frac{y}{f'}$$

Note that $y - y'$ is written instead of $y + y'$ because y', by the convention of signs, is a negative quantity. From the similar triangles QTS and FAS,

$$\frac{y - y'}{s} = \frac{-y'}{f}$$

The sum of these two equations is

$$\frac{y - y'}{s} + \frac{y - y'}{s'} = \frac{y}{f'} - \frac{y'}{f}$$

Since $f = f'$, the two terms on the right may be combined and $y - y'$

canceled out, yielding the desired equation,

$$\frac{1}{s} + \frac{1}{s'} = \frac{1}{f}$$

This is the lens formula in the *Gaussian* * *form*.

Another form of the lens formula, the so-called *Newtonian form*, is obtained in an analogous way from two other sets of similar triangles, QMF and FAS on the one hand, and TAF' and $F'M'Q'$ on the other. We find

$$\frac{y}{x} = \frac{-y'}{f} \quad \text{and} \quad \frac{-y'}{x'} = \frac{y}{f} \qquad (4j)$$

Multiplication of one equation by the other gives

$$xx' = f^2$$

In the Gaussian formula the object distances are measured from the lens, while in the Newtonian formula they are measured from the focal points. Object distances (s or x) are positive if the object lies to the left of its reference point (A or F, respectively), while image distances (s' or x') are positive if the image lies to the right of its reference point (A or F', respectively).

The lateral magnification as given by Eq. 4c corresponds to the Gaussian form. When distances are measured from focal points, one should use the Newtonian form, which may be obtained directly from Eq. 4j.

$$m = \frac{y'}{y} = -\frac{f}{x} = -\frac{x'}{f} \qquad (4k)$$

In the more general case where the medium on the two sides of the lens is different, it will be shown in the next section that the primary and secondary focal distances f and f' are different, being in the same ratio as the two refractive indices. The Newtonian lens formula then takes the symmetrical form

$$xx' = ff'$$

4.15. Derivation of the Lens Makers' Formula. The geometry required for this derivation is shown in Fig. 4L. Let n, n', and n'' represent the refractive indices of the three media as shown, f_1 and f'_1 the focal lengths for the first surface alone, and f'_2 and f''_2 the focal lengths

* Karl Friedrich Gauss (1777–1855). German astronomer and physicist, chiefly known for his contributions in the mathematical theory of magnetism. Coming from a poor family, he received support for his education because of his obvious mathematical ability. In 1841 he published the first general treatment of the first-order theory of lenses in his now famous papers, "Dioptrische Untersuchungen."

for the second surface alone. The oblique ray MT_1 is incident on the first surface as though it came from an axial object point M at a distance s_1 from the vertex A_1. At T_1 the ray is refracted according to Eq. $3b$ and is directed toward the conjugate point M'.

$$\frac{n}{s_1} + \frac{n'}{s_1'} = \frac{n' - n}{r_1} \tag{4l}$$

Arriving at T_2, the same ray is refracted in the new direction T_2M''. For this second surface the object ray T_1T_2 has for its object distance

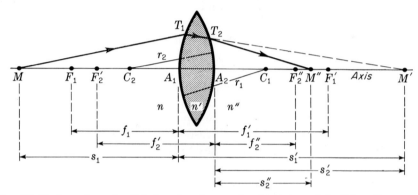

FIG. 4L. Each surface of a thin lens has its own focal points and focal lengths, as well as separate object and image distances.

s_2', and the refracted ray gives an image distance of s_2''. When Eq. $3b$ is applied to this second refracting surface,

$$\frac{n'}{s_2'} + \frac{n''}{s_2''} = \frac{n'' - n'}{r_2} \tag{4m}$$

If we now assume the lens thickness to be negligibly small compared with the object and image distances, we note the image distance s_1' for the first surface becomes equal in magnitude to the object distance s_2' for the second surface. Since M' is a virtual object for the second surface, the sign of the object distance for this surface is negative. As a consequence we can set $s_1' = -s_2'$ and write

$$\frac{n'}{s_1'} = -\frac{n'}{s_2'}$$

If we now add Eqs. $4l$ and $4m$ and substitute this equality, we obtain

$$\frac{n}{s_1} + \frac{n''}{s_2''} = \frac{n' - n}{r_1} + \frac{n'' - n'}{r_2} \tag{4n}$$

If we now call s_1 the object distance and designate it s as in Fig. 4M, and call s_2'' the image distance and designate it s'', we can write Eq. 4n as follows:

$$\frac{n}{s} + \frac{n''}{s''} = \frac{n' - n}{r_1} + \frac{n'' - n'}{r_2} \tag{4o}$$

This is the general formula for a thin lens having different media on the two sides. For such cases we can follow the procedure given in Sec. 3.4 and define primary and secondary focal points F and F'', and

FIG. 4M. When the media on the two sides of a thin lens have different indices, the primary and secondary focal lengths are not equal and the ray through the lens center is deviated.

the corresponding focal lengths f and f'', by setting s or s'' equal to infinity. When this is done, we obtain

$$\frac{n}{f} = \frac{n' - n}{r_1} + \frac{n'' - n'}{r_2} = \frac{n''}{f''} \tag{4p}$$

In words, the focal lengths have the ratio of the refractive indices of the two media n and n'' (see Fig. 4M).

$$\frac{f}{f''} = \frac{n}{n''} \tag{4q}$$

If the medium on both sides of the lens is the same, $n = n''$, Eq. 4o reduces to

$$\frac{n}{s} + \frac{n''}{s''} = (n' - n)\left(\frac{1}{r_1} - \frac{1}{r_2}\right) \tag{4r}$$

NOTE: The minus sign in the last factor arises when n'' and n' are reversed for the removal of like terms in the last factor of Eq. 4o.

Finally, in case the surrounding medium is air ($n = 1$), we obtain the lens makers' formula

$$\frac{1}{s} + \frac{1}{s''} = (n' - 1)\left(\frac{1}{r_1} - \frac{1}{r_2}\right) \tag{4s}$$

In the power notation of Eq. 3i, the general formula (Eq. 4o), can be written

$$V + V'' = P_1 + P_2 \tag{4t}$$

where $\quad V = \dfrac{n}{s} \qquad V'' = \dfrac{n''}{s''} \qquad P_1 = \dfrac{n' - n}{r_1} \qquad P_2 = \dfrac{n'' - n'}{r_2} \tag{4u}$

Equation 4t can be written

$$V + V'' = P \tag{4v}$$

where P is the power of the lens and is equal to the sum of the powers of the two surfaces.

$$P = P_1 + P_2 \tag{4w}$$

PROBLEMS

1. An object, located 16 cm in front of a thin lens, has its image formed on the opposite side 48 cm from the lens. Calculate (a) the focal length of the lens, and (b) the lens power.

2. An object 2 cm high is placed 10 cm in front of a thin lens of focal length 4 cm. Find (a) the image distance, (b) the magnification, and (c) the nature of the image. Solve graphically and by calculation. *Ans.* (a) +6.66 cm. (b) −0.66. (c) Real and inverted.

3. The two sides of a thin lens have radii $r_1 = +12$ cm and $r_2 = -30$ cm, respectively. The lens is made of glass of index 1.600. Calculate (a) the focal length, and (b) the power of the lens.

4. An object 4 cm high is located 20 cm in front of a lens whose focal length $f = -5$ cm. Calculate (a) the power of the lens, (b) the image distance, and (c) the lateral magnification. Graphically locate the image by (d) the parallel-ray method, and (e) the oblique-ray method. *Ans.* (a) −20 D. (b) −4.0 cm. (c) +0.20.

5. An equiconcave lens is to be made of crown glass of index $n = 1.65$. Calculate the radii of curvature if it is to have a power of −2.5 D.

6. A plano-convex lens is to be made of flint glass of index $n = 1.71$. Calculate the radius of curvature necessary to give the lens a power of +5 D. *Ans.* +14.2 cm.

7. Two lenses with focal lengths $f_1 = +12$ cm and $f_2 = +24$ cm, respectively, are located 6 cm apart. If an object 2 cm high is located 20 cm in front of the first lens, find (a) the position of, and (b) the size of the final image.

8. A converging lens is used to focus the image of a candle flame on a distant screen. A second lens with radii $r_1 = +12$ cm and $r_2 = -24$ cm and index $n = 1.60$ is placed in the converging beam 40 cm from the screen. Calculate (a) the power of the second lens, and (b) the position of the final image. *Ans.* (a) +7.5 D. (b) +10.0 cm.

9. A double-convex lens is to be made of glass having a refractive index of 1.52. If one surface is to have twice the radius of the other and the focal length is to be 5 cm, find the radii.

10. Two lenses having focal lengths $f_1 = +8$ cm and $f_2 = -12$ cm are placed 6 cm apart. If an object 3 cm high is located 24 cm in front of the first lens, find (a) the position, and (b) the size of the final image. *Ans.* (a) +12.0 cm. (b) −3.0 cm.

11. A lantern slide 2 in. high is located 10.5 ft from a projection screen. What is the focal length of the lens that will be required to project an image 40 in. high?

12. An object is located 1.4 m from a white screen.   A lens of what focal length will be required to form a real and inverted image on the screen with a magnification of -6?

Ans. $+17.1$ cm.

13. Three thin lenses have the following powers: $+1.0$ D, -2.0 D, and $+4.0$ D. What are all the possible powers obtainable with these lenses using one, two, or three at a time in contact?

14. Two thin lenses having the following radii of curvature and index are placed in contact: For the first lens $r_1 = +16$ cm, $r_2 = -24$ cm, and $n = 1.60$, and for the second lens $r_1 = -32$ cm, $r_2 = +48$ cm, and $n = 1.48$.   Find their combined (*a*) focal length, and (*b*) power.   *Ans.* (*a*) $+26.6$ cm.   (*b*) $+3.75$ D.

15. An object 2 cm high is located 12 cm in front of a lens of $+4$ cm focal length, and a lens of -8 cm focal length is placed 2 cm behind the converging lens.   Find (*a*) the position, and (*b*) the size of the final image.

16. An object 2 cm high is located 6 cm in front of a lens of -2 cm focal length. A lens of $+4$ cm focal length is placed 4 cm behind the first lens.   Find (*a*) the position, and (*b*) the size of the final image.   *Ans.* (*a*) $+14.7$ cm.   (*b*) -1.33 cm.

17. Three lenses with focal lengths of $+12$ cm, -12 cm, and $+12$ cm, respectively, are located one behind the other 2 cm apart.   If parallel light is incident on the first lens, how far behind the third lens will the light be brought to a focus?

18. An object 4 cm high is located 10 cm in front of a lens of $+2$ cm focal length. A lens of -3 cm focal length is placed 12.5 cm behind the first lens.   Find (*a*) the position, and (*b*) the size of the final image.

Ans. (*a*) -2.31 cm from second lens.   (*b*) -0.23 cm.

CHAPTER 5

THICK LENSES

When the thickness of a lens cannot be considered as small compared with its focal length, some of the thin-lens formulas of Chap. 4 are no longer applicable. The lens must be treated as a *thick lens*. This term is used not only for a single homogeneous lens with two spherical surfaces separated by an appreciable distance but also for any system of coaxial surfaces which is treated as a unit. The thick lens may therefore include several component lenses, which may or may not be in contact. We have already investigated one case which comes under this category, namely, the combination of a pair of thin lenses spaced some distance apart as was shown in Fig. 4H.

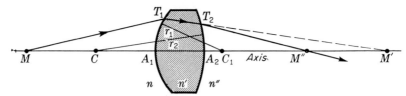

FIG. 5A. Details of the refraction of a ray at both surfaces of a lens.

5.1. Two Spherical Surfaces. A simple form of thick lens comprises two spherical surfaces as shown in Fig. 5A. A treatment of the image-forming capabilities of such a system follows directly from procedures outlined in Chaps. 3 and 4. Each surface, acting as an image-forming component, contributes to the final image formed by the system as a whole.

Let n, n', and n'' represent the refractive indices of three media separated by two spherical surfaces of radius r_1 and r_2. A light ray from an axial object point M is shown refracted by the first surface in a direction T_1M' and then further refracted by the second surface in a direction T_2M''. Since the lens axis may be considered as a second ray of light originating at M and passing through the system, M'' is the final image of the object point M. Hence M and M'' are conjugate points for the thick lens as a whole, and all rays from M should come to a focus at M''.

We shall first consider the parallel-ray method for graphically locating

62

an image formed by a thick lens and then apply the general formulas already given for calculating image distances. The formulas to be used are (see Sec. 3.4)

$$\frac{n}{s_1} + \frac{n'}{s_1'} = \frac{n'-n}{r_1} \qquad \frac{n'}{s_2'} + \frac{n''}{s_2''} = \frac{n''-n'}{r_2} \qquad (5a)$$
$$\text{for first surface} \qquad \text{for second surface}$$

5.2. The Parallel-ray Method. The parallel-ray method of graphical construction, applied to a thick lens of two surfaces, is shown in Fig. 5B.

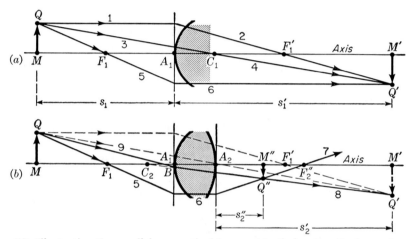

FIG. 5B. Illustrating the parallel-ray method for graphically locating the image formed by a thick lens.

Although the diagram is usually drawn as one, it has been separated into two parts here to simplify its explanation. The points F_1 and F_1' represent the primary and secondary focal points of the first surface, and F_2' and F_2'' represent the primary and secondary focal points of the second surface, respectively.

Diagram (a) is constructed by applying the method of Fig. 3F to the first surface alone and extending the refracted rays as far as is necessary to locate the image $M'Q'$. This real image, $M'Q'$, then becomes the object for the second surface as shown in diagram (b). The procedure is similar to that given for two thin lenses in Fig. 4H. Ray 5 in diagram (b), refracted parallel to the axis by the first surface, is refracted as ray 7 through the secondary focal point F_2'' of the second surface.

Rays 8 and 9 are obtained by drawing a line from Q' back through C_2 and then, through the intersection B, drawing the line BQ. The intersection of rays 7 and 8 locates the final image point Q'' and the final image $M''Q''$.

Example 1: An equiconvex lens 2 cm thick and having radii of curvature of 2 cm is mounted in the end of a water tank. An object in air is placed on the axis of the lens 5 cm from its vertex. Find the position of the final image. Assume refractive indices of 1.00, 1.50, and 1.33 for air, glass, and water, respectively.

Solution: The relative dimensions in this problem are approximately those shown in Fig. 5B(b). If we apply Eq. 5a to the first surface alone, we find the image distance to be,

$$\frac{1.00}{5} + \frac{1.50}{s_1'} = \frac{1.50 - 1.00}{2} \qquad \text{or} \qquad s_1' = +30 \text{ cm}$$

When the same equation is applied to the second surface, we note that the object distance is s_1' minus the lens thickness, or 28 cm, and that since it pertains to a virtual object it has a negative sign. The substitutions to be made are, therefore, $s_2 = -28$ cm, $n' = 1.50$, $n'' = 1.33$, and $r_2 = -2.0$ cm.

$$\frac{1.50}{-28} + \frac{1.33}{s_2''} = \frac{1.33 - 1.50}{-2} \qquad \text{or} \qquad s_2'' = +9.6 \text{ cm}$$

Particular attention should be paid to the signs of the various quantities in this second step. Because the second surface is concave toward the incident light, r_2 must have a negative sign. The incident rays in the glass belong to an object point M', which is virtual, and thus s_2', being to the right of the vertex A_2, must also be negative. The final image is formed in the water ($n'' = 1.33$) at a distance $+9.6$ cm from the second vertex. The positive sign of the resultant signifies that the image is *real*.

It should be noted that Eqs. 5a hold for paraxial rays only. The diagrams in Fig. 5B, showing all refraction as taking place at vertical lines through the vertices A_1 and A_2, are likewise restricted to paraxial rays.

5.3. Focal Points and Principal Points. Diagrams showing the characteristics of the two focal points of a thick lens are given in Fig. 5C. In the first diagram diverging rays from the primary focal point F emerge parallel to the axis, while in the second diagram parallel incident rays are brought to a focus at the secondary focal point F''. In each case the incident and refracted rays have been extended to their point of intersection between the surfaces. Transverse planes through these intersections constitute *primary* and *secondary principal planes*. These planes cross the axis at points H and H'', called the *principal points*. It will be noticed that there is a point-for-point correspondence between the two principal planes, so that each is an erect image of the other, and of the same size. For this reason they have sometimes been called "unit planes." They are best defined by saying that *the principal planes are two planes having unit positive lateral magnification.*

The focal lengths, as shown in the figure, are measured from the focal points F and F'' to their respective principal points H and H'' and not to their respective vertices A_1 and A_2. If the medium is the same on both

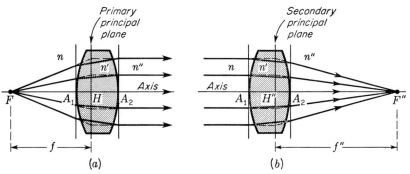

FIG. 5C. Ray diagrams showing the primary and secondary principal planes of a thick lens.

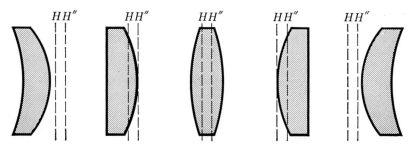

FIG. 5D. Illustrating the variation of the positions of the primary and secondary principal planes as a thick lens of fixed focal length is subjected to "bending."

sides of the lens, $n'' = n$, the primary focal length f is exactly equal to the secondary focal length f''.

If the media on the two sides of the lens are different so that n'' is not equal to n, the two focal lengths are different and have the ratio of their corresponding refractive indices.

$$\frac{n''}{n} = \frac{f''}{f} \tag{5b}$$

In general the focal points and principal points are not symmetrically located with respect to the lens but are at different distances from the vertices. This is true even when the media on both sides are the same and the focal lengths are equal. As a lens with a given material and focal length is "bent" (see Fig. 5D), departing in either direction from the symmetrical shape of an equiconvex lens, the principal points are shifted. For meniscus lenses of considerable thickness and curvature, H and H'' may be completely outside the lens.

5.4. Conjugate Relations. In order to trace any ray through a thick lens, the positions of the focal points and principal points must first be determined. Once this has been done, either graphically or by computation, the parallel-ray construction can be used to locate the image

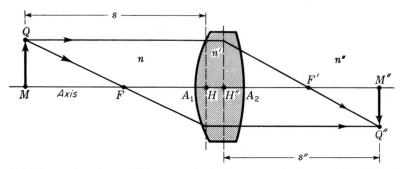

FIG. 5E. Illustrating the parallel-ray method of construction for graphically locating an image formed by a thick lens.

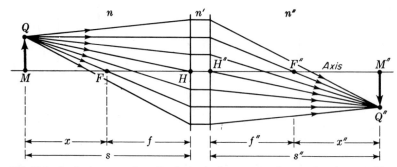

FIG. 5F. Principal planes and antiprincipal planes are planes of unit magnification.

as shown in Fig. 5E. The construction procedure follows that given in Fig. 4M for a thin lens, except that here all rays in the region between the two principal planes are drawn parallel to the axis.

By a comparison of the two figures, and the derivations of Eqs. 4n and 4o, it will be found that, provided the object and image distances are measured to or from the principal points, we may apply the Gaussian lens formula

$$\frac{n}{s} + \frac{n''}{s''} = \frac{n}{f} = \frac{n''}{f''} \tag{5c}$$

or by Eq. 3h

$$V + V'' = P \tag{5d}$$

In the special case where the media on the two sides of the lens are the same, so that $n'' = n$, we find $f'' = f$ and Eq. (5c) becomes

$$\frac{1}{s} + \frac{1}{s''} = \frac{1}{f} = \frac{1}{f''} \tag{5e}$$

Figure 5F shows that for the purposes of graphical construction the lens may be regarded as replaced by its two principal planes.

5.5. The Oblique-ray Method. The oblique-ray method of construction may be used to find graphically the focal points of a thick lens. As an illustration, consider a glass lens of index 1.50, thickness 2 cm, and

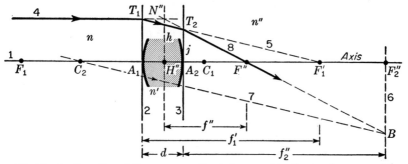

FIG. 5G. Illustrating the oblique-ray method for graphically tracing paraxial rays through a thick lens.

radii $r_1 = +3$ cm, $r_2 = -5$ cm, surrounded by air of index $n = 1.00$. The first step is to calculate the primary and secondary focal lengths of each surface separately by the use of the formulas for a single spherical surface (Eqs. 3c and 3d). Using the present notation, these are

$$\frac{n}{f_1} = \frac{n'}{f_1'} = \frac{n' - n}{r_1} \quad \text{and} \quad \frac{n'}{f_2'} = \frac{n''}{f_2''} = \frac{n'' - n'}{r_2} \tag{5f}$$

The given quantities are

$$r_1 = +3 \text{ cm} \qquad r_2 = -5 \text{ cm} \qquad d = 2 \text{ cm} \qquad n' = 1.50 \qquad n'' = n = 1.00$$

By substituting these values in Eqs. 5f, we obtain

$$f_1 = +6 \text{ cm} \qquad f_1' = +9 \text{ cm} \qquad f_2' = +15 \text{ cm} \qquad f_2'' = +10 \text{ cm}$$

With these focal lengths known, the lens axis can be drawn as in Fig. 5G and the known points measured off to some suitable scale. After drawing lines 2 and 3 through the lens vertices, a parallel incident ray 4 is selected. Upon refraction at the first surface the ray takes the new direction 5 toward F_1', the secondary focal point of that surface. After line 6 is drawn through F_2'', line 7 is drawn through C_2 parallel to ray 5. The point B where line 6 crosses line 7 determines the direction of the final refracted ray 8. The intersection of ray 8 with the axis locates the secondary focal point F'' of the lens, while its intersection N'' with the incident ray locates the corresponding secondary principal plane H''.

By turning the lens around and repeating this procedure, the position of the primary focal point F and the position of the primary principal point H can be determined. The student will find it well worthwhile to carry out this construction and to check the results by measuring the focal lengths to verify the fact that they are equal. It is to be noted that, in accordance with the assumption of paraxial rays, all refraction is assumed to occur at the plane tangent to the boundary at its vertex.

5.6. General Thick-lens Formulas. There is a set of formulas that may be used for the calculation of important constants generally associated with a thick lens. These formulas are presented below in the form of two equivalent sets.

<table>
<tr><td align="center">Gaussian Formulas</td><td align="center">Power Formulas</td></tr>
</table>

$$\frac{n}{f} = \frac{n'}{f_1'} + \frac{n''}{f_2'} - \frac{dn''}{f_1'f_2'} = \frac{n''}{f''}$$

$$P = P_1 + P_2 - \frac{d}{n'}P_1P_2 \qquad (5g)$$

$$A_1F = -f\left(1 - \frac{d}{f_2'}\right)$$

$$A_1F = -\frac{n}{P}\left(1 - \frac{d}{n'}P_2\right) \qquad (5h)$$

$$A_1H = +f\frac{d}{f_2'}$$

$$A_1H = +\frac{n}{P}\cdot\frac{d}{n'}P_2 \qquad (5i)$$

$$A_2F'' = +f''\left(1 - \frac{d}{f_1'}\right)$$

$$A_2F'' = +\frac{n''}{P}\left(1 - \frac{d}{n'}P_1\right) \qquad (5j)$$

$$A_2H'' = -f''\frac{d}{f_1'}$$

$$A_2H'' = -\frac{n''}{P}\cdot\frac{d}{n'}P_1 \qquad (5k)$$

These equations are derived from geometrical relations that may be obtained from a diagram like Fig. 5G. As an illustration, the Gaussian equation 5k is derived as follows: From the two similar right triangles $T_1A_1F_1'$ and $T_2A_2F_1'$, we can write corresponding sides as proportions

$$\frac{A_1F_1'}{A_1T_1} = \frac{A_2F_1'}{A_2T_2} \qquad \text{or} \qquad \frac{f_1'}{h} = \frac{f_1' - d}{j}$$

and, from the two similar right triangles $N''H''F''$ and T_2A_2F'', we can write the proportions

$$\frac{H''F''}{H''N''} = \frac{A_2F''}{A_2T_2} \qquad \text{or} \qquad \frac{f''}{h} = \frac{f'' - H''A_2}{j}$$

If we solve each equation for j/h and then equate the right-hand sides of the resultant equations, we obtain

$$\frac{f_1' - d}{f_1'} = \frac{f'' - H''A_2}{f''} \qquad \text{or} \qquad H''A_2 = f''\frac{d}{f_1'}$$

If we now reverse the segment $H''A_2$ to A_2H'' by changing the sign from $+$ to $-$, we obtain

$$A_2H'' = -f'' \frac{d}{f_1'}$$

In terms of surface power and lens power,

$$P_1 = \frac{n}{f_1} = \frac{n'}{f_1'} \qquad P_2 = \frac{n'}{f_2'} = \frac{n''}{f_2''} \qquad P = \frac{n}{f} = \frac{n''}{f''} \qquad (5l)$$

the same equation can be written

$$A_2H'' = -\frac{n''}{P} \frac{d}{n'} P_1$$

In the design of certain optical systems it is convenient to know the *vertex power* of a lens. This power, sometimes called *effective power*, is given as

$$P_v = \frac{P}{1 - dP_1/n'} \qquad (5m)$$

and is defined as the reciprocal of the distance from the back surface of the lens to the secondary focal point. This distance is commonly called the *back focal length*. Since $P_v = 1/A_2F''$, the above equation for vertex power is obtained by inverting Eq. 5j. In the inversion the lens is assumed to be in air so that $n'' = 1$.

In a similar way the distance from the primary focal point to the front surface of the lens is called the *front focal length*, and the reciprocal of this distance is called the *neutralizing power*. $P_n = 1/A_1F$. Calling P_n the neutralizing power, we can take the reciprocal of Eq. 5h to obtain

$$P_n = \frac{P}{1 - dP_2/n'} \qquad (5n)$$

The name is derived from the fact that a thin lens of this specified power and of opposite sign will, upon contact with the front surface, give zero power to the combination.

The following example will serve as an illustration of the use of thick-lens formulas applied to two surfaces:

Example 2: A lens has the following specifications: $r_1 = +1.5$ cm, $r_2 = +1.5$ cm, $d = 2.0$ cm, $n = 1.00$, $n' = 1.60$, and $n'' = 1.30$. Find (a) the primary and secondary focal lengths of the separate surfaces, (b) the primary and secondary focal lengths of the system, and (c) the primary and secondary principal points.

Solution: To apply the Gaussian formulas, we first calculate the individual focal lengths of the surfaces by means of Eq. 5f.

$$\frac{n}{f_1} = \frac{n' - n}{r_1} = \frac{1.60 - 1.00}{1.5}$$
$$= 0.400$$

$$\frac{n'}{f_2'} = \frac{n'' - n'}{r_2} = \frac{1.30 - 1.60}{1.5}$$
$$= -0.200$$

$$f_1 = \frac{1.00}{0.40} = +2.50 \text{ cm}$$

$$f_1' = \frac{1.60}{0.40} = +4.00 \text{ cm}$$

$$f_2' = \frac{1.60}{-0.20} = -8.00 \text{ cm}$$

$$f_2'' = \frac{1.30}{-0.20} = -6.50 \text{ cm}$$

Ans. (a)

The focal lengths of the system are calculated from Eq. 5g.

$$\frac{n}{f} = \frac{n'}{f_1'} + \frac{n''}{f_2''} - \frac{d\,n''}{f_1'f_2''} = \frac{1.60}{4.00} + \frac{1.30}{-6.50} - \frac{2.00}{4.00}\frac{1.30}{-6.50}$$

$$\frac{n}{f} = 0.40 - 0.20 + 0.10 = 0.30$$

or

$$f = \frac{1.00}{0.30} = +3.333 \text{ cm} \qquad \text{and} \qquad f'' = \frac{n''}{0.30} = \frac{1.30}{0.30} = +4.333 \text{ cm}$$

The focal points of the system are given by Eqs. 5h and 5j.

$$A_1F = -f\left(1 - \frac{d}{f_2'}\right) = -3.333\left(1 - \frac{2.0}{-8.0}\right) = -4.166 \text{ cm}$$

$$A_2F'' = +f''\left(1 - \frac{d}{f_1'}\right) = +4.33\left(1 - \frac{2.0}{4.0}\right) = +2.167 \text{ cm}$$

Ans. (b)

The principal points are given by Eqs. 5i and 5k.

$$A_1H = +f\frac{d}{f_2'} = +3.33\frac{2.0}{-8.0} = -0.833 \text{ cm}$$

$$A_2H'' = -f''\frac{d}{f_1'} = -4.33\frac{2.0}{4.0} = -2.167 \text{ cm}$$

Ans. (c)

Positive signs represent distances measured to the right of the reference vertex and negative signs those measured to the left. By subtracting the magnitudes of the two intervals A_1F and A_1H, the primary focal length $FH = 4.166 - 0.833 = 3.333$ cm is obtained and serves as a check on the calculations in part (b). Similarly the addition of the two intervals A_2F'' and A_2H'' gives the secondary focal length

$$H''F'' = 2.167 + 2.167 = 4.334 \text{ cm}$$

The graphical solution of this same problem is shown in Fig. 5H. After the axis is drawn and the lens vertices A_1 and A_2 and the centers

C_1 and C_2 are located, the individual focal points F_1, F_1', F_2', and F_2'' are laid off according to the results in part (a). The parallel ray (1) is refracted at the first surface toward F_1'. The oblique-ray method is applied to this ray (2) at the second surface, and the final ray (3) is obtained. The point where ray (3) crosses the axis locates the secondary focal point F'', and the point where its backward extension intersects

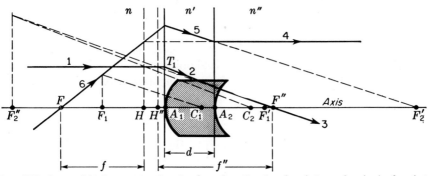

FIG. 5H. A graphical construction for locating the focal points and principal points of a thick lens.

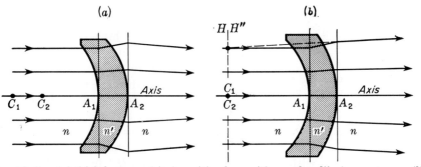

FIG. 5I. Special thick lenses. (a) A positive lens with equal radii of curvature. (b) A negative lens with concentric surfaces.

ray (1) locates the secondary principal plane H''. Ray (4) is constructed backward by drawing it parallel to the axis and from right to left. The first refraction gives ray (5) up and to the left as if it came from F_2'. The oblique-ray method applied to ray (5) at the left-hand surface yields ray (6). The point where ray (6) crosses the axis locates F, and the point where it crosses the extension of ray (4) locates H. Hence parts (b) and (c) of the problem are solved graphically, and they check with the calculated values.

5.7. Special Thick Lenses. Two special lenses of some interest as well as practical importance are presented here. The first, as shown in Fig. 5I, is a lens with spherical surfaces of equal radii, $r_1 = r_2$. A lens of this description, surrounded by a medium of lower index, $n' > n$, has a small but positive power. Its principal planes are located some distance from and to the right of the lens, and their spacing HH'' is equal to the lens thickness d. If the surrounding medium has a greater index, as in the case of an air space between the surfaces of two lenses of equal index, $n' < n$, the power is again positive but the principal planes lie some distance to the left of the lens and a distance d apart.

The second special case is that of a *concentric lens*, both surfaces having the same center of curvature. Where such a lens is surrounded by a medium of lower index, $n' > n$, the system has a negative power with a long focal length and the principal points coincide with the common center of curvature of the two surfaces. In other words, it acts like a thin lens located at C_1C_2.

5.8. Nodal Points and Optical Center. Of all the rays that pass through a lens from an off-axis object point to its corresponding image point, there will always be one for which the direction of the ray in the image space is the same as that in the object space, i.e., the segments of the ray before reaching the lens, and after leaving it, are parallel. The two points at which these segments, if projected, intersect the axis are called the *nodal points*, and the transverse planes through them are called the *nodal planes*. This third pair of points and their associated planes are shown in Fig. 5J, which also shows the optical center of the lens at C. It is readily shown that if the medium on both sides is the same, the nodal points N and N'' coincide with the principal points H and H'', but that if the two media have different indices, the principal points and the nodal points will be separate. Since the incident and emergent rays make equal angles with the axis, the nodal points are called conjugate points of *unit positive angular magnification*.

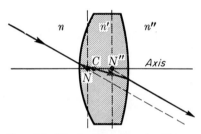

FIG. 5J. Illustrating the significance of the nodal points and nodal planes of a thick lens.

If the ray is to emerge parallel to its original direction, the two surface elements of the lens where it enters and leaves must be parallel to each other so that the effect is like that of a plane-parallel plate. A line between these two points crosses the axis at the *optical center* C. It is therefore through the optical center that the undeviated ray must be drawn in all cases. It has the interesting property that its position, depending as it does only on the radii of curvature and thickness of the lens, does not vary with color of the light. All the six cardinal points (Sec. 5.9) will in general have a slightly different position for each color.

Figure 5K will help to clarify the different significance of the nodal points and the principal points. This figure is drawn for $n'' \neq n$, so that the two sets of points are separate. Ray 11 through the secondary nodal point is parallel to ray 10, the latter being incident in the direction of the primary nodal point N. On the other hand both these segments intersect the principal planes at the same distance above the principal points H and H''. From the small parallelogram at the center of the

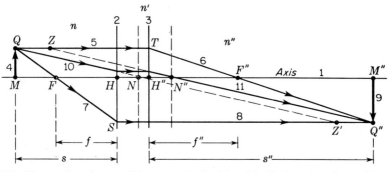

FIG. 5K. Illustrating the parallel-ray method of graphically locating the nodal points and planes of a thick lens.

diagram, it is observed that the distance between nodal planes is exactly equal to the distance between principal planes. In general, therefore,

$$NN'' = HH'' \tag{5o}$$

Furthermore in this case, where the initial and final values of the refractive index differ, the focal lengths, which are measured from the principal points, are no longer equal. The primary focal length FH is equal to the distance $N''F''$, while the secondary focal length $H''F''$ is equal to FN:

$$f = FH = N''F'' \quad \text{and} \quad f'' = H''F'' = FN \tag{5p}$$

Nodal points may be determined graphically, as shown in Fig. 5K, by measuring off the distance $ZQ = HH'' = Z'Q''$ and drawing straight lines through QZ' and ZQ''. From the geometry of this diagram, the lateral magnification y'/y is given by

$$m = \frac{y''}{y} = -\frac{s'' - HN}{s + HN} \tag{5q}$$

where

$$HN = f'' \frac{n'' - n}{n''} \tag{5r}$$

When the object and image distances s and s'' are, as usual, measured from their corresponding principal points H and H'', Eq. 5c is valid for paraxial rays.

The distance from the first vertex to the primary nodal point is given by

$$A_1N = f\left(\frac{d}{f_2'} + \frac{n'' - n}{n}\right) \tag{5s}$$

Example 3: Find the nodal points of the thick lens given in Example 2.

Solution: To locate the primary nodal point N, we may use Eq. 5r and substitute the given values of $n = 1.00$ and $n'' = 1.30$ and the already calculated value of $f'' = +4.333$ cm,

$$HN = 4.333\left(\frac{1.30 - 1.00}{1.30}\right) = +1.00 \text{ cm}$$

Hence the nodal points N and N'' are 1.00 cm to the right of their respective principal points H and H''.

5.9. Other Cardinal Points. In thick-lens problems a knowledge of the six cardinal points, comprising the focal points, principal points, and nodal points, is always adequate to obtain solutions. Other points of lesser importance but still of some interest are (1) negative principal points, and (2) negative nodal points. *Negative principal points* are conjugate points for which the lateral magnification is unity and negative. For a lens in air they lie at twice the focal length and on opposite sides of the lens. *Negative nodal points* lie as far from the focal points as the ordinary cardinal nodal points, but on opposite sides. Their position is such that the angular magnification is unity and negative. Although a knowledge of these two pairs of cardinal points is not essential to the solution of optical problems, in certain cases considerable simplification is achieved by using them.

5.10. Thin-lens Combination as a Thick Lens. A combination of two or more thin lenses may also be referred to as a thick lens. This is because of the fact that the optical properties of a set of coaxially mounted lenses can be conveniently treated in terms of only two focal points and two principal points. If the object space and image space have the same refractive index (and this is nearly always the case), the nodal points and planes coincide with the principal points and planes.

A combination of two thin lenses with focal lengths of 8 and 9 cm respectively is shown in Fig. 5L. By the oblique-ray method the focal points F and F'' and the principal points H and H'' have been determined graphically. In doing so the refraction at each lens was considered in the same way as the refraction at the individual surfaces of the thick lens of Fig. 5G. There is a strong resemblance between these two diagrams; i.e., for a thin lens we assume that all of the deviation occurs at one plane, just as for a single surface. This assumption is justified only when the separation of the principal planes of the lens can be neglected. The definition of a thin lens is just a statement of this fact: *a thin lens in one in which the two principal planes and the optical center coincide at the geometrical center of the lens.* The locations of the centers of the two lenses in this example are labeled A_1 and A_2 in Fig. 5L.

A diagram for a combination of a positive and a negative lens is given in Fig. 5M. The construction lines are not shown, but the graphical procedure used in determining the paths of the two rays is the same as that

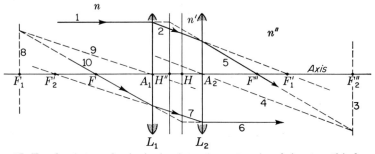

FIG. 5L. Focal points and principal points of a system involving two thin lenses.

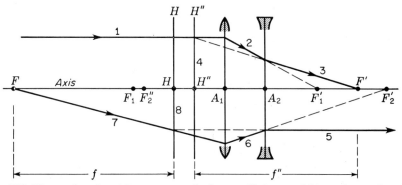

FIG. 5M. Illustrating the oblique-ray method as applied to positive and negative thin lenses in combination.

shown in Fig. 5L. Note here that the final principal points H and H'' lie outside the interlens space but that the focal lengths f and f'' measured from these points are as usual equal. The lower ray, although shown traveling from left to right, is graphically constructed by drawing it from right to left.

The positions of the cardinal points of a combination of two thin lenses in air can be calculated by means of the thick-lens formulas given in Sec. 5.6. As used for thin lenses in place of individual refracting surfaces, A_1 and A_2 become the two lens centers, while f_1, f_2 and P_1, P_2 become their separate focal lengths and powers, respectively. The latter are given by

$$P_1 = \frac{n_1 - n}{r_1} + \frac{n' - n_1}{r_1'} = \frac{n}{f_1} \qquad P_2 = \frac{n_2 - n'}{r_2} + \frac{n'' - n_2}{r_2'} = \frac{n'}{f_2'} \quad (5t)$$

where r_1 and r_1' are the radii of the first lens of index n_1, and r_2 and r_2' are the radii of the second lens of index n_2. The surrounding media have indices n, n', and n'' (see Fig. 5L). The other formulas, Eqs. 5g, 5h, 5i, 5j, and 5k, remain unchanged.

To illustrate the use of these formulas, let us consider the following problem on a lens combination similar to that shown in Fig. 5M:

Example 4: An equiconvex lens with radii of 4 cm and index $n_1 = 1.50$ is located 2 cm in front of an equiconcave lens with radii of 6 cm and index $n_2 = 1.60$. The lenses are to be considered as thin. The surrounding media have indices $n = 1.00$, $n' = 1.33$, and $n'' = 1.00$. Find (a) the power, (b) the focal lengths, (c) the focal points, and (d) the principal points of the system.

Solution: In this instance we shall solve the problem by the use of the power formulas. By Eqs. 5t, the powers of the two lenses in their surrounding media are

$$P_1 = \frac{1.50 - 1.00}{0.04} + \frac{1.33 - 1.50}{-0.04} = 12.50 + 4.17 = +16.67 \text{ D}$$

$$P_2 = \frac{1.60 - 1.33}{-0.06} + \frac{1.00 - 1.60}{0.06} = -4.45 - 10.0 = -14.45 \text{ D}$$

By Eq. 5g, we obtain

$$P = 16.67 - 14.45 + 0.015 \times 16.67 \times 14.45$$

or
$$P = +5.84 \text{ D} \quad Ans. \ (a)$$

Using Eq. 5l, we find

$$f = \frac{n}{P} = \frac{1.00}{5.84} = 0.171 \text{ m} = 17.1 \text{ cm} \left.\begin{array}{l} \\ \\ \\ \\ \end{array}\right\} \quad Ans. \ (b)$$

$$f'' = \frac{n''}{P} = \frac{1.00}{5.84} = 0.171 \text{ m} = 17.1 \text{ cm}$$

By Eqs. 5h, 5i, 5j, and 5k, we obtain

$$A_1F = -\frac{1.00}{5.84}(1 + 0.015 \times 14.45) = -0.208 \text{ m} = -20.8 \text{ cm}$$

$$A_1H = +\frac{1.00}{5.84}0.015 \ (-14.45) \qquad = -0.037 \text{ m} = -3.7 \text{ cm}$$

$$A_2F'' = +\frac{1.00}{5.84}(1 - 0.015 \times 16.67) = +0.128 \text{ m} = +12.8 \text{ cm}$$

$$Ans. \ (c)$$

$$A_2H'' = -\frac{1.00}{5.84}0.015 \times 16.67 \qquad = -0.043 \text{ m} = -4.3 \text{ cm}$$

$$Ans. \ (d)$$

As a check on these results we find that the difference between the first two intervals A_1F and A_1H gives the primary focal length $FH = 17.1$ cm. Similarly the sum of the second two intervals A_2F'' and A_2H'' gives the secondary focal length $H''F'' = 17.1$ cm.

5.11. Thick-lens Combinations. The problem of calculating the positions of the cardinal points of a thick lens consisting of a combination of several component lenses of appreciable thickness is one of considerable difficulty, but one which may be solved by use of the principles already given. If, in a combination of two lenses such as that in Fig. 5L, the individual lenses cannot be considered as thin, each must be represented

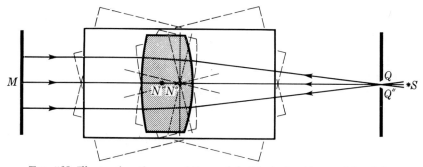

FIG. 5N. Illustrating the use of the nodal slide in locating nodal points.

by a pair of principal planes. There are thus two pairs of principal points, H_1 and H_1' for the first lens and H_2' and H_2'' for the second, and the problem is to combine these to find a single pair H and H'' for the combination, and to determine the focal lengths. By carrying out a construction similar to Fig. 5G for each lens separately, it is possible to locate the principal points and focal points of each. Then the construction of Fig. 5L may be accomplished, taking account of the unit magnification between principal planes.

Formulas may be given for the analytical solution of this problem, but because of their complexity they will not be given here.* Instead, we shall describe a method of determining the positions of the cardinal points of any thick lens by direct experiment.

5.12. Nodal Slide. The nodal points of a single lens, or of a combination of lenses, may be located experimentally by mounting the system on a nodal slide. This is merely a horizontal support which permits rotation of the lens about any desired point on its axis. As is shown in Fig. 5N, light from a source S is sent through a slit Q, adjusted to lie at the secondary focal point of the lens. Emerging as a parallel beam, this

---

* These equations are given, for example, in G. S. Monk, "Light, Principles and Experiments," 1st ed., McGraw-Hill Book Company, Inc., New York, 1937.

light is reflected back on itself by a fixed plane mirror M, passing again through the lens system and being brought to a focus at Q''. This image of the slit is formed slightly to one side of the slit itself on the white face of one of the slit jaws. The nodal slide carrying the lens system is now

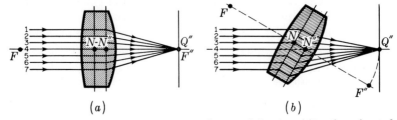

(a)   (b)

FIG. 50. Rotation of a lens about its secondary nodal point shifts the refracted rays but not the image.

rotated back and forth and the lens repeatedly shifted, until the rotation produces no motion of the image Q''. When this condition is reached, the axis of rotation N'' locates one nodal point. By turning the nodal slide end-for-end and repeating the process, the other nodal point N is found. When performed in air, this experiment of course locates the principal points as well, and the distance $N''Q''$ is an accurate measure of the focal length.

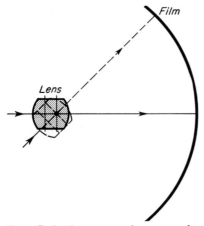

FIG. 5P. In the panoramic camera the lens rotates about a nodal point as a center.

The principle of this method of rotation about a nodal point is illustrated in Fig. 50. In the first diagram ray 4 along the axis passes through N and N'' to the focus at Q''. In the second diagram the lens system has been rotated about N'' and the same bundle of rays passes through the lens, coming to a focus at the same point Q''. Ray 3 is now directed toward N and ray 4 toward N''. When projected across from the plane of N to that of N'', the rays still converge toward Q'' even though F'' is now shifted to one side. Note that ray 3 approaches N in exactly the same direction that it leaves N'', corresponding to the defining condition for the nodal points.

If a camera lens is pivoted about its secondary nodal point and a long strip of photographic film is curved to a circular arc of radius f'', a continuous picture covering a very wide angle may be taken. Such an instrument, shown schematically in Fig. 5P, is known as a *panoramic camera.* The shutter usually consists of a vertical slit just in front of the film, which moves with the rotation so that it always remains centered on the lens axis.

PROBLEMS

1. An equiconvex lens has an index of 1.80, radii of 4.0 cm, and a thickness of 3.6 cm. Calculate (a) the focal length, (b) the power, and (c) the distances from the vertices to the corresponding focal points and principal points.

2. Solve Prob. 1 graphically, locating the focal points and principal points. *Ans.* $A_1F = -1.87$ cm. $A_1H = +1.25$ cm. $A_2F'' = +1.87$ cm. $A_2H'' = -1.25$ cm.

3. A plano-convex lens 3.2 cm thick is made of glass of index 1.60. If the second surface has a radius of 3.2 cm, find (a) the focal length of the lens, (b) the power, and (c) the distances from the vertices to the corresponding focal points and principal points.

4. Solve Prob. 3 graphically, locating the focal points and principal points. *Ans.* $A_1F = -3.33$ cm. $A_1H = +2.00$ cm. $A_2F'' = +5.33$ cm. $A_2H'' = 0$.

5. A glass lens with radii $r_1 = +3.0$ cm and $r_2 = +5.0$ cm has a thickness of 3.0 cm and an index of 1.50. Calculate (a) the focal length, (b) the power, and (c) the distances from the vertices to the corresponding focal points and principal points.

6. Solve Prob. 5 graphically, locating the focal points and principal points. *Ans.* $A_1F = -12.0$ cm. $A_1H = -2.0$ cm. $A_2F'' = +6.66$ cm. $A_2H'' = -3.33$ cm.

7. A glass lens with radii $r_1 = +5.0$ cm and $r_2 = +2.5$ cm has a thickness of 3.0 cm and an index of 1.50. Calculate (a) the focal length, (b) the power, and (c) the distances from the vertices to the corresponding focal points and principal points.

8. Solve Prob. 7 graphically, locating the focal points and principal points. Use the method outlined in Fig. 5H. *Ans.* $A_1F = +23.33$ cm. $A_1H = +6.66$ cm. $A_2F'' = -13.33$ cm. $A_2H'' = +3.33$ cm.

9. A thick lens with radii $r_1 = -8.0$ cm and $r_2 = -4.0$ cm has a thickness of 3.23 cm and an index of 1.615. Calculate (a) the focal length, (b) the power, and (c) the distances from the vertices to the corresponding focal points and principal points.

10. Solve Prob. 9 graphically, locating the focal points and principal points. Use the method shown in Fig. 5H. *Ans.* $A_1F = -6.93$ cm. $A_1H = +3.07$ cm. $A_2F'' = +11.54$ cm. $A_2H'' = +1.54$ cm.

11. A thick glass lens is placed in the end of a tank containing an oil of refractive index 1.30. The lens, with radii $r_1 = +4.2$ cm and $r_2 = -2.0$ cm, is 5.1 cm thick and has a refractive index of 1.70. If r_2 is in contact with the oil, find (a) the primary and secondary focal length, (b) the power, and (c) the distances from the vertices to the corresponding focal points and principal points.

12. Solve Prob. 11 graphically, locating the focal points and principal points. Use the method shown in Fig. 5H. *Ans.* $A_1F = -1.50$ cm. $A_1H = +2.25$ cm. $A_2F'' = +2.44$ cm. $A_2H'' = -2.44$ cm.

13. A glass lens 3.0 cm thick has radii $r_1 = +5.0$ cm and $r_2 = +2.0$ cm and an index of 1.50. If r_2 is in contact with a liquid of index 1.40, find (a) the primary and secondary focal lengths, (b) the power, and (c) the distances from the vertices to the corresponding focal points, principal points, and nodal points.

14. Solve Prob. 13 graphically, locating the six cardinal points of the lens. Use the methods of Figs. 5H and 5K.

Ans. $A_1F = -18.33$ cm. $A_1H = -1.66$ cm. $A_1N = +5.0$ cm. $A_2F'' = +18.66$ cm. $A_2H'' = -4.66$ cm. $A_2N'' = +2.0$ cm.

15. A glass lens with radii $r_1 = +4.0$ cm and $r_2 = +4.0$ cm has an index of 1.50 and a thickness of 1.5 cm. Oil of index 1.30 is in contact with r_2. Find (a) the primary and secondary focal lengths, (b) the power, and (c) the distances from the vertices to the corresponding focal points, principal points, and nodal points.

16. Solve Prob. 15 graphically, locating the six cardinal points of the lens. Use the methods of Figs. 5H and 5K.

Ans. $A_1F = -12.92$ cm. $A_1H = -0.61$ cm. $A_1N = +3.08$ cm. $A_2F'' = +14.00$ cm. $A_2H'' = -2.00$ cm. $A_2N'' = +1.69$ cm.

17. A glass lens 4.8 cm thick and index 1.60 has radii $r_1 = +6.0$ cm and $r_2 = +5.0$ cm. If a liquid of index 1.20 is in contact with r_1 and another liquid of index 2.0 is in contact with r_2, find (a) the primary and secondary focal lengths, (b) the power, and (c) the distances from the vertices to the corresponding focal points, principal points, and nodal points.

18. Solve Prob. 17 graphically, locating the six cardinal points of the lens. Use the method outlined in Figs. 5H and 5K.

Ans. $A_1F = -6.98$ cm. $A_1H = +2.20$ cm. $A_1N = +8.32$ cm. $A_2F'' = +12.24$ cm. $A_2H'' = -3.06$ cm. $A_2N'' = +3.06$ cm.

19. Two thin lenses, each with a focal length of $+10.0$ cm, are placed 4.0 cm apart in air. Find, for the combination, (a) the focal length, (b) the power, and (c) the distances from the lens centers to the focal points and principal points.

20. Solve Prob. 19 graphically, locating the focal points and principal points. Use the method of Fig. 5L.

Ans. $A_1F = -3.75$ cm. $A_1H = +2.50$ cm. $A_2F'' = +3.75$ cm. $A_2H'' = -2.50$ cm.

21. Two thin lenses with focal lengths $f_1 = +10.0$ cm and $f_2 = -10.0$ cm are located 5.0 cm apart in air. Find, for the combination, (a) the focal length, (b) the power, and (c) the distances from the lens centers to the focal points and principal points.

22. Solve Prob. 21 graphically, locating the focal points and principal points. Use the method of Fig. 5M.

Ans. $A_1F = -30.0$ cm. $A_1H = -10.0$ cm. $A_2F'' = +10.0$ cm. $A_2H'' = -10.0$ cm.

23. Two thin lenses with focal lengths $f_1 = -10.0$ cm and $f_2 = +10.0$ cm are located 5.0 cm apart in air. Find, for the combination, (a) the focal length, (b) the power, and (c) the distances from the lens centers to the focal points and principal points.

24. Solve Prob. 23 graphically, locating the focal points and principal points. Use the method of Fig. 5M.

Ans. $A_1F = -10.0$ cm. $A_1H = +10.0$ cm. $A_2F'' = +30.0$ cm. $A_2H'' = +10.0$ cm.

25. Two thin lenses with focal lengths of $f_1 = -10.0$ cm and $f_2 = -20.0$ cm are located 5.0 cm apart in air. Find, for the combination, (a) the focal length, (b) the power, and (c) the distances from the lens centers to the focal points and principal points.

26. Solve Prob. 25 graphically, locating the focal points and principal points. Use the method of Fig. 5L.

Ans. $A_1F = +7.14$ cm. $A_1H = +1.43$ cm. $A_2F'' = -8.57$ cm. $A_2H'' = -2.86$ cm.

27. With Fig. 5G as a guide make a diagram locating the secondary focal point. From similar triangles in your diagram derive Eq. 5j.

28. With Fig. 5G as a guide make a diagram locating the primary focal point. From similar triangles in your diagram derive Eq. 5h.

29. A lens with equal radii of curvature, $r_1 = r_2 = +5.0$ cm, is 3 cm thick and has an index of 1.50. If the lens is surrounded by air, find (*a*) the power, (*b*) the focal length, and (*c*) the focal points and principal points.

30. A concentric lens has radii of -5 cm and -8 cm, respectively, and an index of 1.50. If the lens is surrounded by air, find (*a*) the power, (*b*) the focal length, and (*c*) the focal points and principal points.

Ans. (*a*) -2.5 D. (*b*) -40 cm. (*c*) $A_1F = +35.0$ cm, $A_1H = -5.0$ cm, $A_2F'' = -48.0$ cm, $A_2H'' = -8.0$ cm.

CHAPTER 6

SPHERICAL MIRRORS

A spherical reflecting surface has image-forming properties similar to those of a thin lens or of a single refracting surface. The image from a spherical mirror is in some respects superior to that from a lens, notably in the absence of chromatic effects due to dispersion that always accompany the refraction of white light. Therefore mirrors are occasionally used in place of lenses in optical instruments, but their applications are not so broad as those of lenses because they do not offer the same possibilities for correction of the other aberrations of the image (Chap. 9).

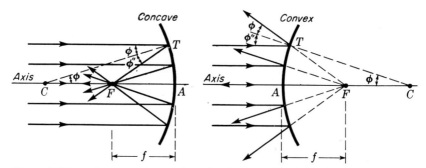

Fig. 6A. The primary and secondary focal points of spherical mirrors coincide.

Because of the simplicity of the law of reflection as compared to the law of refraction, the quantitative study of image formation by mirrors is easier than in the case of lenses. Many features are the same, and these we shall pass over rapidly, putting the chief emphasis upon those characteristics which are different. To begin with, we restrict the discussion to images formed by paraxial rays.

6.1. Focal Point and Focal Length. Diagrams showing the reflection of a parallel beam of light by a concave mirror and by a convex one are given in Fig. 6A. A ray striking the mirror at some point such as T obeys the law of reflection $\phi'' = \phi$. All rays are shown as brought to a common focus at F, although this will be strictly true only for paraxial rays. The point F is called the *focal point* and the distance FA the *focal length*. In the second diagram the reflected rays diverge as though they came from a common point F. Since the angle TCA also equals ϕ, the triangle TCF is an isosceles one, and in general $CF = FT$. But for very small angles ϕ (paraxial rays), FT approaches equality with FA. Hence

$$(FA) = \tfrac{1}{2}(CA) \qquad \text{or} \qquad f = -\tfrac{1}{2}r \qquad (6a)$$

and the focal length equals one-half the radius of curvature (see also Eq. 6d).

The negative sign is introduced in Eq. 6a so that the focal length of a concave mirror, which behaves like a positive or converging lens, will also be positive. According to the sign convention of Sec. 3.5, the radius of curvature is negative in this case. The focal length of a convex mirror, which has a positive radius, will then come out to be negative. This sign convention is chosen as being consistent with that used for lenses; it gives converging properties to a mirror with positive f and diverging properties to a mirror with negative f. By the principle of reversibility it may be seen from Fig. 6A that the primary and secondary focal points of a mirror coincide. In other words, it has but one focal point.

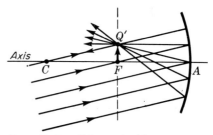

FIG. 6B. Parallel rays incident on a concave mirror but inclined to the axis are brought to a focus in the focal plane.

As before, a transverse plane through the focal point is called the focal plane. Its properties, as shown in Fig. 6B, are similar to those of either focal plane of a lens; for example, parallel rays incident at any angle with the optic axis are brought to a focus at some point in the focal plane. The image Q' of a distant off-axis point object occurs at the intersection with the focal plane of that ray which goes through the center of curvature C.

6.2. Graphical Constructions. Figure 6C, which illustrates the formation of a real image by a concave mirror, is self-explanatory. When the object MQ is moved toward the center of curvature C, the image also approaches C and increases in size until when it reaches C it is the same size as the object. The conditions when the object is between C and F may be deduced from the interchangeability of object and image as applied to this diagram. When the object is inside the focal point, the image is virtual as in the case of a converging lens. The methods of graphically constructing the image follow the same principles as were used for lenses, including the fact that paraxial rays must be represented as deflected at the tangent plane instead of at the actual surface.

An interesting experiment can be performed with a large concave mirror set up under the condition of unit magnification, as shown in Fig. 6D. A bouquet of flowers is suspended upside down in a box and illuminated by a shaded lamp S. The large mirror is placed with its center of curvature C at the top surface of the stand, on which a real vase is placed. The observer's eye at E sees a perfect reproduction of the bouquet, not merely as a picture but as a faithful three-dimensional replica, which creates a strong illusion that it is a real object. As shown in the diagram, the

FIG. 6C. Real image due to a concave mirror.

FIG. 6D. Experimental arrangement for an optical illusion produced by a real image of unit magnification.

rays diverge from points on the image just as they would were the real object in the same position.

The parallel-ray method of construction is given for the case of a concave mirror in Fig. 6E. Three rays leaving Q are, after reflection, brought to the conjugate point Q'. The image is real, inverted, and smaller than the object. Ray 4 drawn parallel to the axis is, by definition of the focal point, reflected through F. Ray 6 drawn through F is reflected parallel to the axis, and ray 8 through the center of curvature strikes the mirror normally and is reflected back on itself. The crossing point of any two of these rays is sufficient to locate the image.

A similar procedure is applied to a convex mirror in **Fig. 6F**. The rays from the object point Q, after reflection, diverge from the conjugate point Q'. Ray 4, starting parallel to the axis, is reflected as if it came from F. Ray 6 toward the center of curvature C is reflected back on itself, while ray 7 going toward F is reflected parallel to the axis. Since the rays never pass through Q', the image $Q'M'$ in this case is virtual.

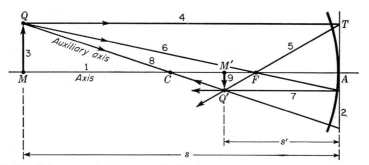

Fig. 6E. Parallel-ray method for graphically locating the image formed by a concave mirror.

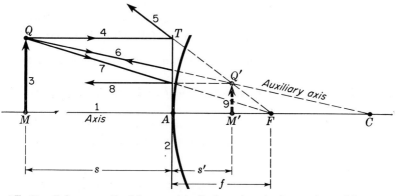

Fig. 6F. Parallel-ray method for graphically locating the image formed by a convex mirror.

The oblique-ray method may also be used for mirrors, as is illustrated in Fig. 6G for a concave mirror. After drawing the axis 1 and the mirror 2, we lay out the points C and F and draw a ray 3 making any arbitrary angle with the axis. Through F, the broken line 4 is then drawn parallel to 3. Where this line intersects the mirror at S, a parallel ray 6 is drawn backward to intersect the focal plane at P. Ray 7 is then drawn through TP and intersects the axis at M'. By this construction M and M' are conjugate points, and 3 and 7 are the parts of the ray in object and image spaces. The principle involved in this construction is obvious from the fact that if 3 and 4 were parallel incident rays they would come to a focus at P in the focal plane. If in place of ray 4 another ray were drawn through C and parallel to ray 3, it too would cross the focal plane at P. A ray through the center of curvature would be reflected directly back upon itself.

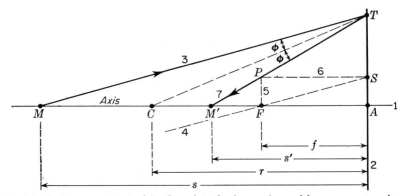

Fig. 6G. Oblique-ray method for locating the image formed by a concave mirror.

6.3. Mirror Formulas. In order to be able to apply the standard lens formulas of the preceding chapters to spherical mirrors with as little change as possible, we must adhere to the following sign conventions:

1. *Distances measured from left to right are positive, while those measured from right to left are negative.*
2. *Incident rays travel from left to right and reflected rays from right to left.*
3. *The focal length is measured from the focal point to the vertex.* This gives f a positive sign for concave mirrors and a negative sign for convex mirrors.
4. *The radius is measured from the vertex to the center of curvature.* This makes r negative for concave mirrors and positive for convex mirrors.
5. *Object distances s and image distances s' are measured from the object and from the image respectively to the vertex.* This makes both s and s' positive and the object and image real when they lie to the left of the vertex, while they are negative and virtual when they lie to the right.

The last of these sign conventions implies that for mirrors the object space and the image space coincide completely, the actual rays of light always lying in the space to the left of the mirror. Since the refractive index of the image space is the same as that of the object space, the n' of the previous equations becomes numerically equal to n.

The following is a simple derivation of the formula giving the conjugate relations for a mirror. Referring to Fig. $6G$ it is observed that by the law of reflection the radius CT bisects the angle MTM'. Using a well-known geometrical theorem, we may then write the proportion

$$\frac{MC}{MT} = \frac{CM'}{M'T}$$

Now, for paraxial rays, $MT \simeq MA = s$ and $M'T \simeq M'A = s'$, where the symbol $\simeq$ means "is approximately equal to." Also, from the diagram,

$$MC = MA - CA = s + r$$

and $$CM' = CA - M'A = -r - s' = -(s' + r)$$

Substituting in the above proportion,

$$\frac{s + r}{s} = -\frac{s' + r}{s'}$$

which may easily be put in the form

$$\frac{1}{s} + \frac{1}{s'} = -\frac{2}{r} \qquad \text{MIRROR FORMULA} \qquad (6b)$$

The primary focal point is defined as that axial object point for which the image is formed at infinity, so substituting $s = f$ and $s' = \infty$ in Eq. $6b$ we have

$$\frac{1}{f} + \frac{1}{\infty} = -\frac{2}{r}$$

from which $$\frac{1}{f} = -\frac{2}{r} \qquad \text{or} \qquad f = -\frac{r}{2} \qquad (6c)$$

The secondary focal point is defined as the image point of an infinitely distant object point. This is, $s' = f'$ and $s = \infty$, so that

$$\frac{1}{\infty} + \frac{1}{f'} = -\frac{2}{r}$$

from which $$\frac{1}{f'} = -\frac{2}{r} \qquad \text{or} \qquad f' = -\frac{r}{2} \qquad (6d)$$

Therefore the primary and secondary focal points fall together, and the magnitude of the focal length is one-half the radius of curvature. When $-r/2$ is replaced by $1/f$, Eq. $6b$ becomes

$$\frac{1}{s} + \frac{1}{s'} = \frac{1}{f} \qquad (6e)$$

just as for lenses.

The lateral magnification of the image from a mirror may be evaluated from the geometry of Fig. 6C. From the proportionality of sides in the similar triangles $Q'AM'$ and QAM, we find that $-y'/y = s'/s$, giving

$$m = \frac{y'}{y} = -\frac{s'}{s} \tag{6f}$$

Example: An object 2 cm high is situated 10 cm in front of a concave mirror of radius 16 cm. Find (*a*) the focal length of the mirror, (*b*) the position of the image, and (*c*) the lateral magnification.

Solution: (*a*) By Eq. 6c,

$$f = -\frac{-16}{2} = 8 \text{ cm}$$

(*b*) By Eq. 6e,

$$\frac{1}{10} + \frac{1}{s'} = \frac{1}{8} \qquad \text{or} \qquad \frac{1}{s'} = \frac{1}{8} - \frac{1}{10} = \frac{1}{40}$$

giving

$$s' = 40 \text{ cm}$$

(*c*) By Eq. 6f,

$$m = -\tfrac{40}{10} = -4$$

The image occurs 40 cm to the left of the mirror, is four times the size of the object, and is real and inverted.

6.4. Power of Mirrors. The power notation that was used in Sec. 4.12 to describe the image-forming properties of lenses may be readily extended to spherical mirrors as follows. As definitions, we let

$$P = \frac{1}{f} \qquad V = \frac{1}{s} \qquad V' = \frac{1}{s'} \qquad K = \frac{1}{r} \tag{6g}$$

Equations 6b, 6e, 6c, and 6f then take the forms

$$V + V' = -2K \tag{6h}$$
$$V + V' = P \tag{6i}$$
$$P = -2K \tag{6j}$$
$$m = \frac{y'}{y} = -\frac{V}{V'} \tag{6k}$$

Example: An object is located 20 cm in front of a convex mirror of radius 50 cm. Calculate (*a*) the power of the mirror, (*b*) the position of the image, and (*c*) its magnification.

Solution: Expressing all distances in meters, we have

$$K = \frac{1}{0.50} = +2 \text{ D} \qquad \text{and} \qquad V = \frac{1}{0.20} = +5 \text{ D}$$

By Eq. 6j,

$$P = -2K = -4 \text{ D} \qquad Ans. \ (a)$$

By Eq. 6i,
$$5 + V' = -4 \quad \text{or} \quad V' = -9 \text{ D}$$
or
$$s' = \frac{1}{V'} = -\frac{1}{9} = -0.111 \text{ m} = -11.1 \text{ cm} \quad Ans. \text{ (b)}$$

By Eq. 6k,
$$m = -\frac{5}{-9} = +0.555 \quad Ans. \text{ (c)}$$

The power $P = -4$ D, and the image is virtual and erect. It is located 11.1 cm to the right of the mirror, and has a magnification of 0.555×.

6.5. Thick Mirrors. The term *thick mirror* is applied to a lens system in which one of the spherical surfaces is a reflector. Under these circumstances the light passing through the system is reflected by the mirror

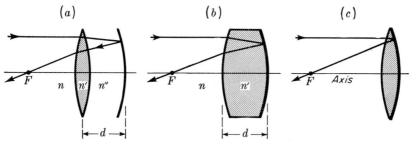

Fig. 6H. Diagrams of several types of "thick mirrors," showing the location of their respective focal points.

back through the lens system, from which it emerges finally into the space from which it entered the lens. Three common forms of optical systems that may be classified as thick mirrors are shown in Fig. 6H. In each case the surface furthest to the right has been drawn with a heavier line than the others, thereby designating the reflecting surface. A parallel incident ray is also traced through each system to where it crosses the axis, thus locating the focal point.

In addition to a focal point and focal plane every thick mirror has a principal point and a principal plane. Two graphical methods by which principal points and planes may be located are given below. The *oblique-ray method* is applied to (a) the thin lens and mirror combination in Fig. 6I, while the *auxiliary-diagram method* is applied to (b) the thick lens and mirror combination in Fig. 6J.

In the first illustration the lens is considered *thin* so that its own principal points may be assumed to coincide at H_1, its center. An incident ray parallel to the axis is refracted by the lens, reflected by the mirror, and again refracted by the lens before it crosses the axis of the system at F. The point T where the incident and final rays, when extended, cross each other locates the principal plane and H represents the principal point. If we follow the sign conventions for a single mirror (Sec. 6.3), the focal length f of this particular combination is positive and is given by the interval FH.

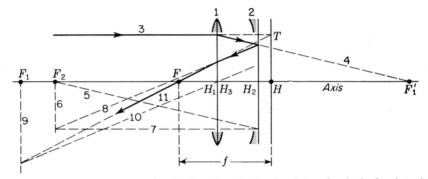

FIG. 6I. Oblique-ray construction for locating the focal point and principal point of a thick mirror.

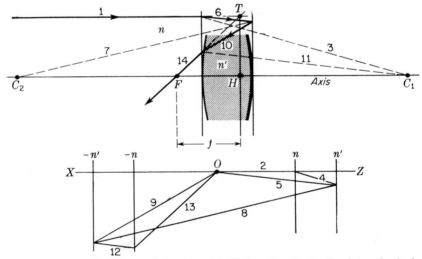

FIG. 6J. Auxiliary-diagram method of graphically locating the focal point and principal point of a thick mirror.

In the second illustration (Fig. 6J) the incident ray is refracted by the first surface, reflected by the second, and finally refracted a second time by the first surface to a point F where it crosses the axis. The point T where the incident and final rays intersect locates the principal plane and principal point H.

The graphical ray-tracing construction for this case, shown in the auxiliary diagram in Fig. 6J, is started by drawing XZ parallel to the axis.

With the origin O near the center, intervals proportional to n and n' are measured off in both directions along XZ. After the vertical lines representing n and n' are drawn the remaining lines are drawn in the order of the numbers 1, 2, 3, ... Each even-numbered line is drawn parallel to its preceding odd-numbered line. The proof that this construction is exact for paraxial rays is similar to that given for Fig. $3I$ in Chap. 3.

6.6. Thick-mirror Formulas. These formulas will be given in the power notation for case (a) shown in Fig. $6H$. Calling r_1, r_2, and r_3 the radii of the three surfaces consecutively from left to right, the power of the combination can be shown* to be given by

$$P = (1 - cP_1)(2P_1 + P_2 - cP_1P_2) \qquad (6l)$$

where, for the case in diagram (a) only, and $n'' = n$,

$$P_1 = (n' - n)(K_1 - K_2) \qquad (6m)$$
$$P_2 = -2nK_3 \qquad (6n)$$

and
$$K_1 = \frac{1}{r_1} \qquad K_2 = \frac{1}{r_2} \qquad K_3 = \frac{1}{r_3}$$

(see Eqs. $4p$ and $6d$). Of the refractive indices, n' represents that of the lens and n that of the surrounding space. The distance from the lens to the principal point of the combination is given by

$$H_1H = \frac{c}{1 - cP_1} \qquad (6o)$$

where
$$c = \frac{d}{n} \qquad (6p)$$

It is important to note from Eq. $6o$ that the position of H is independent of the power P_2 of the mirror and therefore of its curvature K_3.

Example: A thick mirror like that shown in Fig. $6H(a)$ has as one component a thin lens of index $n' = 1.50$ and radii $r_1 = +50$ cm, $r_2 = -50$ cm. This lens is situated 10 cm in front of a mirror of radius -50 cm. Assuming that air surrounds both components, find (a) the power of the combination, (b) the focal length, and (c) the principal point.

Solution: By Eq. $6m$, the power of the lens is

$$P_1 = (1.50 - 1)\left(\frac{1}{0.50} - \frac{1}{-0.50}\right) = +2\ \text{D}$$

Equation $6n$ gives for the power of the mirror

$$P_2 = -2 \cdot \frac{1}{-0.50} = +4\ \text{D}$$

---

* For a derivation of these equations, see J. P. C. Southall, "Mirrors, Prisms, and Lenses," 3d ed., p. 379, The Macmillan Company, New York, 1936.

From Eq. 6p,

$$c = \frac{d}{n} = \frac{0.10}{1} = 0.10 \text{ m}$$

Finally the power of the combination is given by Eq. 6l as

$$P = (1 - 0.10 \times 2)(2 \times 2 + 4 - 0.10 \times 2 \times 4)$$
$$= 0.8(4 + 4 - 0.8) = +5.76 \text{ D}$$

A power of $+5.76$ D corresponds to a focal length

$$f = \frac{1}{P} = \frac{1}{5.76} = 0.173 \text{ m} = 17.3 \text{ cm}$$

The position of the principal point H is determined from Eq. 6o through the distance

$$H_1 H = \frac{0.10}{1 - 0.10 \times 2} = \frac{0.10}{0.80} = 0.125 \text{ m} = 12.5 \text{ cm}$$

It is therefore 12.5 cm to the right of the lens, or 2.5 cm in back of the mirror.

6.7. Other Thick Mirrors. As a second illustration of a thick mirror, consider the case of the thick lens silvered on the back as shown in Fig. 6H(b). A comparison of this system with the one in diagram (a) shows that Eqs. 6l to 6p will apply if the powers P_1 and P_2 are properly defined. For diagram (b), P_1 refers to the power of the first surface alone, and P_2 refers to the power of the second surface as a mirror of radius r_2 in a medium of index n'. In other words,

$$P_1 = \frac{n' - n}{r_1} \qquad P_2 = -\frac{2n'}{r_2} \qquad \text{and} \qquad c = \frac{d}{n'} \tag{6q}$$

With these definitions the power of thick mirror (b) is given by Eq. 6l and the principal point by Eq. 6o.

The third illustration of a thick mirror consists of a thin lens silvered on the back surface as shown in Fig. 6H(c). This system may be looked upon (1) as a special case of diagram (a), where the mirror has the same radius as the back surface of the thin lens and the spacing d is reduced to zero, or (2) as a special case of diagram (b), where the thickness is reduced to practically zero. In either case Eq. 6l reduces to

$$P = 2P_1 + P_2 \tag{6r}$$

and the principal point H coincides with H_1 at the common center of the lens and mirror. P_1 represents the power of the thin lens in air and P_2 the power of the mirror in air, or P_1 represents the power of the first surface of radius r_1 and P_2 represents the power of the second surface as a mirror of radius r_2 in a medium of index n' (see Eq. 6q).

6.8. Spherical Aberration. The discussion of a single spherical mirror in the preceding sections has been confined to paraxial rays. Within this rather narrow limitation, sharp images of objects at any distance may be formed on a screen, since bundles of parallel rays close to the axis and making only small angles with it are brought to a sharp focus in the focal

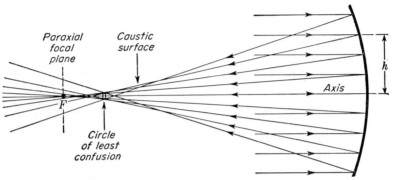

FIG. 6K. Spherical aberration of a concave spherical mirror.

plane. If, however, the light is not confined to the paraxial region, all rays from one object point do not come to a focus at a common point and we have an undesirable effect known as *spherical aberration*. The phenomenon is illustrated in Fig. 6K, where parallel incident rays at increasing distances h cross the axis closer to the mirror. The envelope of all rays forms what is known as a *caustic surface*. If a small screen is placed at the paraxial focal plane F and then moved toward the mirror, a point is reached where the size of the circular image spot is a minimum. This disklike spot is indicated in the diagram and is called the *circle of least confusion*.

The proof that rays from an outer zone of a concave mirror cross the axis inside the paraxial focal point may be simply given by reference to Fig. 6L. According to the law of reflection applied to the ray incident

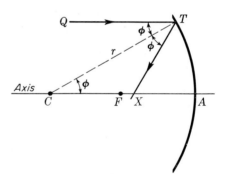

FIG. 6L. Geometry showing how marginal rays parallel to the axis of a spherical mirror cross the axis "inside" the focal point.

at T, the angle of reflection ϕ'' is equal to the angle of incidence ϕ. This in turn is equal to the angle TCA. Having two equal angles, triangle CTX is isosceles, and hence $CX = XT$. Since a straight line is the shortest path between two points,

$$CT < CX + XT$$

Now CT is the radius of the mirror and equals CA, so that

$$CA < 2CX$$

Therefore $$\tfrac{1}{2}CA < CX$$

The geometry of the figure shows that as T is moved toward A, the point X approaches F, and in the limit $CX = XA = FA = \tfrac{1}{2}CA$.

Over the past years numerous methods of reducing spherical aberration have been devised. If instead of a spherical surface the mirror form is that of a paraboloid of revolution, rays parallel to the axis are all brought to a focus at the same point as in Fig. $6M(a)$. Another method is the

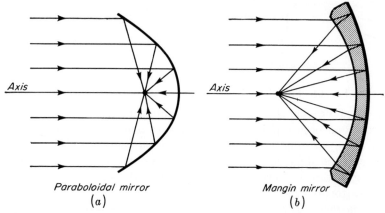

Paraboloidal mirror

(a)

Mangin mirror

(b)

Fig. 6M. Concave spherical mirrors corrected for spherical aberration.

one shown later in Fig. 10Q of inserting a "corrector plate" in front of a spherical mirror, thereby deviating the rays by the proper amount prior to reflection. With the plate located at the center of curvature of the mirror, a very useful optical arrangement known as the "Schmidt system" is obtained. Still a third system known as a "Mangin mirror" is shown in Fig. 6$M(b)$. Here a meniscus lens is employed in which both surfaces are spherical. When the back surface is silvered to form the concave mirror, all parallel rays are brought to a reasonably good focus.

6.9. Astigmatism. This defect of the image occurs when an object point lies some distance from the axis of a concave or convex mirror. The incident rays, whether parallel or not, make an appreciable angle θ with the mirror axis. The result is that, instead of a point image, two mutually perpendicular line images are formed. This effect is known as astigmatism and is illustrated by a perspective diagram in Fig. 6N. Here the incoming rays are parallel, while the reflected rays are converging toward two lines S and T. The reflected rays in the vertical or *tangential* plane $RASE$ are seen to cross or to focus at T, while the fan

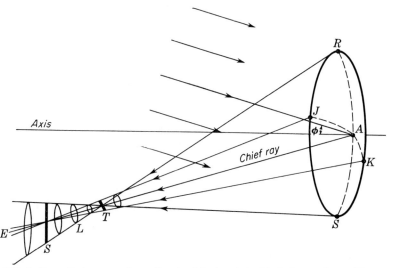

FIG. 6N. Astigmatic images of an off-axis object point at infinity, as formed by a concave spherical mirror. The lines T and S are perpendicular to each other.

of rays in the horizontal or *sagittal* plane $JAKE$ cross or focus at S. If a screen is placed at E and moved toward the mirror, the image will become a vertical line at S, a circular disk at L, and a horizontal line at T.

If the positions of the T and S images of distant object points are determined for a wide variety of angles, their loci will form a paraboloidal and a plane surface respectively, as shown in Fig. 6O. As the obliquity of the rays decreases and they approach the axis, the line images not only come closer together as they approach the paraxial focal plane, but they shorten in length.

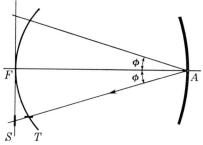

FIG. 6O. Astigmatic surfaces for a concave mirror.

The amount of astigmatism for any pencil of rays is given by the distance between the T and S surfaces measured along the chief ray.

Equations giving the two astigmatic image positions are as follows:*

$$\frac{1}{s} + \frac{1}{s_T'} = -\frac{2}{r \cos \phi}$$

$$\frac{1}{s} + \frac{1}{s_S'} = -\frac{2 \cos \phi}{r}$$

* For a derivation of these equations, see G. S. Monk, "Light, Principles and Experiments," 1st ed., pp. 52 and 424, McGraw-Hill Book Company, Inc., New York, 1937.

In both equations s and s' are measured along the chief ray. The angle ϕ is the angle of obliquity of the chief ray, and r is the radius of curvature of the mirror.

The Schmidt optical system, which will be discussed later (Fig. 10Q), and the Mangin mirror shown in Fig. 6$M(b)$ constitute instruments in which the astigmatism of a spherical mirror is reduced to a minimum. While the two focal surfaces T and S exist for these devices, they lie very close together, and the loci of their mean position (such as L in Fig. 6N) form a nearly spherical surface. The center of this spherical surface is located at the center of curvature of the mirror as is shown in Fig. 10Q.

A paraboloidal mirror, while it is free from spherical aberration even for large apertures, shows unusually large astigmatic $S - T$ differences off the axis. It is for this reason that paraboloidal reflectors are limited in their use to devices that require a small angular spread, such as astronomical telescopes and searchlights.

PROBLEMS

1. The radius of a spherical mirror is -30.0 cm. An object $+4.0$ cm high is located in front of the mirror at a distance of (a) 60.0 cm, (b) 30.0 cm, (c) 15.0 cm, and (d) 10.0 cm. Find the image distance for each of these positions.

2. Solve Prob. 1 graphically. Make separate diagrams for each part.
Ans. (a) $+20$ cm. (b) $+30$ cm. (c) ∞. (d) -30 cm.

3. The radius of a spherical mirror is -20.0 cm. An object 2.0 cm high is located in front of the mirror at a distance of (a) 30.0 cm, (b) 20.0 cm, (c) 12.0 cm, and (d) 6.0 cm. Find the image distance for each of these object distances.

4. Solve Prob. 3 graphically. Make separate diagrams for each part.
Ans. (a) $+15$ cm. (b) $+20$ cm. (c) $+60$ cm. (d) -15 cm.

5. The radius of a spherical mirror is $+20.0$ cm. An object 3.0 cm high is situated in front of the mirror at a distance of (a) 30.0 cm, (b) 20.0 cm, (c) 10.0 cm, and (d) 5.0 cm. Find the image distance for each of these object distances.

6. Solve Prob. 5 graphically. Make separate diagrams for each part.
Ans. (a) -7.5 cm. (b) -6.66 cm. (c) -5.0 cm. (d) -3.33 cm.

7. The radius of a spherical mirror is $+12.0$ cm. An object 2.0 cm high is located in front of the mirror at a distance of (a) 15.0 cm, (b) 10.0 cm, (c) 6.0 cm, and (d) 3.0 cm. Find the image distance for each of these object distances.

8. Solve Prob. 7 graphically. Make separate diagrams for each part.
Ans. (a) -4.28 cm. (b) -3.75 cm. (c) -3.0 cm. (d) -2.0 cm.

9. A concave mirror is to be used to focus the image of a flower on a nearby wall 120 cm from the flower. If a lateral magnification of -16 is desired, what should be the radius of curvature of the mirror?

10. A thin equiconvex lens of index 1.60 and radii 12.0 cm is silvered on one side. Find the power of this system for light entering the unsilvered side. *Ans.* $+36.66$ D.

11. A thin lens of index 1.60 has radii $r_1 = +4.0$ cm and $r_2 = -10.0$ cm. If the second surface is silvered, what is the power of the system?

12. A thin lens of index 1.75 has as radii $r_1 = -5.0$ cm and $r_2 = -10.0$ cm. If the second surface is silvered, what is the power of the system? Use (a) the special-case formulas (Eqs. 6q and 6r), and (b) the thick-lens formulas (Eqs. 6l, 6m, and 6n), with $d = 0$. *Ans.* +5.0 D.

13. A thin lens with a focal length of +12.0 cm is located 2.0 cm in front of a spherical mirror of radius −20.0 cm. Find (a) the power, (b) the focal length, (c) the principal point, and (d) the focal point.

14. Solve Prob. 13 graphically. Use the method of Fig. 6I.
Ans. (a) +20.83 D. (b) +4.80 cm. (c) H_1H = +2.40 cm. (d) H_1F = −2.40 cm

15. A thin lens with a focal length of −14.5 cm is placed 3.0 cm in front of a spherical mirror of radius −12.5 cm. Find (a) the power, (b) the focal length, (c) the principal point, and (d) the focal point.

16. Solve Prob. 15 graphically. Use the method of Fig. 6I.
Ans. (a) +6.65 D. (b) +15.0 cm. (c) H_1H = +2.48 cm. (d) H_1F = −12.52 cm.

17. A thick lens of index 1.60 has radii r_1 = +12.0 cm and r_2 = −32 cm. If the second surface is silvered and the lens is 3.0 cm thick, find (a) the power, (b) the focal length, (c) the principal point, and (d) the focal point.

18. Solve Prob. 17 graphically. Use the method of Fig. 6J.
Ans. (a) +17.2 D. (b) +5.80 cm. (c) H_1H = +2.07 cm. (d) H_1F = −3.73 cm.

19. A lens 3.68 cm thick, of index 1.84 and radii r_1 = −6.0 cm and r_2 = −12.0 cm, has its second surface silvered as a mirror. Find (a) the power, (b) the focal length, (c) the principal point, and (d) the focal point.

20. Solve Prob. 19 graphically. Use the method of Fig. 6J.
Ans. (a) +14.4 D. (b) +6.9 cm. (c) H_1H = +1.56 cm. (d) H_1F = −5.38 cm.

21. The curved surface of a plano-convex lens has a radius of 12.0 cm. The index is 1.60, and the thickness is 3.2 cm. If the curved surface is silvered, find (a) the power, (b) the focal length, (c) the principal point, and (d) the focal point.

22. Solve Prob. 21 graphically. Use the method of Fig. 6J.
Ans. (a) +26.7 D. (b) +3.75 cm. (c) H_1H = +2.0 cm. (d) H_1F = −1.75 cm.

23. If the plane surface of the lens given in Prob. 21 is silvered in place of the curved surface, what are the answers to (a), (b), (c), and (d)?

24. Solve Prob. 23 graphically. Use the method of Fig. 6J.
Ans. (a) +9.0 D. (b) +11.1 cm. (c) H_1H = 2.22 cm. (d) H_1F = −8.89 cm.

25. An object is located 15.0 cm in front of a mirror of radius −20.0 cm. Plot a graph of the two astigmatic surfaces from $\phi = 0°$ to $\phi = 30°$.

26. Plot a graph of the two astigmatic surfaces for a spherical mirror having a radius of −16.0 cm. Assume parallel incident light, and show curves from the axis out to 30°.

CHAPTER 7

THE EFFECTS OF STOPS

There are two subjects in geometrical optics which, though very important from a practical standpoint, are frequently neglected because they do not directly concern the size, position, and sharpness of the image. One of these is the question of the *field of view*, which determines how much of the surface of a broad object can be seen through an optical system. The other subject is that of the *brightness* of images and the distinction between this, which is important for visual effects, and the

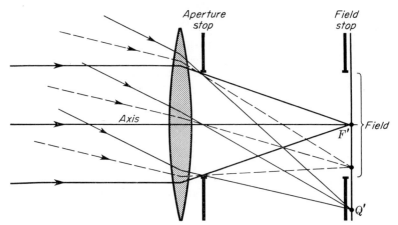

FIG. 7*A*. Diagram showing the difference between a field stop and an aperture stop.

illuminance, which is important for photographic effects. In treating both the field of view and the brightness of images it is of primary importance to understand how and where the bundle of rays traversing the system is limited. The effect of stops or diaphragms, which will always exist if only as the rims of lenses or mirrors, must first be investigated.

7.1. Field Stop and Aperture Stop. In Fig. 7*A* a single lens with two stops is shown forming the image of a distant object. Three bundles of parallel rays from three different points on the object are shown as brought to a focus in the focal plane of the lens. It may be seen from these bundles that the stop close to the lens limits the size of each bundle of rays, while the stop just in front of the focal plane limits the angle at

98

which the incident bundles can get through to this plane. The first is called an *aperture stop*. It obviously determines the amount of light reaching any given point in the image and therefore controls the brightness of the latter. The second, or *field stop*, determines the extent of the object, or the field, that will be represented in the image.

7.2. Entrance and Exit Pupils. A stop $P'E'L'$ placed behind the lens as in Fig. 7B is in the image space and limits the image rays. By a graphical construction or by the lens formula, the image of this real stop,

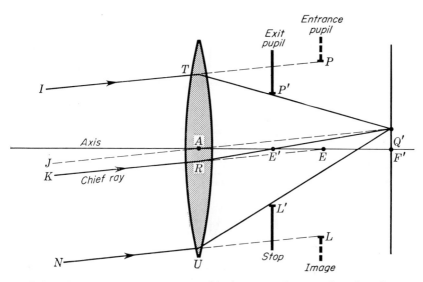

Fig. 7B. Showing how an aperture stop and its image can become the exit and entrance pupils, respectively, of a system.

as formed by the lens, is found to lie at the position PEL shown by the broken lines. Since $P'E'L'$ is inside the focal plane, its image PEL lies in the object space and is virtual and erect. It is called the *entrance pupil*, while the real aperture $P'E'L'$ is, as we have seen, called the aperture stop. When it lies in the image space, as it does here, it becomes the *exit pupil*. (For a treatment of object and image spaces see Sec. 4.11.)

It should be emphasized that P and P', E and E', and L and L' are pairs of conjugate points. Any ray in the object space directed through one of these points will after refraction pass through its conjugate point in the image space. Ray IT directed toward P is refracted through P', ray KR directed toward E is refracted through E', and ray NU directed toward L is refracted through L'. The image point Q' is located graphically by the broken line JQ', parallel to the others and passing undeviated through the optical center A. The aperture stop $P'E'L'$ in the position shown also functions to some extent as a field stop, but the edges of the field will not be sharply limited.   The diaphragm which acts as a field stop is usually made to coincide with a real or virtual image, so that the edges will appear sharp.

7.3. Chief Ray.   Any ray in the object space that passes through the center of the entrance pupil is called a *chief ray*.   Such a ray after refraction also passes through the center of the exit pupil.   In any actual optical instrument the chief ray rarely passes through the center of any lens itself.   The points E and E' at which the chief ray crosses the axis

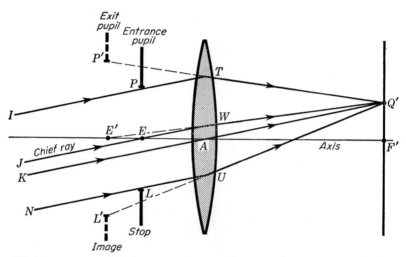

Fig. 7C. A front stop and its image can become the respective entrance and exit pupils of a system.

are known as the *entrance pupil point* and the *exit pupil point*.   The former, as we shall see, is particularly important in determining the field of view.

7.4. Front Stop.   In certain types of photographic lenses a stop is placed close to the lens, either before it (*front stop*) or behind it (*rear stop*). One of the functions of such a stop, as will be seen in Chap. 9, is to improve the quality of the image formed on the photographic film.   With a front stop as shown in Fig. 7C, its small size and its location in the object space make it the entrance pupil.   Its image $P'E'L'$ formed by the lens is in the image space and constitutes the exit pupil.   Parallel rays IT, JW, and NU have been drawn through the two edges of the entrance pupil and through its center.   The lens causes these rays to converge toward the screen as though they had come from the conjugate points P', E', and L' in the exit pupil.   Their intersection at the image point Q' occurs where the undeviated ray KA crosses the secondary focal plane.   Note that the chief ray is directed through the center of the entrance pupil in the object space and emerges from the lens as though it had come from the center of the exit pupil in the image space.

While a certain stop of an optical system may limit the rays getting through the system from one object point, it may not be the aperture stop for other object points at different distances away along the axis. For example, in Fig. 7*D* a lens with a front stop is shown with an object point at *M*. For this point the periphery of the lens itself becomes the aperture stop, and since it limits the object rays it is the entrance pupil.

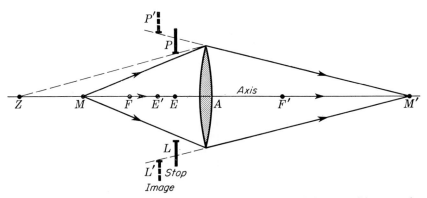

Fig. 7*D*. The entrance and exit pupils are not the same for all object and image points.

Its image, which is again the lens periphery, is also the exit pupil. The lens margin is therefore the aperture stop, the entrance pupil, and the exit pupil for the point *M*. If this object point were to lie to the left of *Z*, *PEL* would become the entrance pupil and the aperture stop, and its image *P'E'L'* the exit pupil.

In the preliminary design of an optical instrument it may not be known which element of the system will constitute the aperture stop. As a result the marginal rays for each element must be investigated one after the other to determine which one actually does the limiting. Regardless of the number of elements the system possesses, it will usually be found to contain but one limiting aperture stop. Once this stop is located, *the entrance pupil of the entire system is the image of the aperture stop formed by all lenses preceding it and the exit pupil is the image formed by all lenses following it.* Figures 7*B* and 7*C*, where there is only a single lens either before or behind the stop, should be studied in connection with this statement.

7.5. Stop between Two Lenses. A common arrangement in photographic lenses is to have two separate lens elements with a variable stop or iris diaphragm between them. Figure 7*E* is a diagram representing such a combination, and in it the elements (1) and (2) are thin lenses while $P_0E_0L_0$ is the stop. By definition the entrance pupil of this system is the image of the stop formed by lens (1). This image is virtual, erect, and located at PEL. Similarly by definition the exit pupil of the entire system is the image of the stop formed by lens (2). This image, located at $P'E'L'$, is also virtual and erect. The entrance pupil PEL lies in the object space of lens (1), the stop $P_0E_0L_0$ lies in the image space of lens (1) as well as in the object space of lens (2), and the exit pupil $P'E'L'$ lies in the image space of lens (2). Points P_0 and P, E_0 and E, and L_0 and L are conjugate pairs of points for the first lens, while P_0 and P', E_0 and E', and L_0 and L' are conjugate pairs for the second lens. This makes

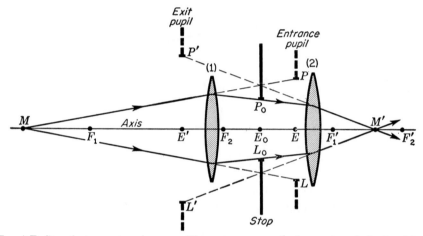

Fig. 7E. Stop between two lenses. The entrance pupil of a system is in its object space, while the exit pupil is in its image space.

points like P and P' conjugate for the whole system. If a point object is located on the axis at M, rays MP and ML limit the bundle that will get through the system. At the first lens these rays are refracted through P_0 and L_0, and at the second lens they are again refracted in such directions that they appear to come from P' and L' as shown. The purpose of using primed and unprimed symbols to designate exit and entrance pupils respectively should now be clear; one lies in the image space, the other in the object space, and they are conjugate images.

The same optical system is shown again in Fig. 7F for the purpose of illustrating the path of a chief ray. Of the many rays that can start from any specified object point Q and traverse the entire system, a chief ray is one which approaches the lens in the direction of E, the entrance pupil point, is refracted through E_0, and finally emerges traveling toward Q' as though it came from E', the exit pupil point.

7.6. Two Lenses with No Stop. The theory of stops is applicable not only to cases where circular diaphragms are introduced into an optical system but to any system whatever, since actually the periphery of any lens in the system is a potential stop.   In Fig. 7G two lenses (1) and (2) are shown, along with their mutual images as possible stops.   Assuming P_1 to be a stop in the object space, its image P' formed by lens (2) lies in the final image space.   Looking upon P_2 as a stop in the image space,

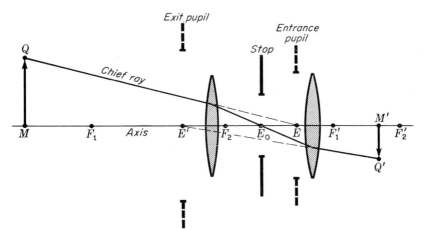

FIG. 7F. The direction taken by any chief ray is such that it passes through the centers of the entrance pupil, the stop, and the exit pupil.

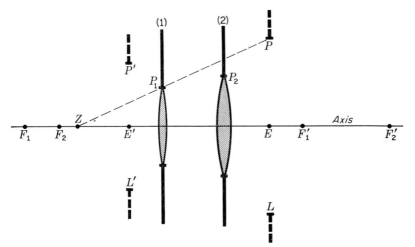

FIG. 7G. The margin of any lens may be the aperture stop of the system.

its image P formed by lens (1) lies in the first object space.   There are therefore two possible entrance pupils, P_1 and P, in the object space of the combination of lenses, and two possible exit pupils, P_2 and P', in the image space of the combination.   For any axial point M lying to the left of Z, P_1 becomes the limiting stop and therefore the entrance pupil of the system.   Its image P' becomes the exit pupil.   If, on the other hand, M lies to the right of Z, P becomes the entrance pupil and P_2 the exit pupil.

7.7. Determination of the Aperture Stop.   In the system of two lenses with a stop between them represented in Figs. $7E$ and $7F$, the lenses were made sufficiently large so that they did not become aperture stops.   If, however, they are not large compared with the stop, as may well be the case with a camera lens when the iris diaphragm is wide open, the system of stops and pupils may become similar to those shown in Fig. $7H$.   This

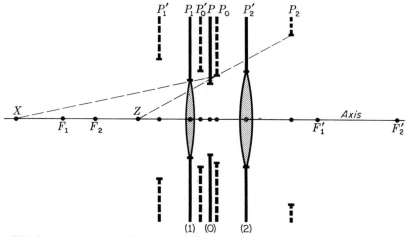

FIG. $7H$. A system composed of several elements has a number of possible stops and pupils.

system consists of two lenses and a stop, each one of which, along with its various images, is a potential aperture stop. P'_1 is the virtual image of the first lens formed by lens (2), P'_0 the virtual image of the stop P formed by lens (2), P_0 the virtual image of P formed by lens (1), and P_2 the virtual image of the second lens formed by lens (1).   In other words, when looking through the system from the left one would see the first lens, the stop, and the second lens in the apparent positions P_1, P_0, and P_2.   Looking from the right, one would see them at P'_1, P'_0, and P'_2. Of all these stops P_0, P_1, and P_2 are potential entrance pupils located in the object space of the system.

For all axial object points lying to the left of X, P_1 limits the entering bundle of rays to the smallest angle and hence constitutes the entrance pupil of the system.   In general the object of which it is the image will be the aperture stop, which in this case is the aperture P_1 of lens (1) itself.   The image of the entrance pupil formed by the entire lens system, namely P'_1, constitutes the exit pupil.   For object points lying between

X and Z, P_0 becomes the entrance pupil, P the aperture stop, and P_0' the exit pupil. Finally, for points to the right of Z, P_2 is the entrance pupil, while P_2' is both the aperture stop and the exit pupil. It is apparent from this discussion that the aperture stop of any system may change with a change in the object position. The general rule is that *the aperture stop of the system is determined by that stop or image of a stop which subtends the smallest angle as seen from the object point.* If it is determined by an image, the aperture stop itself is the corresponding object. In most actual optical instruments the effective stop does not change over the range of object positions normally covered by the instrument when in use.

Having established the methods of determining the positions of the aperture stop and of the entrance and exit pupils, we may now take up the two important properties of an optical system, field of view and brightness. To begin with, let us consider the former property.

7.8. Field of View. When one looks out at a landscape through a window, the field of view outside is limited by the size of the window

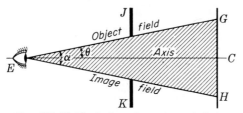

Fig. 7*I*. Field of view through a window.

and by the position of the observer. In Fig. 7*I* the eye of the observer is shown at E, the window opening at JK, and the observed field at GH. In this simple illustration the window is the field stop (Sec. 7.1). When the eye is moved closer to the window the angular field α is widened, while when it is moved farther away the field is narrowed. It is common practice with optical instruments to specify the field of view in terms of the angle α and to express this angle in degrees. The angle θ which the extreme rays entering the system make with the axis is called the *half-field angle*, and limits the width of the object that can be seen. This object field includes the angle 2θ, and in this instance is the same as the image field, of angular width α.

7.9. Field of a Plane Mirror. The field of view afforded by a plane mirror is very similar to that of a simple window. As shown in Fig. 7*J*, TU represents a plane mirror, and $P'E'L'$ the pupil of the observer's eye, which here constitutes the exit pupil. The entrance pupil PEL is the virtual image of the eye pupil formed by the mirror, and is located just as far behind the mirror as the actual pupil is in front of it. The chief rays $E'T$ and $E'U$ limit the field of view in image space, while the corresponding incident rays *ER* and *ES* define the field of view in object space. The latter show the limits of the field in which an object can be situated and still be visible to the eye. In this case also, although not in general, it subtends the same angle as does the image field.

The formation of the image of an object point *Q* within this field is also illustrated. From this point three rays have been drawn toward the points *P*, *E*, and *L* in the entrance pupil. Where these rays encounter the mirror, the reflected rays are drawn toward the conjugate points *P'*, *E'*, and *L'* in the exit pupil. The object *Q* and the entrance pupil

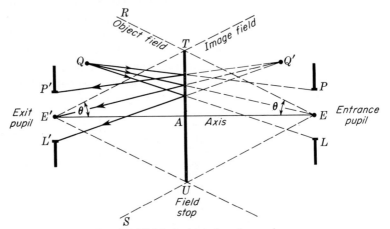

Fig. 7*J*. Field of view of a plane mirror.

PEL are in the object space, while the image *Q'* and the exit pupil *P'E'L'* are in the image space. If *Q* happens to be located close to *RT*, only part of the bundle of rays defined by the entrance pupil will be intercepted by the mirror and will be reflected into the exit pupil. In defining the field of view it is customary to use the chief ray *RTE'*, although in the present case this distinction is not important because of the relative smallness of the pupil of the eye. Its size is obviously greatly exaggerated in the diagram.

Since the limiting chief ray is directed toward the entrance pupil point *E*, the half-field angle θ is in general determined by the smallest angle subtended at *E* by any stop, or image of a stop, in the object space. *The stop determined in this way is the field stop of the system.* For a single mirror the field stop is the border of the mirror itself.

7.10. Field of a Convex Mirror. When the mirror has a curvature the situation is little changed except that the object field and the image field no longer subtend the same angle ($\theta \neq \theta'$ in Fig. 7*K*). In this figure *P'E'L'* represents the real pupil of an eye placed on the axis of a convex mirror *TU*. The mirror forms an image *PEL* of this exit pupil, and this is the entrance pupil which is now smaller in size. Following the same procedure as for a plane mirror, the lines limiting the image field and the object field have been drawn. Rays emanating from an object point Q toward P, E, and L of the entrance pupil are shown as reflected towards

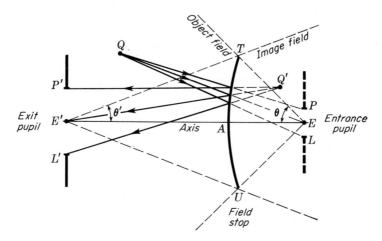

FIG. 7K. Field of view of a convex mirror.

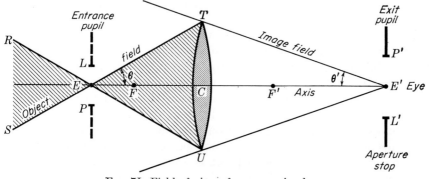

FIG. 7L. Field of view of a converging lens.

P', E', and L' in the exit pupil. When extended backward these rays locate the virtual image Q'. The half-field angle θ is here larger than θ', which determines the field of view to the eye. A similar but somewhat more complicated diagram can be drawn for the field of view of a concave mirror. This case will be left as an exercise for the student, since it is very similar to that of a converging lens to be discussed next.

7.11. Field of a Positive Lens. The method of determining the half-field angles θ and θ' for a single converging lens is shown in Fig. 7L. The pupil of the eye, as an exit pupil, is situated on the right, and its real

inverted image appears at the left.   The chief rays through the entrance
pupil point E which are incident at the periphery of the lens are refracted
through the conjugate point E'.

The shaded areas, or rather cones, ETU and ERS mark the boundaries
within which any object must lie in order to be seen in the image field.
The field stop in this case is the lens TU itself, since it determines the
half-field angle subtended at the entrance pupil point.   If the eye, and
therefore the exit pupil, is moved closer to the lens, thereby increasing
the image-field angle θ', the inverted entrance pupil moves to the left,
causing a lengthening of the object-field cone ETU.

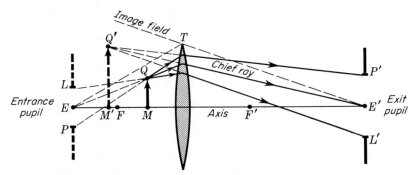

FIG. 7M. Image formation within the field of a converging lens system.

The same lens has been redrawn in Fig. 7M, where an object QM is
shown in a position inside the primary focal point.   Through each of the
three points P, E, and L, rays are drawn from Q to the lens.   From there
the refracted rays are directed through the corresponding points P', E',
and L' on the exit pupil.   Extending them backward to their common
intersection, the virtual image is located at Q'.   The oblique-ray or
parallel-ray methods of construction (not shown) may be used to con-
firm this position of the image.   It will be noted that if objects are to be
placed near the entrance pupil point E, they must be very small; otherwise only a part of them will be visible to an eye placed at E'.   The
student will find it instructive to select object points that lie outside the
object field and to trace graphically the rays from them through the lens.
It will be found that invariably they miss the exit pupil.

When a converging lens is used as a magnifier, the eye should be placed
close to the lens, since this widens the image-field angle and extends the
object field so that the position of the object is less critical.

7.12. Photometric Brightness and Illuminance.   The amount of light
flowing out from a point source Q within the small solid angle subtended
by the element of area dA at the distance r [Fig. 7$N(a)$] is proportional
to the solid angle.   This is found by dividing the area of dA projected

normal to the rays by r^2, so that the *luminous flux* in this elementary pencil may be written

$$dF = \text{const.} \cdot \frac{dA \cos \phi}{r^2} \tag{7a}$$

Since the source in practice is never a mathematical point, we must consider all pencils emitted from an element of area dS, as shown for three of these pencils in part (*b*) of Fig. 7N. Assuming that the source is a so-called "Lambert's-law radiator," the flux will now be proportional to the projected area of dS as well, so that

$$dF = \text{const.} \cdot \frac{dS \, dA \cos \theta \cos \phi}{r^2} \tag{7b}$$

The value of the constant depends only upon the light source, and is called its *photometric brightness B*. To distinguish it from the visual sensation of brightness, it is usually termed the *luminance* in the technical literature, but here we shall use the more common name brightness, with the understanding that it is the photometric quantity that is meant. The unit of B is experimentally defined as one-sixtieth of the brightness of a black body at the temperature of melting platinum, and is called the *candle per square centimeter*. Expressing B in this unit, the flux becomes

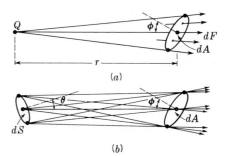

Fig. 7N. An elementary pencil and an elementary beam.

$$dF = B \frac{dS \, dA \cos \theta \cos \phi}{r^2} \qquad \text{lumens} \tag{7c}$$

This is a quantity which must, aside from small losses due to reflection and absorption, remain constant for a bundle of rays as it traverses an optical system.*

The *illuminance E* of a surface is defined as the luminous flux incident per unit area, so that

$$dE = \frac{dF}{dA} = \frac{B \cos \theta \, dS \cos \phi}{r^2} \tag{7d}$$

Illuminance is often expressed in lumens per square meter, or lux. In

---

* To be exact, the expression must be multiplied by n^2 in any medium of index n, but since the initial and final media are usually the same, this factor rarely needs to be taken into account.

order to calculate the illuminance at any point due to a source having a finite area, we must integrate Eq. 7d over this area:

$$E = \iint \frac{B \, dS \, \cos \theta \, \cos \phi}{r^2} \tag{7e}$$

The exact evaluation of this integral is in general difficult, but in most cases the source is sufficiently far from the illuminated surface so that we may regard both $\cos \phi$ and r^2 as constant. In this case

$$E = \frac{\cos \phi}{r^2} \iint B \cos \theta \, dS = \frac{I \cos \phi}{r^2} \tag{7f}$$

where the integral has been designated by I, since it represents what is called the *luminous intensity* of the source. The definition of this, then, is

$$I = \iint B \cos \theta \, dS \tag{7g}$$

The quantities F, B, E, and I are the four basic ones that are dealt with in the subject of photometry.

As an example appropriate to the present subject let us calculate the illuminance due to a luminous disk 6 cm in diameter on a small surface placed normal to the axis of the disk and 20 cm away from it. The brightness of the disk will be taken as 2 candles/cm².

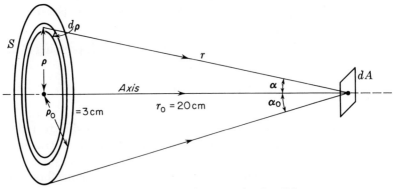

Fig. 70. Illuminance due to a circular disk.

This problem is illustrated in Fig. 70. The distance from dA to the edge of the disk can be calculated to be only 1.1 per cent greater than that to the center; hence r may be regarded as constant. Furthermore the angles θ and ϕ at which the light leaves the source and strikes the surface are small enough so that we may set $\cos \theta = \cos \phi = 1$. Equation 7e may then be written

$$E = \frac{1}{r^2} \iint B \, dS = \frac{1}{r^2} \int B \times 2\pi\rho \, d\rho \qquad (7h)$$

since the area dS of an annular element of radius ρ and width $d\rho$ is its circumference $2\pi\rho$ multiplied by its width $d\rho$. But from the figure

$$\rho = r \sin \alpha \qquad d\rho = r \cos \alpha \, d\alpha$$

where α is the half angle subtended by the element. Making these substitutions in Eq. 7h, one finds

$$E = \frac{1}{r^2} \int_0^{\alpha_0} 2\pi r^2 B \sin \alpha \cos \alpha \, d\alpha$$

$$= 2\pi B \left[\frac{\sin^2 \alpha}{2} \right]_0^{\alpha_0} = \pi B \sin^2 \alpha_0 \qquad (7i)$$

It is instructive to express α_0 in terms of linear dimensions by using the relation $\sin^2 \alpha_0 = \rho_0^2/(\rho_0^2 + r_0^2)$, giving

$$E = \frac{\pi B \rho_0^2}{\rho_0^2 + r_0^2} = \frac{BS}{\rho_0^2 + r_0^2} \qquad (7j)$$

Substituting the numerical values, we have

$$E = \frac{2 \times 28.27}{3^2 + 20^2} = \frac{56.54}{9 + 400} = 0.1382 \text{ lumen/cm}^2 = 1382 \text{ lux}$$

This is not very different from the result that one would obtain by treating the source as a point source of luminous intensity $I = BS$. Using Eq. 7f, this would yield

$$E = \frac{I \cos \phi}{r^2} = \frac{2 \times 28.27 \times 1}{20^2} = 0.1414 \text{ lumen/cm}^2$$

The condition under which it is legitimate to assume a point source is, by Eq. 7j, that ρ_0^2 shall be negligible with respect to r_0^2. Even if ρ_0 is as large as $\frac{1}{10} r_0$, the error is only 1 per cent.

7.13. Brightness of an Image. In Fig. 7P is shown a lens forming the image dA' of a surface element dS of the object. If the image is observed by the eye E, the luminous flux dF entering it is limited by the area dA'' of the pupil so that only the narrow bundle indicated by the broken lines contributes to the image on the retina. Now, since the quantity which characterizes a bundle is the multiplier of B in Eq. 7c and since this remains constant through the system, we have, neglecting losses,

$$\frac{dF}{B} = \frac{dS \, dA \cos \theta \cos \phi}{(r)^2} = \frac{dS' \, dA' \cos \theta' \cos \phi'}{(r')^2}$$

$$= \frac{dS'' \, dA'' \cos \theta'' \cos \phi''}{(r'')^2} \qquad (7k)$$

The last member of this equation refers to the bundle in the region to the right of the image, and since we assume the flux in the bundle to remain constant and equal to dF, we have

$$\frac{dF}{B} = \frac{dF}{B''} \tag{7l}$$

where B'' denotes the brightness of the image. Hence the important result that

$$B'' = B \tag{7m}$$

For an image formed in the same medium as the object by an optical system in which the losses are negligible, *the brightness of the image equals that of the object.*

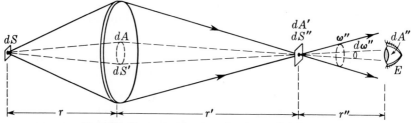

FIG. 7P. Geometry for treating image brightness.

This result may seem surprising to one who has experimented at forming images with a lens, because one always finds that when the image is observed on a screen its brightness to the eye increases as the magnification is made smaller. If, however, the image is observed directly by the eye, without the use of a screen, its brightness does remain unchanged. This is because the brightness represents the flux per unit area *per unit solid angle*, as can be seen from Eqs. 7k and 7l which give, assuming $\cos \theta'' = \cos \phi'' = 1$,

$$B'' = \frac{dF}{dS'' \dfrac{dA''}{(r'')^2}} = \frac{dF}{dS'' \, d\omega''} \tag{7n}$$

When the magnification is decreased the flux incident per unit area of the image is increased, but the total solid angle ω'' (Fig. 7P) is also increased in such a way that the brightness stays constant. The light incident per unit area on a diffusing screen determines its brightness, but this is not the same brightness as the above, since the light is scattered in all directions by such a screen.

7.14. Normal Magnification. In the foregoing discussion, it was assumed that the pupil of the eye acts as the aperture stop of the system. If this is not the case, for example if in Fig. 7P the cone ω'' emerging from the image is not wide enough to fill the eye pupil, the brightness or the image will fall below that of the object. In telescopes and microscopes the eye is usually placed at the exit pupil of the system, and if the full brightness of the object is to be represented in the image, the exit pupil must be at least as large as the pupil of the eye. Now the diameter of the exit pupil is inversely proportional to the magnification, as will be shown for example in the case of a telescope (Eq. 10k). Hence the magnification should not exceed that at which the size of the exit

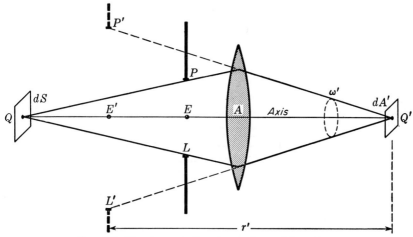

Fig. 7Q. Illuminance of an image formed by a lens.

pupil matches that of the eye. This particular value is called the *normal magnification* of the instrument. We shall see that it represents not only the maximum allowable value in order to avoid sacrifice of brightness but also the minimum value required to realize the full resolving power of the instrument (Sec. 15.9).

7.15. Illuminance of an Image. The illuminance, as defined by Eq. 7e, represents the *total* flux per unit area incident on a surface from all directions. It determines the photographic or other energy effects, as well as the amount of light scattered by unit area of a diffusing screen. To evaluate it in the case of an image formed by a lens or lens system, let us represent this system by A in Fig. 7Q, which also shows the positions of the entrance pupil PEL and the exit pupil $P'E'L'$. The brightness B' of the exit pupil as observed at the image point Q' is equal to that of the source, since, from Eq. 7k,

$$\frac{dF}{B} = \frac{dS'\,dA'\,\cos\theta'\,\cos\phi'}{(r')^2} = \frac{dF}{B'}$$

But the brightness is the flux per unit area per unit solid angle, so that if we wish the total flux incident per unit area we must multiply B' by the solid angle ω' subtended by the exit pupil, and this gives

$$E = B'\omega' = B\omega' \tag{7o}$$

Thus the *illuminance of the image is the product of the brightness of the source and the solid angle subtended by the exit pupil at the image.* This relation is not exact, since as may be seen by referring to Eq. 7e, it assumes that all angles are small. It is, however, a good approximation in most actual cases. As in the previous discussion we are here neglecting losses by absorption and reflection. The occurrence of ω' in Eq. 7o

Fɪɢ. 7R. A spotlight or searchlight beam is often rated in terms of its beam candle power.

is the basis for rating the speed of camera lenses by their f-numbers, as will be explained in Sec. 10.2.

It is interesting to note that the illuminance is the same as that which would be obtained if the lens were removed and the source were placed at the exit pupil and increased in area to the size of the pupil. The result of the calculation given in Sec. 7.12 may be used to prove this proposition. The illuminance due to a disk of brightness B', the diameter of which subtends a plane angle 2α, was there found to be (see Eq. 7i)

$$E = \pi B' \sin^2 \alpha$$

Provided that α is not too large, a disk of radius $r \sin \alpha$ subtends a solid angle $\omega' = (\pi r^2 \sin^2 \alpha)/r^2 = \pi \sin^2 \alpha$, so that

$$E = B\omega'$$

in agreement with Eq. 7o.

As a practical illustration of this principle, consider the intense beam of light produced by a spotlight or searchlight, as illustrated in Fig. 7R. The rim of the reflector of aperture A is the entrance pupil as well as the exit pupil. Neglecting losses of light by reflection and absorption, the illuminance over the region D on a distant screen M is the same as that which would be obtained were the reflector removed and a source of the same brightness as S but having the full size of A placed at the position of A. The equivalent *beam candle power* of a spotlight or searchlight is defined as the candle power of a bare source which, if located at the same distance away from a given point, would produce at that point the same illuminance.

7.16. Image of a Point Source. The above principle is applicable to the illuminance of the image of a source of finite area. If the area of the source is negligible, as it is for example in the telescopic images of stars, the principle deduced above is no longer applicable. The image, instead of being of the very small size predicted by geometrical optics, is actually broadened because of diffraction by the aperture of the lens system (Sec. 1.1). Its illuminance is therefore less than would be predicted by Eq. 7o. The investigation of this case requires the results of the theory of diffraction and will therefore be postponed until we take up this subject (Sec. 15.10).

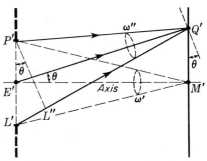

FIG. 7S. Illuminance at an off-axis point in the image.

7.17. Illuminance off the Axis. Supposing the object were a plane surface of uniform brightness, it would be found that the illuminance in the image would fall off with distance away from the axis. This effect is due to more than one cause. In Fig. 7S let $P'E'L'$ represent the exit pupil, which has a uniform brightness B' equal to that of the source. At the axial point M' the illuminance is, according to Eq. 7o, equal to $B'\omega'$. For a point such as Q', however, the following factors act to decrease the illuminance: (a) a factor $\omega''/\omega' = \cos^2 \theta$; (b) a factor $P'L''/P'L' = \cos \theta$, representing the decrease in area of the exit pupil as seen from Q' compared with that seen from M'; and (c) another factor $\cos \theta$ coming from the fact that the light is not incident normally on the surface at Q', as it would be on the surface represented by the broken line. Tilting a surface through an angle θ distributes the flux over an area which is $1/\cos \theta$ times larger, and hence the illuminance, or flux per unit area, is decreased by $\cos \theta$. Putting all these factors together, we have, for the illuminance at Q',

$$E'' = B'\omega' \cos^4 \theta \qquad (7p)$$

Near the axis the factor $\cos^4 \theta$ varies only slightly from unity, but if α becomes as great as 30°, for example, the illuminance is reduced by 44 per cent.

7.18. Vignetting. Another effect, which may cause the illuminance off the axis to fall at an even more rapid rate, is that known as *vignetting*. This is particularly likely to occur in a lens system containing stops, as is illustrated for a single lens in Fig. 7*T*. Although the aperture of the stop is smaller than that of the lens, at the angle of incidence shown some of the rays at the top miss the lens entirely, while the lower part of the lens receives no light. For distant object points, the field that is reproduced without vignetting covers angles up to the value of α shown in the

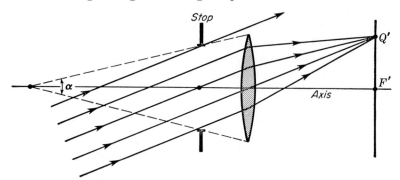

FIG. 7*T*. Illustrating the meaning of the term "vignetting."

diagram. At wider angles the field begins to darken more rapidly than would be indicated by Eq. 7*p*. Vignetting is seldom encountered in telescopes or in other instruments having a relatively small field of view but in instruments like wide-angle cameras it can become serious.

PROBLEMS

1. A thin lens with an aperture of 5.0 cm and a focal length of +4.0 cm has a 3.0-cm stop located 2.0 cm in front of it. An object 1.5 cm high is located with its lower end on the axis 9.0 cm in front of the lens. Locate graphically and by formula (*a*) the position, and (*b*) the size of the exit pupil. (*c*) Locate the image of the object graphically by drawing the two marginal rays and the chief ray from the top end of the object.

2. A thin lens with a focal length of +3.0 cm and aperture 4.0 cm has a 2.5-cm stop located 1.5 cm in front of it. An object 1.0 cm high is located with its lower end on the axis 6.0 cm in front of the stop. Locate graphically and by formula (*a*) the position, and (*b*) the size of the exit pupil. Locate the image of the object graphically by drawing the two marginal rays and the chief ray from the top end of the object. *Ans.* (*a*) −3.0 cm. (*b*) +5.0 cm. (*c*) +5.0 cm.

3. A thin lens with a focal length of −5.0 cm and aperture 4.0 cm has a 2.0-cm stop located 2.0 cm in front of it. An object 4.0 cm high is located with its center on the axis 12.0 cm in front of the lens. Find graphically and by formula (*a*) the position, and (*b*) the size of the exit pupil. (*c*) Graphically locate the image by drawing the two marginal rays and the chief ray from the top end of the object.

4. A thin lens with a focal length of +5.0 cm and an aperture 6.0 cm has a 3.0-cm stop located 3.0 cm behind it. An object 3.0 cm high is located with its center on the axis 12.0 cm in front of the lens. Find graphically and by formula (*a*) the position, and (b) the size of the entrance pupil. (c) Locate the image graphically by drawing the two marginal rays and the chief ray from the top end of the object.

Ans. (a) +7.5 cm. (b) 7.5 cm. (c) +8.6 cm.

5. Two thin lenses with focal lengths of +8.0 cm and +6.0 cm, respectively, and with apertures of 5.0 cm, are located 4.0 cm apart. A stop 2.5 cm in diameter is located midway between the lenses, and an object 4.0 cm high is located with its center 10.0 cm in front of the first lens. Find graphically and by formula (a) the position and size of the entrance pupil, and (b) the position and size of the exit pupil. (c) Locate the final image by drawing the two marginal rays and the chief ray from the top end of the object.

6. A thin lens L_1 with an aperture of 6.0 cm and focal length +6.0 cm is located 4.0 cm in front of another thin lens L_2 with an aperture of 6.0 cm and focal length −10.0 cm. An object 1.0 cm high is located with its center on the axis 18.0 cm in front of L_1, and a stop 3.0 cm in diameter is located 3.0 cm in front of L_1. Calculate the position and size of (a) the entrance pupil, (b) the exit pupil, and (c) the image. (d) Solve graphically.

Ans. (a) $A_1E = -3.0$ cm, $D_n = 3.0$ cm. (b) $A_1E' = -1.0$ cm, $D_x = 3.0$ cm. (c) $A_2M' = +10.0$ cm, $2y' = -1.0$ cm.

7. A thin lens L_2 with an aperture of 5.0 cm and focal length of +8.0 cm is located 5.0 cm behind another thin lens L_1 with an aperture of 6.0 cm and focal length +4.0 cm. An object 2.0 cm high is located with its center on the axis 5.0 cm in front of L_1, and a stop 3.0 cm in diameter is located between the lenses 2.0 cm from L_1. Calculate the position and size of (a) the entrance pupil, (b) the exit pupil, and (c) the image. (d) Solve graphically.

8. A thin lens L_1 with an aperture of 4.0 cm and a focal length of −8.0 cm is located 3.0 cm in front of another thin lens L_2 with an aperture of 4.0 cm and a focal length of +6.0 cm. For light incident on the first lens parallel to the axis calculate the position and size of (a) the entrance pupil, and (b) the exit pupil. (c) Solve graphically.

Ans. (a) $A_1E = +2.2$ cm, $D_n = 2.9$ cm. (b) $A_1E' = +3.0$ cm, $D_x = 4.0$ cm.

9. A Coddington magnifier lens (see Fig. 10H) is made from a glass sphere of index 1.6 and diameter 3.0 cm. The lens aperture is ground to a diameter of 2.0 cm, and a groove 0.40 cm deep is ground around its center. Find the position and size of (a) the entrance pupil, and (b) the exit pupil.

10. An exit pupil with a 4.0-cm aperture is located 8.0 cm in front of a spherical mirror of radius +20.0 cm. An object 2.0 cm high is centrally located on the axis 6.0 cm in front of the mirror. Find graphically (a) the entrance pupil, (b) the image, and (c) the minimum aperture for the mirror required to see the entire object from all points of the exit pupil.

Ans. (a) $AE = -4.44$ cm. (b) $AM' = -3.75$ cm. (c) 2.13 cm.

11. An exit pupil 3.0 cm in diameter is located 10.0 cm in front of a spherical mirror of +16.0 cm radius. An object 4.0 cm high is centrally located on the axis 6.0 cm in front of the mirror. Graphically find (a) the position and size of the entrance pupil. (b) Find the position and size of the image by drawing the two marginal rays and chief ray from the top of the object.

12. An exit pupil with a 4.0-cm aperture is located 8.0 cm in front of a mirror of +12.0 cm radius. An object 5.0 cm high is centrally located on the axis 4.0 cm in front of the mirror. Graphically find (a) the position and size of the entrance pupil (b) Find the position and size of the image by drawing the two marginal rays and chief ray from the top of the object.

Ans. (a) $AE = -3.43$ cm, $D_n = +1.71$ cm. (b) $AM' = -2.40$ cm, $2y' = +3.0$ cm.

13. An exit pupil with a 2.5-cm aperture is located 14.5 cm in front of a mirror of −12.5 cm radius. An object 1.5 cm high is centrally placed on the axis 13.0 cm in front of the mirror. Graphically find (a) the position and size of the entrance pupil. (b) Find the position and size of the image by drawing the two marginal rays and the chief ray from the top of the object.

14. An exit pupil with an aperture of 4.0 cm is located 18.0 cm in front of a mirror of −12.0 cm radius. An object 2.0 cm high is centrally located on the axis 14.0 cm in front of the mirror. (a) Graphically determine the position and size of the entrance pupil. (b) Find the position and size of the image by drawing the marginal rays and chief ray from the top of the object.
Ans. (a) $AE = +9.0$ cm, $D_n = -2.0$ cm. (b) $AM' = +10.5$ cm, $2y' = -1.50$ cm.

15. Construct to scale a diagram of the object field and image field for a lens with an aperture of 4.0 cm and a focal length of +6.0 cm, used as a magnifier. Assume the exit pupil to be 2.0 cm wide and located 3.5 cm to the right of the lens, and an object 3.0 cm high centrally located 4.0 cm to the left of the lens. Graphically find (a) the position and size of the entrance pupil, and (b) the position and size of the image by drawing the marginal rays and chief ray from the top of the object.

16. Make a diagram showing the object field and image field for a lens with an aperture of 3.0 cm and a focal length of +4.0 cm, used as a magnifier. Assume the exit pupil to be 2.0 cm wide and located 2.5 cm to the right of the lens, and an object 3.0 cm high centrally located 2.80 cm to the left of the lens. (a) Graphically find the position and size of the entrance pupil. (b) Find the position and size of the image by drawing the marginal rays and the chief ray from the top of the object.
Ans. (a) $AE = +6.66$ cm, $D_n = +5.33$ cm. (b) $AM' = -9.33$ cm, $2y' = +10.0$ cm.

17. The focal length of a thin lens 4.0 cm in diameter is 12.0 cm. If this lens is placed midway between the eye and a large object 10.0 cm from the eye, what width of the object can be seen through the lens?

18. Calculate the illuminance in lux due to a frosted lamp bulb of projected area 50 cm² and an average brightness of 2.625 candles/cm² on a surface normal to the light and 5.0 m away. (NOTE: Because of Lambert's law the bulb may be treated as a flat surface of the area and brightness given.) *Ans.* 5.25 lux

19. If the lamp in Prob. 17 is displaced 3.0 m in a direction at right angles to the original line joining it and the illuminated surface, what will be the new value of the illuminance?

20. A lens with an aperture of 4.0 cm and a focal length of +10.0 cm has a 3.0-cm stop located 4.0 cm in front of it. A small disk of brightness 50 candles/cm² is placed centrally on the axis 20.0 cm from the lens. Calculate (a) the illuminance at the image, (b) the size of the exit pupil, and (c) the angle at which vignetting begins.
Ans. (a) 1.37 lumens/cm² (b) 5.0 cm. (c) 7.1°.

21. A wide-angle camera lens has a focal length of +12.5 cm and takes photographs on a 9.0- by 12.0-cm film. Assuming no vignetting, find the per cent by which the exposure is diminished at the corners of the film.

22. A stop 2.0 cm in diameter is located 2.0 cm in front of a thin lens having a diameter of 4.0 cm and a focal length of −10.0 cm. Two centimeters behind this lens is another thin lens 6.0 cm in diameter and of focal length +2.5 cm. (a) Find graphically the entrance and exit pupils for parallel incident light. (b) An object 2.0 cm high is located with its lower end on the axis 8.0 cm to the left of the stop. Find the image by drawing three rays from the top end of the object through the system. Two of these rays are to be the *marginal rays*, and the other is to be the *chief ray*. (c) Solve (a) by formula, finding the position and size of both pupils. (d) Find, by calculation, the position and size of the image.
Ans. (a) $A_1E = -2.0$ cm from A_1, $D_n = 2.0$ cm, $A_2E' = +7.86$ cm, $D_x = 3.58$ cm. (b) Graph. (c) Same as (a). (d) $A_2M' = +3.89$ cm, $2y' = -0.56$ cm.

CHAPTER 8

RAY TRACING

The discussion of image formation by a system of one or more spherical surfaces has up to this point been confined to the consideration of paraxial rays. With this limitation it has been possible to derive relatively simple methods of calculating and constructing the position and size of the image. In practice the apertures of most lenses are so large that paraxial rays constitute only a very small fraction of all the effective rays. It is therefore important to consider what happens to rays that are not paraxial. The straightforward method of attacking this problem is to trace the paths of the rays through the system, applying Snell's law to the refraction at each surface.

8.1. Oblique Rays. All rays which lie in a plane through the principal axis and are not paraxial are called *oblique rays*. When the law of refraction is accurately applied to a number of rays through one or more coaxial surfaces, the position of the image point is found to vary with the obliquity of the rays. This leads to a blurring of the image known as lens aberrations, and the study of these aberrations will be the subject of the following chapter. Experience shows that it is possible, by properly choosing the radii and positions of spherical refracting surfaces, to reduce the aberrations greatly. Only in this way have optical instruments been designed and constructed having large usable apertures and at the same time good image-forming qualities.

Lens designers follow two general lines of approach to the problem of finding the optimum conditions. The first is to use graphical methods to find the approximate radii and spacing of the surfaces that should be used for the particular problem at hand. The second is to use well-known aberration formulas to calculate the approximate shapes and spacings. If the results of these methods of approach do not produce image-forming systems of sufficiently high quality and better definition is required, the method known as *ray tracing* is applied. The latter consists in finding the exact paths of several representative rays through the system selected. Some of these rays will be paraxial and some oblique, and each is traced from the object to the image.

If the results are not satisfactory, the surfaces are moved, the radii are

119

changed, and the process is repeated until an apparent minimum of aberration is obtained.   This is a long and tedious cut-and-try process, requiring in some cases hundreds of hours of work.   Five-, six-, or seven-place logarithms may be required, and certain standard tabular forms are printed by the different designers for recording the calculations and results (see Table 8-I).   Recent researches in electronics have led to the development of high-speed calculators capable of ray tracing through complicated systems in a very short time.   Such calculators undoubtedly

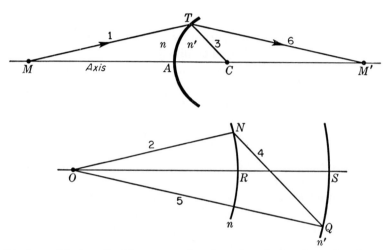

Fig. 8A. A graphical method for ray tracing through a single spherical surface.   The method is exact and obeys Snell's law for all rays.

are leading to the design and production of new and better high-quality optical systems.

In this chapter we shall first consider the method of *graphical ray tracing* and then the method of *calculation ray tracing*.   Lens aberrations and the approximate methods using aberration formulas will be treated in Chap. 9.

8.2. Graphical Method for Ray Tracing.   The graphical method for ray tracing to be presented here is an extension of the procedure given in Sec. 1.3 and shown for refraction at plane surfaces in Figs. $1C$ and $2M$. It is important to note that while the principles used follow Snell's law exactly the accuracy of the results obtained depends upon the precision with which the operator makes his drawing.   A good drawing board, with T square and triangles, or a drafting machine is therefore essential; as large a drawing board as is feasible is to be preferred.   The use of a sharp pencil is a necessity.

The diagrams in Fig. $8A$ illustrate the construction for refraction at a single spherical surface separating two media of index n and n'.   After the axis and the surface with a center at C are drawn, any incident ray like 1 is selected for tracing. An auxiliary diagram is now constructed below, comparable in size, and with its axis parallel to that of the main diagram. With the point O as a center two circular arcs are drawn with radii proportional to the refractive indices. Succeeding steps of the construction are carried out in the following order: Line 2 is drawn through O parallel to ray 1. Line 3 is drawn through points T and C. Line 4 is drawn through N parallel to line 3 and extended to where it

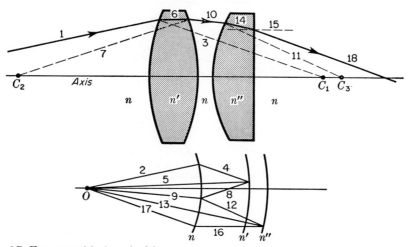

FIG. 8B. Exact graphical method for ray tracing through a centered system of spherical refracting surfaces.

intersects the arc n' at Q. Line 5 connects O and Q, and line 6 is drawn through T parallel to line 5.

In this diagram the radial line TC is normal to the surface at the point T and corresponds to the normal NN' in Fig. 1C. The proof that such construction follows Snell's law exactly is given in Sec. 1.3.

The graphical method applied to a system involving a series of coaxial spherical surfaces is shown in Fig. 8B. Two thick lenses having indices n' and n'', respectively, are surrounded by air of index $n = 1.00$. In the auxiliary diagram below arcs are drawn for the three indices n, n' and n''. All lines are drawn in parallel pairs as before and in consecutive order starting with the incident light ray 1. Each even-numbered line is drawn parallel to the odd-numbered line just preceding it, ending up with the final ray 18. Note that the radius of the fourth surface is infinite and line 15 drawn toward its center at infinity is parallel to the axis. The latter is in keeping with the procedures in Figs. 1C and 2M.

When the graphical method of ray tracing is applied to a thick mirror, the arcs representing the various known indices are drawn on both sides of the origin as shown in Fig. 8*C*. Again in this case the lines are drawn in parallel pairs with each even-numbered line parallel to its preceding odd-numbered line. Where the ray is reflected by the concave mirror, the rays 10 and 14 must make equal angles with the normal. Note that in the auxiliary diagram the corresponding lines 9, 12, and 13

FIG. 8*C*. Ray tracing through a thick mirror.

form an isosceles triangle. The particular optical arrangement shown here is known as a concentric optical system. The fact that all surfaces have a common center of curvature gives rise to some very interesting and useful optical properties (see Sec. 10.19).

8.3. Ray-tracing Formulas. A diagram from which these formulas may be derived is given in Fig. 8*D*. An oblique ray *MT* making an angle θ with the axis is refracted by the single spherical surface at *T* so that it crosses the axis again at *M'*. The line *TC* is the radius of the refracting surface and constitutes the normal from which the angles of incidence and refraction at T are measured. As regards the signs of the angles involved, we consider that

1. Slope angles are positive when the axis must be rotated counterclockwise through an angle of less than $\pi/2$ to bring it into coincidence with the ray.
2. Angles of incidence and refraction are positive when the radius of the surface must be rotated counterclockwise through an angle of less than $\pi/2$ to bring it into coincidence with the ray.

Accordingly, angles θ, ϕ, and ϕ' in Fig. 8D are positive, while angle θ' is negative.

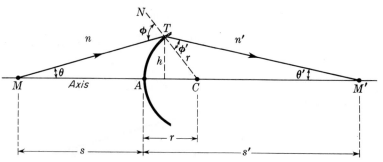

Fig. 8D. Geometry used in deriving the ray-tracing formulas.

Applying the law of sines to the triangle MTC, one obtains

$$\frac{\sin(\pi - \phi)}{r + s} = \frac{\sin \theta}{r}$$

Since the sine of the supplement of an angle equals the sine of the angle itself,

$$\frac{\sin \phi}{r + s} = \frac{\sin \theta}{r}$$

Solving for $\sin \phi$, we find

$$\sin \phi = \frac{r + s}{r} \sin \theta \tag{8a}$$

Now by Snell's law the angle of refraction ϕ' in terms of the angle of incidence ϕ is given by

$$\sin \phi' = \frac{n}{n'} \sin \phi \tag{8b}$$

In the triangle MTM' the sum of all interior angles must equal π. Therefore

$$\theta + (\pi - \phi) + \phi' + (-\theta') = \pi$$

which, upon solving for θ', gives

$$\theta' = \phi' + \theta - \phi \tag{8c}$$

This equation allows us to calculate the slope angle of the refracted ray. To find where the ray crosses the axis and the image distance s', the law of sines may be applied to the triangle TCM', giving

$$\frac{-\sin \theta'}{r} = \frac{\sin \phi'}{s' - r}$$

The image distance is therefore

$$s' = r - r\frac{\sin \phi'}{\sin \theta'} \tag{8d}$$

An important special case is that in which the incident ray is parallel to

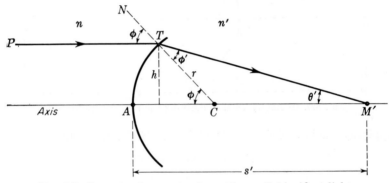

Fig. 8E. Geometry for ray tracing with parallel incident light.

the axis. Under this simplifying condition it may be seen from Fig. 8E that

$$\sin \phi = \frac{h}{r} \tag{8e}$$

where h is the height of the incident ray PT above the axis. For the triangle TCM', the sum of the two interior angles ϕ' and θ' equals the exterior angle at C. When the angles are assigned their proper signs, this gives

$$\theta' = \phi' - \phi \tag{8f}$$

The six of the above equations which are numbered form an important set by which any oblique ray lying in a *meridian plane* may be traced through a number of coaxial spherical surfaces. A meridian plane is defined as any plane containing the axis of the system. While most of the rays emanating from an extra-axial object point do not lie in a meridian plane, the image-forming properties of an optical system can usually be determined from properly chosen meridian rays. *Skew rays*, or rays that are not confined to a meridian plane, do not intersect the axis and are difficult to trace.

8.4. Sample Ray-tracing Calculations. These will be illustrated in the case of a double-convex lens with radii $r_1 = +10$ cm and $r_2 = -10$ cm, the lens being made of crown glass having an index $n' = 1.52300$ for the Fraunhofer D line. If the axial thickness is 2 cm, let us find the focal

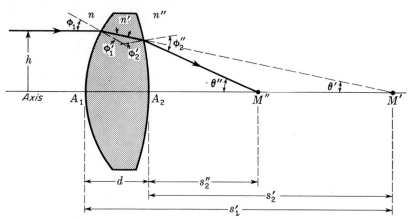

FIG. 8F. Geometry involved in the use of ray-tracing formulas.

points for parallel rays incident at heights above the axis $h = 1.5$ cm, 1.0 cm, 0.5 cm, and 0 cm.

A diagram for this kind of problem is given in Fig. 8F. Refraction at the first surface directs the ray toward the corresponding image point at M'. This becomes the object point for the second surface, at which the refraction determines the final image point M''. The following two tables give the calculations for the refracting surfaces separately. For the first surface the incident light is parallel to the axis, and the four ray-tracing formulas to be used are Eqs. 8b, 8d, 8e, and 8f, namely,

$$\sin \phi = \frac{h}{r} \qquad \sin \phi' = \frac{n}{n'} \sin \phi$$

and

$$\theta' = \phi' - \phi \qquad r - s' = r \frac{\sin \phi'}{\sin \theta'}$$

By substitution of the known values of h and r_1 in the first equation, $\sin \phi$ is determined. Inserting this, along with the known n and n', in the second equation, we obtain $\sin \phi'$. Having found ϕ and ϕ', we may use the third equation to calculate θ'. Finally the values of r_1, ϕ', and θ' are used in the last equation to obtain the image distance s_1'. In the use of logarithms for these calculations, the subtraction of one logarithm from another to find a quotient is avoided by employing the cologarithms of all quantities occurring in the denominator. Thus the operations are reduced to those of addition. The procedure is self-evident as regards the first three columns of figures in Table 8-I, where it is shown for the first refracting surface.

TABLE 8-I. CALCULATIONS FOR THE FIRST SURFACE
$r_1 = +10.0$ cm, $n' = 1.52300$, $n = 1.00000$

	$h = 1.5$ cm	$h = 1.0$ cm	$h = 0.5$ cm	$h = 0$
log h	0.176091	0.000000	9.698970	
colog r_1	9.000000	9.000000	9.000000	
log sin ϕ_1	9.176091	9.000000	8.698970	
log n	0.000000	0.000000	0.000000	
colog n'	9.817300	9.817300	9.817300	
log sin ϕ_1'	8.993391	8.817300	8.516270	
ϕ_1'	5°39'8''	3°45'53''	1°52'53''	0.098490
ϕ_1	8°37'37''	5°44'21''	2°51'58''	0.150000
θ'	2°58'29''	1°58'28''	0°59'8''	0.051510
colog sin θ'	1.284871	1.462764	1.764463	1.288108
log sin ϕ_1'	8.993391	8.817300	8.516270	8.993391
log r_1	1.000000	1.000000	1.000000	1.000000
log $(r_1 - s_1')$	1.278262	1.280067	1.280733	1.281499
$r_1 - s_1'$	−18.9785	−19.0576	−19.0868	−19.1205
s_1'	+28.9785 cm	+29.0576 cm	+29.0868	+29.1205 cm

For the case $h = 0$ in the right-hand column a special procedure is followed. The calculation is started by first finding the number that corresponds to one of the values of log sin ϕ_1' in another column. In the present case either column may be used. This number is entered opposite ϕ_1' in the table under $h = 0$. For example, in the column headed $h = 1.5$ cm, we find log sin $\phi_1' = 8.993391$, and the number corresponding to this logarithm (namely, 0.098490) is entered in the last column. Following the same procedure for the corresponding angle ϕ_1, we find log sin $\phi_1 = 9.176091$, and the number 0.150000 is shown opposite ϕ_1. The difference between these two numbers is next entered for θ'. Then opposite colog sin θ' is written the cologarithm of the number 0.051510, namely, 1.288108. From this point on, the procedure is the same as for the chosen ray, $h = 1.5$, values of log sin ϕ_1' and log r_1 being taken from the column originally selected. The value of s_1' that results will be the same whatever auxiliary ray is chosen for the calculation.*

It is to be noted that the image distance s_1' is greatest for $h = 0$, and about one-half of 1 per cent less for the 1.5-cm ray. These slightly different image points M' become the object points for the second lens surface, and the slope angles ϕ' of Table 8-I become the slope angles θ' for the incident rays in Table 8-II. Since in the latter case the object rays are not parallel to the axis, the four ray-tracing formulas to be used for Table 8-II are Eqs. 8a, 8b, 8c, and 8d, namely,

$$\sin \phi_2' = \frac{r_2 + s_2'}{r_2} \sin \theta' \qquad \sin \phi_2'' = \frac{n'}{n''} \sin \phi_2'$$

and $\qquad \theta' = \phi_2'' + \theta' - \phi_2' \qquad r_2 - s_2'' = r_2 \frac{\sin \phi_2''}{\sin \theta'}$

Starting with the first equation, r_2 is given as -10.0 cm, and s_2' is the distance A_2M' in Fig. 8F. It is obtained by subtracting from the values of s_1' in Table 8-I the lens thickness $d = 2.0$ cm.

Taking the ray having $h = 1.5$ cm as an example, we have s_1' from Table 8-I as 28.9785 cm, which after subtraction of $d = 2.0$ cm yields $s_2' = 26.9785$ cm. The negative sign signifies that the object ray corresponds to a virtual object. Since both r_2 and s_2' have negative signs, the two magnitudes are added in the first equation to give -36.9785 cm.

In the last column of Table 8-II the value for log sin $\theta' = 8.711892$ is obtained from colog sin $\theta' = 1.288108$ of Table 8-I. Instead of angles ϕ_2'', θ', and ϕ_2' in the last column, numbers are obtained by the auxiliary-ray method described above in connection with Table 8-I. For example, the number 0.291210 corresponds to log sin $\phi_2'' = 9.464206$ and is entered opposite ϕ_2'' in Table 8-II. The number 0.051510 corresponds to log sin $\theta' = 8.711892$ and is entered opposite θ' in the table. Then opposite colog sin θ'' is written 0.819550, which is the cologarithm of the *number* 0.151513. From here on, the procedure corresponds to that for the other rays.

The final figures show that, when parallel rays are incident on the lens of Fig. 8F at heights of 1.5 cm, 1.0 cm, 0.5 cm, and 0 cm, the axial intercepts s_2'' are at 8.8820 cm, 9.0842 cm, 9.1809 cm, and 9.2202 cm, respectively. Thus the distance from the lens vertex to the second focal point is not a constant but varies slightly for different zones of the lens. This defect is called *spherical aberration* and will be discussed in detail in the next chapter. The focal distances s_1' and s_2'' for $h = 0$ and for $\theta = 0$ in

* The theory of this auxiliary-ray method is set forth in Lummer, "Photographic Optics," English translation by S. P. Thompson, p. 126, The Macmillan Company, New York, 1900.

TABLE 8-II. CALCULATIONS FOR THE SECOND SURFACE
$r_2 = -10.0$ cm, $n'' = 1.00000$, $n' = 1.52300$, $d = 2.0$ cm

θ'	$\theta' = 2°58'29''$	$\theta' = 1°58'28''$	$\theta' = 0°59'8''$	$\theta' = 0$
$r_2 + s_2'$	-36.9785	-37.0576	-37.0868	-37.1205
$\log (r_2 + s_2')$	1.567949	1.568877	1.569219	1.569614
$\operatorname{colog} r_2$	9.000000	9.000000	9.000000	9.000000
$\log \sin \theta'$	8.715129	8.537233	8.235537	8.711892
$\log \sin \phi_2'$	9.283078	9.106110	8.804756	9.281506
$\log n'$	0.182700	0.182700	0.182700	0.182700
$\operatorname{colog} n''$	0.000000	0.000000	0.000000	0.000000
$\log \sin \phi_2''$	9.465778	9.288810	8.987456	9.464206
ϕ_2''	16°59'37''	11°12'32''	5°34'31''	0.291210
θ'	2°58'29''	1°58'28''	0°59'8''	0.051510
ϕ_2'	11°3'50''	7°20'8''	3°39'27''	0.191207
θ''	8°54'16''	5°50'53''	2°54'12''	0.151513
$\operatorname{colog} \sin \theta''$	0.810265	0.991865	1.295412	0.819550
$\log \sin \phi_2''$	9.465778	9.288810	8.987456	9.464206
$\log r_2$	1.000000	1.000000	1.000000	1.000000
$\log (r_2 - s_2'')$	1.276043	1.280675	1.282868	1.283756
$r_2 - s_2''$	-18.8820	-19.0842	-19.1809	-19.2202
s_2''	$+8.8820$ cm	$+9.0842$ cm	$+9.1809$	$+9.2202$ cm
$\delta s_2''$	0.3382 cm	0.1360 cm	0.0393 cm	0

Tables 8-I and 8-II are identical with the values which would be obtained from the paraxial-ray formulas given in Sec. 5.1.

Whenever a plane surface is encountered, refraction is traced exactly by means of Eq. 2b. If, for example, the second surface of a lens is plane, Snell's law becomes

$$\sin \theta'' = \frac{n'}{n''} \sin \theta'$$

and Eq. 2b becomes

$$s_2'' = s_2' \frac{\tan \theta'}{\tan \theta''}$$

where $\theta'' = \phi_2''$ and $\theta' = \phi_2'$. The calculations are carried out by tabulating the proper logarithms as in Table 8-II.

PROBLEMS

1. A double-convex lens 3 cm thick at the center has radii $r_1 = +14$ cm and $r_2 = -10$ cm and an index of 1.600. If a ray of light parallel to the axis is incident on the first surface at a height of 4 cm, apply the graphical method to find the point where the ray crosses the axis.

2. Solve Prob. 1 if the incident ray is at a height of 3.0 cm.   *Ans.* $+7.92$ cm.

3. Solve Prob. 1 if the incident ray is at a height of 2.0 cm.

4. Solve Prob. 1 if the incident ray is at a height of 1.0 cm.   *Ans.* $+9.23$ cm.

5. Two glass lenses have the following specifications:

Lens 1. $r_1 = +10$ cm, $r_2 = -12$ cm, $n' = 1.50$, and thickness $d = 2.5$ cm.

Lens 2. $r_1 = +10$ cm, $r_2 = +12$ cm, $n'' = 1.70$, and thickness $d = 2.0$ cm.

These lenses are mounted on a common axis with their nearest vertices 1 cm apart. A ray of light, parallel to the axis, is incident on the first lens at a height of 3 cm. Apply the graphical method, and find where the final refracted ray crosses the axis.

6. A thick mirror is composed of a double-concave lens, with radii $r_1 = -11$ cm, $r_2 = +11$ cm, $n' = 1.50$, and thickness 1.5 cm, and a concave mirror of radius -9.5 cm. The two elements are 3.5 cm apart. A light ray is incident on the first lens surface 3.5 cm above, and parallel to, the axis. Apply the graphical method to find where the final emergent ray crosses the axis.   *Ans.* 8.5 cm left of first vertex.

7. A single spherical surface of radius $+10.0$ cm is ground on the end of a glass rod of index 1.65250. Using five-place logarithms, locate the focal points for a parallel incident ray at a height of (a) $h = 1.5$ cm, (b) $h = 1.0$ cm, (c) $h = 0.5$ cm, and (d) $h = 0$ cm.

8. Solve Prob. 7 when $r = +6.25$ cm.
   Ans. (a) 15.6581, (b) 15.7540, (c) 15.8120, (d) 15.8285 cm.

9. Solve Prob. 7 when $r = +4.00$ cm.

10. Solve Prob. 7 when $r = +2.50$ cm.
   Ans. (a) 5.8803, (b) 6.1405, (c) 6.2830, (d) 6.3314 cm.

11. Solve Prob. 7 when $r = -10.0$ cm.

12. A lens 1.0 cm thick is made of dense barium crown glass of index 1.62350. It has radii $r_1 = +10.0$ cm and $r_2 = -10.0$ cm. Using five-place logarithms, locate the focal point for (a) $h = 1.5$ cm, (b) $h = 1.0$ cm, (c) 0.50 cm, and (d) $h = 0$ cm.
   Ans. (a) 7.4907, (b) 7.7011, (c) 7.8220, (d) 7.8623 cm.

13. Solve Prob. 12 when $r_1 = +6.25$ cm and $r_2 = -25.0$ cm.

14. Solve Prob. 12 when $r_1 = +5.00$ cm and $r_2 = $ infinity.
   Ans. (a) 7.0154, (b) 7.3056, (c) 7.3965, (d) 7.4033 cm.

15. Solve Prob. 12 when $r_1 = +2.50$ cm and $r_2 = -6.25$ cm.

16. Solve Prob. 12 when $r_1 = -15.0$ cm and $r_2 = -3.75$ cm.
   Ans. (a) 6.2326, (b) 7.2155, (c) 7.7719, (d) 7.9531 cm.

CHAPTER 9

LENS ABERRATIONS

The processes of ray tracing presented in the last chapter served to emphasize the inability of the paraxial-ray formulas of the Gauss theory to give an accurate account of image detail. A wide beam of rays incident on a lens parallel to the axis, for example, is not brought to a focus at a unique point. The resulting image defect is known as *spherical aberration*. The Gaussian formulas developed and used in the preceding chapters give, therefore, only an idealized account of the images produced with lenses of wide aperture.

When ray tracing is applied to object points located farther and farther off the axis, the observed image defects become more and more pronounced. The methods of reducing these aberrations to a minimum, and thereby permitting the formation of reasonably satisfactory images, are one of the chief problems of geometrical optics. It would be impossible within the scope of this book to give all the details of the extensive mathematical theory involved in this problem.* Instead we shall attempt to show how most of the aberrations manifest themselves and at the same time discuss some of the known formulas to see how they may be used in the design of high-quality optical systems.

9.1. Expansion of the Sine, and First-order Theory. In order to formulate a satisfactory theory of lens aberrations, many theoreticians have found it convenient to start with the correct and precise ray-tracing formulas, as given in Eqs. 8a through 8f, and to expand the sines of each angle into a power series. An expansion of the sine of an angle by Maclaurin's theorem gives

$$\sin \theta = \theta - \frac{\theta^3}{3!} + \frac{\theta^5}{5!} - \frac{\theta^7}{7!} + \frac{\theta^9}{9!} \cdots \tag{9a}$$

For small angles this is a rapidly converging series. Each member is small compared with the preceding member. It shows that for paraxial rays where the slope angles are very small we may, to a first approxima-

* For a more thorough account of lens aberrations the reader is referred to A. E. Conrady, "Applied Optics and Optical Design," vol. 1, Oxford University Press, New York, 1929.

tion, neglect all terms beyond the first and write

$$\sin \theta = \theta$$

When θ is small, the other angles ϕ, ϕ', and θ' are also small, provided the ray lies close to the axis. By substituting θ for $\sin \theta$, ϕ for $\sin \phi$, and θ' for $\sin \theta'$, in Eqs. 8a, 8b, and 8d, we obtain

$$\phi = \frac{r+s}{r} \theta \qquad\qquad \phi' = \frac{n}{n'} \phi$$

$$\theta' = \phi' + \theta - \phi \qquad\qquad s' = r - r \frac{\phi'}{\theta'}$$

By the algebraic substitution of the first equation in the second, the resultant equation in the third, and this resultant in the fourth, all angles may be eliminated. The final equation obtained by these substitutions is found to be none other than the Gaussian formula,

$$\frac{n}{s} + \frac{n'}{s'} = \frac{n' - n}{r}$$

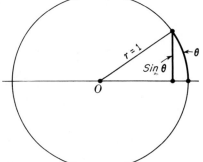

Fig. 9A. Illustrating the arc of an angle θ in relation to its sine.

This equation and others developed from it form the basis of what is usually called *first-order theory*.

The justification for writing $\sin \theta = \theta$, etc., for all small angles, is illustrated in Fig. 9A and in Table 9-I. For an angle of 10°, for example, the arc length θ is only one-half of 1 per cent greater than $\sin 10°$, while for 40° it is about 10 per cent greater. These differences are measures of spherical aberration and, therefore, of image defects.

TABLE 9-I. VALUES OF $\sin \theta$ AND ITS FIRST THREE EXPANSION TERMS

	$\sin \theta$	θ	$\theta^3/3!$	$\theta^5/5!$
10°	0.1736482	0.1745329	0.0008861	0.0000135
20°	0.3420201	0.3490658	0.0070888	0.0000432
30°	0.5000000	0.5235988	0.0239246	0.0003280
40°	0.6427876	0.6981316	0.0567088	0.0013829

9.2. Third-order Theory of Aberrations. If all the sines of angles in the ray-tracing formulas (Eq. 8a to 8f) are replaced by the first two terms of the series in Eq. 9a, the resultant equations, in whatever form they are given, represent the results of *third-order theory*. Thus $\sin \theta$ is replaced by $\theta - \theta^3/3!$, $\sin \phi$ is replaced by $\phi - \phi^3/3!$, etc. The resulting equations give a reasonably accurate account of the principal aberrations.

In this theory the aberration of any ray, i.e., its deviation from the path prescribed by the Gauss formulas, is expressed in terms of five sums, S_1 to S_5, called the *Seidel sums*. If a lens were to be free of all defects in its ability to form images, all five of these sums would have to be equal to zero. No optical system can be made to satisfy all these conditions at once. Therefore it is customary to treat each sum separately, and the vanishing of certain ones corresponds to the absence of certain aberrations. Thus, if for a given axial object point the Seidel

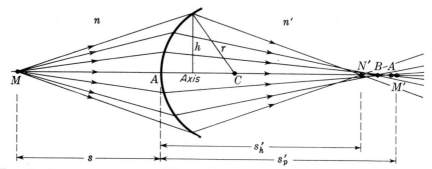

FIG. 9B. Illustration of the spherical aberration in the image of an axial object point as formed by a single spherical refracting surface.

sum $S_1 = 0$, there is no *spherical aberration* at the corresponding image point. If both $S_1 = 0$ and $S_2 = 0$, the system will also be free of *coma*. If, in addition to $S_1 = 0$ and $S_2 = 0$, the sums $S_3 = 0$ and $S_4 = 0$ as well, the images will be free of *astigmatism* and *curvature of field*. If finally S_5 could be made to vanish, there would be no *distortion* of the image. These aberrations are also known as the *five monochromatic aberrations* because they exist for any specified color and refractive index. Additional image defects occur when the light contains various colors. We shall first discuss each of the monochromatic aberrations and then take up the chromatic effects.

9.3. Spherical Aberration of a Single Surface. This is a term introduced in Sec. 6.8, and shown in Fig. 6K, to describe the blurring of the image formed when parallel light is incident on a spherical mirror. A similar blurring of the image that occurs upon refraction by spherical surfaces will now be discussed. In Fig. 9B M is an object point on the axis of a single spherical refracting surface, and M' is its paraxial image point. Oblique rays incident on the surface in a zone of radius h are brought to a focus closer to, and at a distance of s'_h from, the vertex A.

The distance $N'M'$, as shown in the diagram, is a measure of the *longitudinal spherical aberration*, and its magnitude is found from the third-order formula,

$$\frac{n}{s} + \frac{n'}{s'_h} = \frac{n' - n}{r} + \left[\left(\frac{h^2 n^2 r}{2f'n'}\right)\left(\frac{1}{s} + \frac{1}{r}\right)^2\left(\frac{1}{r} + \frac{n' - n}{ns}\right)\right] \quad (9b)$$

Since from the paraxial-ray formula (Eq. 3b) we have

$$\frac{n}{s} + \frac{n'}{s'_p} = \frac{n' - n}{r}$$

the right-hand bracket in Eq. 9b is a measure of the deviations from first-order theory. Its magnitude varies with the position of the object

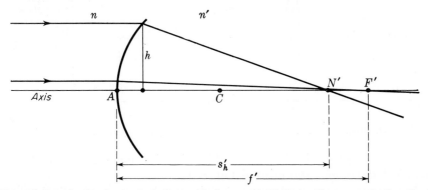

Fig. 9C. Longitudinal spherical aberration for parallel light incident on a single spherical refracting surface.

point and for any fixed point is *approximately proportional to h^2, the square of the radius of the zone on the refracting surface through which the rays pass.*

If the object point is at infinity so that the incident rays are parallel to the axis as shown in Fig. 9C, this equation reduces to

$$\frac{n'}{s'_h} = \frac{n'}{f'} + \frac{h^2 n^2}{2f'r^2n'} \quad (9c)$$

Again the magnitude of the aberration is proportional to h^2, the square of the height of the ray above the axis.

9.4. Spherical Aberration of a Thin Lens. The existence of spherical aberration for a single spherical surface indicates that it may also occur in combinations of such surfaces, as, for example, in a thin lens. Since many of the lenses in optical instruments are used to focus parallel incident or emergent rays, it is usual for comparison purposes to determine the spherical aberration for parallel incident light. Figure 9D(a) illustrates this special case and shows the position of the paraxial focal point F' as well as the focal points A, B, and C for zones of increasing diameter. Diagram (b) in Fig. 9D illustrates the difference between

FIG. 9D. Illustrations of lateral and longitudinal spherical aberration of a lens.

longitudinal spherical aberration, abbreviated Long. S.A., and *lateral spherical aberration*, abbreviated Lat. S.A.

As a measure of the actual magnitudes involved in longitudinal spherical aberration, we may use the focal lengths for three zones of a lens which were accurately calculated in Table 8-II. The results were 9.2202 cm for paraxial rays, 9.1809 cm for rays transversing a zone of radius $h = 0.5$ cm, 9.0842 cm for a zone of radius $h = 1$ cm, and 8.8820 cm for a zone of radius $h = 1.5$ cm. These figures give a spherical aberration of 0.3382 cm for the 1.5-cm zone, or about 4 per cent of the paraxial focal length. A graph showing the variation of f with h for this lens is given in Fig. 9E. For small h the curve approximates to a parabola, and since the marginal rays intersect the axis to the left of the paraxial focal point, the spherical aberration is said to be *positive*. A similar curve for an equiconcave lens would bend over to the right, corresponding to *negative* spherical aberration.

FIG. 9E. A graph of the variation of focal length with ray height h. The differences of f are a measure of spherical aberration.

A series of positive lenses of the same diameter and paraxial focal length but of different shape is presented in Fig. 9F(a). The alteration of shape represented in this series is known as *bending* the lens. Each

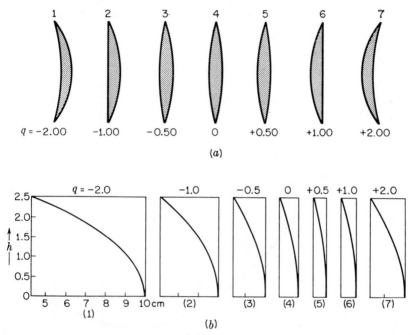

Fig. 9F. (a) Lenses of different shapes but with the same power or focal length. The difference is one of bending. (b) Focal length vs. ray height h for these lenses.

lens is labeled by a number q called its *shape factor*, defined by the formula

$$q = \frac{r_2 + r_1}{r_2 - r_1} \tag{9d}$$

As an example, if the two radii of a converging meniscus lens are $r_1 = -15$ cm and $r_2 = -5$ cm, it has a shape factor

$$q = \frac{-5 - 15}{-5 + 15} = -2$$

The usual reason for considering the bending of a lens is to find that shape for which the spherical aberration is a minimum. That such a minimum exists is shown by the graphs of Fig. 9F(b). These curves are drawn for the same lenses as shown in (a), and the values were taken from Table 9-II. They were calculated by the ray-tracing methods of Chap. 8, Tables 8-I and 8-II. It will be noted that lens (5), for which the shape factor q is +0.5, has the least spherical aberration. The amount of this aberration for the ray having $h = 1$ cm is shown for the same series of lenses by the curves of Fig. 9G.   Over the range of shape factors from about $q = +0.4$ to $q = +1.0$ the spherical aberration varies only slightly, since it is close to a minimum.   At no point, however, does it go to zero.   We therefore see that by choosing the proper radii for the two surfaces of a

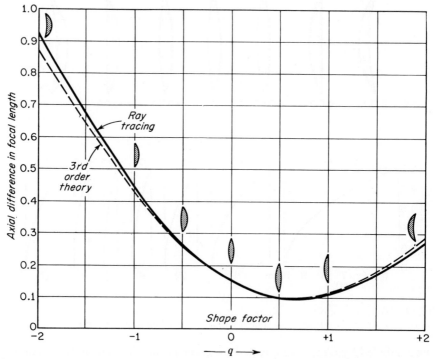

FIG. 9G. A graph of the spherical aberration for lenses of different shape but the same focal length.   For the lenses shown $h = 1$ cm, $f = +10$ cm, $d = 2$ cm, and $n' = 1.51700$.

lens the spherical aberration can be reduced to a minimum but cannot be made to vanish completely.

Reference to the diagrams of Fig. 9D will show that with spherical surfaces the marginal rays are deviated through too large an angle.   Hence any reduction of this deviation will improve the sharpness of the image. The existence of a condition of minimum deviation in a prism (Sec. 2.8) clearly indicates that when the shape of a lens is changed the deviation of the marginal rays will be least when they enter the first lens surface and leave the second at more or less equal angles.   Such an equal division of refraction will yield the smallest spherical aberration.   For parallel light incident on a crown-glass lens, this appears from Fig. 9G to occur at a shape factor of about $q = +0.7$, not greatly different from the plano-convex lens, for which $q = +1.0$.

Spherical aberration can be completely eliminated for a single lens by *aspherizing*. This is a tedious hand-polishing process by which various zones of one or both lens surfaces are given different curvatures. For only a few special instruments are such lenses useful enough so that the added expense of hand figuring is justified. Furthermore, since it is figured for only one object distance, such a lens is not free from spherical aberration for other distances. The most common practice in lens design is to adhere to the simple spherical surfaces and to reduce the spherical aberration by a proper choice of radii.

9.5. Results of Third-order Theory. Although the derivation of an equation for spherical aberration from third-order theory is too lengthy to be given here, some of the resulting equations are of interest. For a thin lens we have the reasonably simple formula

$$L_s = \frac{h^2}{8f^3} \cdot \frac{1}{n(n-1)}$$
$$\left[\frac{n+2}{n-1}q^2 + 4(n+1)pq + (3n+2)(n-1)p^2 + \frac{n^3}{n-1}\right] \quad (9e)$$

where
$$L_s = \frac{1}{s_h'} - \frac{1}{s_p'}$$

As shown in Fig. 9D(b), s_h' is the image distance for an oblique ray traversing the lens at a distance h from the axis, s_p' is the image distance for paraxial rays, and f the paraxial focal length. The constant p is called the *position factor*, and q is the shape factor defined by Eq. 9d. The position factor is defined as

$$p = \frac{s' - s}{s' + s} \quad (9f)$$

Making use of the first-order equation $1/f = (1/s) + (1/s')$, the position factor may also be expressed in terms of f as

$$p = \frac{2f}{s} - 1 = 1 - \frac{2f}{s'} \quad (9g)$$

The difference between the two image distances, $s_p' - s_h'$ is called the *longitudinal spherical aberration*, here abbreviated Long. S.A.

$$\text{Long. S.A.} = s_p' - s_h'$$

The intercept of the oblique ray with the paraxial focal plane is the *lateral spherical aberration* and from Fig. 9D(b) is seen to be given by

$$\text{Lat. S.A.} = (s_p' - s_h') \tan \theta'$$

If we solve Eq. 9e for the difference $s'_p - s'_h$, we obtain

$$\text{Long. S.A.} = s'_p s'_h L_s$$
$$\text{Lat. S.A.} = s'_p h L_s$$

and (9h)

The image distance s'_h for any ray through any zone is given by

$$s'_h = \frac{s'_p}{1 + s'_p L_s}$$

A comparison of the third-order theory with the exact results of ray tracing is included in Fig. 9G. When the shape factor is not far from that corresponding to the minimum, the agreement is remarkably good. The numerical results of third-order theory for the seven lenses of Fig. 9F are presented in the last column of Table 9-II.

TABLE 9-II. SPHERICAL ABERRATION OF LENSES HAVING THE SAME FOCAL
LENGTH BUT DIFFERENT SHAPES q

Lens thickness = 1 cm, f = 10 cm, n = 1.5000, and h = 1 cm

Shape of lens	r_1	r_2	q	Ray tracing	Third-order theory
1. Concavo-convex	−10.000	− 3.333	−2.00	0.92	0.88
2. Plano-convex	∞	− 5.000	−1.00	0.45	0.43
3. Double convex	20.000	− 6.666	−0.50	0.26	0.26
4. Equiconvex	10.000	−10.000	0	0.15	0.15
5. Double convex	6.666	−20.000	+0.50	0.10	0.10
6. Plano-convex	5.000	∞	+1.00	0.11	0.11
7. Concavo-convex	3.333	10.000	+2.00	0.27	0.29

Equations useful in lens design are obtained by finding the shape factor that will make Eq. 9e a minimum. This may be done by differentiating with respect to the shape factor and equating to zero:

$$\frac{dL_s}{dq} = \frac{h^2}{8f^3} \left[\frac{2(n + 2)q + 4(n - 1)(n + 1)p}{n(n - 1)^2} \right]$$

Equating to zero and solving for q, one obtains

$$q = -\frac{2(n^2 - 1)p}{n + 2}$$ (9i)

as the required relation between shape and position factors to produce minimum spherical aberration. As a rule a lens is designed for some particular pair of object and image distances so that p may be calculated from Eq. 9f. For a lens of a given n the shape factor that will produce a minimum lateral spherical aberration may be obtained at once from Eq. 9i. In order to determine the radii that will correspond to such a calculated shape factor and still yield the proper focal length, one may then use the lens makers' formula

$$\frac{1}{s} + \frac{1}{s'} = (n - 1)\left(\frac{1}{r_1} - \frac{1}{r_2}\right) = \frac{1}{f}$$

Substitution of values of s, s' and r_1, r_2 from Eqs. $9g$ and $9d$ gives the following useful set of equations, due to Coddington:

$$\left. \begin{array}{ll} s = \dfrac{2f}{1 + p} & s' = \dfrac{2f}{1 - p} \\[2mm] r_1 = \dfrac{2f(n - 1)}{q + 1} & r_2 = \dfrac{2f(n - 1)}{q - 1} \end{array} \right\} \qquad (9j)$$

The last two relations give the radii in terms of q and f. Division of one of these by the other gives

$$\frac{r_1}{r_2} = \frac{q - 1}{q + 1} \qquad (9k)$$

As a problem let us suppose that a single lens is to be made with a focal length of 10 cm and that we wish to find the radii of the surfaces which will give the minimum spherical aberration for parallel incident light. For simplicity we shall assume that the glass has an index $n = 1.50$. In using Eq. $9i$ the position factor p and the shape factor q must first be determined. Substitution of $s = \infty$ and $s' = 10$ cm in Eq. $9f$ gives

$$p = \frac{10 - \infty}{10 + \infty} = -1$$

It may be seen that if s is not infinite but is allowed to approach infinity, the ratio $(s' + s):(s' - s)$ will approach the value -1, and will in the limit be equal to this. Substituting this position factor in Eq. $9i$, we obtain

$$q = -\frac{2(2.25 - 1)(-1)}{1.5 + 2} = \frac{2.5}{3.5} = 0.714$$

This value falls at the minimum of the curve of Fig. $9G$. The ratio of the two radii is given by Eq. $9k$ as

$$\frac{r_1}{r_2} = \frac{0.714 - 1}{0.714 + 1} = \frac{-0.286}{1.714} = -0.167$$

The negative sign means that the surfaces curve in opposite directions, and the numerical value indicates a ratio of the radii of about 6:1. Their individual values are found from Eq. $9j$ to be

$$r_1 = \frac{10}{1.714} = 5.83 \text{ cm} \qquad \text{and} \qquad r_2 = \frac{10}{0.286} = -35.0 \text{ cm}$$

Such a lens lies between lenses (5) and (6) in Fig. 9F and has essentially the same amount of spherical aberration as either one. For this reason plano-convex lenses are often employed in optical instruments with the convex side facing the parallel incident rays. Should such a lens be turned around so that the flat side is toward the incident light, its shape factor becomes $q = -1.0$, and the spherical aberration increases about fourfold.

Although spherical aberration cannot be entirely eliminated for a single spherical lens, it is possible to do so for a combination of two or more lenses of opposite sign. The amount of spherical aberration introduced by one lens of such a combination must be equal and opposite to that introduced by the other. If for example the doublet is to have a positive power and no spherical aberration, the positive lens should have the greater power and its shape should be at or near that for minimum spherical aberration, while the negative lens should have a smaller power and its shape should not be near that for the minimum. Neutralization by such an arrangement is possible because spherical aberration varies as the cube of the focal length, and therefore changes sign with the sign of f (see Eq. 9e). In a cemented lens of two elements, the two interfaces should have the same radius. The other two may then be varied and then used to correct for spherical aberration. With four radii to manipulate, other aberrations like chromatic aberration can be reduced at the same time. This subject will be considered in Sec. 9.13.

9.6. Fifth-order Spherical Aberration. The two curves that were given in Fig. 9G show that, for a lens having a shape factor anywhere near the optimum, the agreement between the exact results of ray tracing and the approximate results of third-order theory is remarkably good. For larger values of h, however, and for shapes further removed from the optimum, appreciable differences occur. This indicates the necessity of including the fifth-order terms in the theory. The third-order equation 9e shows that spherical aberration should be proportional to h^2, so that the curves in Fig. 9F(b) should be parabolas. Nevertheless accurate measurements show that for larger h departures from proportionality to h^2 do occur and that spherical aberration is more closely represented by an equation of the form

$$\text{Long. S.A.} = ah^2 + bh^4 \tag{9l}$$

where a and b are constants. The term ah^2 represents the third-order effect and bh^4 the fifth-order effect. Some numerical results for a single lens, indicating the necessity for the inclusion of the latter term, are shown in Table 9-III. The **boldface** values in the fifth row are the true values for longitudinal spherical aberration, obtained by ray-tracing methods, while those in the last row correspond to a parabola that has been fitted at $h = 1.0$ cm to the equation

$$\text{Long. S.A.} = a'h^2$$

with $a' = 0.11530$ cm^{-1}.

TABLE 9-III. FIFTH-ORDER CORRECTION TO SPHERICAL ABERRATION
$f = 10$ cm, $r_1 = +5$ cm, $r_2 = \infty$, $n = 1.500$, $d = 1$ cm

1. h, cm	0.5	1.0	1.5	2.0	2.5	3.0
2. ah^2............	0.02839	0.11356	0.25551	0.45424	0.70975	1.02204
3. bh^4............	0.00011	0.00174	0.00881	0.02784	0.06797	0.14094
4. $ah^2 + bh^4$.......	0.02850	**0.11530**	0.26432	**0.48208**	0.77772	1.16928
5. Ray tracing.....	**0.02897**	**0.11530**	**0.26515**	**0.48208**	**0.77973**	**1.16781**
6. Parabola........	0.02882	**0.11530**	0.25942	0.46120	0.71812	1.03770

The second row gives the third-order corrections ah^2 and the third row the fifth-order corrections bh^4. The fourth row contains the values

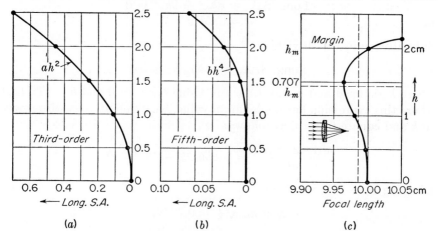

FIG. 9H. (a) Third-order and (b) fifth-order contributions to longitudinal spherical aberration. (c) Longitudinal spherical aberration of a corrected doublet as used in telescopes.

calculated from Eq. 9l by fitting the curve at the two points $h = 1$ cm and $h = 2$ cm. Assuming the values 0.11530 and 0.48208 at these points, the constants become

$$a = 0.11356 \quad \text{and} \quad b = 0.00174$$

A comparison of the totals in the fourth row with the correct values in the fifth row reveals the excellent agreement of the latter with Eq. 9l. Graphs of the values in rows 2 and 3 are given in Fig. 9H, and show the negligible contribution of the fifth-order correction at small values of h. If only the third-order aberration were present in a lens it would be possible to combine a positive and a negative lens having equal aberrations to obtain a combination corrected for all zones. Because they actually would have different amounts of fifth-order aberration, however, such a combination can be corrected for one zone only.

A graph illustrating the spherical aberration of a cemented doublet which is corrected for the marginal zone is shown in Fig. $9H(c)$. It will be seen that the curve comes to zero only at the origin and at the margin. The combination becomes badly overcorrected if the aperture is further increased. The plane of best focus lies a little to the left of the paraxial and marginal focal points, and its position (the vertical broken line) corresponds to that of the circle of least confusion.

Let a and b in Eq. $9l$ represent the constants for a thin-lens doublet. If the combination is to be corrected at the margin, i.e., for a ray at the height h_m, we must have

$$\text{Long. S.A.} = ah_m{}^2 + bh_m{}^4 = 0$$

or

$$a = -bh_m{}^2$$

Substitution in Eq. $9l$ yields

$$\text{Long. S. A.} = -bh_m{}^2h^2 + bh^4$$

where h_m is fixed and h may take any value between 0 and h_m. To find where this expression has a maximum value, we differentiate with respect to h and equate to zero, as follows:

$$\frac{d(\text{long. S.A.})}{dh} = -2bh_m{}^2h + 4bh^3 = 0$$

Dividing by $-2bh$, we obtain

$$h = h_m \sqrt{\tfrac{1}{2}} = 0.707h_m$$

as the radius of the zone at which the aberration reaches a maximum [see Fig. $9H(c)$]. In lens design spherical aberration is always investigated by tracing a ray through the combination for the zone of radius $0.707h_m$.

9.7. Coma. The second of the monochromatic aberrations of third-order theory is called *coma*. It derives its name from the cometlike appearance of the image of a point object located just off the lens axis. Although the lens may be corrected for spherical aberration and may bring all rays to a good focus on the axis, the quality of the images of points just off the axis will not be sharp unless the lens is also corrected for coma. Figure $9I$ illustrates this lens defect for a single object point infinitely distant and off the axis. Of the fan of rays in the meridian plane that is shown, only those through the center of the lens form an image at A'. Two rays through the margin come together at B'. Thus it appears that the magnification is different for different parts of the

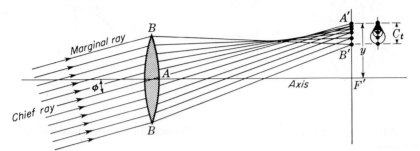

FIG. 9I. Illustrating coma, the second of the five monochromatic aberrations of a lens. Only the tangential fan of rays is shown.

lens. If the magnification for the outer rays through a lens is greater than that for the central rays, the coma is said to be *positive*, while if the reverse is true as in the diagram, the coma is said to be *negative*.

The shape of the image of an off-axis object point is shown at the upper right in Fig. 9I. Each of the circles represents an image from a different zone of the lens. Details of the formation of the *comatic circle* by the light from one zone of the lens are shown in Fig. 9J. Rays (1), which correspond to the *tangential* rays B in Fig. 9I, cross at (1) on the comatic circle, while rays (3), called the *sagittal rays*, cross at the top of that circle. In general all points on a comatic circle

FIG. 9J. Each zone of a lens forms a ring-shaped image called a comatic circle.

are formed by the crossing of pairs of rays passing through two diametrically opposite points of the same zone. Third-order theory shows that the radius of a comatic circle is given by

$$C_s = \frac{jh^2}{f^3}(Gp + Wq) \tag{9m}$$

where j, h, and f are the distances indicated in Fig. 9$K(a)$ and p and q are the Coddington position and shape factors given by Eqs. 9f and 9d. The other two constants are defined as

$$G = \frac{3(2n+1)}{4n} \quad \text{and} \quad W = \frac{3(n+1)}{4n(n-1)}$$

Fɪɢ. 9K. Geometry of coma, showing the relative magnitudes of sagittal and tangential magnifications.

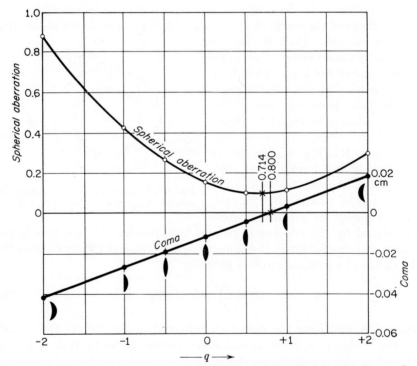

Fɪɢ. 9L. Graphs comparing coma with longitudinal spherical aberration for a series of lenses having different shapes.

The shape of the comatic figure is given by

$$y = C_s(2 + \cos 2\psi) \qquad z = C_s \sin 2\psi$$

which shows that the tangential coma C_t is three times the sagittal coma C_s [see Fig. 9K(b)]. Thus

$$C_t = 3C_s$$

To see how coma is affected by changing the shape of a lens a graph of the height of the comatic figure, C_t, is plotted against the shape factor q in Fig. 9L. The numerical values plotted in this graph are calculated from Eq. 9m and listed in Table 9-IV.

TABLE 9-IV. COMPARISON OF COMA AND SPHERICAL ABERRATION FOR LENSES OF THE SAME FOCAL LENGTH BUT DIFFERENT SHAPE FACTOR
$h = 1.0$ cm, $f = +10.0$ cm, $y = 2.0$ cm, $n = 1.5000$

Shape of lens	Shape factor	Coma	Spherical aberration
1. Concavo-convex........	-2.0	-0.0420 cm	$+0.88$ cm
2. Plano-convex..........	-1.0	-0.0270	$+0.43$
3. Double convex.........	-0.5	-0.0195	$+0.26$
4. Equiconvex............	0	-0.0120	$+0.15$
5. Double convex.........	$+0.5$	-0.0045	$+0.10$
6. Plano-convex..........	$+1.0$	$+0.0030$	$+0.11$
7. Concavo-convex.......	$+2.0$	$+0.0180$	$+0.29$

A parallel beam of light is assumed to be incident on the lens at an angle of 11° with the axis. The values of the longitudinal spherical aberration, given for comparison purposes, are also calculated from third-order theory (Eq. 9e) and assume parallel light incident on the lens parallel to the axis and passing through the same zone.

The fact that the line representing coma crosses the zero axis indicates that a single lens can be made that is entirely free of this aberration. It is important to note, for the lenses shown, that the shape factor $q = 0.800$ for no coma is so near the shape factor $q = 0.714$ for minimum spherical aberration that a single lens designed for $C_T = 0$ will have practically the minimum amount of spherical aberration.

In order to calculate the value of q that will make Eq. 9m vanish, C_s is set equal to zero. There results

$$q = -\frac{G}{W} p \qquad (9n)$$

If the shape and position factors of a single lens obey this relation, the lens is coma-free. A doublet designed to correct for spherical aberration can at the same time be corrected for coma. A graph showing the residual spherical aberration and coma for a telescope objective is given in Fig. 9M.

9.8. Aplanatic Points of a Spherical Surface. An optical system free of both spherical aberration and coma is said to be *aplanatic*. The significance of an aplanatic surface in the simple case of a single surface has already been discussed in Sec. 1.6. An *aplanatic lens* may also be found for any particular pair of conjugate points, although in general it will need to be an aspherical lens. Except for a few special cases, no lens combination with spherical surfaces is completely free of both these aberrations.

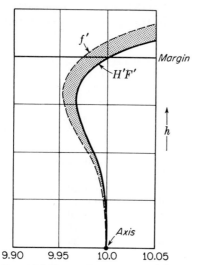

FIG. 9M. Curves for a cemented doublet, showing the variable position of the focal point F' (longitudinal spherical aberration) and the variable focal length f' (coma = $H'F' - f'$).

One special case which is of considerable importance in microscopy is that of a single spherical refracting surface. To demonstrate the existence of aplanatic points for a single surface, a useful construction, originally discovered by Huygens, will first be described. In Fig. 9N(a) the ray RT represents any ray in the first medium, of index n, incident on the surface at T and making an angle ϕ with the normal NC. Around C as a center and with radii

$$\rho = r\frac{n'}{n} \qquad \text{and} \qquad \rho' = r\frac{n}{n'} \qquad (9o)$$

the broken circular arcs are drawn as shown. Where RT, when produced, intersects the larger circle, a line JC is drawn, and this intersects the smaller circle at K. Then TK gives the direction of the refracted ray in accordance with the law of refraction.* Furthermore any ray whatever directed toward J will be refracted through K.

The aplanatic points of a single surface are located where the two construction circles cross the axis [see Fig. 9N(b)]. All rays initially traveling toward M will pass through M', and similarly all rays diverging from M' will after refraction appear to originate at M. The application of this principle to a microscope is illustrated in Fig. 9O. A drop of oil having the same index as the hemispherical lens is placed on the microscope slide and the lens lowered into contact as shown. All rays from an

---

* For a proof of this proposition, see J. P. C. Southall, "Mirrors, Prisms, and Lenses," 3d ed., p. 512, The Macmillan Company, New York, 1936.

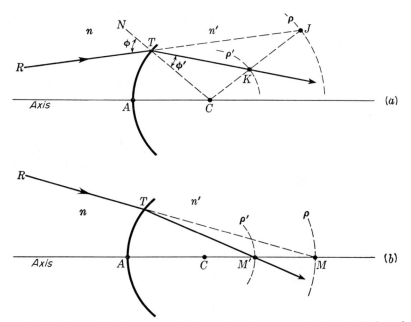

FIG. 9N. (a) A graphical construction for refraction at a single spherical surface. $\rho = rn'/n$, and $\rho' = rn/n'$. (b) Location of the aplanatic points of a single spherical surface.

object at M leave the hemispherical surface after refraction as though they came from M', and this introduces a lateral magnification of $M'A/MA$. If a second lens is added which has the center of its concave surface at M' (and therefore is normal to all rays), refraction at its upper surface, of radius $n' \times CM'$, will give added magnification without introducing spherical aberration. This property of the upper lens, however, holds strictly only for rays from the single point M, and not for points adjacent to it. There is a limit to this process which is set by chromatic aberration (see Sec. 9.13).

9.9. Astigmatism. If the first two Seidel sums vanish, all rays from points on or very close to the axis of a lens will form point images and there will be no spherical aberration or coma. When the

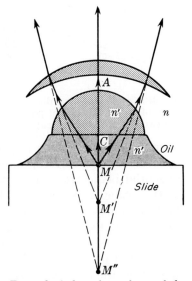

FIG. 9O. Aplanatic surfaces of the first elements of an oil-immersion microscope objective.

object point lies at some distance away from the axis, however, a point image will be formed only if the third sum S_3 is zero.   If the lens fails to satisfy this third condition, it is said to be afflicted with *astigmatism*, and the resulting blurred images are said to be astigmatic.   The formation of real astigmatic images from a concave spherical mirror is discussed in Sec. 6.9. To help understand the formation of astigmatic images by a lens, a ray

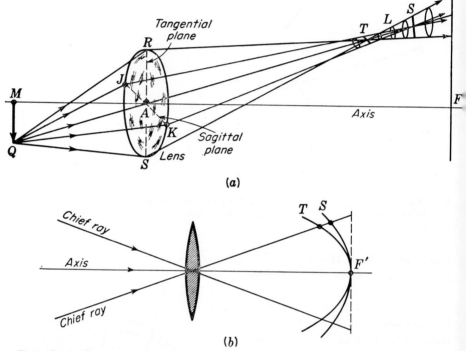

Fig. 9P. (*a*) Perspective diagram showing the two focal lines which constitute the image of an off-axis object point *Q*.   (*b*) Loci of the tangential and sagittal images. The two surfaces approximate paraboloids of revolution.

diagram has been drawn in perspective in Fig. 9P(*a*).   Considering the rays from a point object *Q*, all those in the fan contained in the vertical or tangential plane cross at *T*, while the fan of rays in the horizontal or sagittal plane crosses at *S*.   The tangential and sagittal planes intersect the lens in *RS* and *JK*, respectively.   Rays in these planes are chosen because they locate the two *focal lines* *T* and *S* formed by all rays going through the lens.   These are perpendicular to their respective tangential and sagittal planes.   At *L* the image is approximately disk-shaped, and constitutes the circle of least confusion for this case.

If the positions of the *T* and *S* images are determined for a wide field of distant object points, their loci will form paraboloidal surfaces whose sections are shown in Fig. 9P(*b*).   The amount of astigmatism, or *astig-*

matic difference, for any pencil of rays is given by the distance between these two surfaces measured along the chief ray. On the axis, where the two surfaces come together, the astigmatic difference is zero; away from the axis it increases approximately as the square of the image height. Astigmatism is said to be positive when the T surface lies to the left of S, as shown in the diagram. It should be noted that for a concave mirror (Fig. 60), the sagittal surface is a plane coinciding with the paraxial focal plane.

If, as in Fig. 9Q, the object is a spoked wheel in a plane perpendicular to the axis with its center at M, the rim would be found to be in focus on the T surface while the spokes would be in focus on the S surface. It is for this reason that the terms "tangential" and "sagittal" are applied to the planes and images. On the surface T all images will be lines parallel to the rim as shown at the left in Fig. 9Q, while on the surface S all

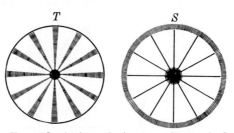

FIG. 9Q. Astigmatic images of a spoked wheel.

images will be lines parallel to the spokes as shown at the right.

Equations giving the astigmatic image distances for a single refracting surface are*

$$\left.\begin{array}{c} \dfrac{n \cos^2 \phi}{s} + \dfrac{n' \cos^2 \phi'}{s'_t} = \dfrac{n' \cos \phi' - n \cos \phi}{r} \\[2ex] \dfrac{n}{s} + \dfrac{n'}{s'_s} = \dfrac{n' \cos \phi' - n \cos \phi}{r} \end{array}\right\} \quad (9p)$$

where ϕ and ϕ' are the angles of incidence and refraction of the chief ray, r the radius of curvature, s the object distance, and s_t and s_s the T and S image distances, the latter being measured along the chief ray. For a spherical mirror these equations reduce to

$$\frac{1}{s} + \frac{1}{s'_t} = \frac{1}{f \cos \phi} \quad \text{and} \quad \frac{1}{s} + \frac{1}{s'_s} = \frac{\cos \phi}{f}$$

Coddington has shown that for a thin lens in air with an aperture stop at the lens, the positions of the tangential and sagittal images are given by

$$\left.\begin{array}{c} \dfrac{1}{s} + \dfrac{1}{s'_t} = \dfrac{1}{\cos \phi}\left(\dfrac{n \cos \phi'}{\cos \phi} - 1\right)\left(\dfrac{1}{r_1} - \dfrac{1}{r_2}\right) \\[2ex] \dfrac{1}{s} + \dfrac{1}{s'_s} = \cos \phi \left(\dfrac{n \cos \phi'}{\cos \phi} - 1\right)\left(\dfrac{1}{r_1} - \dfrac{1}{r_2}\right) \end{array}\right\} \quad (9q)$$

---

* For a derivation of these formulas see G. S. Monk, "Light, Principles and Experiments," 1st ed., p. 424, McGraw-Hill Book Company, Inc., New York, 1937.

The angle ϕ is the angle of obliquity of the incident chief rays, and ϕ' the angle of this ray within the lens. Therefore $n = \sin \phi/\sin \phi'$. The application of these formulas to thin lenses shows that the astigmatism is approximately proportional to the focal length and is very little improved by changing the shape.

Although a contact doublet composed of one positive and one negative lens shows considerable astigmatism, the introduction of another element consisting of a stop *or* a lens can be made to greatly reduce it. By the proper spacing of the lens elements of any optical system, or by the proper location of a stop if one is used, the curvature of the astigmatic

FIG. 9R. Diagrams showing the astigmatic surfaces T and S in relation to the fixed Petzval surface P, as the spacing between lenses (or between lens and stop) is changed.

image surfaces can be changed considerably. Four important stages in the flattening of the astigmatic surfaces due to these alterations are shown in Fig. 9R. Diagram (*a*) represents the normal shape of the T and S surfaces for a contact doublet or a single lens. In diagram (*b*) the separation of lens elements is such that the two surfaces fall together at P. Further alteration of the lens shapes and their spacing may be made and the T and S curves straightened, as in diagram (*c*), or moved still farther apart until they are bisected by the normal plane through the focal point F', as in diagram (*d*). Of these four arrangements, only the second is free of astigmatism. The single paraboloidal surface P, over which point images are formed, is called the *Petzval surface*.

9.10. Curvature of Field. If for an optical system the first three Seidel sums are zero, the system will form point images of point objects on as well as off the axis. Under these circumstances the images fall on the curved Petzval surface where the tangential and sagittal surfaces come together, as in Fig. 9R(*b*). Even though astigmatism is corrected for such a system, the focal surface is curved. If a flat screen is placed in position B, the center of the field will be in sharp focus but the edges will be quite blurred. With a screen at A, the center of the field and the field margins will be blurred, while sharp focus will be obtained about halfway out.

Mathematically a Petzval surface exists for every optical system, and if the powers and refractive indices of the lenses remain fixed the shape of the Petzval surface cannot be changed by altering the shape factors of the lenses or their spacing. Such alterations, however, will change the shapes of the T and S surfaces, but always in such a way that the ratio of the distances PT and PS is $3:1$. It will be noted that this ratio is maintained throughout Fig. $9R$. If a system is designed to make the T surface flat, as in Fig. $9R(c)$, the $3:1$ ratio of distances requires the S surface to be curved, but not strongly so. If a screen is placed

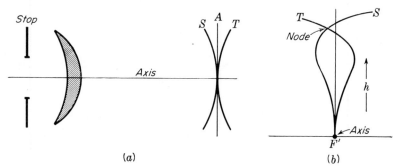

(a)   (b)

FIG. 9S. (a) A properly located stop may be used to reduce field curvature. (b) Astigmatic surfaces for an "antistigmat" camera lens.

at a compromise position A, the images over the entire field will be in reasonably good focus. This condition of correction is commonly used for certain types of photographic lenses. If more negative astigmatism is introduced the condition shown in Fig. $9R(d)$ is reached, in which the T surface is convex and the S surface is concave by an equal amount. In this case a screen placed at the paraxial focus will show considerable blurring at the field edges.

Curvature of field may be corrected for a single lens by means of a stop. Acting as a second element of the system, a stop limits the rays from each object point in such a way that the paths of the chief rays from different points go through different parts of the lens [Fig. $9S(a)$]. Certain manufacturers of inexpensive box cameras employ a single meniscus lens and a stop and with them obtain reasonably good images. The stop is located in front of the lens, with the light incident on the concave surface. Although the compromise field is flat and sharp focus is obtained at the center, astigmatism gives rise to blurred images at the margins.

In complex lens systems it is possible, because of differences in third- and fifth-order corrections, to control the astigmatism and cause the tangential and sagittal surfaces to come together at an outer zone as well as at the center of the field. Typical curves for the camera objective called an "anastigmat" are shown in Fig. $9S(b)$.   Experience has shown that the best state of correction is obtained by making the crossover point, called the node, occur at a relatively short distance in front of the focal plane.

9.11. Distortion.   Even though an optical system were designed so that the first four Seidel sums were zero, it could still be affected by the fifth aberration known as *distortion*.   To be free of distortion a system must

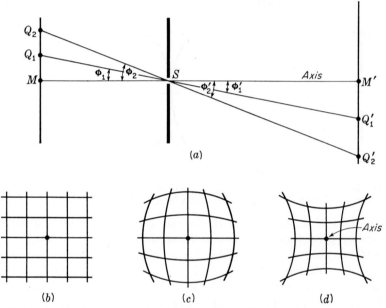

FIG. 9T. (*a*) A pinhole camera shows no distortion.   Images of a rectangular object screen shown with (*b*) no distortion, (*c*) barrel distortion, and (*d*) pincushion distortion.

have uniform lateral magnification over its entire field.   A pinhole camera is ideal in this respect for it shows no distortion; all straight lines connecting each pair of conjugate points in the object and image planes pass through the opening.   Constant magnification for a pinhole camera as well as for a lens implies, as may be seen from Fig. $9T(a)$, that

$$\frac{\tan \phi'}{\tan \phi} = \text{const.}$$

The common forms of image distortion produced by lenses are illustrated in the lower part of Fig. $9T$.   Diagram (*b*) represents the undistorted image of an object consisting of a rectangular wire mesh.   The second diagram shows *barrel* distortion, which arises when the magnification decreases towards the edge of the field.   The third diagram represents *pincushion* distortion, corresponding to a greater magnification at the borders.

A single thin lens is practically free of distortion for all object distances. It cannot, however, be free of all the other aberrations at the same time.

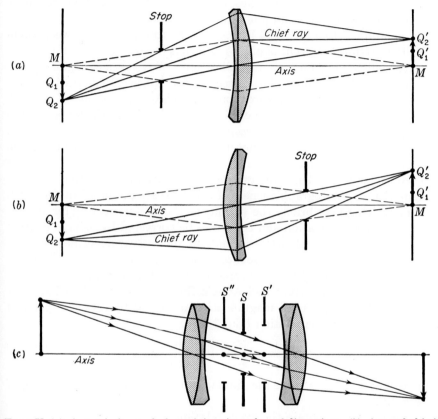

FIG. 9U. (a) A stop in front of a lens giving rise to barrel distortion. (b) A stop behind a lens giving rise to pincushion distortion. (c) A symmetrical doublet with a stop between is relatively free of distortion.

If a stop is placed in front of or behind a thin lens, distortion is invariably introduced; if it is placed at the lens, there is no distortion. Frequently in the design of good camera lenses astigmatism, as well as distortion, is corrected for by a nearly symmetrical arrangement of two lens elements with a stop between them.

To illustrate the principles involved, consider the lens shown in Fig. $9U(a)$, which has a front stop. Rays from object points like M, at or near the axis, go through the central part of the lens, while rays from off-axis object points like Q_2 are refracted only by the upper half. In the latter case the stop decreases the ratio of image to object distances measured along the chief ray, thereby reducing the lateral magnification below that obtaining for object points near the axis. This system therefore suffers from barrel distortion. When the lens and stop are turned around, as in Fig. 9U(b), the ratio of image to object distances is seen to increase as the object point lies farther off the axis. The result is increased magnification and pincushion distortion.

By combining two identical lenses with a stop midway between them as in Fig. 9U(c), a system is obtained which because of its symmetry is free from distortion for unit magnification. With other magnifications however the lenses must be corrected for spherical aberration with respect to the entrance and exit pupils. These two pupils S' and S'' coincide with the principal planes of the combination. Such a corrected lens system is called an *orthoscopic doublet*, or rapid rectilinear lens. Because this combination cannot be corrected for spherical aberration for the object and image planes and for the entrance and exit pupils at the same time, the lens suffers from this aberration as well as from astigmatism. Photographic lenses of this type are discussed in Sec. 10.4.

Summarizing very briefly the various methods of correcting for aberrations, spherical aberration and coma can be corrected by using a contact doublet of the proper shape; astigmatism and curvature of field require for their correction the use of several separated components; and distortion may be minimized by the proper placement of a stop.

9.12. The Sine Theorem and Abbe's Sine Condition. In Chap. 3 it was found that the lateral magnification produced by a *single spherical surface* is given by the relation (Eq. 3g)

$$m = \frac{y'}{y} = -\frac{s' - r}{s + r}$$

This equation follows from the similarity of triangles MQC and $M'Q'C$ in Fig. 3F.

From Eq. 8a we obtain the exact relation

$$s + r = r\frac{\sin \phi}{\sin \theta}$$

and from Eq. 8d

$$s' - r = -r\frac{\sin \phi'}{\sin \theta'}$$

If we substitute these two equations in the first equation, we obtain

$$\frac{y'}{y} = \frac{\sin \phi' \sin \theta}{\sin \theta' \sin \phi}$$

According to Snell's law

$$\frac{\sin \phi'}{\sin \phi} = \frac{n}{n'}$$

which upon substitution gives

$$\frac{y'}{y} = \frac{n \sin \theta}{n' \sin \theta'}$$

or $$ny \sin \theta = n'y' \sin \theta'$$ SINE THEOREM

Here y and y' are the object and image heights, n and n' are the indices of the object and image spaces, and θ and θ' are the slope angles of the ray in these two spaces, respectively (see Fig. 9V). This very general theorem applies to all rays, no matter how large the angles θ and θ' may be.

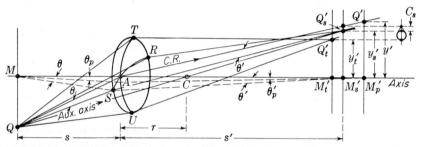

FIG. 9V. Refraction at a spherical surface illustrating the sine theorem as it applies to coma.

For paraxial rays where θ and θ' are both small, $\sin \theta$ and $\sin \theta'$ can be replaced by θ_p and θ'_p, respectively, to give

$$ny\theta_p = n'y'\theta'_p$$ LAGRANGE THEOREM

a relation referred to as the Lagrange theorem. In both these theorems all quantities on the left side refer to object space, while those on the right side refer to image space.

Figure 9V shows a pair of sagittal rays QR and QS from the object point Q through one zone of a single refracting surface. These two particular rays, after refraction, come to a focus at a point Q'_S on the auxiliary axis. On the other hand, a pair of tangential rays QT and QU through the same zone come to a focus at Q'_T, while paraxial rays come to a focus at Q'. Because of the general spherical aberration and astigmatism of the single surface the paraxial, the sagittal, and the tangential focal planes do not coincide. The conventional comatic figure shown at the right in Fig. 9V arises only in the absence of spherical aberration and astigmatism.

Since coma is confined to lateral displacements in the image in which y and y' are relatively small, we can neglect astigmatism and apply the above theorems to the single surface as follows: Note that θ and θ' for the object point Q, which are the slope angles of the zonal rays QS

and $Q_s'S$ relative to the chief ray (c.r.), are virtually equal to the slope angles of the rays from the axial object point M through the same zone of the surface. We can, therefore, apply the sine theorem to find the sagittal image magnification for any zone and obtain

$$m_s = \frac{y_s'}{y} = \frac{n \sin \theta}{n' \sin \theta'}$$

where $y_s' = Q_s'M_s'$, in Fig. 9V.

To show that the sine theorem and the Lagrange theorem can be extended to a complete optical system containing two or more lens surfaces, we recognize that in the image space of the first lens surface the two products are $n_1'y_1' \sin \theta_1'$ and $n_1'y_1'\theta_{p1}'$, respectively. These products are identical for the object space of the second surface because $n_1' = n_2$, $y_1' = y_2$, and $\theta_1' = \theta_2$; hence the products are *invariant* for all the spaces in the system including the original object space and the final image space. This is a most important property.

Now for a complete system to be free of coma and spherical aberration it must satisfy a relation known as the *sine condition*. This is a condition discovered by Abbe, in which the magnification for each zone of the system is the same as for paraxial rays. In other words, if in the final image space $y_s' = y'$, and $m_s = m$, we may combine the two preceding equations and obtain

$$\frac{\sin \theta}{\sin \theta'} = \frac{\theta_p}{\theta_p'} = \text{const.} \quad \text{SINE CONDITION} \quad (9r)$$

Any optical system is therefore free of coma, if in the absence of spherical aberration $\sin \theta/\sin \theta' = $ const. for all values of θ. In lens design coma is sometimes tested for by plotting the ratio $\sin \theta/\sin \theta'$ against the height of the incident ray. Because most lenses are used with parallel incident or emergent light, it is customary to replace $\sin \theta$ by h, the height of the ray above the axis,

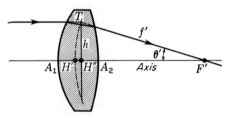

Fig. 9W. For a lens to be free of spherical aberration and coma the principal surface should be spherical and of radius f'.

and to write the sine condition in the special form

$$\frac{h}{\sin \theta'} = \text{const.} \quad (9s)$$

The ray diagram in Fig. 9W shows that the constant in this equation is the focal distance measured along the image ray, which we here call f'. To prevent coma, f' must be the same for all values of h. Since freedom from spherical aberration requires that all rays cross the axis at F', an accompanying freedom from coma requires that the principal "plane" be a spherical surface (represented by the dotted line in the figure) of radius f'. It is thus seen that, whereas spherical aberration is concerned with the crossing of the rays at the focal point, coma is concerned with the shape of the principal surface. It should be noted that the aplanatic points of a single spherical surface (see Sec. 9.8) are unique in that they are

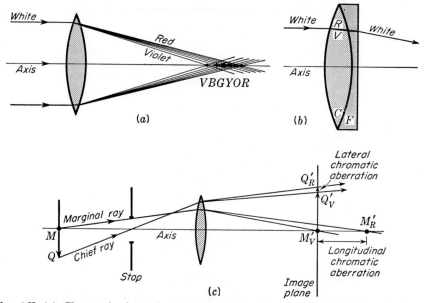

FIG. 9X. (a) Chromatic aberration of a single lens. (b) A cemented doublet corrected for chromatic aberration. (c) Illustrating the difference between longitudinal chromatic aberration and lateral chromatic aberration.

entirely free of spherical aberration and coma and satisfy the sine condition exactly.

9.13. Chromatic Aberration. In the discussion of the third-order theory given in the preceding sections, no account has been taken of the change of refractive index with color. The assumption that n is constant amounts to investigating the behavior of the lens for monochromatic light only. Because the refractive index of all transparent media varies with color, a single lens forms not only one image of an object but a series of images, one for each color of light present in the beam. Such a series of colored images of an infinitely distant object point on the axis of the lens is represented diagramatically in Fig. 9X(a). The prismatic action of the lens, which increases toward its edge, is such as to cause dispersion and to bring the violet light to a focus nearest to the lens.

As a consequence of the variation of focal length of a lens with color, the lateral magnification must vary as well.   This may be seen by the diagram of Fig. $9X(c)$, which shows only the red and violet image heights of an off-axis object point Q.   The horizontal distance between the axial images is called *axial* or *longitudinal chromatic aberration*, while the vertical difference in height is called *lateral chromatic aberration*.   Because these aberrations are often comparable in magnitude with the Seidel

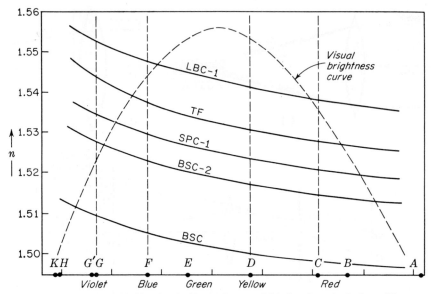

FIG. $9Y$. Graphs of the refractive indices of several kinds of optical glass. These are called dispersion curves.

aberrations, correction for both lateral and longitudinal color is of considerable importance.   As an indication of relative magnitudes, it may be noted that the longitudinal chromatic aberration of an equiconvex lens of spectacle crown glass having a focal length of 10 cm and a diameter of 3 cm is exactly the same (2.5 mm) as the spherical aberration of marginal rays in the same lens.

While there are several general methods for correcting chromatic aberration, the method of employing two thin lenses in contact, one made of crown glass and the other of flint glass, is the commonest and will be considered first.   The usual form of such an *achromatic doublet* is shown in Fig. $9X(b)$.   The crown-glass lens, which has a large positive power, has the same dispersion as the flint-glass lens, for which the power is smaller and negative.   The combined power is therefore positive, while the dispersion is neutralized, thereby bringing all colors to approximately the same focus.   The possibility of achromatizing such a combination rests upon the fact that the dispersions produced by different kinds of glass are not proportional to the deviations they produce (Sec. 1.7). In other words, the dispersive powers $1/\nu$ differ for different materials.

Typical dispersion curves showing the variation of n with color are plotted for a number of common optical glasses in Fig. 9Y, and the actual values of the index n for the different Fraunhofer lines are presented in Table 9-V. The peak of the visual brightness curve* in Fig. 9Y occurs

TABLE 9-V. REFRACTIVE INDICES OF TYPICAL OPTICAL MEDIA FOR FOUR COLORS

Medium	Symbol	I.C.T. type	ν	n_C	n_D	n_F	$n_{G'}$
Borosilicate crown........	BSC	500/665	66.5	1.49776	1.50000	1.50529	1.50937
Borosilicate crown........	BSC-2	517/645	64.5	1.51462	1.51700	1.52264	1.52708
Spectacle crown...........	SPC-1	523/586	58.8	1.52042	1.52300	1.52933	1.53435
Light barium crown.......	LBC-1	541/599	59.7	1.53828	1.54100	1.54735	1.55249
Telescope flint............	TF	530/516	51.6	1.52762	1.53050	1.53790	1.54379
Dense barium flint........	DBF	670/475	47.5	1.66650	1.67050	1.68059	1.68882
Light flint...............	LF	576/412	41.2	1.57208	1.57600	1.58606	1.59441
Dense flint...............	DF-2	617/366	36.6	1.61216	1.61700	1.62901	1.63923
Dense flint...............	DF-4	649/338	33.9	1.64357	1.64900	1.66270	1.67456
Extra dense flint..........	EDF-3	720/291	29.1	1.71303	1.72000	1.73780	1.75324
Fused quartz.............	SiO$_2$		67.9		1.4585		
Crystal quartz (O ray)....	SiO$_2$		70.0		1.5443		
Fluorite.................	CaF$_2$		95.4		1.4338		

not far from the yellow D line. It is for this reason that the index n_D has been chosen by optical designers as the basic index for ray tracing and for the specification of focal lengths. Two other indices, one on either side of n_D, are then chosen for purposes of achromatization. As indicated in the table, the ones most often used are n_C for the red end of the spectrum and n_F or $n_{G'}$ for the blue end.

For two thin lenses in contact, the resultant focal length f_D or power P_D of the combination for the D line is given by Eqs. 4h and 4i:

$$\frac{1}{f_D} = \frac{1}{f'_D} + \frac{1}{f''_D} \qquad \text{or} \qquad P_D = P'_D + P''_D \qquad (9t)$$

where the index D indicates that the quantity depends on n_D, f'_D and P'_D refer to the focal length and power of the crown-glass component, and f''_D and P''_D to the focal length and power of the flint-glass component.

* Brightness is a sensory magnitude in light just as loudness is a sensory magnitude in sound. Over a considerable range both vary approximately as the logarithm of the energy. The curve shown represents the logarithms of the "standard luminosity curve."

In terms of indices of refraction and radii of curvature, the power form of the equation becomes

$$P_D = (n'_D - 1)\left(\frac{1}{r'_1} - \frac{1}{r'_2}\right) + (n''_D - 1)\left(\frac{1}{r''_1} - \frac{1}{r''_2}\right) \tag{9u}$$

For convenience let

$$K' = \left(\frac{1}{r'_1} - \frac{1}{r'_2}\right) \quad \text{and} \quad K'' = \left(\frac{1}{r''_1} - \frac{1}{r''_2}\right) \tag{9u'}$$

Then Eq. (9u) can be more simply written as

$$P_D = (n'_D - 1)K' + (n''_D - 1)K'' \tag{9v}$$

Similarly, for any other colors or wavelengths like the F and C spectrum lines, we may write

$$\left. \begin{array}{l} P_F = (n'_F - 1)K' + (n''_F - 1)K'' \\ P_C = (n'_C - 1)K' + (n''_C - 1)K'' \end{array} \right\} \tag{9v'}$$

To make the combination achromatic we make the resultant focal length the same for F and C light. This means, making $P_F = P_C$,

$$(n'_F - 1)K' + (n''_F - 1)K'' = (n'_C - 1)K' + (n''_C - 1)K''$$

Multiplying out and canceling, this becomes

$$\frac{K'}{K''} = -\frac{n''_F - n''_C}{n'_F - n'_C} \tag{9v''}$$

Since both the numerator and denominator on the right have positive values, the minus sign shows that one K must be negative and the other positive. This means that one lens must be negative.

Now for the D line of the spectrum the separate powers of the two thin lenses are given by

$$P'_D = (n'_D - 1)K' \quad \text{and} \quad P''_D = (n''_D - 1)K'' \tag{9w}$$

Dividing one by the other, this gives

$$\frac{K'}{K''} = \frac{(n''_D - 1)P'_D}{(n'_D - 1)P''_D} \tag{9w'}$$

Equating Eqs. 9v'' and 9w' and solving for P''_D/P'_D gives

$$\frac{P''_D}{P'_D} = -\frac{(n''_D - 1)}{(n''_F - n''_C)} \div \frac{(n'_D - 1)}{(n'_F - n'_C)} = -\frac{v''}{v'} \tag{9w''}$$

where v' and v'' are the dispersion constants of the two glasses.

These constants, usually supplied by manufacturers when optical glass is purchased, are,

$$\nu' = \frac{n'_D - 1}{n'_F - n'_C} \quad \text{and} \quad \nu'' = \frac{n''_D - 1}{n''_F - n''_C} \tag{9x}$$

Values of ν for several common types of glass are given in Table 9-V. Since the dispersive powers are all positive, the negative sign in Eq. $9w''$ indicates that the powers of the two lenses must be of opposite sign. In other words, if one lens is converging the other must be diverging. From the extreme members of Eq. $9w''$, we obtain

$$\frac{P'_D}{\nu'} + \frac{P''_D}{\nu''} = 0 \quad \text{or} \quad \nu'f' + \nu''f'' = 0 \tag{9x'}$$

Substituting the value of P'_D or that of P''_D from Eq. $9t$ in Eq. $9x'$, we obtain

$$P'_D = P_D\left(\frac{\nu'}{\nu' - \nu''}\right) \quad \text{and} \quad P''_D = -P_D\left(\frac{\nu''}{\nu' - \nu''}\right) \tag{9x''}$$

The use of the above formulas to calculate the radii for a desired achromatic lens involves the following steps:

1. *A focal length f_D and a power P_D are specified.*
2. *The types of crown and flint glass to be used are selected.*
3. *If they are not already known, the dispersion constants ν' and ν'' are calculated from Eq. 9x.*
4. *P'_D and P''_D are calculated from Eq. 9x''.*
5. *The values of K' and K'' are determined by Eq. 9w.*
6. *The radii are then found from Eq. 9u'.*

Calculation 6 is usually made with other aberrations in mind.

Example: An achromatic lens having a focal length of 10 cm is to be made as a cemented doublet using crown and flint glasses having the following indices:

Glass	n_C	n_D	n_F	$n_{G'}$
1. Crown.........	1.50868	1.51100	1.51673	1.52121
2. Flint..........	1.61611	1.62100	1.63327	1.64369

Find the radii of curvature for both lenses if the crown-glass lens is to be equiconvex and the combination is to be corrected for the C and F lines.

Solution: The focal length of 10 cm is equivalent to a power of $+10$ D. The dispersion constants ν' and ν'' are, from Eq. 9x,

$$\nu' = \frac{1.51100 - 1.00000}{1.51673 - 1.50868} = 63.4783$$

$$\nu'' = \frac{1.62100 - 1.00000}{1.63327 - 1.61611} = 36.1888$$

Applying Eq. 9x'', we find that the powers of the two lenses must be

$$P'_D = 10 \frac{63.4783}{63.4783 - 36.1888} = +23.2611 \text{ D}$$

$$P''_D = -10 \frac{36.1888}{63.4783 - 36.1888} = -13.2611 \text{ D}$$

The fact that the sum of these two powers $P_D = +10.0000$ D serves as a check on the calculations to this point. Knowing the power required in each lens, we are now free to choose any pair of radii that will give such a power. If two or more surfaces can be made to have the same radius, the necessary number of grinding and polishing tools will be reduced. For this reason the positive element is often made equiconvex, as it is here. Letting $r'_1 = -r'_2$, we apply Eq. 9u' and then Eq. 9w to obtain

$$K' = \frac{1}{r'_1} - \frac{1}{r'_2} = \frac{2}{r'_1} = \frac{P'_D}{n'_D - 1} = \frac{23.2611}{0.51100} = 45.5207$$

from which $r'_1 = 0.0439361 \text{ m} = 4.39361 \text{ cm}$

Since the lens is to be cemented, one surface of the negative lens must fit a surface of the positive lens. This leaves the radius of the last surface to be adjusted to give the proper power of -13.2611 D. Therefore we let $r''_1 = -r'_1$, and apply Eqs. 9u' and 9w as before, to find

$$K'' = \frac{1}{r''_1} - \frac{1}{r''_2} = -\frac{1}{0.0439361} - \frac{1}{r''_2} = \frac{P''_D}{n''_D - 1} = \frac{-13.2611}{0.62100} = -21.3544$$

This gives

$$\frac{1}{r''_2} = 21.3544 - \frac{1}{0.0439361} = 21.3544 - 22.7603$$

and $\dfrac{1}{r''_2} = -1.4059 \qquad r''_2 = -0.71129 \text{ m} = -71.13 \text{ cm}$

The required radii are therefore

$$r'_1 = 4.39 \text{ cm} \qquad r''_1 = -4.39 \text{ cm}$$
$$r'_2 = -4.39 \text{ cm} \qquad r''_2 = -71.13 \text{ cm}$$

It will be noted that, with the crown-glass element of this achromat placed toward incident parallel light, the two exposed surfaces are close to what they should be for minimum spherical aberration and coma. This emphasizes the importance of choosing glasses having the proper dispersive powers.

To see how well this lens has been achromatized, we now calculate its focal length for the four colors corresponding to the C, D, F, and G' lines. By Eq. 9v'

$$P_C = (n'_C - 1)K' + (n''_C - 1)K''$$
$$= 0.50868 \times 45.5207 + 0.61611(-21.3544)$$
$$= 23.1555 - 13.1567$$

giving $$f_C = 10.0012 \text{ cm}$$

Similarly for the colors corresponding to the F and G' lines we obtain

$$P_F = +9.9988 \text{ D} \qquad \text{or} \qquad f_F = 10.0012 \text{ cm}$$
$$P_{G'} = +9.9804 \text{ D} \qquad \text{or} \qquad f_{G'} = 10.0196 \text{ cm}$$

The differences between f_C, f_D, and f_F are negligibly small, but $f_{G'}$ is about $\frac{1}{5}$ mm larger than the others. This difference for light outside the region of the C and F lines results in a small circular zone of color about each image point which is called the *secondary spectrum*.

Although the lens in our example would appear to have been corrected for longitudinal chromatic aberration, it has actually been corrected for lateral chromatic aberration. Equal focal lengths for different colors will produce equal magnification, but the different colored images along the axis will coincide only if the principal points also coincide. Practically speaking, the principal points of a thin lens are so close together that both types of chromatic aberration can be assumed to have been corrected by the above arrangement. In a thick lens, however, longitudinal chromatic aberration is absent if the colors corrected for come together at the same axial image point as shown in Fig. 9Z(a). Because the principal points for blue and red H'_b and H'_r do not coincide, the focal lengths are not equal and the magnification is different for different colors. Consequently the images formed in different colors will have different sizes. This is the lateral chromatic aberration or lateral color mentioned at the beginning of this section.

9.14. Separated Doublet. Another method of obtaining an achromatic system is to employ two thin lenses made of the same glass and separated by a distance equal to half the sum of their focal lengths. To see why this is true, we begin with the thick-lens formula (Eq. 5g) as applied to two thin lenses separated by a distance d:

$$\frac{1}{f} = \frac{1}{f_1} + \frac{1}{f_2} - \frac{d}{f_1 f_2} \qquad \text{or} \qquad P = P_1 + P_2 - dP_1P_2 \qquad (9y)$$

which, by analogy with Eq. 9v, may be written

$$P = (n_1 - 1)K_1 + (n_2 - 1)K_2 - d(n_1 - 1)(n_2 - 1)K_1K_2$$

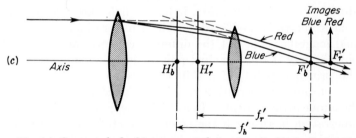

FIG. 9Z. (a) Cemented doublet corrected for longitudinal chromatic aberration. (b) Separated doublet corrected for longitudinal chromatic aberration. (c) Separated doublet corrected for lateral chromatic aberration.

The subscripts 1 and 2 are used here in place of the primes to designate the two lenses, and the K's are given by Eq. 9u'. Since the two lenses are of the same kind of glass, we set $n_1 = n_2$, so that

$$P = (n - 1)(K_1 + K_2) - d(n - 1)^2 K_1 K_2$$

If this power is to be independent of the variation of n with color, dP/dn must vanish. This gives

$$\frac{dP}{dn} = K_1 + K_2 - 2d(n - 1)K_1 K_2 = 0$$

Multiplying by $n - 1$ and substituting for each $(n - 1)K$ the corresponding P, we find

$$P_1 + P_2 - 2dP_1P_2 = 0$$

or
$$d = \frac{P_1 + P_2}{2P_1P_2} \quad \text{and} \quad d = \frac{f_1 + f_2}{2} \tag{9z}$$

This proves the proposition stated above that two lenses made of the same glass separated by half the sum of their focal lengths have the same focal length for all colors near those for which f_1 and f_2 are calculated. For visual instruments this color is chosen to be at the peak of the visual brightness curve (Fig. 9Y). Such spaced doublets are used as oculars in many optical instruments because the lateral chromatic aberration is highly corrected through constancy of the focal length. The longitudinal color, however, is relatively large, due to wide differences in the principal points for different colors. An illustration of a system that has no longitudinal chromatic aberration is shown in Fig. 9$Z(b)$. It is to be contrasted with the system shown in Fig. 9$Z(c)$, in which there is no lateral chromatic aberration.

We have seen in this chapter that a lens may be affected by as many as seven primary aberrations—five monochromatic aberrations of the third and higher orders, and two chromatic aberrations. One might therefore wonder how it is possible to make a good lens at all when rarely can a single aberration be eliminated completely, much less all of them simultaneously. Good usable lenses are nevertheless made by the proper balancing of the various aberrations. The design is guided by the purpose for which the lens is to be used. In a telescope objective, for example, correction for chromatic aberration, spherical aberration, and coma are of primary importance. On the other hand astigmatism, curvature of field, and distortion are not as serious because the field over which the objective is to be used is relatively small. For a good camera lens of wide aperture and field, the situation is almost exactly reversed.

Other treatments of the subject of aberrations will be found in the following texts:

"The Principles of Optics," by A. C. Hardy and F. H. Perrin.
"Light, Principles and Experiments," by G. S. Monk.
"Fundamentals of Optical Engineering," by D. H. Jacobs.
"Applied Optics and Optical Design," by A. E. Conrady.
"Technical Optics," by L. C. Martin.
"A Treatise on Reflexion and Refraction," by H. Coddington.
"A System of Applied Optics," by H. D. Taylor.

PROBLEMS

1. A single spherical surface of radius $r = +10$ cm separates two media of index $n = 1.2$ and $n' = 1.5$, respectively. Calculate (a) the longitudinal and (b) the lateral spherical aberration for parallel incident light through a zone at height $h = 1.0$ cm.

2. A convex surface of 4 cm radius is polished on the end of a glass rod of index 1.60. Calculate (a) the longitudinal and (b) the lateral spherical aberration for parallel incident light through a zone at height $h = 1$ cm. *Ans.* (a) 1.29 mm. (b) 0.12 mm.

3. A thin lens of index 1.5 has radii $r_1 = +60$ cm and $r_2 = -12$ cm. If the lens is used with parallel incident light, find (a) the longitudinal and (b) the lateral spherical aberration for rays through a zone at height $h = 2$ cm.

4. A thin lens of index 1.50 has radii $r_1 = +10$ cm and $r_2 = -10$ cm. Find (a) the longitudinal and (b) the lateral spherical aberration for an axial object point 20 cm in front of the lens and for rays through a zone of radius $h = 1$ cm.
Ans. (a) 4.400 mm. (b) 0.225 mm.

5. A thin lens of index 1.60 has radii $r_1 = +10$ cm and $r_2 = -10$ cm. Find (a) the longitudinal and (b) the lateral spherical aberration for an axial object point 24 cm in front of the lens and for rays through a zone of radius $h = 1$ cm.

6. A thin lens of index 1.60 has radii $r_1 = +36$ cm and $r_2 = -18$ cm. If this lens is to be used with parallel incident light, find (a) the longitudinal and (b) the lateral spherical aberration for rays through a zone of radius $h = 1$ cm.
Ans. (a) 0.974 mm. (b) 0.049 mm.

7. A thin lens of index 1.50 has radii $r_1 = -12$ cm and $r_2 = +60$ cm. If this lens is to be used with parallel incident light, find (a) the longitudinal and (b) the lateral spherical aberration for rays through a zone of radius $h = 2$ cm.

8. A thin lens of index 1.60 has radii $r_1 = -36$ cm and $r_2 = +18$ cm. Find (a) the longitudinal and (b) the lateral spherical aberration for parallel incident light through a zone of radius $h = 1$ cm. *Ans.* (a) -0.974 mm. (b) 0.049 mm.

9. A lens 6 cm in diameter and of index 1.50 has radii $r_1 = \infty$ and $r_2 = -10$ cm. Find the height of the comatic figure if the paraxial image point of parallel incident rays is 4 cm off the principal axis.

10. A thin lens 4 cm in diameter and of index 1.50 has radii $r_1 = +20$ cm and $r_2 = -20$ cm. Find the height of the comatic figure if the paraxial image point of parallel incident rays is 4 cm off the principal axis. *Ans.* -0.120 mm.

11. A thin lens is to be made of glass of index $n = 1.65$ and is to have a minimum spherical aberration when the object is 20 cm in front of the lens and the real image is 80 cm in back of the lens. Determine (a) the position factor, (b) the shape factor, (c) the focal length of the lens, and (d) the radii of curvature.

12. A thin lens is to be made of flint glass of index 1.75 and is to have a focal length of $+5$ cm. An object is located 30 cm in front of the lens. Determine (a) the image distance, and (b) the position factor. If this lens is to have a minimum spherical aberration for these object and image distances, find (c) the shape factor, and (d) the radii of curvature of the two faces.
Ans. (a) $+6.0$ cm. (b) -0.667. (c) $+0.733$. (d) $+4.33$ cm, -28.12 cm.

13. A thin lens is to be made of glass of index 1.50 and is to have a minimum lateral spherical aberration for distant objects. If the focal length is to be $+5$ cm, find (a) the position factor, (b) the shape factor, and (c) the radii of curvature of the two faces.

14. A thin lens is to be made of glass of index 1.550 and is to have a focal length of $+20$ cm. Find (a) the position factor, (b) the shape factor, and (c) the radii of curvature of the two faces if it is to have a minimum amount of spherical aberration for an object placed at its first focal point.
Ans. (a) $+1.0$. (b) -0.790. (c) $+104.81$ cm, -12.29 cm.

15. A thin lens is to be made of glass of index 1.50 and is to have a focal length of $+10$ cm. If an object is located 12 cm in front of the lens, find (a) the image distance, and (b) the position factor. If the lens is to show a minimum amount of spherical aberration, what should be (c) its shape factor, and (d) the radii of curvature of its two faces?

16. Calculate (*a*) the shape factor, and (*b*) the radii of curvature of the two surfaces for the lens in Prob. 11 if it is to have no coma.

Ans. (*a*) −0.633.　(*b*) +56.64 cm, −12.74 cm.

17. If the lens in Prob. 12 is to have no coma, find (*a*) the shape factor, and (*b*) the radii of curvature of the two faces.

18. Calculate (*a*) the shape factor, and (*b*) the radii of curvature of the two surfaces for the lens in Prob. 13 if it is to have no coma.

Ans. (*a*) +0.800.　(*b*) +2.78 cm, −25.00 cm.

19. If the lens in Prob. 14 is to be free of coma, find (*a*) the shape factor, and (*b*) the radii of curvature of the two surfaces.

20. If the lens in Prob. 15 is to be free of coma, what should be its (*a*) shape factor and (*b*) its two radii of curvature?　Ans. (*a*) −5.33.　(*b*) +21.43 cm, −6.52 cm.

21. A meniscus lens 0.5 cm thick and of index 1.60 is to be aplanatic for two points located on the concave side of the lens. If the nearer point is to be 4 cm from the nearest vertex, find (*a*) the radii of the two lens surfaces, and (*b*) the distance from the nearest vertex to the farther point. (NOTE: Both points are in air.)

22. A meniscus lens 0.5 cm thick, and of index 1.50, is to be made aplanatic for two points 6 cm apart. Determine (*a*) the two radii of curvature, and (*b*) the distances from the convex surface to the two points.

Ans. (*a*) −11.50 cm, −7.20 cm.　(*b*) 12.00 cm, 18.00 cm.

23. Apply Abbe's sine condition to the rays traced through the first lens surface listed in Table 8-I, and give the values of the constant for h = 1.5, 1.0, 0.5, and 0 cm.

24. Apply Abbe's sine condition to the final rays traced through the lens in Table 8-II, and give values of the constant for h = 1.5, 1.0, and 0.5 cm.

Ans. 0.335270, 0.338143, and 0.339585.

25. A thin lens of index 1.5 and radii r_1 = +40 cm and r_2 = −10 cm is used with parallel incident light. Calculate (*a*) the position factor, (*b*) the shape factor, (*c*) the focal length, and (*d*) the longitudinal spherical aberration for rays at heights of h = 2.0 cm, 1.5 cm, 1.0 cm, and 0.5 cm. Plot a graph of h vs. *longitudinal spherical aberration*.

26. A thin lens of index 1.50 and radii r_1 = +10 cm and r_2 = −40 cm is used with an object located 32 cm in front of the first surface. Calculate (*a*) the focal length, (*b*) the position factor, (*c*) the shape factor, and (*d*) the longitudinal spherical aberration for rays at heights of 2.0, 1.5, 1.0, and 0.5 cm.

Ans. (*a*) +16.0 cm.　(*b*) Zero.　(*c*) +0.600.　(*d*) 1.474 cm, 0.846 cm, 0.381 cm, 0.196 cm.

27. An achromatic lens with a focal length of +20 cm is to be made of crown and flint glasses of the types BSC and DF-4 (see Table 9-V). If the crown-glass lens is to be equiconvex and the combination is to be cemented, find (*a*) the ν values, (*b*) the two lens powers for sodium light, and (*c*) the radii of the four faces to correct for the C and F lines.

28. An achromatic lens with a focal length of +12.5 cm is to be made of crown and flint glasses of the types LBC-1 and DF-2 (see Table 9-V). If the flint-glass lens is to have its outer face plane and the combination is to be cemented, find (*a*) the ν-values, (*b*) the two lens powers for sodium yellow light, and (*c*) the radii of the three remaining surfaces. The lens is to be corrected for the C and F lines.

Ans. (*a*) 59.6472, 36.6172　(*b*) +20.7198 D, −12.7198 D.　(*c*) +5.6550 cm, −4.8507 cm, −4.8507 cm, infinity.

29. An achromatic lens is to be made of BSC-2 and DF-4 glasses and is to have a focal length of +25 cm (see Table 9-V). If the flint-glass lens is to have its outer face plane and the combination is to be cemented, find the radii of curvature of the other three surfaces. The lens is to be corrected for the C and G' lines.

30. An achromatic lens is to be made of SPC-1 and DF-2 glasses and is to have a focal length of +10 cm (see Table 9-V). If the crown-glass lens is to be equiconvex and the combination is to be cemented, what must be (a) the ν values, (b) the powers of the two lenses for sodium light, and (c) the radii of curvature of the faces? The lens is to be corrected for the C and G' lines.

Ans. (a) 37.5449, 22.7928. (b) +25.4505 D, −15.4505 D. (c) +4.1100 cm, −4.1100 cm, −4.1100 cm, +140.77 cm.

31. Calculate the focal lengths of the lens in Prob. 28 for the C, D, F, and G' lines.

32. Calculate the focal lengths of the lens in Prob. 30 for the C, D, F, and G' lines.

Ans. (a) +10.0044 cm, +10.0000 cm, +9.9927 cm, +10.0044 cm.

CHAPTER 10

OPTICAL INSTRUMENTS

The design of efficient optical instruments is the ultimate purpose of geometrical optics. The principles governing the formation of images by a single lens, and occasionally by simple combinations of lenses, have been set forth in the previous chapters. These principles find a wide variety of applications in the many practical combinations of lenses, frequently including also mirrors or prisms, which fall in the category of optical instruments. This subject is one of such large scope, and has

Fig. 10A. Principle of a camera.

developed so many ramifications, that in a book devoted to the fundamentals of optics it is only possible to describe the principles involved in a few standard types of instrument. In this chapter a description will be given of the more important features of camera lenses, magnifiers, microscopes, telescopes, and oculars. These will serve to illustrate some applications of the basic ideas already discussed and will, it is hoped, be of interest to the student who has used, or expects to use, some of these instruments.

10.1. Photographic Objectives. The fundamental principle of the camera is that of a positive lens forming a real image, as shown in Fig. 10A. Sharp images of distant or nearby objects are formed on a photographic film or plate, which is later developed and printed to obtain the final picture. Where the scene to be taken involves stationary objects, the cheapest camera lens may, if it is stopped down almost to a pinhole and a time exposure used, yield photographs of excellent definition. If, however, the subjects are moving relative to the camera (and this includes the case where the camera is held in the hand), extremely short exposure times are often imperative and lenses of large aperture become a necessity. The most important feature of a good camera, therefore, is that it be equipped with a lens of high relative aperture capable of covering as large an angular field as possible. Because

FIG. 10B. (a) Geometry for determining the speed of a lens. (b) An achromatic meniscus lens with a front stop.

a lens of large aperture is subject to many aberrations, designers of photographic objectives have resorted to the compromises as regards correction that best suit their particular needs. It is the intention here, therefore, to discuss briefly some of these purposes and compromises in connection with a few of the hundreds of well-known makes of photographic objective.

10.2. Speed of Lenses. It was shown in Sec. 7.15 that the total amount of light reaching the image per unit area is given by the product of the brightness B of the source and the solid angle ω' of the bundle of rays converging toward any point on the image. The latter may be computed as the area of the entrance pupil divided by the square of the focal length f. This will be clear from Fig. 10B(a), which shows the lens and stop of Fig. 10A illuminated by a parallel bundle. The solid angle ω' is that subtended at the image point by the exit pupil, but as will be seen, this is equal to that which would be subtended by the *entrance* pupil if it were placed at the secondary principle plane H'. The ratio of the focal length of any lens to the linear diameter a of its entrance pupil is called its *focal ratio*, or f *value*, which is therefore defined as

$$f \text{ value} = \frac{f}{a} \tag{10a}$$

Thus a lens which has a focal length of 10 cm and a linear aperture of 2 cm is said to have an f *value* of 5, or as it is usually stated, the lens is an $f/5$ lens.

The rapidity with which the photographic image is built up depends on the illuminance E of the image, which therefore determines the *speed* of the lens. The speed is inversely proportional to the square of the f value, since by Eq. 7o,

$$E = B\omega' \simeq B \frac{\pi(a/2)^2}{f^2} = \text{const.} \times \frac{a^2}{f^2} = \frac{\text{const.}}{(f \text{ value})^2} \qquad (10b)$$

assuming an object of a given brightness.

In order to take pictures of faintly illuminated subjects, or of ones which are in rapid motion and require a very short exposure, a lens of small f value is required. Thus an $f/2$ lens is "faster" than an $f/4.5$ lens (or than an $f/2$ lens stopped down to $f/4.5$) in the ratio $(4.5/2)^2 = 5.06$. A lens of such large relative aperture is difficult to design, as we shall see.

10.3. Meniscus Lenses. Many of the cheapest cameras employ a single positive meniscus lens with a fixed stop such as was shown in Fig. 10A. Developed in about 1812 and called a *landscape lens*, this simple optical device exhibits considerable spherical aberration, thereby limiting its useful aperture to about $f/11$. Off the lens axis, the astigmatism limits the field to about 40°. The proper location of the stop results in a flat field, but with only a single lens there is always considerable chromatic aberration.

By using a cemented doublet as shown in Fig. 10$B(b)$, lateral chromatism can be corrected. Instead of correcting for the C and F lines of the spectrum, however, the combination is usually corrected for the yellow D line, near the peak sensitivity of the eye, and the blue G' line, near the peak sensitivity of many photographic emulsions. Called "DG achromatism," this type of correction produces the best photographic definition at the sharpest visual focus. In some designs the lens and stop are turned around as in the arrangement of Fig. 9$U(b)$.

10.4. Symmetrical Lenses. Symmetrical lenses consist of two identical sets of thick lenses with a stop midway between them; a number of these are illustrated in Fig. 10$C(a)$. In general, each half of the lens is corrected for lateral chromatic aberration, and by putting them together, curvature of field and distortion are eliminated, as was explained in Sec. 9.11. In the rapid rectilinear lens, flattening of the field was made possible only by the introduction of considerable astigmatism, while spherical aberration limited the aperture to about $f/8$. By introducing three different glasses, as in the Goertz "Dagor," each half of the lens could be corrected for lateral color, astigmatism, and spherical aberration. When combined they are corrected for coma, lateral color, curvature, and distortion. Zeiss calls this lens a "Triple Protar," while Goertz calls it the "DAGor," signifying Double Anastigmat Goertz. The "Speed Panchro" lens developed by Taylor, Taylor, and Hobson in 1920 is noteworthy because of its fine central definition combined with the high speed of $f/2$ and even $f/1.5$. The "Zeiss Topogon" lens is but one of a number of special "wide-angle" lenses, particularly useful in aerial photography. Additional characteristics of symmetrical lenses are (1) the large number

Rapid rectilinear
f/8

Taylor, Taylor and Hobson
Speed Pancro f/2

Goertz "Dagor" f/4.5

Zeiss "Topogon"

Original "Cooke Triplet"

Zeiss "Tessar"

FIG. 10C. Symmetrical and unsymmetrical camera lenses.

of lenses employed, and (2) the rather deep curves, which are expensive to produce.

The greater the number of free glass surfaces in a lens, the greater is the amount of light lost by reflection. The f value alone, therefore, is not the sole factor in the relative speeds of objectives. The development in recent years of lens coatings that practically eliminate reflection at normal incidence has offered greater freedom in the use of more elements in the design of camera lenses (see Sec. 14.6).

10.5. Triplet Anastigmats. A great step forward in photographic lens design was made in 1893 when H. D. Taylor of Cooke and Sons developed the "Cooke Triplet" (Fig. 10C). The fundamental principles involved in this system follow from the fact that (1) the power which a given lens contributes to a system of lenses is proportional to the height at which marginal rays pass through the lens, whereas (2) the contribution each lens makes to field curvature in proportional to the power of the lens regardless of the distance of the rays from the axis. Hence astigmatism and curvature of field can be eliminated by making the power of the central flint element equal and opposite to the sum of the powers of the crown elements. By spacing the negative lens between the two positive lenses, the marginal rays can be made to pass through the negative lens so close to the axis that the system has an appreciable positive power. A proper selection of dispersions and radii enables additional corrections to be made for color and spherical aberration. The "Tessar," one of the best known modern photographic objectives, was developed by Zeiss in 1902. Made in many forms to meet various requirements, the system has

FIG. 10D. Principle of the telephoto lens.

a general structure similar to that of a Cooke Triplet in which the rear crown lens is replaced by a doublet. The Leitz "Hector," working at $f/2$, is also of the Cooke Triplet type, but each element is replaced by a compound lens. This very fast lens is excellent in a motion-picture camera.

10.6. Telephoto Lenses. Since the image size for a distant object is directly proportional to the focal length of the lens, a telephoto lens which is designed to give a large image is a special type of objective with a longer effective focal length than that normally used with the same camera. Because this would require a greater extension of the bellows than most cameras will permit, the principle of a single highly corrected thick lens is modified as follows: As is shown in Fig. 10D by the refraction of an incident parallel ray, with two such lenses considerably separated the principal point H' can be placed well in front of the first lens, thereby giving a long focal length $H'F'$ with a short lens-to-focal-plane distance (f_b in Fig. 10D). The latter distance, or the *back focal length* as it is usually called, is measured from the real lens to the focal plane, as shown.

Although the focal lengths of older types of telephoto lenses could be varied by changing the distance between the front and rear elements, these lenses are almost always made with a fixed focal length. Flexibility is then obtained by having a set of lenses. This has become necessary through the desire for lenses of greater speed and better correction of the aberrations. A "Cooke Telephoto" as produced by Taylor, Taylor, and Hobson is shown in Fig. 10*E*.

10.7. Magnifiers. The magnifier is a positive lens whose function it is to increase the size of the retinal image over and above that which is formed with the unaided eye. The apparent size of any object as seen with the unaided eye depends on the angle subtended by the object (see

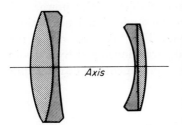

Fig. 10*F*). As the object is brought closer to the eye, from *A* to *B* to *C* in the diagram, accommodation permits the eye to change its power and to form a larger and larger retinal image. There is a limit to how close an object may come to the eye if the latter is still to have sufficient accommodation to produce a sharp image. Although the nearest point varies widely with various individuals, 25 cm is taken

FIG. 10*E*. A well-corrected telephoto lens.

to be the standard *near point*, or as it is sometimes called the *distance of most distinct vision*. At this distance, indicated in Fig. 10*G*(*a*), the angle subtended by object or image will be called θ.

If a positive lens is now placed before the eye in the same position, as in diagram (*b*), the object *y* may be brought much closer to the eye and an image subtending a larger angle θ' will be formed on the retina. What

FIG. 10*F*. The angle subtended by the object determines the size of the retinal image.

the positive lens has done is to form a virtual image *y'* of the object *y* and the eye is able to focus upon this virtual image. Any lens used in this manner is called a *magnifier* or *simple microscope*. If the object *y* is located at *F*, the focal point of the magnifier, the virtual image *y'* will be located at infinity and the eye will be accommodated for distant vision as is illustrated in Fig. 10*G*(*c*). If the object is properly located a short distance inside of *F* as in diagram (*b*), the virtual image may be formed at the distance of most distinct vision and a slightly greater magnification obtained, as will now be shown.

The angular magnification M is defined as the ratio of the angle θ' subtended by the image to the angle θ subtended by the object.

$$M = \frac{\theta'}{\theta} \tag{10c}$$

FIG. 10G. Illustrating the angle subtended by (a) an object at the near point to the naked eye, (b) the virtual image of an object inside the focal point, (c) the virtual image of an object at the focal point.

From diagram (b), the object distance s is obtained by the regular thin-lens formula as

$$\frac{1}{s} + \frac{1}{-25} = \frac{1}{f} \quad \text{or} \quad \frac{1}{s} = \frac{25 + f}{25f}$$

From the right triangles, the angles θ and θ' are given by

$$\tan \theta = \frac{y}{25} \quad \text{and} \quad \tan \theta' = \frac{y}{s} = y\,\frac{25 + f}{25f}$$

For small angles the tangents can be replaced by the angles themselves to give approximate relations

$$\theta = \frac{y}{25} \quad \text{and} \quad \theta' = y\,\frac{25 + f}{25f}$$

giving for the magnification, from Eq. (10c),

$$M = \frac{\theta'}{\theta} = \frac{25}{f} + 1 \qquad (10d)$$

In diagram (c) the object distance s is equal to the focal length, and the small angles θ and θ' are given by

$$\theta = \frac{y}{25} \qquad \text{and} \qquad \theta' = \frac{y}{f}$$

giving for the magnification

$$M = \frac{\theta'}{\theta} = \frac{25}{f} \tag{10e}$$

The angular magnification is therefore larger if the image is formed at the distance of most distinct vision.   For example, let the focal length of a magnifier be 1 in. or 2.5 cm.   For these two extreme cases, Eqs. 10d and 10e give

$$M = \frac{25}{2.5} + 1 = 11\times \qquad \text{and} \qquad M = \frac{25}{2.5} = 10\times$$

Because magnifiers usually have short focal lengths and therefore give approximately the same magnifying power for object distances between 25 cm and infinity, the simpler expression $25/f$ is commonly used in labeling the power of magnifiers.   Hence a magnifier with a focal length of 2.5 cm will be marked 10$\times$ and another with a focal length of 5 cm will be marked 5$\times$, etc.

10.8. Types of Magnifiers.   Several common forms of magnifiers are shown in Fig. 10H.   The first, an ordinary double-convex lens, is the

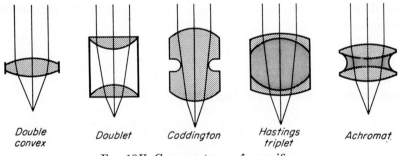

| Double convex | Doublet | Coddington | Hastings triplet | Achromat |

FIG. 10H. Common types of magnifiers.

simplest magnifier and is commonly used as a reading glass, pocket magnifier, or watchmaker's loupe.   The second is composed of two identical plano-convex lenses each mounted at the focal point of the other.   As shown by Eq. 9z this spacing corrects for lateral chromatic aberration but requires the object to be located at one of the lens faces. To overcome this difficulty, color correction is sacrificed to some extent by placing the lenses slightly closer together, but even then the working distance or back focal length (see Eq. 5m) is extremely short.

The third magnifier, cut from a sphere of solid glass, is commonly credited to Coddington but was originally made by Sir David Brewster. It too has a relatively short working distance, as can be seen by the marginal rays, but the image quality is remarkably good due in part to the central groove acting as a stop. Some of the best magnifiers of today are cemented triplets, such as are shown in the last two diagrams. These lenses are symmetrical to permit their use either side up. They have a relatively large working distance and are made with powers up to 20×.

10.9. Microscopes. The microscope, which in general greatly exceeds the power of a magnifier, was invented by Galileo in 1610. In its simplest form, the modern optical microscope consists of two lenses, one of very short focus called the *objective*, and the other of somewhat longer focus called the *ocular* or *eyepiece*. While both these lenses actually contain several elements to reduce aberrations, their principal function is illustrated by single lenses in Fig. 10*I*. The object (1) is located just outside the focal point of the objective so there is formed a real magnified image at (2). This image becomes the object for the second lens, the eyepiece. Func-

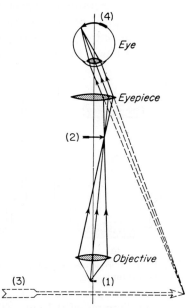

Fig. 10*I*. Principle of the microscope, shown with the eyepiece adjusted to give the image at the distance of most distinct vision.

tioning as a magnifier, the eyepiece forms a large virtual image at (3). This image becomes the object for the eye itself, which forms the final real image on the retina at (4).

Since the function of the objective is to form the magnified image that is observed through the eyepiece, the overall magnification of the instrument becomes the product of the linear magnification m_1 of the objective and the angular magnification M_2 of the eyepiece. By Eqs. 4k and 10e, these are given separately by

$$m_1 = -\frac{x'}{f_1} \quad \text{and} \quad M_2 = \frac{25}{f_2}$$

The over-all magnification is, therefore,

$$M = -\frac{x'}{f_1} \cdot \frac{25}{f_2} \tag{10f}$$

It is customary among manufacturers to label objectives and eyepieces according to their separate magnifications m_1 and M_2.

10.10. Microscope Objectives. A high-quality microscope is usually equipped with a turret nose carrying three objectives, each of a different magnifying power. By turning the turret, any one of the three objectives may be rotated into proper alignment with the eyepiece. Diagrams of three typical objectives are shown in Fig. 10J. The first, composed of two cemented achromats, is corrected for spherical aberration and coma and has a focal length of 1.6 cm, a magnification of 10$\times$, and a

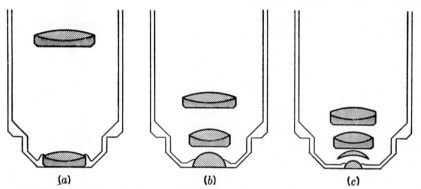

(a) (b) (c)

Fig. 10J. Microscope objectives. (a) Low-power, (b) medium-power, and (c) high-power oil immersion.

working distance of 0.7 cm. The second is also an achromatic objective with a focal length of 0.4 cm, a magnification of 40$\times$, and a working distance of 0.6 cm. The third is an oil-immersion type of objective with a focal length of 0.16 cm, a magnification of 100$\times$, and a working distance of only 0.035 cm. Great care must be exercised in using this last type of lens to prevent scratching of the hemispherical bottom lens. Although oil immersion makes the two lowest lenses aplanatic (see Fig. 9O), lateral chromatic aberration is present. The latter is corrected by the use of a compensating ocular, as will be explained in Sec. 10.16.

10.11. Astronomical Telescopes. Historically the first telescope was probably constructed in Holland in 1608 by an obscure spectacle-lens grinder, Hans Lippershey. A few months later Galileo, upon hearing that objects at a distance could be made to appear close at hand by means of two lenses, designed and made with his own hands the first authentic telescope. The elements of this telescope are still in existence and may be seen on exhibit in Florence. The principle of the astronomical telescopes of today is the same as that of these early devices. A diagram of an elementary telescope is shown in Fig. 10K. Rays from one point of the distant object are shown entering a long-focus objective

lens as a parallel beam. These rays are brought to a focus and form a
point image at Q'. Assuming the distant object to be an upright arrow,
this image is real and inverted as shown. The eyepiece has the same
function in the telescope that it has in a microscope, namely, that of a
magnifier. If the eyepiece is moved to a position where this real image

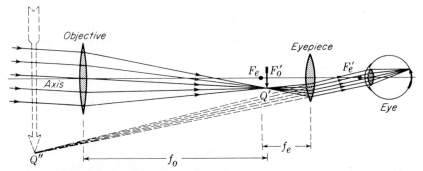

FIG. 10K. Principle of the astronomical telescope, shown with the eyepiece adjusted
to give the image at the distance of most distinct vision.

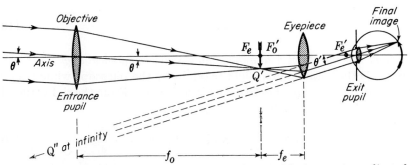

FIG. 10L. Principle of the astronomical telescope, shown with the eyepiece adjusted to
give the image at infinity.

lies just inside its primary focal plane F_e, a magnified virtual image at
Q'' may be seen by the eye at the near point, 25 cm. Normally, however,
the real image is made to coincide with the focal points of both lenses,
with the result that the image rays leave the eyepiece as a parallel bundle
and the virtual image is at infinity. The final image is always the one
formed on the retina by rays which appear to have come from Q''.
Figure 10L is a diagram of the telescope adjusted in this manner.

In all astronomical telescopes the objective lens is the aperture stop.
It is therefore the entrance pupil, and its image as formed by all the
lenses to its right (here, only the eyepiece) is the exit pupil. These

elements are shown in Fig. 10M, which traces the path of one ray incident parallel to the axis and of a chief ray from a distant off-axis object point. The distance from the eye lens, i.e., the last lens of the ocular, to the exit pupil is called the *eye relief* and should normally be about 8 mm.

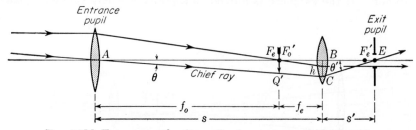

FIG. 10M. Entrance and exit pupils of an astronomical telescope.

The magnifying power of a telescope is defined as the ratio between the angle subtended at the eye by the final image Q'' and the angle subtended at the eye by the object itself. The object, not shown in Fig. 10M, subtends an angle θ at the objective and would subtend approximately the same angle to the unaided eye. The angle subtended at the eye by the final image is the θ'. By definition,

$$M = \frac{\theta'}{\theta} \tag{10g}$$

The angle θ is the object-field angle, and θ' is the image-field angle. In other words, θ is the total angular field taken in by the telescope while θ' is the angle that the field appears to cover (Sec. 7.11). From the right triangles ABC and EBC, in Fig. 10M,

$$\tan \theta = \frac{h}{s} \quad \text{and} \quad \tan \theta' = -\frac{h}{s'} \tag{10h}$$

Applying the general lens formula $1/s + 1/s' = 1/f$,

$$\frac{1}{s'} = \frac{f_o}{f_E(f_o + f_E)} \tag{10i}$$

which, substituted in Eq. 10h, gives

$$\tan \theta = \frac{h}{(f_o + f_E)} \quad \text{and} \quad \tan \theta' = -\frac{h f_o}{f_E(f_o + f_E)}$$

For small angles, $\tan \theta \simeq \theta$ and $\tan \theta' \simeq \theta'$. Substituting them in Eq. 10g, we obtain

$$M = \frac{\theta'}{\theta} = -\frac{f_o}{f_E} \tag{10j}$$

Hence the magnifying power of a telescope is just the ratio of the focal lengths of objective and eyepiece respectively, the minus sign signifying an inverted image.

If D and d represent the diameters of the objective and exit pupil respectively, the marginal ray passing through F'_O and F_E in Fig. 10M forms two similar right triangles, from which the following proportion is obtained

$$-\frac{f_O}{f_E} = \frac{D}{d}$$

giving, as an alternative equation for the angular magnification,

$$M = \frac{D}{d} \qquad (10k)$$

A useful method of determining the magnification of a telescope is, therefore, to measure the ratio of the diameters of the objective lens and of the exit pupil. The latter is readily found by focusing the telescope for infinity and then turning it toward the sky. A thin sheet of white paper held behind the eyepiece and moved back and forth will locate a sharply defined disk of light. This, the exit pupil, is commonly called the *Ramsden circle*. Its size, relative to that of the pupil of the eye, is of great importance in determining the brightness of the image and the resolving power of the instrument (see Secs. 7.15 and 15.9).

Another method of measuring the magnification of a telescope is to sight through the telescope with one eye, observing at the same time the distant object directly with the other eye. With a little practice the image seen in the telescope can be made to overlap the smaller direct image, thereby affording a straightforward comparison of the relative heights of image and object. The object field of the astronomical telescope is determined by the angle subtended at the center of the objective by the eyepiece aperture. In other words, the eyepiece is the field stop of the system. In Fig. 10M the angle θ is the half-field angle (Sec. 7.8).

10.12. Oculars or Eyepieces. Although a simple magnifier of one of the types shown in Fig. 10H may be used as an eyepiece for a microscope or telescope, it is customary to design special lens combinations for each particular instrument. Such eyepieces are commonly called *oculars*. One of the most important considerations in the design of oculars is correction for lateral chromatic aberration. It is for this reason that the basic structure of most of them involves two lenses of the same glass and separated by a distance equal to half the sum of their focal lengths (see Eq. 9z).

The two most popular oculars based on this principle are known as the *Huygens eyepiece* and the *Ramsden eyepiece* (Fig. 10N). In both these systems the lens nearest the eye is called the *eye lens*, while the lens nearest the objective is called the *field lens*.

10.13. Huygens Eyepiece. In eyepieces of this design the two lenses are usually made of spectacle crown glass with a focal-length ratio f_f/f_e varying from 1.5 to 3.0. As shown in Fig. $10N(a)$, rays from an objective to the left (and not shown) are converging to a real image point Q. The field lens refracts these rays to a real image at Q', from which they diverge again to be refracted by the eye lens into a parallel beam. In most telescopes the objective of the instrument is the entrance pupil of the entire system. The exit pupil or *eyepoint* is, therefore, the image of

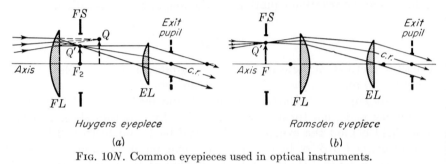

Huygens eyepiece

(a)

Ramsden eyepiece

(b)

Fig. 10N. Common eyepieces used in optical instruments.

the objective formed by the eyepiece and is located at the position marked "Exit pupil" in the figure. Here the chief ray crosses the axis of the ocular. A field stop FS is often located at Q', the primary focal point of the eye lens, and if cross hairs or a reticle are to be employed, they are mounted at this point. Although the eyepiece as a whole is corrected for lateral chromatic aberration, the individual lenses are not, so that image of the cross hairs or reticle formed by the eye lens alone will show considerable distortion and color. Huygens eyepieces with reticles are used in some microscopes, but in this case the reticle is small and is confined to the center of the field. The Huygens eyepiece shows some spherical aberration, astigmatism, and a rather large amount of longitudinal color and pincushion distortion. In general, the eye relief—i.e., the distance between the eye lens of the ocular and the exit pupil—is too small for comfort.

10.14. Ramsden Eyepiece. In eyepieces of this type as well, the two lenses are usually made of the same kind of glass, but here they have equal focal lengths. To correct for lateral color, their separation should be equal to the focal length. Since the first focal plane of the system coincides with the field lens, a reticle or cross hairs must be located there. Under some conditions this is considered desirable, but the fact that any dust particles on the lens surface would also be seen in sharp focus is an undesirable feature. To overcome this difficulty, the lenses are usually moved a little closer together, thus moving the focal plane forward at some sacrifice of lateral achromatism.

The paths of the rays through a Ramsden eyepiece as shown in Fig. 10$N(b)$. The image formed by an objective (not shown) is located at the first focal point F, and it is here that a field stop FS and a reticle or cross hairs are often located. After refraction by both lenses, parallel rays emerge and reach the eye at or near the exit pupil. With regard to aberrations, the Ramsden eyepiece has more lateral color than the Huygens eyepiece but the longitudinal color is only about half as great. It has about one-fifth the spherical aberration, about half the distortion, and no coma. One important advantage over the Huygens ocular is its 50 per cent greater eye relief.

10.15. Kellner or Achromatized Ramsden Eyepiece. Because of the many desirable features of the Ramsden eyepiece, various attempts have been made to improve its chromatic defects. This aberration can be

Kellner achromatized
Ramsden eyepiece

Orthoscopic
eyepiece

Symmetrical
eyepiece

FIG. 100. Three types of achromatized eyepiece.

almost eliminated by making the eye lens a cemented doublet (Fig. 100). Such eyepieces are commonly used in prism binoculars, because the slight amount of lateral color is removed and spherical aberration is reduced through the aberration characteristics of the Porro prisms (Sec. 2.2).

10.16. Special Eyepieces. The orthoscopic eyepiece shown in the middle diagram of Fig. 100 is characterized by its wide field and high magnification. It is usually employed in high-power telescopes and range finders. Its name is derived from the freedom from distortion characterizing the system. The symmetrical eyepiece shown at the right in Fig. 100 has a larger aperture than a Kellner of the same focal length. This results in a wider field as well as a long eye relief, hence its frequent use in various types of telescopic gun sights. The danger of having a short eye relief with a recoiling gun should be obvious.

Since lateral chromatic aberration, as well as the other aberrations of an eyepiece, is affected by altering the separation of the two elements, some oculars are provided with means for making this distance adjustable. Some microscopes come equipped with a set of such compensating eyepieces, thereby permitting the undercorrection of lateral color in any objective to be neutralized by an overcorrection of the eyepiece.

10.17. Prism Binoculars. Prism binoculars are in reality a pair of identical telescopes mounted side by side, one for each of the two eyes. Such an instrument is shown in Fig. 10*P* with part of the case cut away to show the optical parts. The objectives are cemented achromatic pairs, while the oculars are Kellner or achromatized Ramsden eyepieces. The dotted lines show the path of an axial ray through one pair of Porro prisms. The first prism reinverts the image and the second turns it left for right, thereby finally giving an image in the proper position. The

Fig. 10*P*. Diagram of prism binoculars, showing the lenses and totally reflecting Porro prisms.

doubling back of the light rays has the further advantage of enabling longer focus objectives to be used in short tubes, with consequent higher magnification.

There are four general features that go to make up good binoculars: (1) magnification, (2) field of view, (3) light-gathering power, and (4) size and weight. For hand-held use, binoculars with five-, six-, seven-, or eightfold magnification are most generally used. Glasses with powers above 8 are desirable, but require a rigid mount to hold them steady. For powers less than 4, lens aberrations usually offset the magnification, and the average person can usually see better with the unaided eyes. *The field of view is determined by the eyepiece aperture and should be as large as is practicable.* For seven-power binoculars a 6° object field is considered large, since in the eyepiece the same field is spread over an angle of 7 × 6°, or 42°.

The diameter of the objective lenses determines the light-gathering power. Large diameters are important only at night when there is little light available. Binoculars with the specification 6 × 30 have a magnification of 6 and objective lenses with an effective diameter of 30 mm. The specification 7 × 50 means a magnification of 7 and objectives 50 mm in diameter. Although glasses with the latter specifications are excellent for day or night use, they are considerably larger and more cumbersome than the daytime glasses specified as 6 × 30 or 8 × 30. For general civilian use, the latter two are much the most useful.

10.18. The Kellner-Schmidt Optical System. The Kellner-Schmidt optical system combines a concave spherical mirror with an aspheric lens as shown in Fig. 10Q. Kellner devised and patented* this optical system in 1910 as a high-quality source of parallel light. Years later Schmidt introduced the system as a high-speed camera, and it has since become known as a Schmidt camera. While Schmidt was the first to emphasize the importance of placing the corrector plate at the mirror's center of curvature, Kellner shows it in this position in his patent drawing.

FIG. 10Q. Kellner-Schmidt optical system.

The purpose of the lens is to refract incoming parallel rays in such directions that after reflection from the spherical mirror they all come to a focus at the same axial point F. This "corrector plate," therefore, eliminates the spherical aberration of the mirror. With the lens located at the center of curvature of the mirror, parallel rays entering the system at large angles with the axis are brought to a relatively good focus at other points like F'. The focal surface of such a system is spherical, with its center of curvature at C.

Such an optical system has several remarkable and useful properties. First as a camera, with a small film at the center or with a larger film curved to fit the focal surface, it has the very high speed of $f/0.5$. Because of this phenomenal speed, Schmidt systems are used by astronomers to obtain photographs of faint stars or comets. They are used for similar reasons in television receivers to project small images from an oscilloscope tube into a relatively large screen. In this case the convex oscilloscope screen is curved to the focal surface so that the light from the image screen is reflected by the mirror and passes through the corrector lens to the observing screen.

If a convex silvered mirror is located at FF', rays from any distant source will on entering the system form a point image on the focal surface and after reflection will again emerge as a parallel bundle in the exact

* American Patent No. 969,785, 1910.

direction of the source.   When used in this manner the device is called an *autocollimator*.   If the focal surface is coated with fluorescent paint, ultraviolet light from a distant invisible source will form a bright spot at some point on FF', and the visible light emitted from this spot will emerge only in the direction of the source.   If a hole is made in the center of the large mirror, an eyepiece may be inserted in the rear to view the fluorescent screen and any ultraviolet source may be seen as a visible source.   As such, the device becomes a fast, wide-angled, ultraviolet telescope.

10.19. Concentric Optical Systems.* The recent development and use of concentric optical systems warrants at least some mention of their

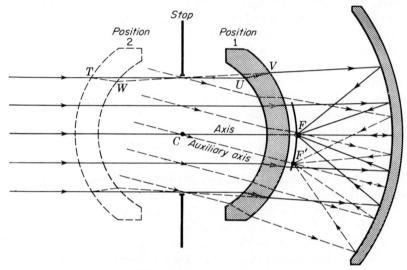

Fig. 10R. Concentric optical system.

remarkable optical properties.   Such systems have the general form of a concave mirror and a concentric lens of the type shown in Fig. 5I.   As the title implies, and as is shown in Fig. 10R, all surfaces have a common center of curvature C.

The purpose of the concentric lens is to reduce spherical aberration to a minimum.   Off-axis rays traversing the lens are bent away from the axis and, by the proper choice of radii, refractive index, and lens thickness, can be made to cross the axis at the paraxial focal point F.   Since any ray through C may be considered as an *axis*, the focal surface is also a sphere with C as a center of curvature.   In some applications the back surface of the lens is made to be the focal surface.

Since the principal planes of the concentric lens both coincide with a plane through C perpendicular to the axial ray of any bundle, it is as if

* A. Bouwers, "Achievements in Optics," Elsevier Press, Inc., Houston, Tex., 1950.

the corrector were a thin lens located at C and oriented at the proper angle for all incident parallel beams.

Since there are no oblique and no sagittal rays, the system is free of coma and astigmatism. The complete performance of the system is known as soon as the imagery of an axial object point is known. Here lies the essential advantage over the Kellner-Schmidt system. Chromatic aberrations resulting from the lens are small as long as the focal length is long compared with that of the mirror, and this is nearly always the case.

Other important features of the concentric system may be seen from the diagram. There is an unusually small decrease in image brightness with increasing angle of incidence. The corrector lens may be placed in front of C, in position 2. In this position the same optical performance is realized. Finally, a concentric convex mirror may be placed about halfway between the lens and the mirror. The reflected light is then brought to a focus through a hole in the center of the large mirror. This latter arrangement, among other things, makes an excellent objective system for a reflecting microscope.

PROBLEMS

1. A magnifier is made of two thin plano-convex lenses, each with a 2-cm focal length, and spaced 1.5 cm apart. Applying Gaussian formulas, find (a) its focal length, (b) its magnifying power, and (c) its back focal length.

2. A Coddington magnifier made from a sphere of 1.5 cm diameter is made of crown glass of index 1.50. Find by calculation (a) its focal length, (b) its magnifying power, and (c) its back focal length. *Ans.* (a) $+1.12$ cm. (b) $22.2\times$. (c) 0.375 cm.

3. A Ramsden eyepiece is made of two thin plano-convex lenses, each of 2.5 cm focal length, and spaced 1.8 cm apart. Applying thin-lens formulas, find (a) its focal length, (b) its magnifying power, and (c) its back focal length.

4. A Ramsden eyepiece is made of two thin lenses, each with a 22.5-mm focal length, and spaced 16 mm apart. Applying thin-lens formulas, find (a) its focal length, (b) its magnifying power, and (c) its back focal length.
Ans. (a) $+1.745$ cm. (b) $14.3\times$. (c) 5.05 mm.

5. A Huygens eyepiece is made of two thin lenses, with focal lengths of 2 cm and 1 cm, respectively. If the lenses are spaced to correct for chromatic aberration, find (a) the focal length of the combination, (b) the magnifying power, and (c) the back focal length.

6. A microscope has an objective with a focal length of 3 mm and an ocular marked $20\times$. What is the total magnification if the objective forms its image 16 cm beyond its secondary focal plane? *Ans.* $1067\times$.

7. A microscope has an objective with a focal length of 3.5 mm and an ocular with a focal length of 10 mm. What is the total magnification if the objective forms its image 16 cm beyond its secondary focal plane?

8. The eyepiece and objective of a microscope are 20.6 cm apart, and each has a focal length of 0 mm. Treating these lenses as though they were thin lenses, find (a) the distance from the objective to the object viewed, (b) the linear magnification produced by the objective, and (c) the over-all magnification if the final image is formed at infinity.   *Ans.* (a) 6.19 mm.   (b) −32.3×.   (c) 1347×.

9. The ocular and objective of a microscope are 21.2 cm apart, and each has a focal length of 1.2 cm.   Treating these as thin lenses, find (a) the distance from the objective to the object viewed, (b) the linear magnification produced by the objective, and (c) the over-all magnification if the final image is formed at infinity.

10. An objective of an astronomical telescope has a diameter of 10 cm and a focal length of 120 cm.   When it is used with an eyepiece having a focal length of 2 cm and a field lens with a diameter of 10 mm, find (a) the angular magnification, (b) the diameter of the exit pupil, (c) the object-field angle, (d) the image-field angle, and (e) the eye relief.   *Ans.* (a) 60×.   (b) 1.67 mm.   (c) 0.47°.   (d) 28.2°.   (e) 2.03 cm.

11. An astronomical telescope has an objective with a diameter of 6 cm and a focal length of 60 cm.   When used with a 20× ocular having a field lens 1.2 cm in diameter, find (a) the angular magnification, (b) the diameter of the exit pupil, (c) the object-field angle, and (d) the image-field angle.

12. The objectives of a pair of binoculars have apertures of 60 mm and focal lengths of 250 mm.   The oculars have apertures of 10 mm and focal lengths of 22 mm.   Find (a) the angular magnification, (b) the diameter of the exit pupils, (c) the object-field angle, (d) the image-field angle, (e) the eye relief, and (f) the field at 1000 m.

Ans. (a) 11.4×.   (b) 5.28 mm.   (c) 2.1°.   (d) 24.5°.   (e) 2.4 cm.   (f) 36.8 m.

PART II

PHYSICAL OPTICS

CHAPTER 11

LIGHT WAVES

The preceding chapters were concerned with the subject of geometrical optics, the basis of which is furnished by the laws of reflection and refraction. We now turn to *physical optics*, which comprises those phenomena bearing on the nature of light. As thus defined, this field includes processes which involve the interactions of light with matter, as for example the emission and absorption of light. Many of these processes require the quantum theory for their complete explanation, but the systematic treatment of this theory lies beyond the scope of this book. A large and homogeneous class of optical phenomena can be explained by assuming that light consists of waves, and it has therefore seemed desirable to restrict the meaning of the term "physical optics" to include only the classical wave theory of light. The way in which this theory forms part of the more complete one called quantum mechanics will then be briefly described in the final chapter (Chap. 30).

As we have seen, large-scale optical effects can be explained by the use of light rays. Finer details require the wave picture which we are now to consider. Most of these details are not commonly observed in everyday life but appear when, for example, we make a close examination of the effects of passing light through narrow openings or of reflecting it from ruled surfaces. Finally, processes which occur on a still smaller scale, involving individual atoms or molecules, require quantum theory for their rigorous treatment. Any case of the interaction of two or more beams of light with each other may, however, be treated quantitatively by wave theory. As an introduction to this theory, the present chapter deals with wave motion in general and indicates at appropriate points how the various characteristics of light depend on those of the waves of which we assume it to consist.

11.1. Wave Motion. Waves of the type with which we are most familiar, i.e., waves on the surface of water, are of considerable complexity. However, they may serve to illustrate an important feature present in any wave motion. If the waves are traveling in the x direction and the y direction is vertical, an instantaneous picture of the contour of the waves in the x,y plane is given in Fig. 11A by the continuous curve.   Let this curve be represented by an equation $y = f(x)$.   If the wave contour is to move toward $+x$ with a constant velocity v, we must introduce the time t in such a way that, as t increases, a given ordinate such as y_1 will, after a time Δt has elapsed, be found at y_1', farther to the right by an amount $\Delta x = v\,\Delta t$.   This is accomplished by writing the equation $y = f(x - vt)$, since we have, at the two times t and $t + \Delta t$,

$$y_1 = f(x - vt)$$
$$y_1' = f[(x + \Delta x) - v(t + \Delta t)]$$

If now we substitute $\Delta x = v\,\Delta t$, we find that $y_1' = y_1$, and the above requirement is realized.   The wave is in the position of the broken curve

Fig. 11A. Illustrating the propagation of water waves.

at the instant $t + \Delta t$.   The general equation for any transverse wave motion in a plane is

$$y = f(x \pm vt) \tag{11a}$$

The plus sign is to be used if the wave is to travel to the left, i.e., in the $-x$ direction.

This equation is the solution of the so-called *wave equation*, a partial differential equation which for waves traveling along the x axis may be written

$$\frac{\partial^2 y}{\partial t^2} = v^2 \frac{\partial^2 y}{\partial x^2} \tag{11b}$$

To prove that Eq. 11a satisfies it, we evaluate the derivatives, using, for example, the negative sign.   Partial differentiations with respect to t give

$$\frac{\partial y}{\partial t} = -vf'(x - vt)$$

and

$$\frac{\partial^2 y}{\partial t^2} = v^2 f''(x - vt)$$

while the differentiations with respect to x give

$$\frac{\partial^2 y}{\partial x^2} = f''(x - vt)$$

The proportionality factor v^2 is therefore obtained. Now the second derivative with respect to t represents the acceleration of a particle at a given instant, while that with respect to x determines the curvature of the wave contour at the same point and instant. Thus, if one can evaluate these derivatives for a given kind of waves, he has a means of finding their velocity. This method will be used in Sec. 11.4 for transverse elastic waves and again in Sec. 20.4 for electromagnetic waves.

The above equations represent the progression of the wave contour with time and specify that, whatever the initial form, the form at time t is the same but is displaced by a distance vt. This does not imply that the particles of the medium are carried along with the wave. On the contrary, the only thing that moves along continuously is the contour, while each particle merely oscillates about its position of equilibrium. Nor do the equations set any restriction on the type of oscillations involved. In water waves, for example, they are circular or elliptical ones in the x,y plane of Fig. 11A. This figure, of

FIG. 11B. Generation of transverse waves in an elastic solid.

course, represents merely a cross section perpendicular to the crests of the waves. The complete waves are spread over the x,z plane, and their crests are straight since the displacement y in Eq. 11a is independent of z.

Turning now from surface waves to waves in three dimensions such as sound waves or earthquake waves, the same equations may be applied. For this to be so, it is necessary that the locus of equal displacements occur in a plane, and we speak of *plane waves*. Such waves could be produced in a block of elastic material, for example, as is illustrated in Fig. 11B. A board attached to one surface of the block will, if given a periodic motion in its own plane, generate plane waves. Equations 11a and 11b will represent such waves if the perpendicular to the wave fronts is parallel to x. To generalize the equations so that they can represent plane waves going in any direction, one merely substitutes for x the expression $lx + my + nz$, where l, m, and n are the cosines of the angles between the given direction and the x, y, and z axes, respectively.

A small source of light generates waves which are not plane but spherical, with the source at the center of the curved wave fronts. Since the curvature decreases with distance, one may realize what are essentially plane waves of light by placing the source sufficiently far away. The required distance depends on the aperture, i.e., on the area of the wave front used, the distance obviously increasing for larger apertures. A more common way of obtaining plane light waves is to place a point source at the primary focal point of a lens or mirror, as was shown in Chaps. 4 and 6. It is true that in practice the source is never a mathematical point and that the beam obtained actually consists of many plane waves slightly inclined to each other, each originating from a different point on the source. To reduce this effect to a minimum, the usual laboratory practice is to employ as the point source an illuminated pinhole of diameter not exceeding a few wavelengths of light.

11.2. Sine Waves. The simplest type of wave is that for which the function f in Eq. 11a is a sine or cosine. The motion of the individual particles is then simple harmonic.* This is the type of motion that one expects for elastic substances, where the forces due to distortion obey Hooke's law. Let us consider *transverse waves*, in which the motions of the particles are perpendicular to the direction of travel of the waves. The instantaneous displacements y may then be represented by writing

$$y = a \sin \frac{2\pi x}{\lambda}$$

The significance of the constants a and λ may be seen from the curve

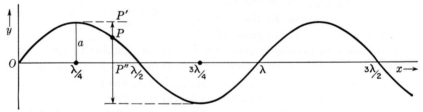

FIG. 11C. Contour of a sine wave at time $t = 0$.

of Fig. 11C, which is a plot of the above equation. The maximum displacement a is called the *amplitude* of the wave, and the distance λ after which the curve repeats, its *wavelength*.

To represent the wave in time as well as in space, i.e., to make the wave move, one introduces the time as in Eq. 11a, obtaining

$$y = a \sin \frac{2\pi}{\lambda} (x - vt) \tag{11c}$$

Then the contour will be displaced toward $+x$ with the velocity v. Any one particle, such as P in the figure, will carry out a simple harmonic

---

* For a discussion of simple harmonic motion, and of its mathematical representation, the reader may refer to any textbook on elementary mechanics, such as F. W. Sears, "Principles of Physics," vol. I, Mechanics, Heat and Sound, 2d ed., Addison-Wesley Publishing Company, Cambridge, Mass., 1946.

vibration, occupying the successive positions P, P', P'', etc., as the wave moves. The time for a whole vibration of any particle is the *period T*, and its reciprocal, the number of vibrations per second, is the *frequency ν*. We have

$$v = \frac{\lambda}{T} = \nu\lambda \tag{11d}$$

A useful and concise way of expressing the equation for simple harmonic waves is in terms of the *angular frequency* $\omega = 2\pi\nu$ and the *propagation number* $k = 2\pi/\lambda$. Equation 11c then becomes

$$y = a \sin (kx - \omega t) = a \sin (\omega t - kx + \pi)$$

$$= a \cos \left(\omega t - kx + \frac{\pi}{2} \right)$$

Now the addition of a constant to the quantity in parentheses is of little physical significance, since such a constant may be eliminated by suitably adjusting the zero of the time scale. Thus the equations when written

$$y = a \cos (\omega t - kx)$$

and
$$y = a \sin (\omega t - kx) \tag{11e}$$

will describe the wave of Fig. 11C, if the curve applies at times $t = T/4$, and $T/2$, respectively, instead of at $t = 0$.

A beam of light to which equations of the above type would apply has the following characteristics: Not only is it a perfectly parallel beam, but it is absolutely *monochromatic* because it possesses one accurately defined wavelength. It is also *plane-polarized*, since the vibrations occur in a plane passing through the direction of propagation. Particularly as regards its monochromatic character, such light is idealized, and impossible of actual realization. One obvious reason is that an equation like Eq. 11e sets no limit on x and requires an infinitely long train of waves. The light of a single, sharp spectrum line does, however, approach this ideal rather closely.

11.3. Phase and Phase Difference. The important characteristic of plane waves is that the vibratory motion of every part of the medium is the same except for its phase. This term refers to the quantity in parentheses in Eq. 11e, namely, the argument of the sine or cosine, and tells us what fraction of a complete vibration the particle has executed at a given instant. In one vibration, the phase increases by 2π. Giving t a particular value in the equations, we see that the phase varies along

---

* The physical meaning of k is that it represents the number of waves in a distance of 2π cm. Hence it is sometimes called the *wave number*. We shall reserve this term for the number of waves in 1 cm. See Sec. 14.14, where this quantity is designated by σ.

the wave in direct proportion to x. The proportionality constant is the propagation number k, usually expressed in radians per centimeter. The *phase difference* at any instant between two particles at positions x_2 and x_1 is therefore

$$\delta = k(x_2 - x_1) = \frac{2\pi}{\lambda} \Delta$$

Here we have represented by Δ the difference in the x coordinate of the two particles, which, for reasons to be explained shortly, we call the *path difference*.

Only differences of phase are important. The absolute value of a particular phase cannot be measured for light, and need never concern us. Differences, on the other hand, may be determined to a high degree of precision, and there is no arbitrariness in their definition. Similarly, the instantaneous displacement y is of little significance, since it is specified by the amplitude and absolute phase. Amplitudes and phase differences are the essential quantities, as will become clear in the chapters immediately following.

An example of the kind of optical experiment where phase differences play an important part is as follows: a beam of monochromatic light is divided into two beams, by partial reflection or otherwise. The two are then sent over different paths and afterward recombined. The intensity resulting from this superposition will depend greatly on the exact phase difference between the two sets of waves. This difference, in turn, is determined by the distances traversed by the two beams in reaching the point of observation. The use of the term path differences for the quantity Δ indicates that it is usually a difference for two separate waves, not for two points in a single wave, that is of interest. In an experiment of this type it may be that one or more segments of the paths are in a substance for which the velocity of light is appreciably different from that in vacuum or air. In computing phase differences, one then uses not the actual geometrical path through such a segment, but the *optical path* [d] (Sec. 1.5), which is the product of the distance and the refractive index n. The necessity for this follows from the fact that the velocity of light waves is less in the denser medium by the factor $1/n$. Hence, if one requires the equivalent path in vacuum, or the path the light would traverse in vacuum in the same time, he uses the optical path instead of the geometrical one. The following important relations then apply:

$$\text{Phase difference } \delta = \frac{2\pi}{\lambda} \times \text{(optical path difference)}$$

$$= \frac{2\pi}{\lambda} \Delta = \frac{2\pi}{\lambda} \left(\sum_i n_i d_i - \sum_j n_j d_j \right) \tag{11f}$$

Here the two sums represent the total optical paths of the two light beams mentioned above.

11.4. Phase Velocity or Wave Velocity. It is now possible to state more precisely what actually moves with a wave. The discussion given in connection with Fig. 11A may be summed up by saying that a wave constitutes the progression of a condition of constant phase. This condition might be, for instance, the crest of the wave, where the phase is such as to yield the maximum upward displacement. The speed with which a crest moves along is usually called the wave velocity, although the more specific term phase velocity is sometimes used. That it is identical with the quantity v in our previous equations is shown by evaluating the rate of change of the x coordinate under the condition that the phase remain constant. Using the form of the phase in Eq. 11e, the latter requirement becomes

$$\omega t - kx = \text{const.}$$

and the wave velocity

$$v = \frac{dx}{dt} = \frac{\omega}{k} \qquad (11g)$$

Substitution of $\omega = 2\pi\nu$ and $k = 2\pi/\lambda$ gives agreement with Eq. 11d. For a wave traveling toward $-x$, the constant phase takes the form $\omega t + kx$, and the corresponding $v = -\omega/k$.

The ratio ω/k for a given kind of waves depends on the physical properties of the medium in which the waves travel and also, in general, on the frequency ω itself. For transverse elastic waves involving distortions small enough so that the forces obey Hooke's law, the wave velocity is independent of frequency and is given simply as

$$v = \sqrt{\frac{N}{\rho}} \qquad (11h)$$

FIG. 11D. Illustrating the shear caused by a transverse wave.

N being the shear modulus and ρ the density. The proof of this relation is not difficult. From Fig. 11D it will be seen that the sheet of small thickness δx is sheared through the angle α. The shear modulus is the constant ratio of stress to strain. The strain is measured by $\tan \alpha$, so that

$$\text{Strain} = \frac{\delta f}{\delta x}$$

where f is the function giving the shape of the wave at a particular instant. The stress is the tangential force F per unit area acting on the surface of the sheet, and this by Hooke's law must equal the product of the shear modulus and the strain, so that

$$\text{Stress} = F_x = N\,\frac{\delta f}{\delta x}$$

Because of the curvature of the wave, the stress will vary with x, and the force acting on the left side of the sheet will not be exactly balanced by the force acting on its right side.   The net force per unit area is

$$F_x - F_{x+\delta x} = \frac{\partial F}{\partial x}\,\delta x = N\,\frac{\partial^2 f}{\partial x^2}\,\delta x$$

We now apply Newton's second law of motion, equating this force to the product of the mass and the acceleration of unit area of the sheet.

$$N\,\frac{\partial^2 f}{\partial x^2}\,\delta x = \rho\,\delta x\,\frac{\partial^2 f}{\partial t^2}$$

Comparison with the wave equation 11b then verifies the expression for the velocity given in Eq. 11h.

From the fact that they can be polarized (Chap. 24), light waves are known to be transverse waves.   Measurements show that their velocity in vacuum is approximately 3×10^{10} cm/sec.   If one assumes then to be elastic waves, as was commonly done in the nineteenth century, the question arises as to the medium that transmits them.   Since the velocity is so large, Eq. 11h would require that the ratio of rigidity to density would have to be very great.   In the early *elastic-solid theory*, a medium called the "aether" having this property was assumed to occupy all space.   Its density was supposed to increase in material substances to account for the lower velocity.   There are obvious objections to such a hypothesis.   For example, in spite of its resistance to shear, which had to be postulated because light waves are transverse, the aether produces no detectable effects on the motions of astronomical bodies. All the difficulties disappeared when Maxwell developed the present *electromagnetic theory* of light (Chap. 20).   Here the mechanical displacement of an element of the medium is replaced by a variation of the electric field (or more generally of the dielectric displacement) at the corresponding point.

The elastic-solid theory was successful in explaining a number of properties of light.   There are many parallelisms in the two theories, and much of the mathematics of the earlier theory can be rewritten in electromagnetic terms without difficulty.   Consequently, we shall frequently find mechanical analogies useful in understanding the behavior of light.   In fact, for the material presented in the next seven chapters, it is immaterial what type of waves are assumed.

11.5. Amplitude and Intensity. Waves transport energy, and the amount of it that flows per second across unit area perpendicular to the direction of travel is called the *intensity* of the wave. If the wave flows continuously with the velocity v, there is a definite energy density, or total energy per unit volume. All the energy contained in a column of the medium of unit cross section and of length v will pass through the unit of area in 1 sec. Thus the intensity is given by the product of v and the energy density. Either the energy density or the intensity is proportional to the square of the amplitude and to the square of the frequency. To prove this proposition for sine waves in an elastic medium, it is necessary only to determine the vibrational energy of a single particle executing simple harmonic motion.

Consider for example the particle P in Fig. 11C. At the time for which the figure is drawn, it is moving upward and possesses both kinetic and potential energy. A little later it will have the position P'. Here it is instantaneously at rest, with zero kinetic energy and the maximum potential energy. As it subsequently moves downward, it gains kinetic energy, while the potential energy decreases in such a way that the total energy stays constant. When it reaches the center, at P'', the energy is all kinetic. Hence we may find the total energy either from the maximum potential energy at P' or from the maximum kinetic energy at P''. The latter procedure gives the desired result most easily.

According to Eq. 11e, the displacement of a particular particle varies with time according to the relation

$$y = a \sin (\omega t - \alpha)$$

where α is the value of kx for that particle. The velocity of the particle is

$$\frac{dy}{dt} = \omega a \cos (\omega t - \alpha)$$

When $y = 0$, the sine vanishes and the cosine has its maximum value. Then the velocity becomes $-\omega a$, and the maximum kinetic energy

$$\frac{1}{2} m \left[\frac{dy}{dt} \right]^2_{max} = \frac{1}{2} m\omega^2 a^2$$

Since this is also the total energy of the particle and is proportional to the energy per unit volume, it follows that

$$\text{Energy density} \sim \omega^2 a^2 \tag{11i}$$

The intensity, v times this quantity, will then also be proportional to ω^2 and a^2.

In spherical waves, the intensity decreases as the inverse square of the distance from the source. This law follows directly from the fact that, provided there is no conversion of the energy into other forms, the same amount must pass through any sphere with the source as its center. Since the area of a sphere increases as the square of its radius, the energy per unit area at a distance r from the source, or the intensity, will vary as $1/r^2$. The amplitude must then vary as $1/r$, and one may write the equation of a spherical wave as

$$y = \frac{a}{r} \sin (\omega t - kr) \tag{11j}$$

Here a means the amplitude at unit distance from the source.

If any of the energy is transformed to heat, that is to say, if there is *absorption*, the amplitude and intensity of plane waves will not be constant but will decrease as the wave passes through the medium. Similarly with spherical waves, the loss of intensity will be more rapid than is required by the inverse-square law. For plane waves, the fraction dI/I of the intensity lost in traversing an infinitesimal thickness dx is proportional to dx, so that

$$\frac{dI}{I} = -\alpha \, dx$$

To obtain the decrease in traversing a finite thickness x, the equation is integrated to give

$$\int_0^x \frac{dI}{I} = -\alpha \int_0^x dx$$

Evaluating these definite integrals, we find

$$I_x = I_0 e^{-\alpha x} \tag{11k}$$

This law, which has been attributed to both Bouguer[*] and Lambert,[†] we shall refer to as the *exponential law of absorption*. Figure 11E is a plot of the intensity against thickness according to this law for a medium having $\alpha = 0.4$ per cm. The wave equations may be modified to take account of absorption by multiplying the amplitude by the factor $e^{-\alpha x/2}$, since the amplitude varies with the square root of the intensity.

For light, the intensity can be expressed in ergs per square centimeter per second. Full sunlight, for example, has an intensity in these units of about 1.4×10^6. Here it is important to realize that not all this energy flux affects the eye, and not all that does is equally efficient. Hence the intensity as defined above does not necessarily correspond to

[*] Pierre Bouguer (1698–1758). Royal Professor of Hydrography at Le Havre.
[†] Johann Lambert (1728–1777). German physicist, astronomer, and mathematician. Worked primarily in the field of heat radiation. Another law, which is always called Lambert's law, refers to the variation with angle of the radiation from a surface.

the sensation of brightness, and it is more usual to find light flux expressed in visual units.* The intensity and the amplitude are the purely physical quantities, however, and according to modern theory the latter must be expressed in electrical units. Thus it may be shown that according to equations to be derived in Chap. 20 the amplitude in a beam of sunlight having the above-mentioned value of the intensity represents an electric field strength of 7.3 volts/cm and an accompanying magnetic field of 0.024 gauss.

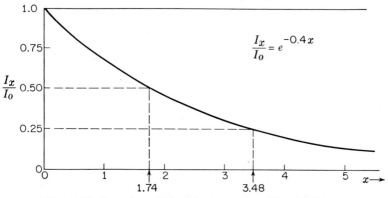

Fig. 11E. Decrease of intensity in an absorbing medium.

The amplitude of light always decreases more or less rapidly with the distance traversed. Only for plane waves traveling in vacuum, such as the light from a star coming through outer space, is it nearly constant. The inverse-square law of intensities may be assumed to hold for a small source in air at distances greater than about ten times the lateral dimension of the source. Then the finite size of the source causes an error of less than one-tenth of 1 per cent in computing the intensity, and for laboratory distances the absorption of air may be neglected. In greater thicknesses, however, all "transparent" substances absorb an appreciable fraction of the energy. We shall take up this subject again in some detail in Chap. 22.

11.6. Frequency and Wavelength. Any wave motion is generated by some sort of vibrating source, and the frequency of the waves is equal to that of the source. The wavelength in a given medium is then determined by the velocity in that medium and by Eq. 11d is obtained by dividing the velocity by the frequency. Passage from one medium to another causes a change in the wavelength in the same proportion as it does in the velocity, since the frequency is not altered. If we remember that a wave front represents a surface on which the phase of motion is

* See, for example, F. W. Sears, "Principles of Physics," vol. 3, Optics, 3d ed., chap. 13, Addison-Wesley Publishing Company, Cambridge, Mass., 1948.

constant, it should be clear that, regardless of any changes of velocity, two different wave fronts are separated by a certain number of waves. That is, the length of any ray between two such surfaces is the same, provided this length is expressed in wavelengths in the appropriate media.

As applied to light, the last statement is equivalent to saying that the optical path is the same along all rays drawn between two wave fronts. For since wavelengths are proportional to velocities, we have

$$\frac{\lambda}{\lambda_m} = \frac{c}{v} = n$$

when the light passes from a vacuum, where it has wavelength λ and velocity c, into a medium where the corresponding quantities are λ_m and v. The optical path corresponding to a distance d in any medium is therefore

$$nd = \frac{\lambda}{\lambda_m} d$$

or the number of wavelengths in that distance multiplied by the wavelength in vacuum. It is customary in optics and spectroscopy to refer to the "wavelength" of a particular radiation, of a single spectral line, for example, as its wavelength in air under normal conditions. This we shall designate by λ (without subscript), and except in rare circumstances it may be taken as the same as the wavelength in vacuum.

The wavelengths of visible light extend between about 4×10^{-5} cm for the extreme violet and 7.2×10^{-5} cm for the deep red. Just as the ear becomes insensitive to sound above a certain frequency, so the eye fails to respond to light vibrations of frequencies greater than that of the extreme violet or less than that of the extreme red. The limits, of course, depend somewhat upon the individual, and there is evidence that most persons can see an image with light of wavelength as short as 3.0×10^{-5} cm, but this is a case of fluorescence in the retina. In this case the light appears to be bluish gray in color and is harmful to the eye. Radiation of wavelength shorter than that of the visible is termed "ultraviolet light" down to a wavelength of about 5×10^{-7} cm, and beyond this we are in the region of X rays to 6×10^{-10} cm. Shorter than these, in turn, are the γ rays from radioactive substances. On the long-wavelength side of the visible lies the infrared, which may be said to merge into the radio waves at about 4×10^{-2} cm. Figure 11F shows the names which have been given to the various regions of the spectrum of radiation, though we know that no real lines of demarcation exist. It is not convenient to use the same units of length throughout such an enormous range. Hence radio wavelengths are expressed in meters

(10^2 cm), infrared in microns (1 $\mu = 10^{-4}$ cm), visible and ultraviolet in angstrom* units (1 Å $= 10^{-8}$ cm) and X rays in angstroms, or, commonly in accurate work, in X units (1 XU $= 10^{-11}$ cm).

It will be seen that visible light covers an almost insignificant fraction of this range. Therefore, although all these radiations are similar in nature, differing only in wavelength, the term "light" is conventionally extended only to the adjacent portions of the spectrum, namely, the ultraviolet and infrared. Many of the results that we shall discuss for light are common to the whole range of radiation, but naturally there

ELECTROMAGNETIC WAVES

FIG. 11F. Scale of wavelengths for the range of known electromagnetic waves.

are qualitative differences in behavior between the very long and very short waves, which we shall occasionally point out. The divisions between the different types of radiation are purely formal and are roughly fixed by the fact that in the laboratory the different types are generated and detected in different ways. Thus the infrared is emitted copiously by hot bodies, and is detected by an energy-measuring instrument such as the thermopile. The shortest radio waves are generated by electric discharges between fine metallic particles immersed in oil and are detected by electrical devices. Nichols and Tear, in 1917, produced infrared waves having wavelengths up to 0.42 mm and radio waves down to 0.22 mm. The two regions may therefore be said to overlap, keeping in mind, however, that the waves themselves are of the same nature for both. The same holds true for the boundaries of all the other regions of the spectrum.

In sound and other mechanical waves, a change of wavelength occurs when the source has a translational motion. The waves sent out in the direction of motion are shortened, and, in the opposite direction, lengthened. No change is produced in the velocity of the waves them-

* A. J. Ångström (1814–1874). Professor of physics at Uppsala, Sweden. Chiefly known for his famous atlas of the solar spectrum, which was used for many years as the standard for wavelength determinations.

selves; so a stationary observer receives a frequency which is larger or smaller than that of the source. If, on the other hand, the source is at rest and the observer in motion, a change of frequency is also observed, but for a different reason. Here there is no change of wavelength, but the frequency is altered by the change in relative velocity of the waves with respect to the observer. The two cases involve approximately the same change of frequency for the same speed of motion, provided this is small compared with the velocity of the waves. These phenomena are known as the Doppler effect* and are most commonly experienced in sound as changes in the acoustic pitch.

Doppler mistakenly attributed the different colors of stars to their motions toward or away from the earth. Because the velocity of light is so large, an appreciable change in color would require that a star have a component of velocity in the line of sight impossibly large compared with the measured velocities at right angles to it. For most stars, the latter usually range between 10 and 30 km/sec, with a few as high as 300 km/sec. Since light travels at nearly 300,000 km/sec, the expected shifts of frequency are small. Furthermore, it makes little difference whether one assumes that the observer or the source is in motion. Suppose that the earth were moving with a velocity u directly toward a fixed star. An observer would then receive u/λ waves in addition to the number $\nu = c/\lambda$ that would reach him if he were at rest. The apparent frequency would be

$$\nu' = \frac{c + u}{\lambda} = \nu\left(1 + \frac{u}{c}\right) \tag{11l}$$

With the velocities mentioned, this would differ from the true frequency by less than 1 part in 1000. A good spectroscope can, however, easily detect and permit the measurement of such a shift as a displacement of the spectrum lines. In fact, this legitimate application of Doppler's principle has become a powerful method of studying the radial velocities of stars. Figure 11G shows an example where the spectrum of μ Cassiopeiae, in the center strip, is compared with the lines of iron from a laboratory source, photographed above and below. All the iron lines also appear in the stellar spectrum as white lines (absorption lines) but are shifted toward the left, i.e., toward shorter wavelengths. Measurement shows that the increase of frequency corresponds to a velocity of approach of 115 km/sec, which is unusually high for stars in our own galaxy. The spectra of other galaxies (spiral nebulae) all show displace-

* J. C. Doppler (1803–1853). Native of Salzburg, Austria. At the age of thirty-two, unable to secure a position, he was about to emigrate to America. However, at that time he was made professor of mathematics at the Realschule in Prague and later became professor of experimental physics at the University of Vienna.

ments toward the red, which for the most distant ones amount to several hundreds of angstrom units. Such values would indicate recessional velocities of tens of thousands of kilometers per second, and have been so interpreted. It is rather interesting that here there is enough reddening to change the color of the object, as postulated by Doppler, but in this case it occurs for objects far too faint to be seen by the naked eye.

In the laboratory, there have been found two ways of achieving velocities sufficient to produce detectable Doppler shifts. By reflecting light

Fig. 11G. Doppler shift of spectrum lines in a star. Both spectra are negatives. (*After McKellar.*)

from mirrors mounted on the rim of a wheel rotating at high speed, one may produce speeds of a virtual source as high as 400 m/sec. Much larger values are attained by beams of atoms moving in vacuum, as will be discussed later in Sec. 19.17. There, it is also shown that with the abandonment of the material aether necessitated by relativity theory the distinction between the cases of source in motion and of observer in motion disappears. Relativity leads to an equation which is substantially Eq. 11*l*, with *u* representing the relative velocity of approach or recession.

11.7. Wave Packets. As was mentioned at the end of Sec. 11.2, no source of waves vibrates indefinitely, as would be required for it to produce a true sine wave. More commonly the vibrations die out because of the dissipation of energy or are interrupted in some way. Then a group of waves of finite length, such as that illustrated in Fig. 11*H*, is produced.

Fig. 11*H*. Example of a wave packet.

The mathematical representation of a wave packet of this type is rather more complex and will be briefly discussed in the next chapter. Since wave packets are of frequent occurrence, however, some features of their behavior should be mentioned here. In the first place, the wavelength is not well defined. If the packet be sent through any device for measuring wavelengths (as, for example, light through a diffraction grating), it will be found to yield a continuous spread over a certain range $\Delta\lambda$. The maximum intensity will occur at the value of λ_0 indicated in Fig. 11H, but energy will appear in other wavelengths, the intensity dying off more or less rapidly on either side of λ_0. The larger the number N of waves in the group, the smaller will be the spread $\Delta\lambda$, and in fact theory shows* that $\Delta\lambda/\lambda_0$ is approximately equal to $1/N$. Hence only when N is very large may we consider the wave to have an accurately defined wavelength.

If the medium through which the packet travels is such that the velocity depends on frequency, two further phenomena will be observed. The individual wave crests will travel with a velocity different from that of the packet as a whole, and the packet will spread out as it progresses. We then have two velocities, the wave (or phase) velocity and the group velocity. The relation between these will be derived in Sec. 12.7.

In light sources, the radiating atoms emit wave trains of finite length. Usually, because of collisions or damping arising from other causes, these packets are very short. According to the theorem mentioned above, the consequence is that the spectrum lines will not be very narrow but will have an appreciable width $\Delta\lambda$. A measurement of this width will yield the effective "lifetime" of the electromagnetic oscillators in the atoms and the average length of the wave packets. A low-pressure discharge through the vapor of mercury containing the single isotope Hg^{198} yields very sharp spectral lines, of width about 0.005 Å. Taking the wavelength of one of the brightest lines, 5461 Å, we may estimate that there are roughly 10^6 waves in a packet and that the packets themselves are some 50 cm long.

11.8. Reflection and Refraction. When waves are incident on a boundary between two media in which the velocity is appreciably different, the incident wave train is divided into reflection and refracted (or transmitted) trains. The reflected energy will be relatively greater the larger the change in velocity. Furthermore, transverse elastic waves will be partly converted into longitudinal waves at such a boundary. The fact that the latter are not observed for light constituted another serious objection to the elastic-solid theory. The refracted waves are purely transverse and contain all of the energy that is not reflected. In general, both the reflected and refracted waves travel in directions different from that of the incident wave.

The relations between the latter directions agree, of course, with the

* This theorem is proved, for example, in J. A. Stratton, "Electromagnetic Theory," p. 292, McGraw-Hill Book Company, Inc., New York, 1941.

behavior of light *rays* stated in Chap. 1, since a ray represents the direction of flow of the energy of the waves, and this is usually perpendicular to the wave front (for an exception, see Sec. 26.2). The laws of reflection and refraction were deduced in Sec. 1.6 from Fermat's principle, but it is well known that they also follow from the application of Huygens' construction to the reflection and refraction of a plane wave.* In Fig. 11I(a), a ray incident on a plane surface of water is indicated by a, while the reflected and refracted rays are indicated by ar and at, respectively.

A question of particular interest from the standpoint of physical optics is that of a possible abrupt *change of phase* of waves when they are reflected

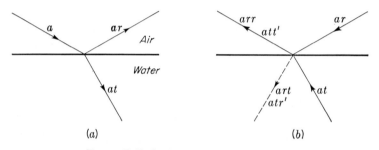

FIG. 11I. Stokes' treatment of reflection.

from a boundary. For a given boundary the result will differ, as we shall now show, according to whether the waves approach from the side of higher velocity or from that of lower velocity. Thus, let the symbol a in the left-hand part of Fig. 11I represent the amplitude (not the intensity) of a set of waves striking the surface, let r be the fraction of the amplitude reflected, and let t be the fraction transmitted. The amplitudes of the two sets of waves will then be ar and at, as shown. Now, following a treatment given by Stokes,† imagine the two sets reversed in direction, as in part (b) of the figure. Provided there is no dissipation of energy by absorption, a wave motion is a strictly reversible phenomenon. It must conform to the law of mechanics known as the *principle of reversibility*, according to which the result of an instantaneous reversal of all the velocities in a dynamical system is to cause the system to retrace its whole previous motion. That the paths of light rays are in conformity with this principle has already been stated in Sec. 1.4. The

* See, for example, J. K. Robertson, "Introduction to Physical Optics," 3d ed., pp. 60–67, D. Van Nostrand Company, Inc., New York, 1941.

† Sir George Stokes (1819–1903). Versatile Englishman of Pembroke College, Cambridge, and pioneer in the study of the interaction of light with matter. He is known for his laws of fluorescence (Sec. 22.6) and of the rate of fall of spheres in viscous fluids. The treatment referred to here was given in his "Mathematical and Physical Papers," vol. 2, pp. 89ff., especially p. 91.

two reversed trains, of amplitude ar and at, should accordingly have as their net effect after striking the surface a wave in air equal in amplitude to the incident wave in part (a) but traveling in the opposite direction. The wave of amplitude ar gives a reflected wave of amplitude arr and a refracted wave of amplitude art. If we call r' and t' the fractions of the amplitude reflected and refracted when the reversed wave at strikes the boundary from below, this contributes amplitudes att' and atr' to the two waves, as indicated. Now, since the resultant effect must consist only of a wave in air of amplitude a, we have

$$att' + arr = a \qquad (11m)$$

and

$$art + atr' = 0 \qquad (11n)$$

The second equation states that the two incident waves shall produce no net disturbance on the water side of the boundary. From Eq. 11m we obtain

$$tt' = 1 - r^2 \qquad (11o)$$

and from Eq. 11n

$$r' = -r \qquad (11p)$$

It might at first appear that Eq. 11o could be carried further by using the fact that intensities are proportional to squares of amplitudes and by writing, by conservation of energy, $r^2 + t^2 = 1$. This would immediately yield $t = t'$. The result is not correct, however, for two reasons. First, although the proportionality of intensity with square of amplitude holds for light traveling in a single medium, passage into a different medium brings in the additional factor of the index of refraction in determining the intensity. Second, it is not to the intensities that the conservation law is to be applied, but rather to the total energies of the beams. When there is a change in width of the beam, as in refraction, it must also be taken into account.

The second of Stokes' relations, Eq. 11p, shows that the *reflectance*, or fraction of the intensity reflected, is the same for a wave incident from either side of the boundary, since the negative sign disappears upon squaring the amplitudes. It should be noted, however, that the waves must be incident at angles such that they correspond to angles of incidence and refraction. The difference in sign of the amplitudes in Eq. 11p indicates a difference of phase of π between the two cases, since a reversal of sign means a displacement in the opposite sense. If there is no phase change on reflection from above, there must be a phase change of π on reflection from below; or correspondingly, if there is no change on reflection from below, there must be a change of π on reflection from above.

The principle of reversibility as applied to light waves is often useful in optical problems; for example, it proves at once the interchangeability of object and image. The conclusion reached above about the change of phase is not dependent on the applicability of the principle, i.e., on the absence of absorption, but holds for reflection from any boundary. It is a matter of experimental observation that in the reflection of light under the above conditions, the phase change of π occurs when the light strikes the boundary from the side of higher velocity,* so that the second of the two alternatives mentioned is the correct one in this case. A change of phase of the same type is encountered in the reflection of simple mechanical waves, such as transverse waves in a rope. Reflection with change of phase where the velocity decreases in crossing the boundary corresponds to the reflection of waves from a fixed end of a rope. Here the elastic reaction of the fixed end of the rope immediately produces a reflected train of opposite phase traveling back along the rope. The case where the velocity increases in crossing the boundary has its parallel in reflection from a free end of a rope. The end of the rope undergoes a displacement of twice the amount it would have if the rope were continuous, and it immediately starts a wave in the reverse direction having the same phase as the incident wave. We shall make use of the conclusions embodied in Eqs. 11o and 11p in discussing the interference of light (Sec. 14.1) and shall return to the question of the phase relations for reflection at any angle of incidence in Chap. 25.

PROBLEMS

1. Using the relations of Eq. 11d, show that the phase of a sine wave may be variously expressed as

$$\frac{2\pi}{T}\left(t - \frac{x}{v}\right) \qquad 2\pi\left(\frac{t}{T} - \frac{x}{\lambda}\right) \qquad \text{and} \qquad 2\pi\nu\left(t - \frac{x}{v}\right)$$

2. Plot a sine wave having $v = 20$ cm/sec, $\lambda = 15$ cm, and $a = 5$ cm, as a function of x at time $t = 0$. Assume that the particle at the origin has its extreme positive displacement at this time.

Ans. Sine curve of amplitude 5, having zeros at $x = 3.75, 11.25, 18.75, 26.25, \ldots$ cm.

3. In the wave of Prob. 2, plot the motion of a particle at $x = 78$ cm as a function of time, from $t = 0$ to $t = 5$ sec.

4. A wave is expressed by $y = 10 \sin (6t - 0.5x)$, where the time is in seconds and the distances in centimeters. Find the velocity and acceleration of a particle 3 cm from the origin at time $t = 24$. *Ans.* -25.72 cm/sec; 325.2 cm/sec^2.

5. What will be the phase difference in radians between two particles 90 cm apart, measured along the wave train represented by $y = 2 \sin 7\pi(x - 24t)$, in which x and t are in centimeters and seconds, respectively?

6. Spherical waves from a point source generate the motion $y = 4.2 \cos 6t$ mm

* See the discussion in Sec. 13.6 in connection with Lloyd's mirror.

at a distance of 3 m from the source. Write an equation for such waves and another describing the motion 50 cm from the source.

Ans. $y = (12,600/r) \sin (6t - kr); y = 25.2 \cos (6t + \phi.)$

7. A source of plane waves vibrates according to the equation $y = a \sin (2\pi t/T)$, where $a = 0.8$ cm and $T = 0.023$ sec. If the waves travel at the rate of 30 cm/sec, find (a) the equation of the wave, $y = f(x,t)$, and (b) the equation of motion of a particle 8 cm from the source.

8. Plane sine waves having a wavelength of 62 cm traverse a certain medium. At a particular instant, one of the particles has a displacement of $+2.6$ mm, and this displacement is increasing. Find (a) the amplitude of the wave if the phase of the particle is 72° at that instant, counting the zero phase from the time the particle passes through its equilibrium position in the positive direction, (b) the displacement and phase of another particle 19 cm farther on.

Ans. (a) 2.73 mm. (b) -0.015 mm; 180.32°.

9. Find the velocity of transverse waves in bulk aluminum.

10. One arm of a Michelson interferometer has a transparent, plane-parallel glass plate 5 mm thick, and of index $n_D = 1.5360$, set at exactly 45° with the light beam. The beam traverses the plate twice. Find the change in the optical path when the inclination of the plate is altered by 30 minutes of arc. *Ans.* 0.0298 mm.

11. On comparing the spectra from the east and west limbs (edges) of the sun, it is found that a spectrum line at 4126 Å is shifted by 0.029 Å from one spectrum to the other. What quantitative information regarding the motion of the sun can be derived from this observation?

12. Calculate the ratio of the intensities of two waves represented by $y_1 = 6 \sin (0.4t - 25x)$ and $y_2 = 2.5 \sin (3.2t - 200x)$. *Ans.* 0.09.

13. The *transmission coefficient* of a substance is defined as the fraction of light that is transmitted by unit thickness. Derive a relation between this coefficient and the absorption coefficient as it occurs in the exponential law of absorption.

14. Visible light spreads out from a point source under water that has a coefficient of absorption $\alpha = 0.08$ per m. If the intensity is 2300 ergs/cm² sec at 50 cm from the source, what will it be 10 m away? *Ans.* 2.691 ergs/cm² sec.

15. If a spectrum line in the infrared at $\lambda = 6.3$ μ is found to have a true width (corrected for any instrumental broadening) of 6×10^{-4} μ, find the average number of waves in the wave packets and the average life of the molecular oscillators emitting the line.

16. A parallel beam of light enters water ($n = 1.330$) at an angle of incidence of 60°. Find the ratio of the width of the beam in water to that in air. Will this effect tend to make t' greater or smaller with respect to t? *Ans.* 1.518. Greater.

CHAPTER 12

THE SUPERPOSITION OF WAVES

When two sets of waves are made to cross each other, as, for example, the waves created by dropping two stones simultaneously in a quiet pool, very interesting and complicated effects are observed. In the region of crossing there are places where the disturbance is practically zero, and others where it is greater than that which would be given by either wave alone. A very simple law can be used to explain these effects, which states that the resultant displacement of any point is merely the sum of the displacements due to each wave separately. This is known as the *principle of superposition* and was first clearly stated by Young* in 1802. The truth of this principle is at once evident when we observe that after the waves have passed out of the region of crossing, they appear to have been entirely uninfluenced by the other set of waves. Amplitude, frequency, and all other characteristics are just as if they had crossed an undisturbed space. This could hold only provided the principle of superposition were true. Two different observers can see different objects through the same aperture with perfect clearness, whereas the light reaching the two observers has crossed in going through the aperture. The principle is therefore applicable with great precision to light, and we may use it in investigating the disturbance in regions where two or more light waves are superimposed.

12.1. Addition of Simple Harmonic Motions along the Same Line. Considering first the effect of superimposing two sine waves of the same frequency, the problem resolves itself into finding the resultant motion when a particle executes two simple harmonic motions at the same time. The displacements due to the two waves are here taken to be along the same line, which we shall call the y direction. If the amplitudes of the two waves are a_1 and a_2, these will be the amplitudes of the two periodic

---

* Thomas Young (1773–1829). English physician and physicist, usually called the founder of the wave theory of light. An extremely precocious child (he had read the Bible twice through at the age of four), he developed into a brilliant investigator. His work on interference constituted the most important contribution on light since Newton. His early work proved the wave nature of light but was not taken seriously by others until it was corroborated by Fresnel.

211

motions impressed on the particle, and, according to Eq. 11e of the last chapter, we may write the separate displacements as follows:

$$y_1 = a_1 \sin (\omega t - \alpha_1) \Big\}$$
$$y_2 = a_2 \sin (\omega t - \alpha_2) \Big\} \qquad (12a)$$

Note that ω is the same for both waves, since we have assumed them to be of the same frequency. According to the principle of superposition, the resultant displacement y is merely the sum of y_1 and y_2, and we have

$$y = a_1 \sin (\omega t - \alpha_1) + a_2 \sin (\omega t - \alpha_2)$$

Using the expression for the sine of the difference of two angles, this may be written

$$y = a_1 \sin \omega t \cos \alpha_1 - a_1 \cos \omega t \sin \alpha_1 + a_2 \sin \omega t \cos \alpha_2$$
$$- a_2 \cos \omega t \sin \alpha_2$$
$$= (a_1 \cos \alpha_1 + a_2 \cos \alpha_2) \sin \omega t - (a_1 \sin \alpha_1 + a_2 \sin \alpha_2) \cos \omega t \qquad (12b)$$

Now since the a's and α's are constants, we are justified in setting

$$a_1 \cos \alpha_1 + a_2 \cos \alpha_2 = A \cos \theta \Big\}$$
$$a_1 \sin \alpha_1 + a_2 \sin \alpha_2 = A \sin \theta \Big\} \qquad (12c)$$

provided that constant values of A and θ can be found which satisfy these equations. Squaring and adding Eqs. 12c, we have

$$A^2(\cos^2 \theta + \sin^2 \theta) = a_1{}^2(\cos^2 \alpha_1 + \sin^2 \alpha_1) + a_2{}^2(\cos^2 \alpha_2 + \sin^2 \alpha_2)$$
$$+ 2a_1a_2(\cos \alpha_1 \cos \alpha_2 + \sin \alpha_1 \sin \alpha_2)$$

or
$$A^2 = a_1{}^2 + a_2{}^2 + 2a_1a_2 \cos (\alpha_1 - \alpha_2) \qquad (12d)$$

Dividing the lower equation 12c by the upper one, we obtain

$$\tan \theta = \frac{a_1 \sin \alpha_1 + a_2 \sin \alpha_2}{a_1 \cos \alpha_1 + a_2 \cos \alpha_2} \qquad (12e)$$

Equations 12d and 12e show that values of A and θ exist which satisfy Eqs. 12c, and we may rewrite Eq. 12b, substituting the right-hand members of Eq. 12c. This gives

$$y = A \cos \theta \sin \omega t - A \sin \theta \cos \omega t$$

which has the form of the sine of the difference of two angles and can be expressed as

$$y = A \sin (\omega t - \theta) \qquad (12f)$$

This equation is the same as either of our original equations for the separate simple harmonic motions but contains a new amplitude A and a new phase constant θ. Hence we have the important result that the sum of two simple harmonic motions of the same frequency and along the same line is also a simple harmonic motion of the same frequency. The amplitude and phase constant of the resultant motion can easily be calculated from those of the component motions by Eqs. 12d and 12e, respectively.

The addition of three or more simple harmonic motions of the same frequency will likewise give rise to a resultant motion of the same type, since the motions can be added successively, each time giving an equation of the form of Eq. 12f.   Unless considerable accuracy is desired, it is usually more convenient to use the graphical method described in the following section.   A knowledge of the resultant phase constant θ, given by Eq. 12e, is not of interest unless it is needed in combining the resultant motion with still another.

The resultant amplitude A depends, according to Eq. 12d, upon the amplitudes a_1 and a_2 of the component motions and upon their difference of phase $\delta = \alpha_1 - \alpha_2$.   When we bring together two beams of light, as is done in the Michelson interferometer (Sec. 13.8), the intensity of the light at any point will be proportional to the square of the resultant amplitude.   By Eq. 12d we have, in the case where $a_1 = a_2$,

$$I \sim A^2 = 2a^2(1 + \cos \delta) = 4a^2 \cos^2 \frac{\delta}{2} \qquad (12g)$$

If the phase difference is such that $\delta = 0, 2\pi, 4\pi, \ldots$, then this gives $4a^2$, or four times the intensity of either beam.   If $\delta = \pi, 3\pi, 5\pi, \ldots$, the intensity is zero.   For intermediate values, the intensity varies between these limits according to the square of the cosine.   These modifications of intensity obtained by combining waves are referred to as *interference* effects, and we shall discuss in the next chapter several ways in which they may be brought about and used experimentally.

12.2. Vector Addition of Amplitudes.   A very simple geometrical construction can be used to find the resultant amplitude and phase constant of the combined motion in the above case of two simple harmonic motions along the same line.   If we represent the amplitudes a_1 and a_2 by vectors making angles α_1 and α_2 with the x axis,* as in Fig. 12A(a), the resultant amplitude A is the vector sum of a_1 and a_2 and makes an angle θ with that axis.   To prove this proposition, we first note from Fig. 12A(b) that, in the triangle formed by a_1, a_2, and A, the law of cosines gives

$$A^2 = a_1{}^2 + a_2{}^2 - 2a_1a_2 \cos [\pi - (\alpha_1 - \alpha_2)] \qquad (12h)$$

which readily reduces to Eq. 12d.   Furthermore, Eq. 12e is obtained at once from the fact that the tangent of the angle θ is the quotient of the

---

* Here we depart from the usual convention of measuring positive angles in the counterclockwise direction, because it is customary in optics to represent an advance of phase by a clockwise rotation of the amplitude vector.

sum of the projections of a_1 and a_2 on the y axis by the sum of their projections on the x axis.

That the resultant motion is also simple harmonic can be concluded if we remember that this type of motion may be represented as the projection on one of the coordinate axes of a point moving with uniform

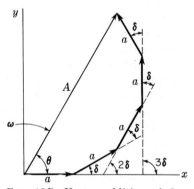

FIG. 12A. Graphical composition of amplitudes as vectors.

circular motion. Figure 12A is drawn for the time $t = 0$, and as time progresses, the displacements y_1 and y_2 will be given by the vertical components of the vectors a_1 and a_2, if the latter revolve clockwise with the same angular velocity ω. The resultant, A, will then have the same angular velocity, and the projection P' of its terminus P will undergo the resultant motion. If one imagines the vector triangle in part (b) of the figure to revolve as a rigid frame, it will be seen that the motion of P' will agree with Eq. 12f.

The graphical method is particularly useful where we have more than two motions to compound. Figure 12B shows the result of adding five motions of equal amplitudes a and having equal phase differences δ. Clearly the intensity $I = A^2$ can here vary between zero and $25a^2$, according to the phase difference δ. This is the problem which arises in finding the intensity pattern from a diffraction grating, as discussed in Chap. 17. The five equal amplitudes shown in the figure might be contributed by five

FIG. 12B. Vector addition of five amplitudes having the same magnitude and phase differences δ.

apertures of a grating, an instrument which has as its primary purpose the introduction of an equal phase difference in the light from each successive pair of apertures. It will be noted that as Fig. 12B is drawn the vibrations, starting with that at the origin, lag successively further *behind* in phase.

Either the trigonometric or graphical methods for compounding vibrations may be used to find the resultant of any number of motions with given amplitudes and phases. It is even possible, as we shall see, to apply these methods to the addition of infinitesimal vibrations, so that the summations become integrations. In such cases, and especially if the amplitudes of the individual contributions vary, it is simpler to use a method of adding the amplitudes as complex numbers. We shall take up this method in Sec. 14.8, where it first becomes necessary.

12.3. Superposition of Two Wave Trains of the Same Frequency. From the preceding section we may conclude directly that the result of superimposing two trains of sine waves of the same frequency and traveling along the same line is to produce another sine wave of that frequency, but having a new amplitude which is determined for given values of a_1 and a_2 by the phase difference δ between the motions imparted to any particle by the two waves. As an example, let us find the resultant wave produced by two waves of equal frequency and amplitude traveling in the same direction $+x$, but with one a distance Δ ahead of the other. The equations of the two waves, in the form of Eq. 11e, will be

$$y_1 = a \sin (\omega t - kx) \tag{12i}$$
$$y_2 = a \sin [\omega t - k(x + \Delta)] \tag{12j}$$

By the principle of superposition, the resultant displacement is the sum of the separate ones, so that

$$y = y_1 + y_2 = a\{\sin (\omega t - kx) + \sin [\omega t - k(x + \Delta)]\}$$

Applying the trigonometric formula

$$\sin A + \sin B = 2 \sin \tfrac{1}{2}(A + B) \cos \tfrac{1}{2}(A - B) \tag{12k}$$

we find

$$y = 2a \cos \frac{k\Delta}{2} \sin \left[\omega t - k \left(x + \frac{\Delta}{2} \right) \right] \tag{12l}$$

This corresponds to a new wave of the same frequency but with the amplitude $2a \cos (k\Delta/2) = 2a \cos (\pi\Delta/\lambda)$. When Δ is a small fraction of a wavelength, this amplitude will be nearly $2a$, while if Δ is in the neighborhood of $\tfrac{1}{2}\lambda$, it will be practically zero. These cases are illustrated in Fig. 12C, where the waves represented by Eqs. 12i and 12j (light curves) and 12l (heavy curve) are plotted at the time $t = 0$. In these figures it will be noted that the algebraic sum of the ordinates of the light curves at any value of x equals the ordinate of the heavy curve. The student may easily verify by such graphical construction the facts that the two amplitudes need not necessarily be equal to obtain a sine wave as the resultant and that the addition of any number of waves of the same frequency and wavelength also gives a similar result. In any case, the resultant wave form will have a constant amplitude, since the component waves and their resultant all move with the same velocity and maintain the same relative position. The true state of affairs may

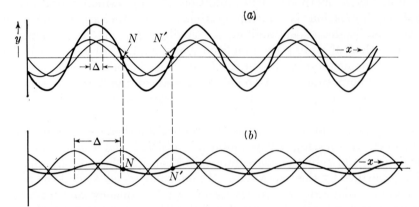

FIG. 12C. (a) Superposition of two wave trains almost in phase. (b) Superposition of two wave trains almost 180° out of phase.

be pictured by having all the waves in Fig. 12C move toward the right with a given velocity.

The formation of the so-called "standing waves" in a vibrating cord, giving rise to nodes and loops, is an example of the superposition of two wave trains of the same frequency and amplitude but traveling in *opposite* directions. A wave in a cord is reflected from the end, and the direct and reflected waves must be added to obtain the resultant motion of the cord. Two such waves may be represented by the equations

$$y_1 = a \sin (\omega t - kx)$$
$$y_2 = a \sin (\omega t + kx)$$

By addition one obtains, in the same manner as for Eq. 12l,

$$y = 2a \cos (-kx) \sin \omega t$$

which represents the standing waves. For any value of x we have a simple harmonic motion, whose amplitude varies with x between the limits $2a$, when $kx = 0, \pi, 2\pi, 3\pi, \ldots$, and zero, when $kx = \pi/2, 3\pi/2, 5\pi/2, \ldots$. The latter positions correspond to the nodes and are separated by a distance $\Delta x = \pi/k = \lambda/2$. Figure 12C may also serve to illustrate this case if one pictures the two lightly drawn waves as moving in opposite directions. The resultant curve, instead of moving unchanged toward the right, now oscillates between a straight-line position, when $\omega t = \pi/2,\ 3\pi/2,\ 5\pi/2,\ \ldots$, and a sine curve of amplitude $2a$, when $\omega t = 0,\ \pi,\ 2\pi,\ \ldots$. At the nodes, such as N and N' in the figure, the resultant displacement is zero at all times.

The standing waves produced by reflecting light at normal incidence from a polished mirror may be observed by means of an experiment due to Wiener,[*] which is illustrated in Fig. 12D. A specially prepared photo-graphic film only one-thirtieth of a wavelength thick is placed in an inclined position in front of the re-flecting surface so that it will cross the nodes and loops successively, as at $A,\ a,\ B,\ b,\ C,\ c,\ D,\ d,\ \ldots$. The light will affect the plate only where there is an appreciable amount of vibration, and not at all at the nodes. As expected, the developed plate showed a system

FIG. 12D. Formation and detection of standing waves in Wiener's experiment.

of dark bands, separated by lines of no blackening where it crossed the nodes. Decreasing the angle of inclination of the plate with the reflect-ing surface caused the bands to move farther apart, since a smaller number of nodal planes are cut in a given distance. On measuring these bands, an important fact was established: the standing waves have a node at the reflecting surface. The phase relations of the direct and reflected waves at this point are therefore such that they continu-ously annul each other. This is analogous to the reflection of the waves in a rope from a fixed end. Other experiments of a similar nature were performed by Wiener and these will be discussed more in detail in Sec. 25.12.

12.4. Superposition of Many Waves with Random Phases. Suppose that we now consider a large number of wave trains of the same frequency and amplitude to be traveling in the same direction, and specify that the amount by which each train is ahead or behind any other is a matter of pure chance. From what has been said above, we can conclude that the resultant wave will be another sine wave of the same frequency, and it becomes of interest to inquire as to the amplitude and intensity of this wave. Let the individual amplitudes be a, and let there be n wave trains superimposed. The amplitude of the resultant wave will be the ampli-tude of motion of a particle undergoing n simple harmonic motions at once, each of amplitude a. If these motions were all in the same phase,

[*] O. Wiener, *Ann. Physik*, **40**, 203, 1890.

the resultant amplitude would be na and the intensity n^2a^2, or n^2 times that of one wave. In the case we are considering, however, the phases are distributed purely at random. If one were to use the graphical method of compounding amplitudes (Sec. 12.2), he would now obtain a picture like Fig. 12E. The phases α_1, α_2, . . . take perfectly arbitrary values between 0 and 2π. The intensity due to the superposition of such waves will now be determined by the square of the resultant A. To find A^2, we must square the sum of the projections of all vectors a on the x axis and add the square of the corresponding sum for the y axis. The sum of the x projections is

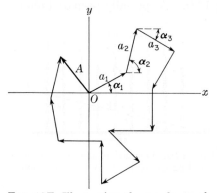

$$a(\cos \alpha_1 + \cos \alpha_2$$
$$+ \cos \alpha_3 + \cdots + \cos \alpha_n)$$

When the quantity in parentheses is squared, we obtain terms of the form $\cos^2 \alpha_1$ and others of the form $2 \cos \alpha_1 \cos \alpha_2$. When n is large, one might expect the latter terms to cancel out, because they take both positive and negative values. In any *one* arrangement of the vectors this is far from true, however, and in

Fig. 12E. Illustrating the resultant of 12 amplitude vectors drawn with phases at random.

fact the sum of these cross-product terms actually increases approximately in proportion to their number. Thus we do not obtain a definite result with one given array of randomly distributed waves. In computing the intensity in any physical problem, we are always presented with a large number of such arrays, and we wish to find their average effect. In this case it is safe to conclude that the cross-product terms will average to zero, and we have only the $\cos^2 \alpha$ terms to consider. Similarly, for the y projections of the vectors one obtains $\sin^2 \alpha$ terms, and the terms like $2 \sin \alpha_1 \sin \alpha_2$ cancel. Therefore we have

$$I \sim A^2 = a^2(\cos^2 \alpha_1 + \cos^2 \alpha_2 + \cos^2 \alpha_3 + \cdots + \cos^2 \alpha_n)$$
$$+ a^2(\sin^2 \alpha_1 + \sin^2 \alpha_2 + \sin^2 \alpha_3 + \cdots + \sin^2 \alpha_n)$$

Now since $\sin^2 \alpha_k + \cos^2 \alpha_k = 1$, we find at once that

$$I \sim a^2 \times n$$

Thus the average intensity resulting from the superposition of n waves with random phases is just n times that due to a single wave. This means that the amplitude A in Fig. 12E, instead of averaging to zero when a large number of vectors a are repeatedly added in random directions, must actually increase in length as n increases, being proportional to $\sqrt{n}$.

The above considerations may be used to explain why, when a large number of violins in an orchestra are playing the same note, interference between the sound waves need not be considered. Owing to the random condition of phases, 100 violins would give about 100 times the intensity due to one alone. The atoms in a sodium flame are emitting light without any systematic relation of phases, and furthermore each is shifting its phase many million times per second. Thus we may safely conclude that the observed intensity is exactly that due to one atom multiplied by the number of atoms.

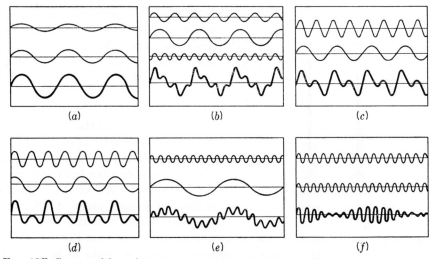

FIG. 12F. Superposition of two or more waves traveling in the same direction with different relative frequencies, amplitudes, and phases.

12.5. Complex Waves. The waves we have considered so far have been of the simple type in which the displacements at any instant are represented by a sine curve. As we have seen, superposition of any number of such waves having the same frequency, but arbitrary amplitudes and phases, still gives rise to a resultant wave of the same type. However, if only two waves having appreciably different frequencies are superimposed, the resulting wave is complex; i.e., the motion of one particle is no longer simple harmonic, and the wave contour is not a sine curve. The analytical treatment of such waves will be referred to in the following section, and here we shall consider only some of their more qualitative aspects.

It is instructive to examine the results of adding graphically two or more waves traveling along the same line and having various relative frequencies, amplitudes, and phases. The wavelengths are determined by the frequencies according to the relation $\nu\lambda = v$, so that greater frequency means shorter wavelength, and vice versa. Figure 12F illustrates the addition for a number of cases, the resultant curves in each case being obtained, according to the principle of superposition, by merely adding algebraically the displacements due to the individual waves at every point. Figure 12F(a) illustrates the case, mentioned in Sec. 12.3, of the addition of two waves of the same frequency but different amplitudes. The resultant amplitude depends on the phase difference, which in the figure is taken as zero. Other phase differences would be represented by shifting one of the component waves laterally with respect to the other

and will give a smaller amplitude for the resultant sine wave, its smallest value being the difference in the amplitudes of the components. In (b) three waves of different frequencies, amplitudes, and phases are added, giving a complex wave as the resultant, which is evidently very different from a sine curve. In (c) and (d), where two waves of the same amplitude but frequencies in the ratio 2:1 are added, it is seen that changing the phase difference may produce a resultant of very different form. If these represent sound waves, the eardrum would actually vibrate in

Fig. 12G. Mechanical and optical arrangement for illustrating the superposition of two waves.

a manner represented by the resultant in each case, yet the ear mechanism would respond to two frequencies and these would be heard and interpreted as the two original frequencies regardless of their phase difference. If the resultant wave forms represent visible light, the eye would similarly receive the sensation of a mixture of two colors, which would be the same regardless of the phase difference. Finally (e) shows the effect of adding a wave of very high frequency to one of very low frequency, and (f) the effect of adding two of nearly the same frequency. In the latter case, the resultant wave divides up into groups, which in sound produce the well-known phenomenon of beats. In any of the above cases, if the component waves all travel with the same velocity, the resultant wave form will evidently move with this velocity, keeping its contour unchanged.

Experimental illustrations of the superposition of waves are easily accomplished with the apparatus shown in Fig. 12G. Two small mirrors, M_1 and M_2, are cemented to thin strips of spring steel which are clamped vertically and illuminated by a narrow beam of light. Such a beam is conveniently produced by the concentrated-arc lamp described in Sec. 21.2. An image of this source S is focused on the screen by the lens L.

The beam is reflected in succession from the two mirrors, and if one of them is set vibrating, the reflected beam will vibrate up and down with simple harmonic motion. If now this beam on its way to the screen is reflected from a rotating mirror, the spot of light will trace out a sine wave form which will appear continuous by virtue of the persistence of vision. When both M_1 and M_2 are set vibrating at once, the resultant wave form is the superposition of that produced by each separately. In this way all the curves of Fig. 12F may be produced by using two or more strips of suitable frequencies. The frequencies may be easily altered by changing the free length of the strips above the clamps.

Since for visible light the frequency determines the color, complex waves of light are produced when beams of light of different colors are used. The "impure" colors which are not found in the spectrum will therefore have waves of a complex form. White light, which, since Newton's original experiments with prisms, we usually speak of as composed of a mixture of all colors, is the extreme example of the superposition of a great number of waves having frequencies differing by only infinitesimal amounts. We shall discuss the resultant wave form for white light in the following section. It was mentioned in the preceding chapter that even the most monochromatic light we can produce in the laboratory still has a finite spread of frequencies. The question of the actual wave forms in such cases, and of how they may be described mathematically, should therefore be considered.

12.6. Fourier Analysis. Since we may build up a wave of very complex form by the superposition of a number of simple waves, it is of interest to ask to what extent the converse process may be accomplished—that of decomposing a complex wave into a number of simple ones. According to a theorem due to Fourier, any *periodic* function may be represented as the sum of a number (possibly infinite) of sine and cosine functions. By a periodic function we mean one that repeats itself exactly in successive equal intervals, such as the lower curve in Fig. 12F(b). The wave is given by an equation of the type

$$y = a_0 + a_1 \sin \omega t + a_2 \sin 2\omega t + a_3 \sin 3\omega t + \cdots$$
$$+ a_1' \cos \omega t + a_2' \cos 2\omega t + a_3' \cos 3\omega t + \cdots \quad (12m)$$

This is known as a *Fourier series* and contains, besides the constant term a_0, a series of terms having amplitudes a_1, a_2, . . . , a_1', a_2', . . . and angular frequencies ω, 2ω, 3ω, ... Therefore the resultant wave is regarded as built up of a number of waves whose wavelengths are as $1 : \frac{1}{2} : \frac{1}{3} : \frac{1}{4} : \cdots$. In the case of sound, these represent the fundamental note and its various harmonics. The evaluation of the amplitude coefficients a_i for a given wave form can be carried out by a straightforward mathematical process for some fairly simple wave forms but in general is a difficult matter. Usually one must have recourse to one of the various forms of "harmonic analyzer," a mechanical device for determining the amplitudes and phases of the fundamental and its harmonics.*

Fourier analysis is not often of direct use in studying light waves, because it is impossible to observe directly the form of a light wave. For sound this can be done, and it is in the investigation of the quality of sounds that the Fourier analysis of waves has been most used. However, it is important for us to understand the principles of the method, because, as we shall see, a grating or a prism essentially performs a

FIG. 12H. Distribution of amplitudes in different frequencies for various types of wave disturbance of finite length.

Fourier analysis of the incident light, revealing the various component frequencies which it contains and which appear as *spectral lines*.

Fourier analysis is not limited to waves of a periodic character. The upper part of Fig. 12H shows three types of waves which are not periodic, because, instead of repeating their contour indefinitely, the waves have zero displacement beyond a certain finite range. These "wave packets" (Sec. 11.7) cannot be represented by Fourier series, but instead *Fourier integrals* must be used, in which the component waves differ only by infinitesimal increments of wavelength. By suitably distributing the amplitudes for the various components, any arbitrary wave form may be expressed by such an integral.† The three lower curves in Fig. 12H represent qualitatively the frequency distribution of the amplitudes which will produce the corresponding wave groups shown above. That is, the upper

---

* For a detailed account of harmonic analyzers, see D. C. Miller, "The Science of Musical Sounds," The Macmillan Company, New York, 1922. A good discussion of Fourier analysis may be found in E. H. Barton, "Textbook of Sound," 1st ed., pp. 83ff., The Macmillan Company, New York, 1908.

† For a brief discussion of these integrals, and for further references, see J. A. Stratton, "Electromagnetic Theory," pp. 285–292, McGraw-Hill Book Company, Inc. New York, 1941.

curves represent the actual wave contour of the group, and this contour may be synthesized by adding up a very large (strictly, an infinite) number of wave trains, each of frequency differing only infinitesimally from the next. The curves shown immediately below each group show the necessary amplitudes of the components of each frequency, in order that their superposition may produce the wave form indicated above. They represent the so-called *Fourier transforms* of the corresponding wave functions.

Curve (*a*) shows the typical wave packet discussed before, and has the Fourier transform (*b*) corresponding to a single spectral line of finite width. The group shown in (*c*) would be produced by passing perfectly monochromatic light through a shutter which is opened for an extremely short time. It is worth remarking here that the corresponding amplitude distribution, shown in curve (*d*), is exactly that obtained for the Fraunhofer diffraction by a single slit, as will be described in Sec. 15.3. Another interesting case, shown in curve (*e*), is that of a single *pulse*, such as the sound pulse sent out by a pistol shot or (better) by the discharge of a spark. The form of such a pulse may resemble that shown, and when a Fourier analysis is made, it yields the broad distribution of wavelengths shown in curve (*f*). For light, such a distribution is called a *continuous spectrum* and is obtained with sources of white light such as an incandescent solid. The distribution of intensity in different wavelengths, which is proportional to the square of the ordinates in the curve, is determined by the exact shape of the pulse. This view of the nature of white light is one which has been emphasized by Gouy and others,* and raises the question as to whether Newton's experiments on refraction by prisms, which are usually said to prove the composite nature of white light, were of much significance in this respect. Since white light may be regarded as consisting merely of a succession of random pulses, of which the prism performs a Fourier analysis, the view that the colors are manufactured by the prism, which was held by Newton's predecessors, may be regarded as equally correct.

12.7. Group Velocity. It will be readily seen that, if all the component simple waves making up a group travel with the same velocity, the group will move with this velocity and maintain its form unchanged. If, however, the velocities vary with wavelength, this is no longer true, and the group will change its form as it progresses. This situation exists for water waves, and if one watches the individual waves in the group sent out by dropping a stone in still water, they will be found to be moving faster than the group as a whole, dying out at the front of the group

---

* The reader will find the more detailed discussion of the various representations of white light given in R. W. Wood, "Physical Optics" 1st or 2d ed., The Macmillan Company, New York, of interest in this connection.

and reappearing at the back. Hence in this case the group velocity is less than the wave velocity, a relation which always holds when the velocity of longer waves is greater than that of shorter ones. It is important to establish a relation between the group velocity and wave velocity, and this can easily be done by considering the groups formed by superimposing two waves of slightly different wavelength, such as those already discussed and illustrated in Fig. 12F(f). We shall suppose that the two waves have equal amplitudes, but that they have slightly different wavelengths, λ and λ', and slightly different velocities, v and v'.

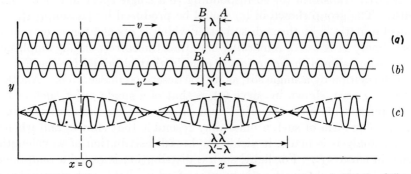

FIG. 12I. Illustrating groups and group velocity of two waves of slightly different wavelength and frequency.

The primed quantities in each case will be taken as the larger. Then the propagation numbers and angular frequencies will also differ, such that $k > k'$ and $\omega > \omega'$. The resultant wave will be given by the sum

$$y = a \sin (\omega t - kx) + a \sin (\omega' t - k'x)$$

Again applying the trigonometric relation of Eq. 12k, this equation becomes

$$y = 2a \sin \left(\frac{\omega + \omega'}{2} t - \frac{k + k'}{2} x \right) \cos \left(\frac{\omega - \omega'}{2} t - \frac{k - k'}{2} x \right) \quad (12n)$$

In Figs. 12I(a) and (b) the two waves are plotted separately, while (c) gives their sum, represented by this equation with $t = 0$. The resultant waves have the average wavelength of the two, but the amplitude is modulated to form groups. The individual waves, having the average of the two k's, correspond to variations of the sine factor in Eq. 12n, and according to Eq. 11g their phase velocity is the quotient of the multipliers of t and x.

$$v = \frac{\omega + \omega'}{k + k'} \simeq \frac{\omega}{k}$$

That is, the velocity is essentially that of either of the component waves, since these velocities are very nearly the same.   The envelope of modulation, indicated by the broken curves shown in Fig. 12I, is given by the cosine factor.   This has a much smaller propagation number, equal to the difference of the separate ones, and a correspondingly greater wavelength. The velocity of the groups is

$$u = \frac{\omega - \omega'}{k - k'} \simeq \frac{d\omega}{dk} \qquad (12o)$$

Since no limit has been set on the smallness of the differences, they may be treated as infinitesimals and the approximate equality becomes exact. Then, since $\omega = vk$, we find for the relation between the *group velocity* u and the *wave velocity* v

$$u = v + k \frac{dv}{dk}$$

If the variable is changed to λ, through $k = 2\pi/\lambda$, one obtains the useful form

$$u = v - \lambda \frac{dv}{d\lambda} \qquad (12p)$$

It should be emphasized that λ here represents the actual wavelength *in the medium*.   For light, this will not in most problems be the ordinary wavelength in air (see Sec. 23.7).

Equations 12o and 12p, although derived for an especially simple type of group, are quite general and can be shown to hold for any group whatever, as, for example, the three illustrated in Fig. 12H(a), (c), and (e).

The relation between wave and group velocities may also be derived in a less mathematical way by considering the motions of the two component wave trains in Fig. 12I(a) and (b).   At the instant shown, the crests A and A' of the two trains coincide to produce a maximum for the group.   A little later the faster waves will have gained a distance $\lambda' - \lambda$ on the slower ones, so that B' coincides with B, and the maximum of the group will have moved back a distance λ.   Since the difference in velocity of the two trains is dv, the time required for this is $d\lambda/dv$.   But in this time both wave trains have been moving to the right, the upper one moving a distance $v\,d\lambda/dv$.   The net displacement of the maximum of the group is thus $v(d\lambda/dv) - \lambda$ in the time $d\lambda/dv$, so that we obtain, for the group velocity,

$$u = \frac{v(d\lambda/dv) - \lambda}{d\lambda/dv} = v - \lambda \frac{dv}{d\lambda}$$

in agreement with Eq. 12p.

A picture of the groups formed by two waves of slightly different frequency may easily be produced with the apparatus described in Sec.

12.5.   It is merely necessary to adjust the two vibrating strips until the frequencies differ by only a few vibrations per second.

The group velocity is the important one for light, since it is the only velocity which we can observe experimentally.   We know of no means of following the progress of an individual wave in a group of light waves; instead, we are obliged to measure the rate at which a wave train of finite length conveys the *energy*, a quantity which can be observed.   The wave and group velocities become the same in a medium having no dispersion, i.e., in which $dv/d\lambda = 0$, so that waves of all lengths travel with the same speed.   This is accurately true for light traveling in a vacuum, so that there is no difference between group and wave velocities in this case.

Fig. 12J. Graphical determination of group velocity from a wave velocity curve.

12.8. Graphical Relation between Wave and Group Velocity.   There is a very simple geometrical construction by which we may determine the group velocity from a curve of the wave velocity against wavelength. It is based upon the graphical interpretation of Eq. 12p.   As an example, the curve of Fig. 12J represents the variation of the wave velocity with λ for water waves in deep water (gravity waves) and is drawn according to the theoretical equation $v = \text{const.} \times \sqrt{\lambda}$.   At a certain wavelength λ_1, the waves have a velocity v, and the slope of the curve at the corresponding point P gives $dv/d\lambda$.   The line PR, drawn tangent to the curve at this point, intersects the v axis at the point R, the ordinate of which is the group velocity u for waves of wavelength in the neighborhood of λ_1. This is evident from the fact that PQ equals $\lambda_1\, dv/d\lambda$, that is, the abscissa of P multiplied by the slope of PR.   Hence QS, which is drawn equal to RO, represents the difference $v - \lambda\, dv/d\lambda$, and this is just the value of u, by Eq. 12p.   In the particular example chosen here, it will be left as a problem for the student to prove that $u = \frac{1}{2}v$ for any value of λ. In water waves of this type, the individual waves therefore move with twice the velocity with which the group as a whole progresses.

12.9. Addition of Simple Harmonic Motions at Right Angles.   Consider the effect when two sine waves of the same frequency but having displacements in two perpendicular directions act simultaneously at a point.   Choosing the directions as y and z, we may express the two component motions as follows:

$$y = a_1 \sin\,(\omega t - \alpha_1)$$
$$z = a_2 \sin\,(\omega t - \alpha_2) \tag{12q}$$

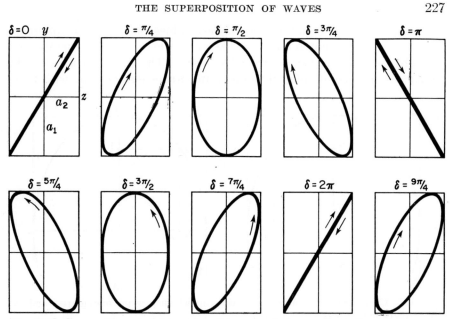

FIG. 12K. Composition at right angles of two simple harmonic motions of the same frequency but different phase.

These are to be added, according to the principle of superposition, to find the path of the resultant motion. One does this by eliminating t from the two equations, obtaining

$$\frac{y}{a_1} = \sin \omega t \cos \alpha_1 - \cos \omega t \sin \alpha_1 \qquad (12r)$$

$$\frac{z}{a_2} = \sin \omega t \cos \alpha_2 - \cos \omega t \sin \alpha_2 \qquad (12s)$$

Multiplying Eq. 12r by $\sin \alpha_2$ and Eq. 12s by $\sin \alpha_1$ and subtracting the first equation from the second, there results

$$-\frac{y}{a_1} \sin \alpha_2 + \frac{z}{a_2} \sin \alpha_1 = \sin \omega t (\cos \alpha_2 \sin \alpha_1 - \cos \alpha_1 \sin \alpha_2) \qquad (12t)$$

Similarly, multiplying Eq. 12r by $\cos \alpha_2$ and Eq. 12s by $\cos \alpha_1$, and subtracting the second from the first, we obtain

$$\frac{y}{a_1} \cos \alpha_2 - \frac{z}{a_2} \cos \alpha_1 = \cos \omega t (\cos \alpha_2 \sin \alpha_1 - \cos \alpha_1 \sin \alpha_2) \qquad (12u)$$

We may now eliminate t from Eqs. 12t and 12u by squaring and adding these equations. This gives

$$\sin^2 (\alpha_1 - \alpha_2) = \frac{y^2}{a_1{}^2} + \frac{z^2}{a_2{}^2} - \frac{2yz}{a_1 a_2} \cos (\alpha_1 - \alpha_2) \qquad (12v)$$

as the equation for the resultant path. In Fig. 12K the heavy curves are graphs of this equation for various values of the phase difference $\delta = \alpha_1 - \alpha_2$. Except for the special cases where they degenerate into straight lines, these curves are all ellipses. The principal axes of the ellipse are in general inclined to the y and z axes but coincide with them

FIG. 12L. Graphical composition of motions in which y is (a) one-quarter and (b) three-quarters of a period ahead of z.

when $\delta = \pi/2, 3\pi/2, 5\pi/2, \ldots$, as can readily be seen from Eq. 12v. In this case

$$\frac{y^2}{a_1{}^2} + \frac{z^2}{a_2{}^2} = 1$$

which is the equation of an ellipse with semiaxes a_1 and a_2, coinciding with the y and z axes, respectively. When $\delta = 0, 2\pi, 4\pi, \ldots$, we have

$$y = \frac{a_1}{a_2} z$$

representing a straight line passing through the origin, with a slope a_1/a_2. If $\delta = \pi, 3\pi, 5\pi, \ldots$,

$$y = -\frac{a_1}{a_2} z$$

a straight line with the same slope, but of opposite sign.

That the two cases $\delta = \pi/2$ and $\delta = 3\pi/2$, although giving the same path, are physically different may be seen by graphical constructions such as those of Fig. 12L. In both parts of the figure the motion in the y direction is in the same phase, the point having executed one-eighth of a vibration beyond its extreme positive displacement. The z motion in part (a) lacks one-eighth of a vibration of reaching this extreme position, while in part (b) it lacks five-eighths. Consideration of the directions of the individual motions, and of that of their resultant, will show that the latter corresponds to the indications of the curved arrows. In the two cases the ellipse is traversed in opposite senses.

Light may be produced for which the form of vibration is an ellipse of any desired eccentricity. The so-called *plane-polarized* light (Chap. 24) approximates a sine wave lying in a plane—say the x,y plane of Fig. 12M —and the displacements are linear displacements in the y direction. If

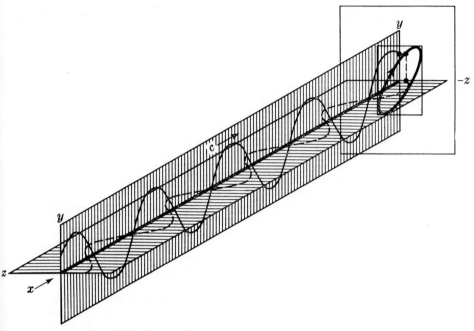

Fig. 12M. Composition of two sine waves at right angles.

one combines a beam of this light with another consisting of plane-polarized waves lying in the x,z plane (dotted curve) and having a constant phase difference with the first, the resultant motion at any value of x will be a certain ellipse in the y,z plane. Such light is said to be *elliptically polarized* and may readily be produced by various means (Chap. 27). A special case occurs when the amplitudes a_1 and a_2 of the two waves are equal and the phase difference is an odd multiple of $\pi/2$. The vibration form is then a circle, and the light is said to be *circularly polarized*. When the direction of rotation is clockwise ($\delta = \pi/2, 5\pi/2, \ldots$) looking opposite to the direction in which the light is traveling, the light is called *right* circularly polarized, while if the rotation is counterclockwise ($\delta = 3\pi/2, 7\pi/2, \ldots$), it is called *left* circularly polarized.

The various types of motion shown in Fig. 12K may be readily demonstrated with the apparatus described in Sec. 12.5. For this purpose, the two strips are arranged to vibrate at right angles to each other, and the rotating mirror eliminated. Then one strip imparts a horizontal vibration to the spot of light, and the other a vertical vibration. When both are actuated simultaneously, the spot will trace out an ellipse. This will remain fixed if the two strips are tuned to exactly the same frequency. If they are only slightly detuned, the figure will progress through the forms corresponding to all possible values of the phase difference, passing in succession a sequence like that shown in Fig. 12K.

PROBLEMS

1. If two simple harmonic motions in the same line are added, these having at a given instant amplitudes of two and nine units and phases $\pi/4$ and π, respectively, find (a) the resultant amplitude, and (b) the phase difference between the resultant and the first of the two motions.

2. Plot the two equations $y_1 = 3 \sin 6\pi t$ and $y_2 = \sin (6\pi t - \pi/3)$, and obtain their resultant, $y = A \sin (6\pi t - \theta)$ by addition of ordinates. Compute an exact value of A, and compare with that measured from the resultant curve. *Ans.* 3.60 cm.

3. Find the equation for the resultant of the three motions $y_1 = \sin (\omega t - 10°)$, $y_2 = 3 \cos (\omega t + 100°)$, and $y_3 = 2 \sin (\omega t - 30°)$. The solution is to be made (a) by vector addition of amplitudes and (b) by computation.

4. Find graphically the resultant amplitude when seven simple harmonic motions are added, each having the same period and amplitude, but each differing in phase from the next by 20°. Take the amplitude as 3 cm. For what value of the phase difference does the resultant first go to zero? *Ans.* 16.23 cm; 51°26′.

5. Two waves having amplitudes of three and five units, and equal frequencies, are traveling in the same direction. If the phase difference is $3\pi/8$, find the resultant intensity relative to that of the separate waves.

6. Calculate the energy of the vibration resulting from the addition of five simple harmonic motions having individual amplitudes a and phases 0°, 45°, 90°, 135°, and 180°. Is the resultant amplitude increased or decreased when the fourth motion (having phase 135°) is removed? *Ans.* $5.83a^2$; decreased.

7. Compound graphically two wave trains having wavelengths in the ratio 4:3 and equal amplitudes.

8. Two sources vibrating according to the equations $y_1 = 3 \sin \pi t$ and $y_2 = \sin \pi t$ send out plane waves which travel with a velocity of 150 cm/sec. Find the equation of motion of a particle 6 m from the first source and 4 m from the second. *Ans.* $y = 2.65 \sin (\pi t + 19.1°)$.

9. Standing waves are produced by the superposition of the two waves $y_1 = 18 \sin (3\pi t - 6x)$ and $y_2 = 18 \sin (3\pi t + 6x)$. Find the amplitude of the motion at $x = 23$.

10. Wiener's experiment is performed with red light ($\lambda = 6000$ Å). The photographic film is inclined at $\frac{1}{2}°$ with the mirror, one end being in contact with it. Find the distances from this end of the first three dark bands produced. *Ans.* 0, 0.034, 0.069 mm.

11. Four vibrations are capable of emitting waves of the same frequency, but of phases differing by only zero or π. Assuming that each possible combination of phases is equally probable (there are 16 of these), show that the average intensity is just four times that of one of the waves. Remember that the intensity due to each combination is given by the square of the resultant amplitude.

12. Suppose that a beam of green light ($\lambda \simeq 5200$ Å) consists of wave trains 6 cm long. What is the approximate spread of wavelengths, or the width of the spectrum line? *Ans.* 0.045 Å.

13. A square wave may be represented by a Fourier series of the form $y = a \sin kx$ $+ (a/3) \sin 3kx + (a/5) \sin 5kx + \cdots$. By plotting the first three terms of the series, and their sum, find how closely the resultant approximates a square wave.

14. As suggested in Sec. 12.8, prove that for water waves controlled by gravity the group velocity equals half the wave velocity.

$$Ans.\ u = v - \lambda(dv/d\lambda) = C\sqrt{\lambda} - \tfrac{1}{2}C\sqrt{\lambda} = \tfrac{1}{2}C\sqrt{\lambda}$$

15. The velocity of rather short waves on the surface of a liquid is given by

$$v = \sqrt{\frac{\lambda}{2\pi}\left(g + \frac{4\pi^2 T}{\lambda^2 d}\right)}$$

where T is the surface tension and d the density. Calculate the wave and group velocities of water waves at $\lambda = 1$ cm, 5 cm, and 25 cm.

16. For the type of waves described in Prob. 15, find the exact value of the wavelength for which the wave and group velocities become equal, and determine this velocity. *Ans.* 1.711 cm; 23.10 cm/sec.

17. The phase velocity of waves in a certain medium is represented by $v = C_1 + C_2\lambda$, where the C's are constants. What is the value of the group velocity?

18. The refractive indices for carbon disulfide at 4900 and 6200 Å are 1.65338 and 1.62425, respectively. Assuming a Cauchy equation for n vs. λ (Sec. 23.3), calculate the wave and group velocities of light in carbon disulfide at the mean wavelength, 5550 Å. Compare with Michelson's experimental results (group velocities, see Sec. 19.10) of 1/1.758 of the velocity in vacuum for white light and 1.4 per cent faster for "orange-red" light than for "greenish-blue."
Ans. 1.83215×10^{10} cm/sec.; 1.70603×10^{10} cm/sec. or $c/1.7572$; 4.83%.

19. Two simple harmonic motions at right angles are represented by $y = 2 \sin 2\pi t$ and $z = 5 \sin (2\pi t - 5\pi/4)$. Find the equation for the resultant path, and plot this path by the method indicated in Fig. 12L. Verify at least two points on this path by substitution in your resultant equation.

20. How must the equation for the z motion in Prob. 19 be changed to yield an ellipse having its major axis coincident with z? To yield a circular motion with clockwise rotation?
Ans. Phase constant changed to $\pi/2$, $-\pi/2$, $3\pi/2$, $-3\pi/2$, etc.; same, but amplitude of z motion changed to 2.

CHAPTER 13

INTERFERENCE OF TWO BEAMS OF LIGHT

It was stated at the beginning of the last chapter that two beams of light may be made to cross each other without either one producing any modification of the other after it passes beyond the region of crossing. In this sense the two beams do not interfere with each other. However, in the region of crossing, where both beams are acting at once, we are led to expect from the considerations of the preceding chapter that the resultant amplitude and intensity may be very different from the sum of those contributed by the two beams acting separately. This modification of intensity obtained by the superposition of two or more beams of light we call *interference*. If the resultant intensity is zero or in general less than we expect from the separate intensities, we have *destructive* interference, while if it is greater, we have *constructive* interference. The phenomenon in its simpler aspects is rather difficult to observe, because of the very short wavelength of light, and therefore was not recognized as such in the time prior to 1800 when the corpuscular theory of light was predominant. The first man successfully to demonstrate the interference of light, and thus establish its wave character, was Thomas Young. In order to understand his crucial experiment performed in 1801, we must first consider the application to light of an important principle which holds for any type of wave motion.

13.1. Huygens' Principle. When waves pass through an aperture, or past the edge of an obstacle, they always spread to some extent into the region which is not directly exposed to the oncoming waves. This phenomenon is called *diffraction*. In order to explain this bending of light, Huygens nearly three centuries ago proposed the rule that *each point on a wave front may be regarded as a new source of waves.** This principle has very far-reaching applications and will be used later in discussing the diffraction of light, but we shall consider here only a very simple proof

---

* The "waves" envisioned by Huygens were not continuous trains but rather a series of random pulses. Furthermore, he supposed the secondary waves to be effective only at the point of tangency to their common envelope, thus denying the possibility of diffraction. The correct application of the principle was first made by Fresnel, more than a century later.

of its correctness.   In Fig. 13A let a set of plane waves approach the barrier AB from the left, and let the barrier contain an opening S of width somewhat smaller than the wavelength.   At all points except S the waves will be either reflected or absorbed, but S will be free to produce a disturbance behind the screen.   It is found experimentally, in agreement with the above principle, that the waves spread out from S in the form of semicircles.

Huygens' principle as shown in Fig. 13A can be illustrated very successfully with water waves.   An arc lamp on the floor, with a glass-bottomed tray or tank above it, will cast shadows of waves on a white ceiling.   A vibrating strip of metal or a wire fastened to one prong of a tuning fork of low frequency will serve as a source of waves at one end of the tray.   If an electrically driven tuning fork is used, the waves may be made apparently to stand still by placing a slotted disk on the shaft of a motor in front of the arc lamp. The disk is set rotating with the same frequency as the tuning fork to give the stroboscopic effect.   The

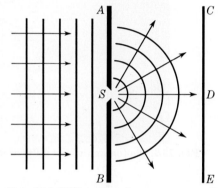

FIG. 13A. Diffraction of waves at a small aperture.

latter experiment can be performed for a fairly large audience and is well worth doing.   Descriptions of diffraction experiments in light will be given in Chap. 15.

If the experiment in Fig. 13A be performed with light, one would naturally expect, from the fact that light generally travels in straight lines, that merely a narrow patch of light would appear at D.   However, if the slit is made very narrow, an appreciable broadening of this patch is observed, its breadth increasing as the slit is further narrowed.   This remarkable evidence that light does not always travel in straight lines was mentioned at the very beginning of this book (Sec. 1.1 and Fig. 1A). When the screen CE is replaced by a photographic plate, a picture like the one shown in Fig. 13B is obtained.   The light is most intense in the forward direction, but its intensity decreases slowly as the angle increases. If the slit is small compared with the wavelength of light, the intensity does not come to zero even when the angle of observation becomes 90°. While this brief introduction to Huygens' principle will be sufficient for an understanding of the interference phenomena we are to discuss, we shall return in Chaps. 15 and 18 to a more detailed consideration of diffraction at a single opening.

13.2. Young's Experiment. The original experiment performed by Young is shown schematically in Fig. 13C. Sunlight was first allowed to pass through a pinhole S and then, at a considerable distance away, through two pinholes S_1 and S_2. The two sets of spherical waves emerging from the two holes interfered with each other in such a way as to form a symmetrical pattern of varying intensity on the screen AC. Since

Fig. 13B. Photograph of the diffraction of light from a slit of width 0.001 mm.

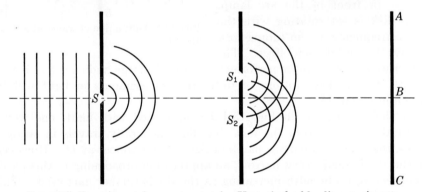

Fig. 13C. Experimental arrangement for Young's double-slit experiment.

this early experiment was performed, it has been found convenient to replace the pinholes by narrow slits and to use a source giving monochromatic light, i.e., light of a single wavelength. In place of spherical wave fronts we now have cylindrical wave fronts, represented equally well in two dimensions by the same Fig. 13C. If the circular lines represent crests of waves, the intersections of any two lines represent the arrival at those points of two waves with the same phase or with phases differing by a multiple of 2π. Such points are therefore those of maximum disturbance or brightness. A close examination of the light on the screen will reveal evenly spaced light and dark bands or fringes, similar to those shown in Fig. 13D. Such photographs are obtained by replacing the screen AC of Fig. 13C by a photographic plate.

A very simple demonstration of Young's experiment can be accomplished in the laboratory or lecture room by setting up a single-filament lamp L (Fig. 13E) at the front of the room. The straight vertical filament S acts as the source and first slit. Double slits for each observer can be easily made from small photographic plates about 1 to 2 in.

FIG. 13D. Interference fringes produced by a double slit using the arrangement shown in Fig. 13C.

FIG. 13E. Simple method for observing interference fringes.

square. The slits are made in the photographic emulsion by drawing the point of a penknife across the plate, guided by a straight edge. The plates need not be developed or blackened but can be used as they are. The lamp is now viewed by holding the double slit D close to the eye E and looking at the lamp filament. If the slits are close together, e.g., 0.2 mm apart, they give widely spaced fringes, whereas slits farther apart, e.g., 1 mm, give very narrow fringes. A piece of red glass F, placed adjacent to and above another of green glass in front of the lamp, will show that the red waves produce wider fringes than the green, which we shall see is due to their greater wavelength.

Frequently one wishes to perform accurate experiments by using more nearly monochromatic light than that obtained by white light and a red or green glass filter. Perhaps the most convenient method is to use the sodium arc now available on the market, or a mercury arc plus a filter to isolate the green line, λ5461. A suitable filter consists of a combination of didymium glass, to absorb the yellow lines, and a light yellow glass, to absorb the blue and violet lines.

13.3. Interference Fringes from a Double Source. We shall now derive an equation for the intensity at any point P on the screen (Fig. 13F) and investigate the spacing of the interference fringes. Two waves arrive at P, having traversed different distances S_2P and S_1P. Hence

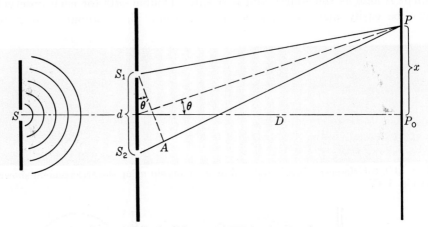

Fig. 13F. Path difference in Young's experiment.

they are superimposed with a phase difference which, according to Eq. 11f, is

$$\delta = k\Delta = \frac{2\pi}{\lambda} (S_2P - S_1P) \tag{13a}$$

It is assumed that the waves start out from S_1 and S_2 in the same phase, because these slits were taken to be equidistant from the source slit S. Furthermore, the amplitudes are practically the same if, as is usually the case, S_1 and S_2 are of equal width and very close together. The problem of finding the resultant intensity at P therefore reduces to that discussed in Sec. 12.1, where we considered the addition of two simple harmonic motions of the same frequency and amplitude, but of phase difference δ. The intensity was given by Eq. 12g as

$$I \sim A^2 = 4a^2 \cos^2 \frac{\delta}{2} \tag{13b}$$

where a is the amplitude of the separate waves and A that of their resultant.

It now remains to evaluate the phase difference in terms of the distance x on the screen from the central point P_0, the separation d of the two slits, and the distance D from the slits to the screen. The corresponding path difference is the distance S_2A in Fig. 13F, where the dashed line S_1A has been drawn to make S_1 and A equidistant from P. As Young's experiment is usually performed, D is some thousand times larger than d or x. Hence the angles θ and θ' are very small and practically equal. Under these conditions, S_1AS_2 may be regarded as a right triangle, and the path difference becomes $d \sin \theta' \simeq d \sin \theta$. To the same approximation, we may set the sine of the angle equal to the tangent, so that $\sin \theta \simeq x/D$. With these assumptions, we obtain

$$\Delta = d \sin \theta = d \frac{x}{D} \tag{13c}$$

This is the value of the path difference to be substituted in Eq. 13a to obtain the phase difference δ. Now Eq. 13b for the intensity has maximum values equal to $4a^2$ whenever δ is an integral multiple of 2π, and according to Eq. 13a this will occur when the path difference is an integral multiple of λ. Hence we have

$$\frac{xd}{D} = 0, \lambda, 2\lambda, 3\lambda, \ldots = m\lambda$$

or
$$x = m\lambda \frac{D}{d} \qquad \text{BRIGHT FRINGES} \tag{13d}$$

The minimum value of the intensity is zero, and this occurs when $\delta = \pi$, 3π, 5π, ... For these points

$$\frac{xd}{D} = \frac{\lambda}{2}, \frac{3\lambda}{2}, \frac{5\lambda}{2}, \cdots = \left(m + \frac{1}{2}\right)\lambda$$

or
$$x = \left(m + \frac{1}{2}\right)\lambda \frac{D}{d} \qquad \text{DARK FRINGES} \tag{13e}$$

The whole number m, which characterizes a particular bright fringe, is called the *order* of interference. Thus the fringes with $m = 0, 1, 2, \ldots$ are called the *zero, first, second*, etc., *orders.*

According to these equations the distance on the screen between two successive fringes, which is obtained by changing m by unity in either Eq. 13d or Eq. 13e, is constant and equal to $\lambda D/d$. Not only is this equality of spacing verified by measurement of an interference pattern such as Fig. 13D, but one also finds by experiment that its magnitude *is directly proportional to the slit-screen distance D, inversely proportional to the separation of the slits d, and directly proportional to the wavelength λ.* Knowledge of the spacing of these fringes thus gives us a direct determination of λ in terms of known quantities.

These maxima and minima of intensity exist throughout the space behind the slits. A lens is not required to produce them, although they are usually so fine that a magnifier or eyepiece must be used to see them visually. Because of the approximations made in deriving Eq. 13c, careful measurements would show that, particularly in the region near the slits, the fringe spacing departs from the simple linear dependence required by Eq. 13d. A section of the fringe system in the plane of the paper of Fig. 13C, instead of consisting of a system of straight lines radiating from the mid-point between the slits, is actually a set of hyperbolas. The hyperbola, being the curve for which the difference in the distance from two fixed points is constant, obviously fits the condition for a given fringe, namely, the constancy of the path difference.

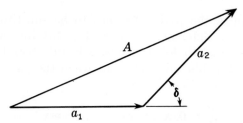

Fig. 13G. Illustrating the composition of two waves of the same frequency and amplitude but different phase.

Although this deviation from linearity may become important with sound and other waves, it is usually negligible when the wavelengths are as short as those of light.

13.4. Intensity Distribution in the Fringe System. To find the intensity on the screen at points between the maxima, we may apply the vector method of compounding amplitudes described in Sec. 12.2 and illustrated for the present case in Fig. 13G. For the maxima, the angle δ is zero, and the component amplitudes a_1 and a_2 are parallel, so that if they are equal, the resultant $A = 2a$. For the minima, a_1 and a_2 are in opposite directions, and $A = 0$. In general, for any value of δ, A is the closing side of the triangle. The value of A^2, which measures the intensity, is then given by Eq. 13b and varies according to $\cos^2(\delta/2)$. In Fig. 13H the solid curve represents a plot of the intensity against the phase difference.

In concluding our discussion of these fringes, one question of fundamental importance should be considered. If the two beams of light arrive at a point on the screen exactly out of phase, they interfere destructively and the resultant intensity is zero. One may well ask what becomes of the *energy* of the two beams, since the law of conservation of energy tells us that energy cannot be destroyed. The answer to this question is that the energy which apparently disappears at the minima actually is still present at the maxima, where the intensity is greater than would be produced by the two beams acting separately. In other words, the energy is not destroyed but merely redistributed in the interference pattern. The *average* intensity on the screen is exactly that which would exist in the absence of interference. Thus, as shown in Fig. 13H, the, intensity in the interference pattern varies between $4a^2$ and zero. Now each beam acting separately would contribute a^2, and so without interference we would have a uniform intensity of $2a^2$, as indicated by the broken line. To obtain the average intensity on the screen for n fringes, we note that the average value of the square of the cosine is $\frac{1}{2}$. This gives, by Eq. 13b, $I \sim 2a^2$, justifying the statement made above, and

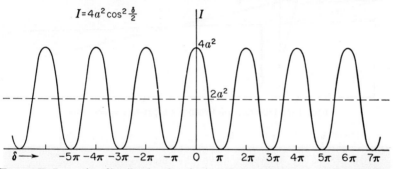

Fig. 13H. Intensity distribution for the interference fringes from two beams.

it shows that no violation of the law of conservation of energy is involved in the interference phenomenon.

13.5. Fresnel's Biprism.* Soon after the double-slit experiment was performed by Young, the objection was raised that the bright fringes he observed were probably due to some complicated modification of the light by the edges of the slits and not to true interference. Thus the wave theory of light was still questioned. Not many years passed, however, before Fresnel brought forward several new experiments in which the interference of two beams of light was proved in a manner not open to the above objection. One of these, the so-called Fresnel biprism experiment, will be described in some detail.

A schematic diagram of the biprism experiment is shown in Fig. 13I. The thin double prism P refracts the light from the slit source S into two overlapping beams ac and be. If screens M and N are placed as shown in the figure, interference fringes are observed only in the region bc. When the screen ae is replaced by a photographic plate, a picture

---

* Augustin Fresnel (1788–1827). Most notable French contributor to the theory of light. Trained as an engineer, he became interested in light, and in 1814–1815 he rediscovered Young's principle of interference and extended it to complicated cases of diffraction. His mathematical investigations gave the wave theory a sound foundation.

like the upper one in Fig. 13*J* is obtained. The closely spaced fringes in the center of the photograph are due to interference, while the wide fringes at the edge of the pattern are due to diffraction. These wider bands are produced by the vertices of the two prisms, each of which acts

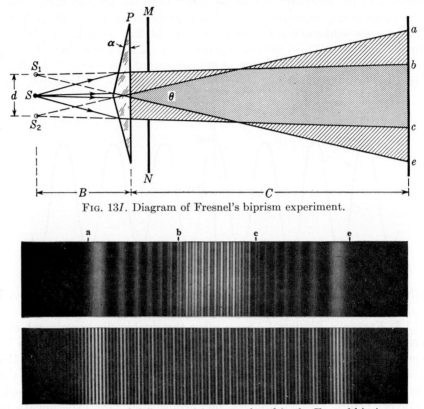

FIG. 13*I*. Diagram of Fresnel's biprism experiment.

FIG. 13*J*. Interference and diffraction fringes produced in the Fresnel biprism experiment.

as a straight edge, giving a pattern which will be discussed in detail in Chap. 18. When the screens *M* and *N* are removed from the light path, the two beams will overlap over the whole region *ae*. The lower photograph in Fig. 13*J* shows for this case the equally spaced interference fringes superimposed on the diffraction pattern of a wide aperture. (For the diffraction pattern above, without the interference fringes, see lowest figures in Fig. 18*U*). With such an experiment Fresnel was able to produce interference without relying upon diffraction to bring the interfering beams together.

Just as in Young's double-slit experiment, the wavelength of light can be determined from measurements of the interference fringes produced by the biprism.   Calling B and C the distances of the source and screen, respectively, from the prism P, d the distance between the virtual images S_1 and S_2, and Δx the distance between the successive fringes on the screen, the wavelength of the light is given from Eq. 13d as

$$\lambda = \frac{\Delta x d}{B + C} \tag{13f}$$

Thus the virtual images S_1 and S_2 act as did the two slit sources in Young's experiment.

In order to find d, the linear separation of the virtual sources, one may measure their angular separation θ on a spectrometer and assume, to sufficient accuracy, that $d = B\theta$.   If the parallel light from the collimator covers both halves of the biprism, two images of the slit are produced and the angle θ between these is easily measured with the telescope.   An even simpler measurement of this angle may be made by holding the prism close to one eye and viewing a round frosted light bulb.   At a certain distance from the light the two images may be brought to the point where their inner edges just touch.   The diameter of the bulb divided by the distance from the bulb to the prism then gives θ directly.

Fresnel biprisms are easily made from a small piece of glass, such as half a microscope slide, by beveling about $\frac{1}{8}$ to $\frac{1}{4}$ in. on one side.   This requires very little grinding with ordinary abrasive materials, and polishing with rouge, since the angle required is only about 1°.

13.6. Other Apparatus Depending on Division of the Wave Front. Two beams may be brought together in other ways to produce interference.   In the arrangement known as *Fresnel's mirrors*, light from a slit is reflected in two plane mirrors slightly inclined to each other.   The mirrors produce two virtual images of the slit, as shown in Fig. 13K. They act in every respect like the images formed by the biprism, and interference fringes are observed in the region bc, where the reflected beams overlap.   The symbols in this diagram correspond to those in Fig. 13I, and Eq. 13f is again applicable.   It will be noted that the angle 2θ subtended at the point of intersection M by the two sources is twice the angle between the mirrors.

The Fresnel double-mirror experiment is usually performed on an optical bench, with the light reflected from the mirrors at nearly grazing angles.   Two pieces of ordinary plate glass about 2 in. square make a very good double mirror.   One plate should have an adjusting screw for changing the angle θ, and the other a screw for making the edges of the two mirrors parallel.

An even simpler device, shown in Fig. 13L, produces interference between the light reflected in one long mirror and the light coming directly from the source without reflection.   In this arrangement, known as

Lloyd's mirror, the quantitative relations are similar to those in the foregoing cases, with the slit and its virtual image constituting the double
source.   An important feature of the Lloyd's-mirror experiment lies
in the fact that when the screen is placed in contact with the end of the

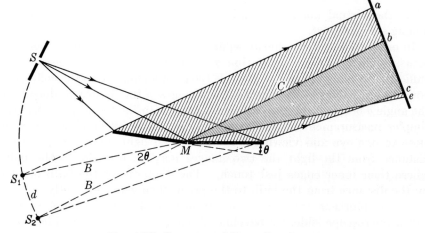

FIG. 13K. Geometry of Fresnel's mirrors.

FIG. 13L. Lloyd's mirror.

mirror (in the position MN, Fig. 13L), the edge O of the reflecting surface
comes at the center of a *dark* fringe, instead of a bright one as might be
expected.   This means that one of the two beams has undergone a phase
change of π.   Since the direct beam could not change phase, this experimental observation is interpreted to mean that the reflected light has
changed phase at reflection.   Two photographs of the Lloyd's mirror

fringes taken in this way are reproduced in Fig. 13M, one taken with visible light and the other with X rays.

If the light from source S_1 in Fig. 13L is allowed to enter the end of the glass plate by moving the latter up, and to be internally reflected from the upper glass surface, fringes will again be observed in the interval OP, with a dark fringe at O. This shows that there is again a phase change of π at reflection. As will be shown in Chap. 25, this is not in contradiction with the discussion of phase change given in Sec. 11.8. In this instance the light is incident at an angle greater than the critical angle for total reflection.

(a)   (b)

FIG. 13M. Interference fringes produced with Lloyd's mirror.   (a) Taken with visible light, $\lambda = 4358$ Å.   (*After White.*)   (b) Taken with X rays, $\lambda = 8.33$ Å.   (*After Kellstrom.*)

Lloyd's mirror is readily set up for demonstration purposes as follows: A carbon arc, followed by a colored glass filter and a narrow slit, serves as a source. A strip of ordinary plate glass 1 to 2 in. wide and a foot or more long makes an excellent mirror. A magnifying glass focused on the far end of the mirror enables one to observe the fringes shown in Fig. 13M. Internal fringes can be observed by polishing the ends of the mirror to allow the light to enter and leave the glass, and by roughening one of the glass faces with coarse emery.

Other ways exist* for dividing the wave front into two segments and subsequently recombining these at a small angle with each other. For example, one may cut a lens into two halves on a plane through the lens axis and separate the parts slightly, to form two closely adjacent real images of a slit. The images produced in this device, known as *Billet's split lens*, act like the two slits in Young's experiment. A single lens followed by a biplate (two plane-parallel plates at a slight angle) will accomplish the same result.

13.7. Coherent Sources.   It will be noticed that the various methods of demonstrating interference so far discussed have one important feature

* Good descriptions will be found in T. Preston, "Theory of Light, 5th ed., chap. 7, The Macmillan Company, New York, 1928.

in common: The two interfering beams are always derived from the same source of light. We find by experiment that it is impossible to obtain interference fringes from two separate sources, such as two lamp filaments set side by side. This failure is caused by the fact that the light from any one source is not an infinite train of waves. On the contrary, there are sudden changes in phase occurring in very short intervals of time (of the order of 10^{-8} sec). This point has already been mentioned in Secs. 11.7 and 12.6. Thus, although interference fringes may exist on the screen for such a short interval, they will shift their position each time there is a phase change, with the result that no fringes at all will be seen. In Young's experiment and in Fresnel's mirrors and biprism, the two sources S_1 and S_2 always have a point-to-point correspondence of phase, since they are both derived from the same source. If the phase of the light from a point in S_1 suddenly shifts, that of the light from the corresponding point in S_2 will shift simultaneously. The result is that the *difference* in phase between any pair of points in the two sources always remain constant, and so the interference fringes are stationary. It is a characteristic of any interference experiment with light that the sources must have this point-to-point phase relation, and sources that have this relation are called *coherent sources*.

While special arrangements are necessary for producing coherent sources of light, the same is not true of *microwaves*, which are radio waves of a few centimeters wavelength. These are produced by an oscillator which emits a continuous wave, the phase of which remains constant over a time long compared with the duration of an observation. Two independent microwave sources of the same frequency are therefore coherent and may be used to demonstrate interference. Because of the convenient magnitude of their wavelength, microwaves may be used for illustrating many common optical interference and diffraction effects.*

If in Young's experiment the source slit S (Fig. 13C) is made too wide, or the angle between the rays which leave it too large, the double slit no longer represents two coherent sources and the interference fringes disappear. This subject will be discussed in more detail at the end of Chap. 16, The Double Slit.

13.8. Division of Amplitude. Michelson† Interferometer. Interference apparatus may be conveniently divided into two main classes,

---

* The technique of such experiments is discussed by G. F. Hull, Jr., *Am. J. Phys.*, **17**, 599, 1949.

† A. A. Michelson (1852–1931). American physicist of great genius. He early became interested in the velocity of light, and began experiments while an instructor in physics and chemistry at the Naval Academy, from which he graduated in 1873. It is related that the superintendent of the Academy asked young Michelson why he wasted his time on such useless experiments. Years later Michelson was awarded

those based on *division of wave front* and those based on *division of ampli-tude*. The previous examples all belong to the former class, in which the wave front is divided laterally into segments by mirrors or dia-phragms. It is also possible to divide a wave by partial reflection, the two resulting wave fronts maintaining the original width but having reduced amplitudes. The Michelson interferometer is an important example of this second class. Here the two beams obtained by amplitude division are sent in quite different directions against plane mirrors, whence they are brought together again to form interference fringes.

The arrangement is shown sche-matically in Fig. 13*N*. The main optical parts consist of two highly polished plane mirrors M_1 and M_2 and two plane-parallel plates of glass G_1 and G_2. Sometimes the rear side of the plate G_1 is lightly silvered (shown by the heavy line in the figure) so that the light coming from the source S is di-vided into (1) a reflected and (2) a transmitted beam of equal in-tensity. The light reflected nor-mally from mirror M_1 passes through G_1 a third time and reaches the eye as shown. The light reflected from the mirror M_2

FIG. 13*N*. Diagram of the Michelson interferometer.

passes back through G_2 for the second time, is reflected from the surface of G_1 and into the eye. The purpose of the plate G_2, called the compen-sating plate, is to render the path *in glass* of the two rays equal. This is not essential for producing fringes in monochromatic light, but it is indispensable when white light is used (Sec. 13.11). The mirror M_1 is mounted on a carriage C and can be moved along the well-machined waves or tracks T. This slow and accurately controlled motion is accom-plished by means of the screw V which is calibrated to show the exact distance the mirror has been moved. To obtain fringes, the mirrors M_1 and M_2 are made exactly perpendicular to each other by means of screws shown on mirror M_2.

Even when the above adjustments have been made, fringes will not

the Nobel prize (1907) for his work on light. Much of his work on the velocity of light (Sec. 19.5) was done during 10 years spent at the Case Institute of Technology. During the latter part of his life he was professor of physics at the University of Chicago, where many of his famous experiments on the interference of light were done.

be seen unless two important requirements are fulfilled. First, the light must originate from an *extended* source. A point source or a slit source, as used in the methods previously described, will not produce the desired system of fringes in this case. The reason for this will appear when we consider the origin of the fringes. Second, the light must in general be *monochromatic*, or nearly so. Especially is this true if the distances of M_1 and M_2 from G_1 are appreciably different.

An extended source suitable for use with a Michelson interferometer may be obtained in any one of several ways. A sodium flame or a mercury arc, if large enough, may be used without the screen L shown in Fig. 13N. If the source is small, a ground glass screen or a lens at L will extend the field of view. Looking at the mirror M_1 through the plate G_1, one then sees the whole mirror filled with light. In order to obtain the fringes, the next step is to measure the distances of M_1 and M_2 to the back surface of G_1 roughly with a millimeter scale, and to move M_1 until they are the same to within a few millimeters. The mirror M_2 is now adjusted to be perpendicular to M_1 by observing the images of a common pin, or any sharp point, placed between the source and G_1. Two pairs of images will be seen, one coming from reflection at the front surface of G_1 and the other from reflection at its back surface. When the tilting screws on M_2 are now turned until one pair of images falls exactly on the other, the interference fringes should appear. When they first appear, the fringes will not be clear unless the eye is focused on or near the back mirror M_1, so the observer should look constantly at this mirror while searching for the fringes. When they have been found, the adjusting screws should be turned in such a way as to continually increase the width of the fringes, and finally a set of concentric circular fringes will be obtained. M_2 is then exactly perpendicular to M_1, if the latter is at an angle of 45° with G_1.

13.9. Circular Fringes. These are produced with monochromatic light when the mirrors are in exact adjustment and are the ones used in most kinds of measurement with the interferometer. Their origin may be understood by reference to the diagram of Fig. 13O. Here the real mirror M_2 has been replaced by its virtual image M_2' formed by reflection in G_1. M_2' is then parallel to M_1. Owing to the several reflections in the real interferometer, we may now think of the extended source as being at L, behind the observer, and as forming two virtual images L_1 and L_2 in M_1 and M_2'. These virtual sources are coherent in that the phases of corresponding points in the two are exactly the same at all instants. If d is the separation M_1M_2', the virtual sources will be separated by $2d$. When d is exactly an integral number of half wavelengths, i.e., the path difference $2d$ equal to an integral number of whole wavelengths, all rays of light reflected normal to the mirrors will be in phase.

Rays of light reflected at an angle, however, will in general not be in phase. The path difference between the two rays coming to the eye from corresponding points P' and P'' is $2d \cos \theta$, as shown in the figure. The angle θ is necessarily the same for the two rays when M_1 is parallel to M_2' so that the rays are parallel. Hence when the eye is focused to receive parallel rays (a small telescope is more satisfactory here, especially

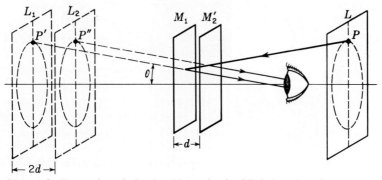

FIG. 130. Formation of circular fringes in the Michelson interferometer.

for large values of d) the rays will reinforce each other to produce maxima for those angles θ satisfying the relation

$$2d \cos \theta = m\lambda \tag{13g}$$

Since for a given m, λ, and d the angle θ is constant, the maxima will lie in the form of circles about the foot of the perpendicular from the eye to the mirrors. By expanding the cosine, it can be shown from Eq. 13g that the radii of the rings are proportional to the square roots of integers, as in the case of Newton's rings (Sec. 14.5). The intensity distribution across the rings follows Eq. 13b, in which the phase difference is given by

$$\delta = \frac{2\pi}{\lambda} 2d \cos \theta$$

Fringes of this kind, where parallel beams are brought to interference with a phase difference determined by the angle of inclination θ, are often referred to as *fringes of equal inclination*. In contrast to the type to be described in the next section, this type may remain visible over very large path differences. The eventual limitation on the path difference will be discussed in Sec. 13.12.

The upper part of Fig. 13P shows how the circular fringes look under different conditions. Starting with M_1 a few centimeters beyond M_2', the fringe system will have the general appearance shown in (a) with the rings very closely spaced. If M_1 is now moved slowly toward M_2' so that d is decreased, Eq. 13g shows that a given ring, characterized by a given value of the order m, must decrease its radius because the product $2d \cos \theta$ must remain constant. The rings therefore shrink and vanish at the center, a ring disappearing each time $2d$ decreases by λ, or d by $\lambda/2$.

(a)	(b)	(c)	(d)	(e)

(f)	(g)	(h)	(i)	(j)

Fig. 13P. Appearance of the various types of fringes observed in the Michelson interferometer. *Upper row*, circular fringes. *Lower row*, localized fringes. Path difference increases outward, in both directions, from the center.

This follows from the fact that at the center $\cos \theta = 1$, so that Eq. 13g becomes

$$2d = m\lambda \qquad (13h)$$

To change m by unity, d must change by $\lambda/2$. Now as M_1 approaches M_2' the rings become more widely spaced, as indicated in Fig. 13$P(b)$, until finally we reach a critical position where the central fringe has spread out to cover the whole field of view, as shown in (c). This happens when M_1 and M_2' are exactly coincident, for it is clear that under these conditions the path difference is zero for all angles of incidence. If the mirror is moved still farther, it effectively passes through M_2', and new widely spaced fringes appear, growing out from the center. These will gradually become more closely spaced as the path difference increases, as indicated in (d) and (e) of the figure.

13.10. Localized Fringes. If the mirrors M_2' and M_1 are not exactly parallel, fringes will still be seen with monochromatic light for path differences not exceeding a few millimeters. In this case the space between the mirrors is wedge-shaped, as indicated in Fig. 13Q. The two rays* reaching the eye from a point P on the source are now no longer parallel, but appear to diverge from a point P' near the mirrors. For various positions of P on the extended source, it can be shown† that the path difference between the two rays remains constant, but that the distance of P' from the mirrors changes. If the angle between the mirrors is not too small, however, the latter distance is never great, and hence, in order to see these fringes clearly, the eye must be focused on or near the rear mirror M_1. The localized fringes are practically straight

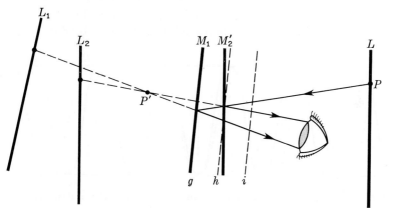

FIG. 13Q. Diagram illustrating the formation of fringes with inclined mirrors in the Michelson interferometer.

because the variation of the path difference across the field of view is now due primarily to the variation of the thickness of the "air film" between the mirrors. With a wedge-shaped film, the locus of points of equal thickness is a straight line parallel to the edge of the wedge. The fringes are not exactly straight, however, if d has an appreciable value, because there is also some variation of the path difference with angle. They are in general curved and are always convex toward the thin edge of the wedge. Thus, with a certain value of d, we might observe fringes shaped like those of Fig. 13P(g). M_1 could then be in a position such as g of Fig. 13Q. If the separation of the mirrors is decreased, the fringes will move to the left across the field, a new fringe crossing the center each time d changes by $\lambda/2$. As we approach zero path difference, the fringes become straighter, until the point is reached where M_1 actually intersects M_2', when they are perfectly straight, as in (h). Beyond this

* When the term "ray" is used, here and elsewhere in discussing interference phenomena, it merely indicates the direction of the *perpendicular to a wave front* and is in no way to suggest an infinitesimally narrow pencil of light.

† R. W. Ditchburn, "Light," 1st ed., pp. 132–134, Interscience Publishers, Inc., New York, 1953.

point, they begin to curve in the opposite direction, as shown in (*i*). The blank fields (*f*) and (*j*) indicate that this type of fringe cannot be observed for large path differences. Because the principal variation of path difference results from a change of the thickness *d*, these fringes have been termed *fringes of equal thickness*.

13.11. White-light Fringes. If a source of white light is used, no fringes will be seen at all except for a path difference so small that it does not exceed a few wavelengths. In observing these fringes, the mirrors are tilted slightly as for localized fringes, and the position of M_1 is found where it intersects M_2'. With white light there will then be observed a central dark fringe, bordered on either side by 8 or 10 colored

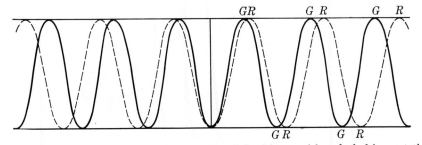

Fig. 13*R*. Illustrating the formation of white-light fringes with a dark fringe at the center.

fringes. This position is often rather troublesome to find using white light only. It is best located approximately beforehand by finding the place where the localized fringes in monochromatic light becomes straight. Then a very *slow* motion of M_1 through this region, using white light, will bring these fringes into view.

The fact that only a few fringes are observed with white light is easily accounted for when we remember that such light contains all wavelengths between 4000 and 7500 Å. The fringes for a given color are more widely spaced the greater the wavelength. Thus the fringes in different colors will only coincide for *d* = 0, as indicated in Fig. 13*R*. The solid curve represents the intensity distribution in the fringes for green light, and the broken curve that for red light. Clearly, only the central fringe will be uncolored, and the fringes of different colors will begin to separate at once on either side, producing various impure colors which are not the saturated spectral colors. After 8 or 10 fringes, so many colors are present at a given point that the resultant color is essentially white. Interference is still occurring in this region, however, because a spectroscope will show a continuous spectrum with dark bands at those wavelengths for which the condition for destructive interference is fulfilled. White-light fringes are also observed in all the other methods of producing interference described above, if white light is substituted for monochromatic light.   They are particularly important in the Michelson interferometer, where they may be used to locate the position of zero path difference, as we shall see in Sec. 13.13.

An excellent reproduction in color of these white-light fringes is given in one of Michelson's books.*   The fringes in three different colors are also shown separately, and a study of these in connection with the white-light fringes is instructive as showing the origin of the various impure colors in the latter.

It was stated above that the central fringe in the white-light system, i.e., that corresponding to zero path difference, is black when observed in the Michelson interferometer.   One would ordinarily expect this fringe to be white, since the two beams should be in phase with each other for any wavelength at this point, and in fact this is the case in the fringes formed with the other arrangements, such as the biprism.   In the present case, however, it will be seen by referring to Fig. 13N that while ray (1) undergoes an internal reflection in the plate G_1, ray (2) undergoes an external reflection, with a consequent change of phase (Sec. 11.8).   Hence the central fringe is black, if the back surface of G_1 is unsilvered.   If it is silvered, the conditions are different and the central fringe may be white.

13.12. Visibility of the Fringes.   There are three principal types of measurement that can be made with the interferometer: (1) width and fine structure of spectrum lines, (2) lengths or displacements in terms of wavelengths of light, and (3) refractive indices.   As was explained in the preceding section, when a certain spread of wavelengths is present in the light source, the fringes become indistinct and eventually disappear as the path difference is increased.   With white light they become invisible when d is only a few wavelengths, whereas the circular fringes obtained with the light of a single spectrum line may still be seen after the mirror has been moved several centimeters.   Since no line is perfectly sharp, however, the different component wavelengths produce fringes of slightly different spacing, and hence there is a limit to the usable path difference even in this case.   For the measurements of length to be described below, Michelson tested the lines from various sources and concluded that a certain red line in the spectrum of cadmium was the most satisfactory.   He measured the *visibility*, defined as

$$V = \frac{I_{\max} - I_{\min}}{I_{\max} + I_{\min}} \tag{13i}$$

where $I_{\max}$ and $I_{\min}$ are the intensities at the maxima and minima of the fringe pattern.   The more slowly V decreases with increasing path

* A. A. Michelson, "Light Waves and Their Uses," plate II, University of Chicago Press, Chicago, 1906.

difference, the sharper the line. With the red cadmium line, it dropped
to 0.5 at a path difference of some 10 cm, or at $d = 5$ cm.

With certain lines, the visibility does not decrease uniformly but
fluctuates with more or less regularity. This behavior indicates that
the line has a fine structure, consisting of two or more lines very close
together. Thus it is found that with sodium light the fringes become
alternately sharp and diffuse, as the fringes from the two D lines get in
and out of step. The number of fringes between two successive positions
of maximum visibility is about 1000, indicating that the wavelengths of

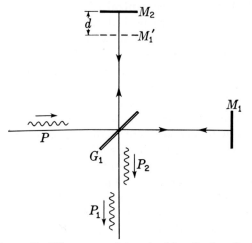

FIG. 13S. Limiting path difference as determined by the length of wave packets.

the components differ by approximately 1 part in 1000. In more complicated cases, the separation and intensities of the components could
be determined by a Fourier analysis of the visibility curves.* Since
this method of inferring the structure of lines has now been superseded
by more direct methods, to be described in the following chapter, it will
not be discussed in any detail here.

There is an alternative way of interpreting the eventual vanishing of
interference at large path differences, which it is instructive to consider
at this point. In Sec. 12.6 it was indicated that a finite spread of wavelengths corresponds to wave packets of limited length, this length
decreasing as the spread becomes greater. Thus, when the two beams
in the interferometer traverse distances that differ by more than the
length of the individual packets, these can no longer overlap and no
interference is possible. The situation upon complete disappearance
of the fringes is shown schematically in Fig. 13S. The original wave

* A. A. Michelson, "Studies in Optics," chap. 4, University of Chicago Press,
Chicago, 1927.

packet P has its amplitude divided at G_1 so that two similar packets are produced, P_1 traveling to M_1, and P_2 to M_2. When the beams are reunited, P_2 lags a distance $2d$ behind P_1. Evidently a measurement of this limiting path difference gives a direct determination of the length of the wave packets. This interpretation of the cessation of interference seems at first sight to conflict with the one given above. A consideration of the principle of Fourier analysis shows, however, that mathematically the two are entirely equivalent and are merely alternative ways of representing the same phenomenon.

13.13. Interferometric Measurements of Length. The principal advantage of Michelson's form of interferometer over the earlier methods of producing interference lies in the fact that the two beams are here widely separated, and the path difference can be varied at will by moving the mirror or by introducing a refracting material in one of the beams. Corresponding to these two ways of changing the optical path, there are two other important applications of the interferometer. Accurate measurements of distance in terms of the wavelength of light will be discussed in this section, while interferometric determinations of refractive indices are described in Sec. 13.15.

When the mirror M_1 of Fig. 13N is moved slowly from one position to another, counting the number of fringes in monochromatic light which cross the center of the field of view will give a measure of the distance the mirror has moved in terms of λ, since by Eq. 13h we have, for the position d_1 corresponding to the bright fringe of order m_1,

$$2d_1 = m_1\lambda$$

and for d_2, giving a bright fringe of order m_2,

$$2d_2 = m_2\lambda$$

Subtracting these two equations, we find

$$d_1 - d_2 = (m_1 - m_2)\frac{\lambda}{2} \tag{13j}$$

Hence the distance moved equals the number of fringes counted, multiplied by a half wavelength. Of course, the distance measured need not correspond to an integral number of half wavelengths. Fractional parts of a whole fringe displacement can easily be estimated to one-tenth of a fringe, and, with care, to one-fiftieth. The latter figure then gives the distance to an accuracy of $\frac{1}{100}\lambda$, or 5×10^{-7} cm for green light.

A small Michelson interferometer in which a microscope is attached to the moving carriage carrying M_1 is frequently used in the laboratory for measuring the wavelength of light. The microscope is focused on a fine glass scale, and the number of fringes, $m_1 - m_2$, crossing the mirror

between two readings d_1 and d_2 on the scale gives λ, by Eq. 13*j*. The
bending of a beam, or even of a brick wall, under pressure from the hand
can be made visible and measured by attaching M_1 directly to the beam or wall.

The most important measurement made with the interferometer was the comparison of the standard meter in Paris with the wavelengths of intense red, green, and blue lines of cadmium by Michelson and Benoit. For reasons discussed in the last section,

FIG. 13*T*. One of the nine etalons used by Michelson.

it would be impossible to count
directly the number of fringes for a displacement of the movable mirror
from one end of the standard meter to the other.   Instead, nine intermediate standards (etalons) were used, of the form shown in Fig. 13*T*,
each approximately twice the length of the other.   The two shortest

FIG. 13*U*. Special Michelson interferometer used in accurately comparing the wavelength of light with the standard meter.

etalons were first mounted in an interferometer of special design (Fig.
13*U*), with a field of view covering the four mirrors, M_1, M_2, M_1', and M_2'.
With the aid of the white light fringes the distances of M, M_1, and
M_1' from the eye were made equal, as shown in the figure.   Substituting
the light of one of the cadmium lines for white light, M was then moved

slowly from A to B, counting the number of fringes passing the cross hair. The count was continued until M reached the position B, which was exactly coplanar with M_2, as judged by the appearance of the white-light fringes in the upper mirror of the shorter etalon. The fraction of a cadmium fringe in excess of an integral number required to reach this position was determined, giving the distance M_1M_2 in terms of wavelengths. The shorter etalon was then moved through its own length, without counting fringes, until the white-light fringes reappeared in M_1. Finally M was moved to C, when the white-light fringes appeared in M_2' as well as in M_2. The additional displacement necessary to make M coplanar with M_2 was measured in terms of cadmium fringes, thus giving the exact number of wavelengths in the longer etalon. This was in turn compared with the length of a third etalon of approximately twice the length of the second, by the same process.

The length of the largest etalon was about 10 cm. This was finally compared with the prototype meter by alternately centering the white-light fringes in its upper and lower mirrors, each time the etalon was moved through its own length. Ten such steps brought a marker on the side of the etalon nearly into coincidence with the second fiducial mark on the meter, and the slight difference was evaluated by counting cadmium fringes. The 10 steps involve an accumulated error which does not enter in the intercomparison of the etalons, but nevertheless this was smaller than the uncertainty in setting on the end marks.

The final results were, for the three cadmium lines:

Red line............ 1 m = 1,553,163.5λ or λ = 6438.4722 Å
Green line........... 1 m = 1,966,249.7λ or λ = 5085.8240 Å
Blue line............ 1 m = 2,083,372.1λ or λ = 4799.9107 Å

Not only has the standard meter been determined in terms of what we now believe to be an invariable unit, the wavelength of light, but we have also obtained absolute determinations of the wavelength of three spectrum lines, the red line of which is at present the primary standard in spectroscopy. More recent measurements on the red cadmium line have been made (see Sec. 14.11). It now is internationally agreed that in dry atmospheric air at 15°C and a pressure of 760 mm Hg the red cadmium line, produced under the conditions described by Michelson, has the wavelength

$$\lambda_r = 6438.4696 \text{ Å}$$

A still more satisfactory line for use as a standard of wavelength has now been discovered,[*] namely, the green line of mercury as emitted by the single isotope, Hg^{198}. This kind of mercury can be produced entirely free of the other mercury isotopes by the bombardment of gold

[*] J. H. Wiens and L. W. Alvarez, *Phys. Rev.*, **58**, 1005, 1940.

with neutrons. The line is considerably sharper than the cadmium standard, and its wavelength has been measured* as 5460.7532 Å. Probably it will replace λ6438 as the primary standard of wavelength.

13.14. Twyman and Green Interferometer. If a Michelson interferometer is illuminated with strictly parallel monochromatic light, produced by a point source at the principal focus of a well-corrected lens, it becomes a very powerful instrument for testing the perfection of optical parts such as prisms and lenses. The piece to be tested is placed in one of the light beams, and the mirror behind it is so chosen that the reflected waves, after traversing the test piece a second time, again become plane. These waves are then brought to interference with the plane waves from the other arm of the interferometer by another lens, at the focus of which the eye is placed. If the prism or lens is optically perfect, so that the returning waves are strictly plane, the field will appear uniformly illuminated. Any local variation of the optical path will, however, produce fringes in the corresponding part of the field, which are essentially the "contour lines" of the distorted wave front. Even though the surfaces of the test piece may be accurately made, the glass may contain regions that are slightly more or less dense. With the Twyman and Green interferometer these may be detected, and corrected for by local polishing of the surface.†

13.15. Index of Refraction by Interference Methods. If a thickness t of a substance having an index of refraction n is introduced into the path of one of the interfering beams in the interferometer, the optical path in this beam is increased because of the fact that light travels more slowly in the substance and consequently has a shorter wavelength. The optical path (Eq. 11f) is now nt through the medium, whereas it was practically t through the corresponding thickness of air ($n = 1$). Thus the increase in optical path due to insertion of the substance is $(n - 1)t$.‡ This will introduce $(n - 1)t/\lambda$ extra waves in the path of one beam; so if we call Δm the number of fringes by which the fringe system is displaced when the substance is placed in the beam, we have

$$(n - 1)t = (\Delta m)\lambda \tag{13k}$$

In principle a measurement of Δm, t, and λ thus gives a determination of n.

In practice, the insertion of a plate of glass in one of the beams pro-

---

* W. F. Meggers and F. O. Westfall, *J. Research Natl. Bur. Standards*, **44**, 447–455, 1950.

† For a more complete description of the use of this instrument, see F. Twyman, "Prism and Lens Making," 2d ed., chap. 12, Hilger and Watts, London, 1952.

‡ In the Michelson interferometer, where the beam traverses the substance twice in its back-and-forth path, t is *twice* the actual thickness.

duces a discontinuous shift of the fringes so that the number Δm cannot be counted. With monochromatic fringes it is impossible to tell which fringe in the displaced set corresponds to one in the original set. With white light, the displacement in the fringes of different colors is very different because of the variation of n with wavelength, and the fringes disappear entirely. This illustrates the necessity of the compensating plate G_2 in Michelson's interferometer if white-light fringes are to be observed. If the plate of glass is very thin, these fringes may still be visible, and this affords a method of measuring n for very thin films. For thicker pieces, a practicable method is to use two plates of identical

Fig. 13V. (a) The Jamin and (b) the Mach-Zehnder interferometers.

thickness, one in each beam, and to turn one gradually about a vertical axis, counting the number of monochromatic fringes for a given angle of rotation. This angle then corresponds to a certain known increase in effective thickness.

For the measurement of the index of refraction of gases, which can be introduced gradually into the light path by allowing the gas to flow into an evacuated tube, the interference method is the most practicable one. Several forms of refractometers have been devised especially for this purpose, of which we shall describe three, the Jamin, the Mach-Zehnder, and the Rayleigh refractometers.

Jamin's refractometer is shown schematically in Fig. 13V(a). Monochromatic light from a broad source S is broken into two parallel beams (1) and (2) by reflection at the two parallel faces of a thick plate of glass G_1. These two rays pass through to another identical plate of glass G_2 to recombine after reflection, forming interference fringes known as Brewster's fringes (see Sec. 14.11). If now the plates are parallel, the light paths will be identical. Suppose as an experiment we wish to measure the index of refraction of a certain gas at different temperatures and pressures. Two similar evacuated tubes T_1 and T_2 of equal length are placed in the two parallel beams. Gas is slowly admitted to tube T_2. Counting the number of fringes Δm crossing the field while the gas reaches the desired pressure and temperature, the value of n can be found by applying Eq. 13k. It is found experimentally that at a given temperature the value $(n - 1)$ is directly proportional to the pressure. This is a special case of a theoretical law known as the *Lorenz-Lorentz** law according to which

$$\frac{n^2 - 1}{n^2 + 2} = (n - 1)\frac{(n + 1)}{(n^2 + 2)} = \text{const.} \times \rho \qquad (13l)$$

Here ρ is the density of the gas. When n is very nearly unity, the factor $(n + 1)/(n^2 + 2)$ is nearly constant, as required by the above experimental observation.

The interferometer devised by Mach and Zehnder, and shown in Fig. 13$V(b)$, has a similar arrangement of light paths, but they may be much farther apart. The role of the two glass blocks in the Jamin instrument is here taken by two pairs of mirrors, the pair M_1 and M_2 functioning like G_1, and the pair M_3 and M_4 like G_2. The first surface of M_1 and the second surface of M_4 are half-silvered. Although it is more difficult to adjust, the Mach-Zehnder interferometer is the only one suitable for studying slight changes of refractive index over a considerable area and is used, for example, in measuring the flow patterns in wind tunnels. Contrary to the situation in the Michelson interferometer, the light traverses a region such as T in the figure in only one direction, a fact which simplifies the study of local changes of optical path in that region.

The purpose of the compensating plates C_1 and C_2 in Figs. 13$V(a)$ and 13W is to speed up the measurement of refractive index. As the two plates, of equal thickness, are rotated together by the single knob attached to the dial D, one light path is shortened and the other lengthened. The device can therefore compensate for the path difference in the two tubes. The dial, if previously calibrated by counting fringes, can be made to read the index of refraction directly. The sensitivity of this device can be varied at will, a high sensitivity being obtained when the angle between the two plates is small, and a low sensitivity when the angle is large.

* H. A. Lorentz (1853–1928). For many years professor of mathematical physics at the University of Leyden, Holland. Awarded the Nobel prize (1902) for his work on the relations between light, magnetism, and matter, he also contributed notably to other fields of physics. Gifted with a charming personality and kindly disposition, he traveled a great deal, and was widely known and liked. By a strange coincidence L. Lorenz of Copenhagen derived the above law from the elastic-solid theory only a few months before Lorentz obtained it from the electromagnetic theory.

In Rayleigh's* refractometer (Fig. 13W) monochromatic light from a linear source S is made parallel by a lens L_1 and split into two beams by a fairly wide double slit.   After passing through two exactly similar tubes and the compensating plates, these are brought to interfere by the

FIG. 13W. Rayleigh's refractometer.

lens L_2.   This form of refractometer is often used to measure slight differences in refractive index of liquids and solutions.

PROBLEMS

1. Young's experiment is performed with light of the green mercury line.   If the fringes are measured with a micrometer eyepiece 80 cm behind the double slit, it is found that 20 of them occupy a distance of 10.92 mm.   Find the distance between the two slits.

2. A double slit of separation $\frac{1}{2}$ mm is illuminated by light of the blue cadmium line.   How far behind the slits must one go to obtain fringes that are 1 mm apart?

Ans. 104.2 cm.

3. Describe what would be observed if a double slit were illuminated by light of the two yellow mercury lines, $\lambda\lambda 5769$ and 5790 Å.   Assuming the two lines to be perfectly sharp and of equal intensity, calculate the visibility of the fringes near $m = 50$.

4. In Young's double-slit experiment, when a thin film of transparent material is placed over one of the slits, the central bright fringe of the white-light fringe system is displaced by 3.6 fringes.   The refractive index of the material is 1.40, and the effective wavelength of the light 5500 Å.   (*a*) By how much does the film increase the optical path?   (*b*) What is the exact thickness of the film?   (*c*) What would probably be observed if a piece of the material 1 mm thick were used, and why?

Ans. (*a*) 1.98×10^{-4} cm.   (*b*) 4.95×10^{-4} cm.   (*c*) No fringes.

5. Lloyd's mirror is easily demonstrated with microwaves, using as a reflector a sheet of metal lying on a table.   If the source has a frequency of 10,000 Mc and is placed 6 cm above the surface of the table, find the height above this surface of the first two maxima, 4 m away from the source.

6. In Fresnel's biprism and mirrors, coherent parts of the two virtual sources are in corresponding positions, whereas in Lloyd's mirror they are inverted with respect to each other.   What effect will this difference have on the appearance of the fringes produced when the source slit is not extremely narrow?

Ans. Fringes of higher order become indistinct in Lloyd's mirror.

* Lord Rayleigh (third Baron) (1842–1919).   Professor of physics at Cambridge University and the Royal Institution of Great Britain.   Gifted with great mathematical ability and physical insight, he made important contributions to many fields of physics.   His works on sound and on the scattering of light (Sec. 22.9) are the best known.   He was a Nobel prize winner in 1904.

7. A Fresnel biprism is to be constructed for use on a 2-m optical bench. The source slit is to be at one end of the bench, and the eyepiece at the other. Because of the finite width of the source slit, it is not permitted to place the biprism less than 50 cm from it. Find the value of the refracting angles of the biprism necessary to produce sodium fringes having a separation of 0.8 mm, if the glass has $n = 1.55$.

8. A Fresnel biprism with apex angles 1°30′ is used to form interference fringes. The refractive index is 1.52. Find the fringe separation for red light, λ6563, when the distance between the source and the prism is 20 cm and that between the prism and the screen 80 cm. *Ans.* 0.1205 mm.

9. With Fresnel's mirrors, what must be the angle between the mirrors, in degrees, in order to produce sodium fringes 0.5 mm apart, if the slit is 30 cm from the intersection of the mirrors and the screen 120 cm from the slit?

10. It is desired to determine the unknown concentration of a solution to ±0.002 per cent by comparing its refractive index with that of a standard solution in the Rayleigh refractometer using a sodium lamp as a source. A 5 per cent standard solution has $n = 1.4316$, a 10 per cent solution $n = 1.4425$, and n varies linearly with concentration between these values. What lengths should the tubes have in order to achieve the required accuracy, assuming that one can estimate fringe displacements to one-twentieth of a fringe? *Ans.* 6.76 mm.

11. How far must the movable mirror of a Michelson interferometer be displaced for 2000 fringes of the green cadmium line to cross the center of the field of view?

12. Find the angular radius of the sixth bright fringe in a Michelson interferometer when the central path difference $(2d)$ is 4 mm, and when it is 30 mm. Assume blue light of wavelength 4358 Å and that the interferometer is adjusted in each case so that the first bright fringe forms a maximum at the center of the pattern.
Ans. 1.892°. 0.690°.

13. Investigate the effect on the white-light fringes of placing a thin sheet of telescope crown glass in one arm of a Michelson interferometer. The refractive indices of this glass are given in Table 23-I. Assuming that the colored fringes disappear at a path difference equal to six wavelengths of sodium light, what would be the maximum allowable thickness of the glass sheet in order to see any fringes when it is inserted?

14. Prove that the increase in optical path produced by rotating a plane-parallel compensating plate of thickness t and index n through an angle ϕ from the perpendicular is given by
$$\Delta = t(\sqrt{n^2 - \sin^2 \phi} - \cos \phi - n + 1)$$
(HINT: Take account of the change of path through air, as well as through glass.)

15. The two compensating plates of a Jamin refractometer are fixed at an angle of 5° with each other. One plate is vertical when the fringes are first observed. Through what angle should the pair be rotated to produce a shift of 20 fringes of green light, $\lambda = 5500$ Å, the refractive index being 1.500? Assume that the plates are turned toward the symmetrical position.

16. For a spectrum line having the contour due to Doppler broadening, it can be proved that the path difference at which the visibility curve falls to its half value is $2.77/\Delta k$, where Δk is the width of the line at half maximum, expressed in propagation numbers. From the data given in Sec. 13.12, calculate the width in angstroms of the red cadmium line. *Ans.* 0.018 Å.

17. The two tubes of a Jamin interferometer are each 40 cm long. One is evacuated, and the other contains argon at atmospheric pressure. The refractive index of the latter is 1.00028. How many fringes of the green mercury line would be counted when the argon is pumped out?

CHAPTER 14

INTERFERENCE INVOLVING MULTIPLE REFLECTIONS

Some of the most beautiful effects of interference result from the multiple reflection of light between the two surfaces of a thin film of transparent material. These effects require no special apparatus for their production or observation and are familiar to anyone who has noticed the colors shown by thin films of oil on water, by soap bubbles, or by cracks in a piece of glass. We begin our investigation of this class of interference by considering the somewhat idealized case of reflection from a film with perfectly plane sides which are parallel to each other.

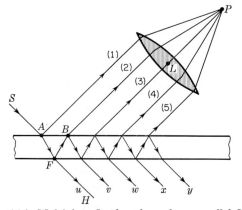

Fig. 14A. Multiple reflections in a plane-parallel film.

14.1. Reflection from a Plane-parallel Film. Let a ray of light from a source S be incident on the surface of such a film at A (Fig. 14A). Part of this will be reflected as ray (1) and part refracted in the direction AF. Upon arrival at F, part of the latter will be reflected to B and part refracted toward H. At B the ray FB will be again divided. A continuation of this process yields two sets of parallel rays, one on each side of the film. In each of these sets, of course, the intensity decreases rapidly from one ray to the next. If the set of parallel reflected rays is now collected by a lens and focused at the point P, each ray will have traveled a different distance, and the phase relations may be such as to produce destructive or constructive interference at that point. It is such interference that produces the colors of thin films when they are viewed by the naked eye. In such a case L is the lens of the eye, and P lies on the retina.

In order to find the phase difference between these rays, we must first evaluate the difference in the optical path traversed by a pair of successive rays, such as rays (1) and (2). In Fig. 14B let d be the thickness of the film, n its index of refraction, λ the wavelength of the light, and ϕ and ϕ' the angles of incidence and refraction. If BD is perpendicular to ray (1), the optical paths from D and B to the focus of the lens will be equal. Starting at A, ray (2) has the path AFB in the film and ray (1) the path AD in air. The difference in these optical paths (Eq. 11f) is given by

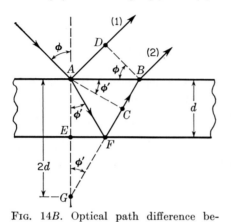

FIG. 14B. Optical path difference between two consecutive rays in multiple reflection (see Fig. 14A).

$$\Delta = n(AFB) - AD$$

If BF is extended to intersect the perpendicular line AE at G, $AF = GF$ because of the equality of the angles of incidence and reflection at the lower surface. Thus we have

$$\Delta = n(GB) - AD = n(GC + CB) - AD$$

Now AC is drawn perpendicular to FB; so the broken lines AC and DB represent two successive positions of a wave front reflected from the lower surface. The optical paths, as was shown in Sec. 11.6, must be the same by any ray drawn between two wave fronts; so we may write

$$n(CB) = AD$$

The path difference then reduces to

$$\Delta = n(GC) = n(2d \cos \phi') \tag{14a}$$

If this path difference is a whole number of wavelengths, we might expect rays (1) and (2) to arrive at the focus of the lens in phase with each other and produce a maximum of intensity. However, we must take account of the fact that ray (1) undergoes a phase change of π at reflection, while ray (2) does not, since it is internally reflected (Sec. 11.8). The condition

$$2nd \cos \phi' = m\lambda \qquad \text{MINIMA} \tag{14b}$$

then becomes a condition for *destructive* interference as far as rays (1) and (2) are concerned.   As before, $m = 0, 1, 2, \ldots$ is the order of interference.

Next we examine the phases of the remaining rays, (3), (4), (5), ... Since the geometry is the same, the path difference between rays (3) and (2) will also be given by Eq. 14*a*, but here there are only internal reflections involved, so that if Eq. 14*b* is fulfilled, ray (3) will be in the same phase as ray (2).   The same holds for all succeeding pairs, and so we conclude that under these conditions rays (1) and (2) will be out of

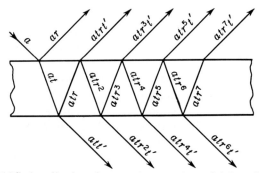

Fig. 14*C*. Amplitudes of successive rays in multiple reflection.

phase, but rays (2), (3), (4), . . . , will be in phase with each other. On the other hand, if conditions are such that

$$2nd \cos \phi' = (m + \tfrac{1}{2})\lambda \qquad \text{MAXIMA} \qquad (14c)$$

ray (2) will be in phase with (1), but (3), (5), (7), . . . will be out of phase with (2), (4), (6), ...   Since (2) is more intense than (3), (4) more intense than (5), etc., these pairs cannot cancel each other, and since the stronger series combines with (1), the strongest of all, there will be a maximum of intensity.

For the minima of intensity, ray (2) is out of phase with ray (1), but (1) has a considerably greater amplitude than (2), so that these two will not completely annul each other.   We can now prove that the addition of (3), (4), (5), . . . , which are all in phase with (2), will give a net amplitude just sufficient to make up the difference and to produce complete darkness at the minima.   Using a for the amplitude of the incident wave, r for the fraction of this reflected, and t or t' for the fraction transmitted in going from rare to dense or dense to rare, as was done in Stokes' treatment of reflection in Sec. 11.8, Fig. 14*C* is constructed and the amplitudes labeled as shown.   In accordance with Eq. 11*p*, we have taken the fraction reflected internally and externally to be the same.   Adding the amplitudes of all the reflected rays but the first on the upper side of the film, we obtain the resultant amplitude,

$$A = atrt' + atr^3t' + atr^5t' + atr^7t' + \cdots$$
$$= atrt'(1 + r^2 + r^4 + r^6 + \cdots)$$

Since r is necessarily less than 1, the geometrical series in parentheses has a finite sum equal to $1/(1 - r^2)$, giving

$$A = atrt' \frac{1}{(1 - r^2)}$$

But from Stokes' treatment (Eq. 11o), $tt' = 1 - r^2$; so we obtain finally

$$A = ar \tag{14d}$$

This is just equal to the amplitude of the first reflected ray, so we conclude that under the conditions of Eq. 14b there will be complete destructive interference.

14.2. Fringes of Equal Inclination.   If the image of an *extended* source reflected in a thin plane-parallel film be examined, it will be found to be crossed by a system of distinct interference fringes, provided the source emits monochromatic light and provided the film is sufficiently thin. Each bright fringe corresponds to a particular path difference giving an integral value of m in Eq. 14c.   For any fringe, the value of ϕ is fixed; so the fringe will have the form of the arc of a circle whose center is at the foot of the perpendicular drawn from the eye to the plane of the film. Evidently we are here concerned with fringes of equal inclination, and the equation for the path difference has the same form as for the circular fringes in the Michelson interferometer (Sec. 13.9).

The necessity of using an extended source will become clear upon consideration of Fig. 14A.   If a very distant point source S is used, the parallel rays will necessarily reach the eye at only one angle (that required by the law of reflection), and will be focused to a point P.   Thus only one point will be seen, either bright or dark, according to the phase difference at this particular angle.   It is true that, if the source is not very far away, its image on the retina will be slightly blurred, because the eye must be focused for parallel rays to observe the interference. The area illuminated is small, however, and in order to see an extended system of fringes, we must obviously have many points S, spread out in a broad source so that the light reaches the eye from various directions.

These fringes are seen by the eye only if the film is very thin, unless the light is reflected practically normal to the film.   At other angles, since the pupil of the eye has a small aperture, increasing the thickness of the film will cause the reflected rays to get so far apart that only one enters the eye at a time.   Obviously no interference can occur under these conditions.   Using a telescope of large aperture, the lens may include enough rays for the fringes to be visible with thick plates, but unless viewed nearly normal to the plate, they will be so finely spaced as to be invisible. The fringes seen with thick plates near normal incidence are often called *Haidinger* fringes*.

14.3. Interference in the Transmitted Light. The rays emerging from the lower side of the film, shown in Fig. 14A and 14C, may also be brought together with a lens and caused to interfere. Here, however, there are no phase changes at reflection for any of the rays, and the relations are such that Eq. 14b now becomes the condition for maxima and Eq. 14c the condition for minima. For maxima the rays u, v, w, . . . of Fig. 14A are all in phase, while for minima v, x, . . . are out of phase with u, w, ... When the reflectance r^2 has a low value, as is the case with the surfaces of unsilvered glass, the amplitude of u is much the greatest in the series, and the minima are not by any means black. Figure 14D shows quantitative curves for the intensity transmitted, I_T, and reflected, I_R, plotted in this instance for $r = 0.2$ according to Eqs. 14j and 14k, ahead. The corresponding reflectance of 4 per cent is closely that of glass at normal incidence. The abscissas δ in the figure repre-

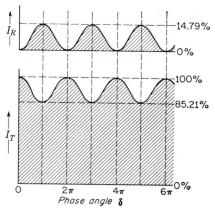

Fig. 14D. Intensity contours of the reflected and transmitted fringes from a film having a reflectance of 4 per cent.

sent the phase difference between successive rays in the transmitted set, or between all but the first pair in the reflected set, which by Eq. 14a is

$$\delta = k\Delta = \frac{2\pi}{\lambda} \Delta = \frac{4\pi}{\lambda} nd \cos \phi' \qquad (14e)$$

It will be noted that the curve for I_R looks very much like the cos² contour obtained from the interference of two beams. It is not exactly the same, however, and the resemblance holds only when the reflectance is small. Then the first two reflected beams are so much stronger than the rest that the latter have little effect. The important changes that come in at higher values of the reflectance will be discussed in Sec. 14.7.

14.4. Fringes of Equal Thickness. If the film is not plane parallel, so that the surfaces make an appreciable angle with each other as in Fig. 14$E(a)$, the interfering rays do not enter the eye parallel to each other,

---

* W. K. Haidinger (1795–1871). Austrian mineralogist and physicist, for 17 years director of the Imperial Geological Institute in Vienna.

but appear to diverge from a point near the film. The resulting fringes resemble the localized fringes in the Michelson interferometer, and appear to be formed in the film itself. If the two surfaces are plane, so that the film is wedge-shaped, the fringes will be practically straight following the lines of equal thickness. In this case the path difference for a given

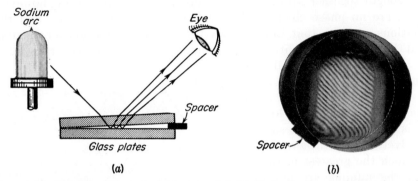

FIG. 14E. Fringes of equal thickness. (a) Method of visual observation. (b) Photograph taken with a camera focused on the plates.

pair of rays is practically that given by Eq. 14a. Provided that observations are made almost normal to the film, the factor cos ϕ' may be considered equal to 1, and the condition for bright fringes becomes

$$2nd = (m + \tfrac{1}{2})\lambda \tag{14f}$$

In going from one fringe to the next m increases by 1, and this requires that the optical thickness of the film, nd, should change by $\lambda/2$.

Fringes formed in thin films are easily shown in the laboratory or lecture room by using two pieces of ordinary plate glass. If they are laid together with a thin strip of paper along one edge, we obtain a wedge-shaped film of air between the plates. When a sodium flame or arc is viewed as in Fig. 14E, yellow fringes are clearly seen. If a carbon arc and filter are used, the fringes may be projected on a screen with a lens. On viewing the reflected image of a monochromatic source, one will find it to be crossed by more or less straight fringes, such as those in Fig. 14E(b).

This class of fringes has important practical applications in the testing of optical surfaces for planeness. If an air film is formed between two surfaces, one of which is perfectly plane and the other not, the fringes will be irregular in shape. Any fringe is characterized by a particular value of m in Eq. 14f, and hence will follow those parts of the film where d is constant. That is, the fringes form the equivalent of *contour lines* for the uneven surface. The contour interval is $\lambda/2$, since for air $n = 1$, and going from one fringe to the next corresponds to increasing d by this amount. The standard method of producing optically plane surfaces uses repeated observation of the fringes formed between the working surface and an optical flat, the polishing being continued until the fringes are straight. In Fig. 14E(b) it will be noticed that there is considerable distortion of one of the plates near the bottom.

14.5. Newton's Rings. If the fringes of equal thickness are produced in the air film between a convex surface of a long-focus lens and a plane glass surface, the contour lines will be circular. The ring-shaped fringes thus produced were studied in detail by Newton,[*] although he was not able to explain them correctly.

For purposes of measurement, the observations are usually made at normal incidence by an arrangement such as that in Fig. 14F, where the glass plate G reflects the light down on the plates. After reflection, it is transmitted by G and observed in the low-power microscope T. Under these conditions the positions of the maxima are given by Eq. 14f, where d is the thickness of the air film.

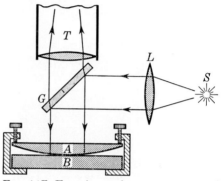

FIG. 14F. Experimental arrangement used in viewing and measuring Newton's rings.

Now if we designate by R the radius of curvature of the surface A, and assume that A and B are just touching at the center, the value of d for any ring of radius r is the sagitta of the arc, given by

$$d = \frac{r^2}{2R} \tag{14g}$$

Substitution of this value in Eq. 14f will then give a relation between the radii of the rings and the wavelength of the light. For quantitative work, one may not assume the plates to barely touch at the point of contact, since there will always be either some dust particles or distortion by pressure. Such disturbances will merely add a small constant to Eq. 14g, however, and their effect may be eliminated by measuring the diameters of at least two rings.

Because the ring diameters depend on wavelength, white light will

---

[*] Isaac Newton (1642–1727). Besides laying foundations of the science of mechanics, Newton devoted considerable time to the study of light and embodied the results in his famous "Opticks." It seems strange that one of the most striking demonstrations of the interference of light, Newton's rings, should be credited to the chief proponent of the corpuscular theory of light. Newton's advocacy of the corpuscular theory was not so uncompromising as it is generally represented. This is evident to anyone consulting his original writings. The original discovery of Newton's rings is now attributed to Robert Hooke.

produce only a few colored rings near the point of contact. With monochromatic light, however, an extensive fringe system such as that shown in Fig. 14G(a) is observed. When the contact is perfect, the central spot is found to be black. This is direct evidence of the relative phase change of π between the two types of reflection, air-to-glass and glass-to-air, mentioned in Sec. 14.1. If there were no such phase change, the rays reflected from the two surfaces in contact should be in the same phase,

(a)   (b)

Fig. 14G. Newton's rings (a) by reflection; (b) by transmission.

and produce a bright spot at the center. In an interesting modification of the experiment, due to Thomas Young, the lower plate has a higher index of refraction than the lens, and the film between is filled with an oil of intermediate index. Then both reflections are at "rare-to-dense" surfaces, no relative phase change occurs, and the central fringe of the reflected system is bright. The experiment does not tell us at which surface the phase change in the ordinary arrangement occurs, but it is now definitely known (Sec. 25.4) that it occurs at the lower (air-to-glass) surface.

A ring system is also observed in the light transmitted by the Newton's-ring plates. These rings are exactly complementary to the reflected ring system, so that the center spot is now bright. The contrast between bright and dark rings is small, for reasons already discussed in Sec. 14.3. A reproduction of the transmitted pattern is shown in Fig. 14G(b).

14.6. Nonreflecting Films. A simple and very important application of the principles of interference in thin films has been the production of the so-called *coated* surfaces. If a film of a transparent substance of refractive index n' be deposited on glass of a larger index n, to a thickness of one-quarter of the wavelength of light in the film, so that

$$d = \frac{\lambda}{4n'}$$

the light reflected at normal incidence is almost completely suppressed by interference. This corresponds to the condition $m = 0$ in Eq. 14c, which here becomes a condition for *minima* because the reflections at both surfaces are "rare-to-dense." The waves reflected from the lower surface have an extra path of one-half wavelength over those from the upper surface, and the two, combined with the weaker waves from multiple reflections, therefore interfere destructively. For the destruction to be complete, however, it is necessary that the fraction of the amplitude reflected at each of the two surfaces be exactly the same, since this specification is made in proving the relation of Eq. 14d. It will be true for a film in contact with a medium of higher index only if the index of the film obeys the relation

$$n' = \sqrt{n}$$

This can be proved from Eq. 25e of the chapter on reflection by substituting n' for the refractive index of the upper surface and n/n' for that of the lower. Similar considerations will show that such a film will give zero reflection from the glass side as well as from the air side. Of course no light is destroyed by a nonreflecting film; there is merely a redistribution such that a decrease of reflection carries with it a corresponding increase of transmission.

The practical importance of these films is that by their use one can greatly reduce the loss of light by reflection at the various surfaces of a system of lenses or prisms. Stray light reaching the image as a result of these reflections is also largely eliminated, with a resulting increase in contrast. Almost all optical parts of high quality are now coated to reduce reflection. The coatings were first made by depositing several monomolecular layers of an organic substance on glass plates. More durable ones are now made by evaporating calcium or magnesium fluoride on the surface in vacuum, or by chemical treatment with acids which leave a thin layer of silica on the surface of the glass. Properly coated lenses have a purplish hue by reflected light. This is a consequence of the fact that the condition for destructive interference can be fulfilled for only one wavelength, which is usually chosen to be one near the middle of the visible spectrum. The reflection of red and violet light is then somewhat larger. Furthermore, coating materials of sufficient durability have too high a refractive index to fulfill the condition stated above. Considerable improvement in these respects can be achieved by using two or more superimposed layers, and such films are capable of reducing the total reflected light to one-tenth of its value for the uncoated glass. This refers, of course, to light incident perpendicularly on the surface. At other angles, the path difference will change because of the factor cos ϕ' in Eq. 14a. Since, however, the cosine does not change rapidly in the neighborhood of 0°, the reflection remains low over a fairly large range of angles about the normal. The multiple films, now called *multilayers*, may also be used, with suitable thicknesses, to accomplish the opposite purpose, namely, to increase the reflectance. They may be used, for example, as "beam-splitting" mirrors to divide a beam of light into two parts of a given intensity ratio. The division can thus be accomplished without the losses of energy by absorption that are inherent in the transmission through, and reflection from, a thin metallic film.

14.7. Sharpness of the Fringes. As the reflectance of the surfaces is increased, either by the above method or by lightly silvering them, the fringes due to multiple reflections become much narrower. The striking

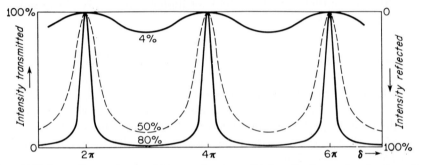

FIG. 14*H*. Intensity contours of fringes due to multiple reflections, showing how the sharpness depends on reflectance.

changes that occur are shown in Fig. 14*H*, which is plotted for $r^2 = 0.04$, 0.40, and 0.80 according to the theoretical equations to be derived below. The curve labeled 4% is just that for unsilvered glass which was given in Fig. 14*D*. Since, in the absence of any absorption, the intensity transmitted must be just the complement of that reflected, the same plot will represent the contour of either set. One is obtained from the other by merely turning the figure upside down, or by inverting the scale of ordinates, as is shown at the right in Fig. 14*H*.

In order to understand the reason for the narrowness of the transmitted fringes when the reflectance is high, we may use the graphical method of compounding amplitudes already discussed in Secs. 12.2 and 13.4. Referring back to Fig. 14*C* we notice that the amplitudes of the transmitted rays are given by att', $att'r^2$, $att'r^4$, . . . , or in general for the mth ray by $att'r^{2m}$. We thus have to find the resultant of an infinite number of amplitudes which decrease in magnitude more rapidly the smaller the fraction r. In Fig. 14*I*(*a*) the magnitudes of the amplitudes of the first 10 transmitted rays are drawn to scale for the 50 per cent and 80 per cent cases in Fig. 14*H*, i.e., essentially for $r = 0.7$ and 0.9. Starting at any principal maximum, with $\delta = 2\pi m$, these individual amplitudes will all be in phase with each other, so the vectors are all drawn parallel to give a resultant that has been made equal for the two cases. If we now go slightly to one side of the maximum, where the phase difference introduced between successive rays is $\pi/10$, each of the individual vectors must be drawn making an angle of $\pi/10$ with the preceding one, and the resultant found by joining the tail of the first to the head of the last.   The result is shown in diagram (b).   It will be seen that in the case $r = 0.9$, in which the individual amplitudes are much more nearly equal to each other, the resultant R is already considerably less than in the other case.   In diagram (c), where the phase has changed by $\pi/5$, this effect is much more pronounced; the resultant has fallen to a considerably smaller value

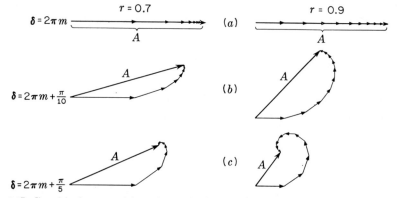

Fig. 14I. Graphical composition of amplitudes for the first 10 multiply reflected rays, with two difference reflectances.

in the right-hand picture.   Although a correct picture would include an infinite number of vectors, the later ones will have vanishing amplitudes, and we would reach a result similar to that found with the first 10.

These qualitative considerations may be made more precise by deriving an exact equation for the intensity.   To accomplish this, we must find an expression for the resultant amplitude A, the square of which determines the intensity.   Now A is the vector sum of an infinite series of diminishing amplitudes having a certain phase difference δ given by Eq. 14e.   Here we may apply the standard method of adding vectors by first finding the sum of the horizontal components, then that of the vertical components, squaring each sum, and adding to get A^2.   In doing this, however, the use of trigonometric functions as in Sec. 12.1 becomes too cumbersome.   Hence an alternative way of compounding vibrations, which is mathematically simpler for complicated cases, will be used.

14.8. Method of Complex Amplitudes.   In place of using the sine or the cosine to represent a simple harmonic wave, one may write the equation in the exponential form*

$$y = ae^{i(\omega t - kx)} = ae^{i\omega t}e^{-i\delta}$$

* For the mathematical background of this method, see E. T. Whittaker and G. N. Watson, "Modern Analysis," chap. 1, Cambridge University Press, New York, 1935.

where $\delta = kx$, and is constant at a particular point in space. The presence of $i = \sqrt{-1}$ in this equation makes the quantities complex. We may nevertheless use this representation, and at the end of the problem take either the real (cosine) or the imaginary (sine) part of the resulting

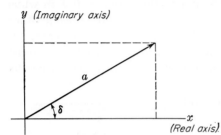

expression. Now the time-varying factor $\exp(i\omega t)$ is of no importance in combining waves of the same frequency, since the amplitudes and relative phases are independent of time. The other factor, $a \exp(-i\delta)$, is called the *complex amplitude*. It is a complex number, whose modulus a is the real amplitude, and whose argument δ gives the phase relative to some standard phase. The negative sign merely indicates that the phase is behind the standard phase. In general, the vector $\mathbf{a}$ is given by

Fig. 14*J*. Representation of a vector in the complex plane.

$$\mathbf{a} = ae^{i\delta} = x + iy = a(\cos \delta + i \sin \delta)$$

Then it will be seen that

$$a = \sqrt{x^2 + y^2} \qquad \tan \delta = \frac{y}{x}$$

Thus if $\mathbf{a}$ is represented as in Fig. 14*J*, plotting horizontally its real part and vertically its imaginary part, it will have the magnitude a and will make the angle δ with the x axis, as we require for vector addition.

The advantage of using complex amplitudes lies in the fact that the algebraic addition of two or more is equivalent to vector addition of the real amplitudes. Thus for two such quantities

$$Ae^{i\theta} = a_1 e^{i\delta_1} + a_2 e^{i\delta_2}$$

so that if

$$x_1 + x_2 = a_1 \cos \delta_1 + a_2 \cos \delta_2 = X$$

and

$$y_1 + y_2 = a_1 \sin \delta_1 + a_2 \sin \delta_2 = Y$$

it will be found that our previous Eqs. 12*d* and 12*e* require that

$$A = \sqrt{X^2 + Y^2} \qquad \tan \theta = \frac{Y}{X} \qquad (14h)$$

Thus, to get a vector sum, we need only obtain the *algebraic* sums $X = \Sigma x_i$ and $Y = \Sigma y_i$ of the real and imaginary parts, respectively, of the complex amplitudes. In obtaining the resultant intensity as proportional to the square of the real amplitude, we multiply the resultant complex amplitude by its complex conjugate, which is the same expression with i replaced by $-i$ throughout. The justification for this procedure follows from the relations

$$(X + iY)(X - iY) = X^2 + Y^2 = A^2 \left.\begin{matrix} \\ \\ \end{matrix}\right\}$$
$$Ae^{i\theta} \cdot Ae^{-i\theta} = A^2 \qquad (14i)$$

14.9. Derivation of the Intensity Function. For the fringe system formed by the transmitted light, the sum of the complex amplitudes is (see Fig. 14C)

$$Ae^{i\theta} = att' + att'r^2 e^{i\delta} + att'r^4 e^{i2\delta} + \cdots$$
$$= a(1 - r^2)(1 + r^2 e^{i\delta} + r^4 e^{i2\delta} + \cdots)$$

where $(1 - r^2)$ has been substituted for tt', according to Stokes' relation (Eq. 11o). The infinite geometric series in the second parentheses has the common ratio $r^2 \exp(i\delta)$, and has a finite sum because $r^2 < 1$. Summing the series, one obtains

$$Ae^{i\theta} = \frac{a(1 - r^2)}{1 - r^2 e^{i\delta}}$$

By Eq. 14i, the intensity is the product of this quantity by its complex conjugate, which yields

$$I_T \sim \frac{a(1 - r^2)}{1 - r^2 e^{i\delta}} \frac{a(1 - r^2)}{1 - r^2 e^{-i\delta}} = \frac{a^2(1 - r^2)^2}{1 - r^2(e^{i\delta} + e^{-i\delta}) + r^4}$$

Since $(e^{i\delta} + e^{-i\delta})/2 = \cos \delta$, and $a^2 \sim I_0$, the intensity of the incident beam, we obtain the result, in terms of real quantities only, as

$$I_T = I_0 \frac{(1 - r^2)^2}{1 - 2r^2 \cos \delta + r^4} = \frac{I_0}{1 + \dfrac{4r^2}{(1 - r^2)^2} \sin^2 \dfrac{\delta}{2}} \qquad (14j)$$

The main features of the intensity contours in Fig. 14H can be read from this equation. Thus at the maxima, where $\delta = 2\pi m$, we have $\sin^2 (\delta/2) = 0$, and $I_T = I_0$. When the reflectance r^2 is large, approaching unity, the quantity $4r^2/(1 - r^2)^2$ will also be large, and even a small departure of δ from its value for the maximum will result in a rapid drop of the intensity.

For the reflected fringes it is not necessary to carry through the summation, since we know from the conservation of energy that, if no energy is lost through absorption,

$$I_R + I_T = 1 \qquad (14k)$$

The reflected fringes are complementary to the transmitted ones, and for high reflectances become narrow dark fringes. These can be used to make more precise the study of the contour of surfaces.* If there is appreciable absorption on transmission through the surfaces, as will be the case if they are lightly silvered, one may no longer assume that Stokes' relations, nor Eq. 14k, hold. Going back to the derivation of Eq. 14j, it will be found that in this case the expression for I_T must be multiplied by $(tt')^2/(1 - r^2)^2$. Here tt' and r^2 are essentially the fractions of the intensity transmitted and reflected, respectively, by a single surface. Where the surfaces are metallized, there will be slight differences between t and t', as well as small phase changes upon reflection. The

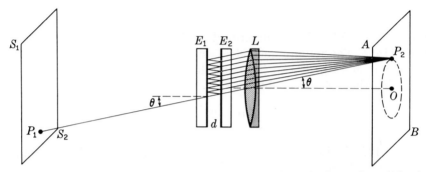

FIG. 14K. Fabry-Perot interferometer E_1E_2 set up to show the formation of circular interference fringes from multiple reflections.

transmitted fringes may still be represented by Eq. 14j, however, with an over-all reduction of intensity, and a correction to δ which merely changes slightly the effective thickness of the plate.

14.10. Fabry-Perot Interferometer. This instrument utilizes the fringes produced in the transmitted light after multiple reflection in the air film between two plane plates thinly silvered on the inner surfaces (Fig. 14K). Since the separation d between the reflecting surfaces is usually fairly large (from 0.1 to 10 cm) and observations are made near the normal direction, the fringes come under the class of fringes of equal inclination (Sec. 14.2). To observe the fringes, the light from a broad source (S_1S_2) of monochromatic light is allowed to traverse the interferometer plates E_1E_2. Since any ray incident on the first silvered surface is broken by reflection into a series of *parallel* transmitted rays, it is essential to use a lens L, which may be the lens of the eye, to bring these parallel rays together for interference. In Fig. 14K a ray from the point P_1 on the source is incident at the angle θ, producing a series of parallel rays at the same angle, which are brought together at the point P_2 on the screen AB. It is to be noted that P_2 is *not* an image of P_1. The

* S. Tolansky, "Multiple-beam Interferometry," Oxford University Press, New York, 1948.

condition for reinforcement of the transmitted rays is given by Eq. 14b with $n = 1$ for air, and $\phi' = \theta$, so that

$$2d \cos \theta = m\lambda \qquad \text{MAXIMA} \qquad (14l)$$

This condition will be fulfilled by all points on a circle through P_2 with its center at O, the intersection of the axis of the lens with the screen AB. When the angle θ is decreased, the cosine will increase until another maximum is reached for which m is greater by 1, 2, . . . , so that we have for the maxima a series of concentric rings on the screen with O as their center. Since Eq. 14l is the same as Eq. 13g for the Michelson interferometer, the spacing of the rings is the same as for the circular fringes in that instrument, and they will change in the same way with change in the distance d. In the actual interferometer one plate is fixed, while the other may be moved toward or away from it on a carriage riding on accurately machined ways by a slow-motion screw.

14.11. Brewster's* Fringes. In a single Fabry-Perot interferometer it is not practicable to observe white-light fringes, since the condition of zero path difference occurs only when the two silvered surfaces are brought into direct contact. By the use of two interferometers in series, however, it is possible to obtain interference in white light, and the resulting fringes have had important applications. The two plane-parallel "air plates" are adjusted to exactly the same thickness, or else one to some exact multiple of the other, and the two interferometers are inclined to each other at an angle of 1° or 2°. A ray that bisects the angle between the normals to the two sets of plates can then be split into two, each of which after two or more reflections emerges, having traversed the same path. In Fig. 14L these two paths are drawn as separate for the sake of clarity, though actually the two interfering beams are derived from the same incident ray, and are superimposed when they leave the system. The reader is referred to Fig. 13V, where the formation of Brewster's fringes by two thick glass plates in Jamin's interferometer is illustrated. A ray incident at any other angle than that mentioned above will give a path difference between the two emerging ones which increases with the angle, so that a system of straight fringes is produced.

The usefulness of Brewster's fringes lies chiefly in the fact that when they appear, the ratio of the two interferometer spacings is very exactly

---

* Sir David Brewster (1781–1868). Professor of physics at St. Andrew's, and later principal of the University of Edinburgh. Educated for the church, he became interested in light through repeating Newton's experiments on diffraction. He made important discoveries in double refraction and in spectrum analysis. Oddly enough, he opposed the wave theory of light in spite of the great advances in this theory that were made during his lifetime.

a whole number. Thus, in the redetermination of the length of the standard meter in terms of the wavelength of the red cadmium line, a series of interferometers was made, each having twice the length of the preceding, and these were intercompared using Brewster's fringes. The number of wavelengths in the longest, which was approximately 1 m long, could be found in a few hours by this method. It should finally be emphasized that this type of fringe results from the interference of

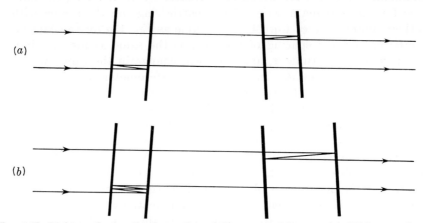

FIG. 14L. Light paths for the formation of Brewster's fringes. (a) With two plates of equal thickness. (b) With one plate twice as thick as the other. The inclination of the two plates is exaggerated.

only *two* beams, and therefore cannot be made very narrow, as can the usual fringes due to multiple reflections.

14.12. Chromatic Resolving Power. The great advantage of the Fabry-Perot interferometer over the Michelson instrument lies in the sharpness of the fringes. Thus it is able to reveal directly those details of fine structure and line width that previously could only be inferred from the behavior of the visibility curves. The difference in the appearance of the fringes for the two instruments is illustrated in Fig. 14*M*, where the circular fringes produced by a single spectral line are compared. If a second line were present, it would merely reduce the visibility in (a) but would show as a separate set of rings in (b). As will appear later, this fact also permits more exact intercomparisons of wavelength.

It is important to know how close together two wavelengths may be and still be distinguished as separate rings. The ability of any type of spectroscope to discriminate wavelengths is expressed as the ratio $\lambda/\Delta\lambda$, where λ is the mean wavelength of a barely resolved pair and $\Delta\lambda$ is the wavelength difference between the components. This ratio is called the *chromatic resolving power* of the instrument at that wavelength. In the present case, it is convenient to say that the fringes formed by λ and

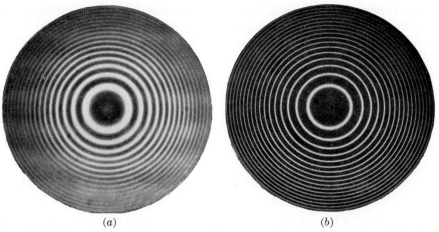

(a) (b)

FIG. 14M. Comparison of the types of fringes produced with (a) the Michelson interferometer and (b) the Fabry-Perot interferometer with surfaces of reflectance 0.8.

$\lambda + \Delta\lambda$ are just resolved when the intensity contours of the two in a particular order lie in the relative positions shown in Fig. 14N(a). If the separation $\Delta\theta$ is such as to make the curves cross at the half-intensity point, $I_T = 0.5 I_0$, there will be a central dip of 17 per cent in the sum of the two, as shown in (b) of the figure. The eye can then easily recognize the presence of two lines.

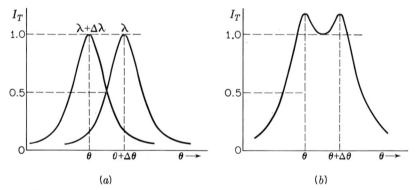

(a) (b)

FIG. 14N. Intensity contour of two Fabry-Perot fringes that are just resolved. (a) Shown separately. (b) Added, to give the observed effect.

In order to find the $\Delta\lambda$ corresponding to this separation, we note first that, in going from the maximum to the halfway point, the phase difference in either pattern must change by the amount necessary to make the second term in the denominator of Eq. 14j equal to unity. This requires that

$$\sin^2 \frac{\delta}{2} = \frac{(1 - r^2)^2}{4r^2}$$

If the fringes are reasonably sharp, the change of $\delta/2$ from a multiple of π will be small. Then the sine may be set equal to the angle, and if we denote by $\Delta\delta$ the change in going from one maximum to the position of the other, we have

$$\sin \frac{1}{2}\left(\frac{\Delta\delta}{2}\right) \simeq \frac{\Delta\delta}{4} = \frac{1 - r^2}{2r} \qquad (14m)$$

Now the relation between an angular change $\Delta\theta$ and a phase change $\Delta\delta$ may be found by differentiating Eq. 14e, setting $\phi' = \theta$ and $n = 1$.

$$\Delta\delta = -\frac{4\pi d}{\lambda} \sin \theta \, \Delta\theta \qquad (14n)$$

Furthermore, if the maximum for $\lambda + \Delta\lambda$ is to occur at this same angular separation $\Delta\theta$, Eq. 14l requires that

$$-2d \sin \theta \, \Delta\theta = m \, \Delta\lambda \qquad (14o)$$

The combination of Eqs. 14m, 14n, and 14o yields, for the chromatic resolving power,

$$\frac{\lambda}{\Delta\lambda} = m \frac{\pi r}{1 - r^2} \qquad (14p)$$

It thus depends on two quantities, the order m, which may be taken as $2d/\lambda$, and the reflectance r^2 of the surfaces. If the latter is close to unity, very large resolving powers are obtained. For example, with $r^2 = 0.9$ the second factor in Eq. 14p becomes 30, and, with a plate separation d of only 1 cm, the resolving power at $\lambda5000$ becomes 1.20×10^6. The components of a doublet only 0.0042 Å wide could be seen as separate.

14.13. Comparison of Wavelengths with the Interferometer. The ratio of the wavelengths of two lines which are not very close together, for example, the yellow mercury lines, is sometimes measured in the laboratory with the form of interferometer in which one mirror is movable. The method is based on observation of the positions of coincidence and discordance of the fringes formed by the two wavelengths, a method which has already been mentioned in Sec. 13.12. Starting with the two mirrors nearly in contact, the ring systems owing to the two wavelengths practically coincide. As d is increased, they gradually separate, and the maximum discordance occurs when the rings of one set are halfway between those of the other set. Confining our attention to the rings at the center ($\cos \theta = 1$), we may write from Eq. 14l

$$2d_1 = m_1\lambda = (m_1 + \tfrac{1}{2})\lambda' \qquad (14q)$$

where, of course, $\lambda > \lambda'$. From this,

$$m_1(\lambda - \lambda') = \frac{2d_1}{\lambda}(\lambda - \lambda') = \frac{\lambda'}{2}$$

and

$$\lambda - \lambda' = \frac{\lambda\lambda'}{4d_1} = \frac{\lambda^2}{4d_1}$$

if the difference between λ and λ' is small. On displacing the mirror still farther, the rings will presently coincide and then separate out again. At the next discordance

$$2d_2 = m_2\lambda = (m_2 + 1\tfrac{1}{2})\lambda' \tag{14r}$$

Subtracting Eq. 14q from Eq. 14r, we obtain

$$2(d_2 - d_1) = (m_2 - m_1)\lambda = (m_2 - m_1)\lambda' + \lambda'$$

whence, assuming λ approximately equal to λ', we find

$$\lambda - \lambda' = \frac{\lambda^2}{2(d_2 - d_1)} \tag{14s}$$

We can determine $d_2 - d_1$ either directly from the scale or by counting the number of fringes of the known wavelength λ between discordances.

Fig. 14O. Mechanical details of a Fabry-Perot etalon, showing spacer ring, adjusting screws, and springs.

For the most accurate work, the above method is replaced by one in which the fringe systems of the lines are photographed simultaneously with a fixed separation d of the plates. For this purpose the plates are held rigidly in place by quartz or invar spacers. A pair of Fabry-Perot plates thus mounted is called an *etalon* (Fig. 14O). The etalon can be used to determine accurately the relative wavelengths of several spectral lines from a single photographic exposure. If it were mounted with a lens as in Fig. 14K, the light containing several wavelengths, the fringe systems of the various wavelengths would be concentric with O and would be confused with each other. However, they can be separated

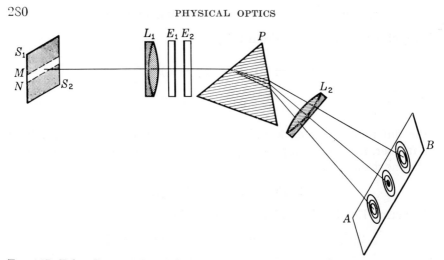

F IG . 14P. Fabry-Perot etalon and prism arrangement for separating the ring systems produced by different lines.

by inserting a prism between the etalon and the lens L. The experimental arrangement is then similar to that shown in Fig. 14P. A photograph of the visible spectrum of mercury taken in this way is shown in the upper part of Fig. 14Q. It will be seen that the fringes of the green

F IG . 14Q. Interference rings of the visible mercury spectrum taken with the Fabry-Perot etalon as shown in Fig. 14P.

and yellow lines still overlap. To overcome this, it is merely necessary to use an illuminated slit (MN of Fig. 14P) of the proper width as the source. When the interferometer is in a collimated beam of parallel light, as it is here, each point on the extended source corresponds to a given point in the ring system. Therefore only vertical sections of the ring system are obtained, as shown in the lower part of Fig. 14Q, and these no longer overlap.   When the spectrum is very rich in lines, as in Fig. 14R, the source slit must be made rather narrow.   In this photograph only sections of the upper half of the fringe systems appear. Measurements of the radii of the rings in a photograph of this type permit very accurate comparisons of wavelengths.   The determination of the correct values of m in the different systems and of the exact value

A   A A   A A   XX C   A   X

FIG. 14R. Interference patterns of the lanthanum spectrum taken with a Fabry-Perot etalon. $d = 5$ mm.   (*After Anderson.*)

of d is a rather involved process which we shall not discuss here.*   By this method the wavelengths of several hundred lines from the iron arc have been measured relative to the red cadmium line within an accuracy of a few ten-thousandths of an angstrom.

14.14. Study of Hyperfine Structure and of Line Shape.   Because of its bearing on the properties of atomic nuclei, the investigation of hyperfine structure with the Fabry-Perot interferometer has become of considerable importance in modern research.   Occasionally it will be found that a line which appears sharp and single in an ordinary spectroscope will yield ring systems consisting of two or more sets.   Examples are found in the lines marked X in the lanthanum spectrum (Fig. 14R). Those marked A are sharp to a greater or less extent.   These multiple ring systems arise from the fact that the line is actually a group of lines of wavelengths very close together, differing by perhaps a few hundredths of an angstrom.   If d is sufficiently large, these will be separated, so that in each order m we obtain effectively a short spectrum very powerfully resolved.   Any given fringe of a wavelength λ_1 is formed at such an angle that

$$2d \cos \theta_1 = m\lambda_1 \tag{14t}$$

The next fringe farther out for this same wavelength has

$$2d \cos \theta_2 = (m - 1)\lambda_1 \tag{14u}$$

* See W. E. Williams, "Applications of Interferometry," 1st ed., pp. 83–88, Methuen & Co., Ltd., London, 1930, for a description of this method.

Suppose now that λ_1 has a component line λ_2 which is very near λ_1, so that we may write $\lambda_2 = \lambda_1 - \Delta\lambda$. Suppose also that $\Delta\lambda$ is such that this component, in order m, falls on the order $m - 1$ of λ_1. Then

$$2d \cos \theta_2 = m(\lambda_1 - \Delta\lambda) \tag{14v}$$

Equating the right-hand members of Eqs. 14u and 14v,

$$\lambda_1 = m\Delta\lambda$$

Substituting the value of m from Eq. 14t and solving for $\Delta\lambda$,

$$\Delta\lambda = \frac{\lambda_1{}^2}{2d \cos \theta_1} \simeq \frac{\lambda_1{}^2}{2d} \tag{14w}$$

if θ is nearly zero. This is the wavelength interval in a given order when the fringe of the same wavelength in the next higher order is reached. We see that it is constant, independent of m. Knowing d and λ (approximately), the wavelength difference of component lines lying in this small range may be evaluated.*

The equation for the separation of orders becomes still simpler when expressed in terms of frequency. Since the frequencies of light are awkwardly large numbers, spectroscopists commonly use an equivalent quantity called the *wave number*. This is the number of waves per centimeter path in vacuum, and varies from roughly 15,000 to 25,000 cm^{-1} in going from red to violet. Denoting wave number by σ, we have

$$\sigma = \frac{1}{\lambda} = \frac{k}{2\pi}$$

To find the wave-number difference $\Delta\sigma$ corresponding to the $\Delta\lambda$ in Eq. 14w, we may differentiate the above equation to obtain

$$\Delta\sigma = -\frac{\Delta\lambda}{\lambda^2}$$

Substitution in Eq. 14w then yields

$$\Delta\sigma = -\frac{1}{2d} \tag{14x}$$

Hence, if d is expressed in centimeters, $1/2d$ gives the wave-number difference, which is seen to be independent of the order (neglecting the variation of θ) and of wavelength as well.

The study of the width and shape of individual spectrum lines, even though they may have no hyperfine structure, is of interest because it can

* For a good account of the methods, see K. W. Meissner, *J. Opt. Soc. Am.*, **31**, 405, 1941.

give us information as to the conditions of temperature, pressure, etc., in the light source.   If the interferometer has a high resolving power, the fringes will have a contour corresponding closely to that of the line itself. The small width which is inherent in the instrument can be determined by observations with an extremely small etalon spacer, and appropriate corrections made.

The difficult adjustment of the Fabry-Perot interferometer lies in the attainment of accurate parallelism of the silvered surfaces.   This operation is usually accomplished by the use of screws and springs, which hold the plates against the spacer rings shown in Fig. 140.   A brass ring A with three quartz or invar pins constitutes the spacer.   A source of light such as a mercury arc is set up with a sheet of ground glass G on one side of the etalon, and then viewed from the opposite side as shown at E.   With the eye focused for infinity, a system of rings will be seen with the reflected image of the pupil of the eye at its center.   As the eye is moved up and down or from side to side, the ring system will also move along with the image of the eye.   If the rings on moving up expand in size, the plates are farther apart at the top than at the bottom. Tightening the top screw will then depress the corresponding separator pin enough to produce the required change in alignment.   When the plates are properly adjusted, and if they are exactly plane, the rings will remain the same size as the eye is moved to any point of the field of view.

Sometimes it is convenient to place the etalon in front of the slit of a spectrograph rather than in front of the prism.   In such cases the light incident on the etalon need not be parallel.   A lens must, however, follow the etalon, and this must always be set with the slit at its focal plane.   This lens selects parallel rays from the etalon and focuses interference rings on the slit.   Both these methods are used in practice.

14.15. Other Interference Spectroscopes.   When the light is monochromatic, or nearly so, it is not necessary that the material between the highly reflecting surfaces be air.   A single accurately plane-parallel glass plate having its surfaces lightly silvered will function as a Fabry-Perot etalon.   The use of two such plates with thicknesses in the ratio of whole numbers will result in the suppression of several of the maxima produced by the thicker plate, since any light getting through the system at a particular angle must satisfy Eq. 14l for both plates.   This arrangement, known as the *compound interferometer*, gives the resolving power of the thicker plate and the free wavelength range (Eq. 14w) of the thinner one.

The spacing of the fringes of equal inclination becomes extremely small when θ departs much from 0°.   It opens out again, however, near grazing incidence.   The *Lummer-Gehrcke plate* makes use of the first few maxima near $\theta = 90°$.   In order to get an appreciable amount of light to enter the plate, it is necessary to introduce it by a total-reflection prism cemented on one end. It then undergoes multiple internal reflections very near the critical angle, and the beams emerging at a grazing angle are brought to interference by a lens. High reflectance and resolving power are thus obtained with unsilvered surfaces.

Because of its flexibility, the Fabry-Perot interferometer has for research purposes largely replaced such instruments having a fixed spacing of the surfaces. For special purposes, however, they may be valuable.*

14.16. Channeled Spectra. Interference Filter. Our discussion of the Fabry-Perot interferometer was concerned primarily with the dependence of the intensity on plate separation and on angle for a single wavelength, or perhaps for two or more wavelengths close together. If the instrument is placed in a parallel beam of white light, interference will also occur for all the monochromatic components of such light, but this will not manifest itself until the transmitted beam is dispersed by an auxiliary spectroscope. One then observes a series of bright fringes in the spectrum, each formed by a wavelength somewhat different from the next. The maxima will occur, according to Eq. 14l, at wavelengths given by

$$\lambda = \frac{2d \cos \theta}{m} \tag{14y}$$

where m is any whole number. If d is a separation of a few millimeters, there will be very many narrow fringes (more than 12,000 through the visible spectrum when $d = 5$ mm), and high dispersion is necessary in order to separate them. Such fringes are referred to as a *channeled spectrum*, or as Edser-Butler bands, and have been used, for example, in the calibration of spectroscopes for the infrared and in accurate measurements of wavelengths of the absorption lines in the solar spectrum.

An application of these fringes having considerable practical importance uses the situation where d is extremely small, so that only one or two maxima occur within the visible range of wavelengths. With white light incident, only one or two narrow bands of wavelength will then be transmitted, the rest of the light being reflected. The pair of semitransparent metallic films thus can act as a *filter* passing nearly monochromatic light. The curves of transmitted energy against wavelength resemble those of Fig. 14H, since according to Eq. 14e the phase difference δ is inversely proportional to wavelength for a given separation d.

In order that the maxima shall be widely separated, it is necessary that m be a small number. This is attained only by having the reflecting

* For a more detailed description of these and other similar instruments, see A. C. Candler, "Modern Interferometers," Hilger and Watts, London, 1951.

surfaces very close together.   If one wishes to have the maximum for $m = 2$ occur at a given wavelength λ, the metal films would have to be a distance λ apart.   The maximum $m = 1$ will then appear at a wavelength of 2λ.   Such minute separations can be attained, however, with modern techniques of evaporation in vacuum.   A semitransparent metal film is first evaporated on a plate of glass.   Next, a thin layer of some dielectric material such as cryolite ($3\mathrm{NaF \cdot AlF_3}$) is evaporated on top of this, and then the dielectric layer is in turn coated with another similar film of metal.   Finally another plate of glass is placed over the films for mechanical protection. The completed filter then has the cross section shown schematically in Fig. 14S, where the thickness of the films is greatly exaggerated relative to that of the glass plates.   Since the path difference is now in the dielectric of index n, the wavelengths of maximum transmission for normal incidence are given by

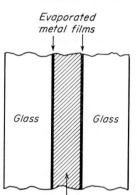

Evaporated metal films

Glass   Glass

$$\lambda = \frac{2nd}{m} \tag{14z}$$

Evaporated layer of transparent material

Fig. 14S. Cross section of an interference filter.

If there are two maxima in the visible spectrum, one of them can easily be eliminated by using colored glass for the protecting cover plate. Interference filters are now made which transmit a band of wavelengths of width (at half transmission) only 15 Å, with the maximum lying at any desired wavelength.   The transmission at the maximum can be as high as 45 per cent.   It is very difficult to obtain combinations of colored glass or gelatin filters which will accomplish this purpose.   Furthermore, since the interference filter reflects rather than absorbs the unwanted wavelengths, there is no trouble with its overheating.

PROBLEMS

1. Fringes of equal thickness are often used to compare the lengths of standard end gauges, which consist of cylindrical pieces of steel with ends that are accurately flat and parallel.   Suppose that two of these which are nominally of equal length are placed on an optical flat, and another glass flat laid across the top.   If sodium fringes are then formed between the latter and the top surfaces of the gauges, it is found that there are eight fringes per centimeter.   The points of contact of the flat with the two gauges are 5 cm apart.   Find the difference in length of the gauges.

2. In an experiment with Newton's rings, the diameters of the sixth and twentieth bright rings formed by the green mercury line are measured to be 1.76 and 3.22 mm, respectively.   Calculate the radius of curvature of the convex surface.   *Ans.* 23.78 cm.

3. Three spherical surfaces of large radius are to be compared by observing Newton's rings when they are placed together in pairs.   The diameters of the sixteenth bright ring in the three possible combinations are found to be 16.0, 20.8, and 12.8 mm, with light of wavelength 5000 Å. Find the three radii of curvature.

4. A nonreflecting layer is to be deposited on the surface of a lens having $n = 1.780$. Assuming that the coating material has an index of 1.334, what would be the necessary thickness for zero reflection at 5500 Å? What would be the reflectance of the layer at 6500 Å? The reflectance of either surface may be taken as 2.05 per cent in both cases. *Ans.* 1.031×10^{-5} cm; 0.47%.

5. Using vector diagrams, find the resultant amplitude and intensity in the interference pattern from a Fabry-Perot interferometer having a reflectance of 70 per cent, when the phase difference is (a) 0, (b) $\pi/8$, (c) $\pi/4$. Carry the vectors far enough to obtain the relative intensities to within 2 per cent.

6. The plates of a Fabry-Perot interferometer have a reflectance of 0.85. Calculate the minimum separation of the plates required to resolve the components of the H_α line of hydrogen, which is a doublet of wavelength difference 0.136 Å.

Ans. 0.82 mm.

7. Prove that the fringes in a channeled spectrum produced by means of an air film are separated by equal wave-number intervals.

8. The method of coincidences of Fabry-Perot rings is used to compare two wavelengths, one of which is exactly 4800 Å and the other slightly greater. If coincidences occur at plate separations of 1.90, 2.50, and 3.10 mm, find the unknown wavelength.

Ans. 4801.92 Å

9. If in taking the Fabry-Perot spectrogram of Fig. 14R the plate spacing had been exactly 5 mm, what would be the wavelength separation of orders for a line at 5000 Å? What would be the linear diameter of the tenth order from the center if the focal length of the camera lens were 1 m?

10. A channeled spectrum is formed by placing a microscope slide 1 mm thick in front of the slit of a spectroscope illuminated by white light. If the glass has $n_D = 1.546$, find the separation of maxima in angstroms near the sodium D lines.

Ans. 1.12 Å.

11. The Fabry-Perot rings for a line at 4649 Å, which has hyperfine structure, are photographed with an etalon spacer of 9.0 mm. The difference in the squares of the diameters of the rings formed by the strongest component is constant and equal to 28.65 mm². Two weaker components lie adjacent to the strong one, on the side opposite the center of the ring system. The squares of their diameters differ by 7.95 and 14.43 mm², respectively, from those for the strong component. Find their respective separations, in angstroms, from the main line, including the sign of the shift.

12. Design an interference filter using a layer of cryolite ($n = 1.35$) to separate two semitransparent silver layers. The filter is to transmit the yellow mercury lines (those of longest wavelength in Table 21-I) with a maximum of intensity and reduce the green line to less than 1 per cent. Find (a) the thickness of the cryolite, neglecting phase changes at the silver surfaces, and (b) the minimum reflectance required for the silver layers. *Ans.* (a) 2.141×10^{-5} cm. (b) 96.4%.

13. Prove that in the fringe system formed by a Fabry-Perot interferometer the contrast, or the ratio of the intensity of maxima to the intensity midway between maxima, is given by $(1 + r^2)^2/(1 - r^2)^2$.

14. Show that the second factor in Eq. 14p, namely $\pi r/(1 - r^2)$, represents the ratio of the separation of the fringes to their width at half intensity. (HINT: To find δ for half intensity, put $I_T/I_o = 0.5$ in Eq. 14j.)

15. A glass Lummer-Gehrcke plate is 10 cm long and 6 mm thick. If the refractive index for light of the blue cadmium line, λ4799.91, is 1.632, find the order of interference at grazing emergence. Find also the number of beams brought to interference.

16. Fringes of equal inclination are formed with a plane-parallel glass plate of index 1.50 and 2 mm thick. How many fringes are formed in the entire range from normal incidence to grazing incidence? Calculate the maximum and minimum values of their angular spacing. Take $\lambda = 6000$ Å.

Ans. 2546 fringes. $1.22°$ near $\phi = 0$. $0.0225°$ at $\phi = 49°12'$.

17. The plates of a Fabry-Perot interferometer are silvered to such a density that each reflects 90 per cent, transmits 4 per cent, and absorbs 6 per cent at a given wavelength. Find the intensity at the maximum of the rings, as compared with the value it would have were there no absorption.

CHAPTER 15

FRAUNHOFER DIFFRACTION BY A SINGLE OPENING

When a beam of light passes through a narrow slit, it spreads out to a certain extent into the region of the geometrical shadow. This effect, already noted and illustrated at the beginning of Chaps. 1 and 13, is one of the simplest examples of *diffraction*, i.e., of the failure of light to travel in straight lines. It can be satisfactorily explained only by assuming a wave character for light, and in this chapter we shall investigate quantitatively the *diffraction pattern*, or distribution of intensity of the light behind the aperture, using the principles of wave motion already discussed.

15.1. Fresnel and Fraunhofer Diffraction. Diffraction phenomena are conveniently divided into two general classes, (1) those in which the source of light and the screen on which the pattern is observed are effectively at infinite distances from the aperture causing the diffraction, and (2) those in which either the source or the screen, or both, are at finite distances from the aperture. The phenomena coming under class (1) are called, for historical reasons, *Fraunhofer diffraction*, and those coming under class (2) *Fresnel diffraction*. Fraunhofer diffraction is much simpler to treat theoretically. It is easily observed in practice by rendering the light from a source parallel with a lens, and focusing it on a screen with another lens placed behind the aperture, an arrangement which effectively removes the source and screen to infinity. In the observation of Fresnel diffraction, on the other hand, no lenses are necessary, but here the wave fronts are divergent instead of plane, and the theoretical treatment is consequently more complex. Only Fraunhofer diffraction will be considered in this chapter.

15.2. Diffraction by a Single Slit. A slit is a rectangular aperture of length large compared to its breadth. Consider a slit S to be set up as in Fig. 15A, with its long dimension perpendicular to the plane of the page, and to be illuminated by parallel monochromatic light from the narrow slit S', at the principal focus of the lens L_1. The light focused by another lens L_2 on a screen or photographic plate P at its principal focus will form a diffraction pattern, as indicated schematically. Figure 15B(b) and (c) shows two actual photographs, taken with different exposure times, of such a pattern, using violet light of wavelength 4358 Å.

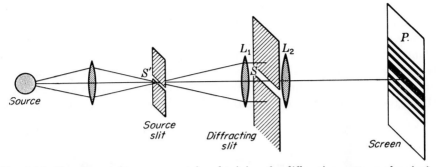

Fɪɢ. 15*A*. Experimental arrangement for obtaining the diffraction pattern of a single slit.   Fraunhofer diffraction.

The distance $S'L_1$ was 25 cm, and L_2P was 100 cm.   The width of the slit S was 0.090 mm, and of S', 0.10 mm.   If S' was widened to more than about 0.3 mm, the details of the pattern began to be lost.   On the original plate, the half width d of the central maximum was 4.84 mm.   It is important to notice that the width of the central maximum is *twice* as great as that of the fainter side maxima.   That this effect comes under

Fɪɢ. 15*B*. Photographs of the single-slit diffraction pattern.

the heading of diffraction as previously defined is clear when we note that the strip drawn in Fig. 15*B*(*a*) is the width of the geometrical image of the slit S', or practically that which would be obtained by removing the second slit and using the whole aperture of the lens.   This pattern can easily be observed by ruling a single transparent line on a photographic plate and using it in front of the eye as explained in Sec. 13.2.

The explanation of the single-slit pattern lies in the interference of the Huygens secondary wavelets which can be thought of as sent out from every point on the wave front at the instant that it occupies the plane of the slit. To a first approximation, one may consider these wavelets to be uniform spherical waves, the emission of which stops abruptly at the edges of the slit. The results obtained in this way, although they give a fairly accurate account of the observed facts, are subject to

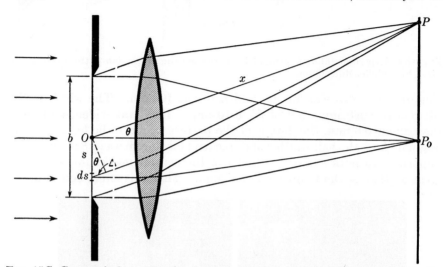

Fig. 15C. Geometrical construction for investigating the intensity in the single-slit diffraction pattern.

certain modifications in the light of the more rigorous theory to be mentioned in Sec. 18.17.

Figure 15C represents a section of a slit of width b, illuminated by parallel light from the left. Let ds be an element of width of the wave front in the plane of the slit, at a distance s from the center O, which we shall call the origin. The parts of each secondary wave which travel normal to the plane of the slit will be focused at P_0, while those which travel at any angle θ will reach P. Considering first the wavelet emitted by the element ds situated at the origin, its amplitude will be directly proportional to the length ds, and inversely proportional to the distance x. At P it will produce an infinitesimal displacement which, according to Eq. 11j for a spherical wave, may be expressed as

$$dy_0 = \frac{a\,ds}{x} \sin\,(\omega t\,-\,kx)$$

As the position of ds is varied, the displacement it produces will vary in phase because of the different path length to P. When it is at a distance

s below the origin, the contribution will be

$$dy_s = \frac{a\,ds}{x} \sin\left[\omega t - k(x + \Delta)\right]$$

$$= \frac{a\,ds}{x} \sin\left(\omega t - kx - ks \sin\theta\right) \tag{15a}$$

We now wish to sum the effects of all elements from one edge of the slit to the other. This may be done by integrating Eq. 15a from $s = -b/2$ to $b/2$. The simplest way* is to integrate the contributions from pairs of elements symmetrically placed at s and $-s$, each contribution being

$$dy = dy_{-s} + dy_s$$

$$= \frac{a\,ds}{x}\left[\sin\left(\omega t - kx - ks \sin\theta\right) + \sin\left(\omega t - kx + ks \sin\theta\right)\right]$$

By the identity $\sin\alpha + \sin\beta = 2 \cos\frac{1}{2}(\alpha - \beta) \sin\frac{1}{2}(\alpha + \beta)$, we have

$$dy = \frac{a\,ds}{x}\left[2 \cos\left(ks \sin\theta\right) \sin\left(\omega t - kx\right)\right]$$

which must be integrated from $s = 0$ to $b/2$. In doing so, x may be regarded as constant, insofar as it affects the amplitude. Thus

$$y = \frac{2a}{x} \sin\left(\omega t - kx\right) \int_0^{b/2} \cos\left(ks \sin\theta\right) ds$$

$$= \frac{2a}{x}\left[\frac{\sin\left(ks \sin\theta\right)}{k \sin\theta}\right]_0^{b/2} \sin\left(\omega t - kx\right)$$

$$= \frac{ab}{x} \frac{\sin\left(\frac{1}{2}kb \sin\theta\right)}{\frac{1}{2}kb \sin\theta} \sin\left(\omega t - kx\right) \tag{15b}$$

The resultant vibration will therefore be a simple harmonic one, the amplitude of which varies with the position of P, since the latter is determined by θ. We may represent its amplitude as

$$A = A_0 \frac{\sin\beta}{\beta} \tag{15c}$$

where $\beta = \frac{1}{2}kb \sin\theta = (\pi b \sin\theta)/\lambda$ and $A_0 = ab/x$. The quantity β is a convenient variable, which signifies one-half the phase difference between the contributions coming from opposite edges of the slit. The intensity on the screen is then

$$I \sim A^2 = A_0^2 \frac{\sin^2\beta}{\beta^2} \tag{15d}$$

* The method of complex amplitudes (Sec. 14.8) starts with $(ab/x)\int e^{iks \sin\theta}\,ds$, and yields the real amplitude upon multiplication of the result by its complex conjugate. No simplification results from using the method here.

If the light, instead of being incident on the slit perpendicular to its plane, makes an angle i, a little consideration will show that it is merely necessary to replace the above expression for β by the more general expression

$$\beta = \frac{\pi b(\sin i + \sin \theta)}{\lambda} \tag{15e}$$

15.3. Further Investigation of the Single-slit Diffraction Pattern.
In Fig. 15$D(a)$ graphs are shown of Eq. 15c for the *amplitude* (dotted curve)

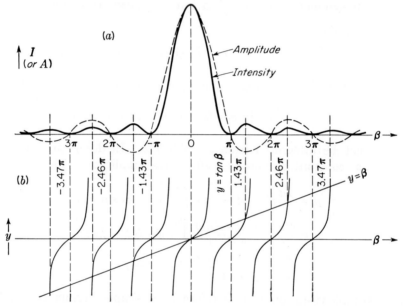

Fig. 15D. Amplitude and intensity contours for Fraunhofer diffraction of a single slit, showing positions of maxima and minima.

and Eq. 15d for the *intensity*, taking the constant A_0 in each case as unity. The intensity curve will be seen to have the form required by the experimental result in Fig. 15B. The maximum intensity of the strong central band comes at the point P_0 of Fig. 15C, where evidently all the secondary wavelets will arrive in phase because the path difference $\Delta = 0$. For this point $\beta = 0$, and although the quotient $(\sin \beta)/\beta$ becomes indeterminate for $\beta = 0$, it will be remembered that $\sin \beta$ approaches β for small angles, and is equal to it when β vanishes. Hence for $\beta = 0$, $(\sin \beta)/\beta = 1$. We now see the significance of the constant A_0. Since for $\beta = 0$, $A = A_0$, it represents the amplitude when all the wavelets arrive in phase. $A_0{}^2$ is then the value of the maximum intensity, at the center of the pattern. From this *principal maximum* the intensity falls to zero at $\beta = \pm\pi$, then passes through several *secondary maxima*, with equally spaced points of zero intensity at $\beta = \pm\pi$, $\pm 2\pi$, $\pm 3\pi$, . . . , or in general $\beta = m\pi$. The secondary maxima do not fall halfway between these points, but are displaced toward the center of the pattern by an amount which decreases with increasing m. The exact values of β for these maxima can be found by differentiating Eq. 15c with respect to β and equating to zero. This yields the condition

$$\tan \beta = \beta$$

The values of β satisfying this relation are easily found graphically as the intersections of the curve

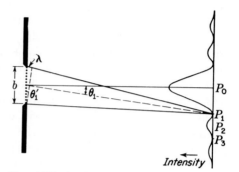

FIG. 15E. Angle of the first minimum of the single-slit diffraction pattern.

$y = \tan \beta$ and the straight line $y = \beta$. In Fig. 15D(b) these points of intersection lie directly below the corresponding secondary maxima.

The intensities of the secondary maxima may be calculated to a very close approximation by finding the values of $(\sin^2 \beta)/\beta^2$ at the halfway positions, i.e., where $\beta = 3\pi/2$, $5\pi/2$, $7\pi/2$, ... This gives $4/(9\pi^2)$, $4/(25\pi^2)$, $4/(49\pi^2)$, . . . , or $\dfrac{1}{22.2}$, $\dfrac{1}{61.7}$, $\dfrac{1}{121}$, . . . , of the intensity of the principal maximum. Reference to Table 15-I ahead, where the exact values of the maxima are given, will show that the approximation is very good. The first secondary maximum, where the deviation is largest, is actually 4.72 per cent of the central intensity, whereas the above figure of 1/22.2 corresponds to 4.50 per cent.

A very clear idea of the origin of the single-slit pattern is obtained by the following simple treatment. Consider the light from the slit of Fig. 15E coming to the point P_1 on the screen, this point being just one wavelength farther from the upper edge of the slit than from the lower. The secondary wavelet from the point in the slit adjacent to the upper edge will travel approximately $\lambda/2$ farther than that from the point at the center, and so these two will produce vibrations with a phase difference of π and will give a resultant displacement of zero at P_1. Similarly the wavelet from the next point below the upper edge will cancel that from the next point below the center, and we may continue this pairing off to include all points in the wave front, so that the resultant effect at P_1 is zero. At P_3 the path difference is 2λ, and if we divide the slit into four parts, the pairing of points again gives zero resultant, since the parts cancel in pairs. For the point P_2, on the other hand, the path difference is $3\lambda/2$, and we may divide the slit into thirds, two of which will cancel, leaving one third to account for the intensity at this point. The resultant amplitude at P_2 is, of course, not even approximately one-third that at P_0, because the phases of the wavelets from the remaining third are not by any means equal.

The above method, though instructive, is not exact if the screen is at a finite distance from the slit. As Fig. 15E is drawn, the shorter broken line is drawn to cut off equal distances on the rays to P_1. It will be seen from this that the path difference to P_1 between the light coming from the upper edge and that from the center is slightly greater than $\lambda/2$, and that between the center and lower edge slightly less than $\lambda/2$. Hence the resultant intensity will not be zero at P_1 and P_3, but it will be more nearly so the greater the distance between slit and screen, or the narrower the slit. This corresponds to the transition from Fresnel diffraction to Fraunhofer diffraction. Obviously, with the relative dimensions shown in the figure, the geometrical shadow of the slit would considerably widen the central maximum as drawn. Just as was true with Young's experiment (Sec. 13.3), when the screen is at infinity, the relations become simpler. Then the two angles θ_1 and θ_1' in Fig. 15E become exactly equal (i.e., the two broken lines are perpendicular to each other), and $\lambda = b \sin \theta_1$ for the first minimum corresponding to $\beta = \pi$.

In practice θ_1 is usually a very small angle, so we may put the sine equal to the angle. Then

$$\theta_1 = \frac{\lambda}{b}$$

a relation which shows at once how the dimensions of the pattern vary with λ and b. The *linear* width of the pattern on a screen will be proportional to the slit-screen distance, which is the focal length f of a lens placed close to the slit. The linear distance d between successive minima corresponding to the angular separation $\theta_1 = \lambda/b$ is thus

$$d = \frac{f\lambda}{b}$$

The width of the pattern increases in proportion to the wavelength, so that for red light it is roughly twice as wide as for violet light, the slit width, etc., being the same. If white light is used, the central maximum is white in the middle, but is reddish on its outer edge, shading into a purple and other impure colors farther out.

The angular width of the pattern for a given wavelength is inversely proportional to the slit width b, so that as b is made larger, the pattern shrinks rapidly to a smaller scale. In photographing Fig. 15B, if the slit S had been 9 mm wide, the whole visible pattern (of five maxima) would be included in a width of 0.24 mm on the original plate instead of 2.4 cm.   This fact, that when the width of the aperture is large compared to a wavelength the diffraction is practically negligible, led the early investigators to conclude that light travels in straight lines and that it could not be a wave motion.   Sound waves, whose lengths are measured in feet, will evidently be diffracted through large angles in passing through an aperture of ordinary size, such as an open window.

15.4. Graphical Treatment of Amplitudes.   The Vibration Curve. The addition of the amplitude contributions from all the secondary wavelets originating in the slit may be carried out by a graphical method based on the vector addition of amplitudes discussed in Sec. 12.2.   It will be worth while to consider this method in some detail, because it may be applied to advantage in other more complicated cases to be treated in later chapters, and because it gives a very clear physical picture of the origin of the diffraction pattern.   Let us divide the width of the slit into a fairly large number of equal parts, say 9.   The amplitude r contributed at a point on the screen by any one of these parts will be the same, since they are of equal width.   The phases of these contributions will differ, however, for any point except that lying on the axis, i.e., on the normal to the slit at its center (P_0, Fig. 15C).   For a point off the axis, each of the 9 segments will contribute vibrations differing in phase, because the segments are at different average distances from the point.   Furthermore the difference in phase δ between the contributions from adjacent segments will be constant, since each element is on the average the same amount farther away (or nearer) than its neighbor.

Now, using the fact that the resultant amplitude and phase may be found by the vector addition of the individual amplitudes making angles with each other equal to the phase difference, a vector diagram like that shown in Fig. 15F(b) may be drawn.   Each of the 9 equal amplitudes a is inclined at an angle δ with the preceding one, and their vector sum A is the resultant amplitude required.   Now suppose that instead of dividing the slit into 9 elements, we had divided it into many thousand or, in the limit, an infinite number of equal elements.   The vectors a would become shorter, but at the same time δ would decrease in the same proportion, so that in the limit our vector diagram would approach the arc of a circle, shown as in (b').   The resultant amplitude A is still the same and equal to the length of the chord of this arc.   Such a continuous curve, representing the addition of infinitesimal amplitudes, we shall refer to as a *vibration curve*.

To show that this method is in agreement with our previous result, we note that the length of the arc is just the amplitude A_0 obtained when all of the component vibrations are in phase, as in (a) of the figure. Introducing a phase difference between the components does not alter

their individual amplitudes or the algebraic sum of these. Hence the
ratio of the resultant amplitude A at any point in the screen to A_0, that
on the axis, is the ratio of the chord to the arc of the circle. Since β
stands for half the phase difference from opposite edges of the slit, the angle
subtended by the arc is just 2β, because the first and last vectors a will
have a phase difference of 2β. In Fig. 15$F(b')$, the radius of the arc is

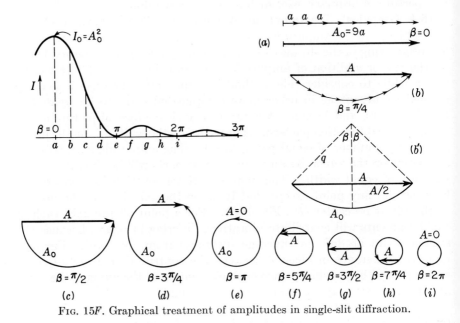

FIG. 15F. Graphical treatment of amplitudes in single-slit diffraction.

called q, and a perpendicular has been dropped from the center on the
chord A. From the geometry of the figure, we have

$$\sin \beta = \frac{A/2}{q} \qquad A = 2q \sin \beta$$

and hence

$$\frac{A}{A_0} = \frac{\text{chord}}{\text{arc}} = \frac{2q \sin \beta}{q \times 2\beta} = \frac{\sin \beta}{\beta}$$

in agreement with Eq. 15c.

As we go out from the center of the diffraction pattern, the length of
the arc remains constant and equal to A_0, but its curvature increases
owing to the larger phase difference δ introduced between the infinitesimal component vectors a. The vibration curve thus winds up on itself
as β increased. The successive diagrams (a) to (i) in Fig. 15F are
drawn for the indicated values of β at intervals of $\pi/4$, and the corresponding points are similarly lettered on the intensity diagram. A study

of these figures will bring out clearly the cause of the variations in intensity occurring in the single-slit pattern.   In particular, one sees that the asymmetry of the secondary maxima follows from the fact that the radius of the circle is shrinking with increasing β.   Thus A will reach its maximum length slightly before the condition represented in Fig. $15F(g)$.

15.5. Rectangular Aperture.   In the preceding sections the intensity function for a slit was derived by summing the effects of the spherical wavelets originating from a linear section of the wave front by a plane

FIG. 15G. Diffraction pattern from a rectangular opening.   (*After A. Köhler.*)

perpendicular to the length of the slit, i.e., by the plane of the page in Fig. 15C.   Nothing was said about the contributions from parts of the wave front out of this plane.   A more thorough mathematical investigation, involving a double integration over both dimensions of the wave front,* shows, however, that the above result is correct when the slit is very long compared to its width.   The complete treatment gives, for a slit of width b and length l, the following expression for the intensity:

$$I \sim b^2 l^2 \frac{\sin^2 \beta}{\beta^2} \cdot \frac{\sin^2 \gamma}{\gamma^2} \tag{15f}$$

where $\beta = (\pi b \sin \theta)/\lambda$, as before, and $\gamma = (\pi l \sin \Omega)/\lambda$.   The angles θ and Ω are measured from the normal to the aperture at its center, in planes through the normal parallel to the sides b and l, respectively. The diffraction pattern given by Eq. 15f when b and l are comparable with each other is illustrated in Fig. 15G.   The dimensions of the aper-

* See R. W. Wood, "Physical Optics," 2d ed., pp. 195–202, The Macmillan Company, New York, 1921.

ture are shown by the white rectangle in the lower left-hand part of the figure. The intensity in the pattern is concentrated principally in two directions coinciding with the sides of the aperture, and in each of these directions it corresponds to the simple pattern for a slit width equal to the width of the aperture in that direction. Owing to the inverse proportionality between the slit width and the scale of the pattern, the fringes are more closely spaced in the direction of the longer dimension of the aperture. In addition to these patterns there are other faint maxima, as shown in the figure. This diffraction pattern may easily be observed by illuminating a small rectangular aperture with monochromatic light from a source which is effectively a *point*, the disposition of the lenses and the distance of the source and screen being similar to those described for observation of the slit pattern (Sec. 15.2). The cross formed by the brightest spots in the photograph is the one always observed when a bright street light is seen through a wet umbrella.

Now for a slit having l very large, the factor $(\sin^2 \gamma)/\gamma^2$ in Eq. 15f is zero for all values of Ω except extremely small ones. This means that the diffraction pattern will be limited to a line on the screen perpendicular to the slit and will resemble a section of the central horizontal line of bright spots in Fig. 15G. We do not ordinarily observe such a line pattern in diffraction by a slit, because its observation requires the use of a *point source*. In Fig. 15A the primary source was a slit S', with its long dimension perpendicular to the page. In this case, each point of the source slit forms a line pattern, but these fall adjacent to each other on the screen, adding up to give a pattern like Fig. 15B. If we were to use a slit source with the rectangular aperture of Fig. 15G, the slit being parallel to the side l, the result would be the summation of a number of such patterns, one above the other, and would be identical with Fig. 15B.

These considerations can easily be extended to cover the effect of widening the primary slit. With a slit of finite width, each line element parallel to the length of the slit forms a pattern like Fig. 15B. The resultant pattern is equivalent to a set of such patterns displaced laterally with respect to each other. If the slit is too wide, the single-slit pattern will therefore be lost. No great change will occur until the patterns from the two edges of the slit are displaced about one-fourth of the distance from the central maximum to the first minimum. This condition will hold when the width of the primary slit subtends an angle of $\frac{1}{4} (\lambda/b)$ at the first lens, as can be seen by reference to Fig. 15H below.

15.6. Resolving Power with a Rectangular Aperture. By the resolving power of an optical instrument we mean its ability to produce separate images of objects very close together. Using the laws of geometrical optics, a telescope or a microscope is designed to give an image of a point source which is as small as possible. However, in the final analysis, it is the diffraction pattern that sets a theoretical upper limit to the resolving power. We have seen that whenever parallel light passes through any aperture, it cannot be focused to a point image, but instead gives a diffraction pattern in which the central maximum has a certain finite width, inversely proportional to the width of the aperture. The images of two objects will evidently not be resolved if their separation is much less than the width of the central diffraction maximum. The aperture here involved is usually that of the objective lens of the telescope or microscope and is therefore circular. Diffraction by a circular aperture will be considered below in Sec. 15.8, and here we shall treat the somewhat simpler case of a rectangular aperture.

Fig. 15H. Diffraction images of two slit sources formed by a rectangular aperture.

Figure 15H shows two plano-convex lenses (equivalent to a single double-convex lens) limited by a rectangular aperture of vertical dimension b. Two narrow slit sources S_1 and S_2 perpendicular to the plane of the figure form real images S_1' and S_2' on a screen. Each image consists of a single-slit diffraction pattern for which the intensity distribution is plotted in a vertical direction. The angular separation α of the central maxima is equal to the angular separation of the sources, and with the value shown in the figure is adequate to give separate images. The condition illustrated is that in which each principal maximum falls exactly on the second minimum of the adjacent pattern. This is the smallest possible value of α which will give zero intensity between the two strong maxima in the resultant pattern. The angular separation from the center to the second minimum in either pattern then corresponds to $\beta = 2\pi$ (see Fig. 15D), or $\sin \theta \simeq \theta = 2\lambda/b = 2\theta_1$. As α is made smaller than this, and the two images move closer together, the intensity between the maxima will rise, until finally no minimum remains at the center. Figure 15I illustrates this by showing the resultant curve (heavy line) for four different values of α. In each case the resultant pattern has been obtained by merely adding the intensities due to the separate patterns (dotted and light curves), as was done in the case of the Fabry-Perot fringes (Sec. 14.12).

Inspection of this figure shows that it would be impossible to resolve the two images if the maxima were much closer than $\alpha = \theta_1$, corresponding to $\beta = \pi$. At this separation the maximum of one pattern falls exactly on the first minimum of the other, so that the intensities of the maxima in the resultant pattern are equal to those of the separate maxima. The calculations are therefore simpler than for Fabry-Perot fringes, where at no point does the intensity actually become zero. To find the intensity at the center of the resultant minimum for diffraction

FIG. 15I. Diffraction images of two slit sources.   (a) and (b) Well resolved.   (c) Just resolved.   (d) Not resolved.

fringes separated by θ_1, we note that the curves cross at $\beta = \pi/2$ for either pattern and

$$\frac{\sin^2 \beta}{\beta^2} = \frac{4}{\pi^2} = 0.4053$$

the intensity of either relative to the maximum. The sum of the contributions at this point is therefore 0.8106, which shows that the intensity of the resultant pattern drops almost to four-fifths of its maximum value. This change of intensity is easily visible to the eye, and in fact a considerably smaller change could be seen, or at least detected with a sensitive intensity-measuring instrument such as a microphotometer. However, the depth of the minimum changes very rapidly with separation in this region, and in view of the simplicity of the relations in this particular case, it was decided by Rayleigh to arbitrarily fix the separation $\alpha = \theta_1 = \lambda/b$ as the criterion for resolution of two diffraction patterns. This quite arbitrary choice is known as "Rayleigh's criterion." The angle θ_1 is sometimes called the "resolving power" of the aperture b, although the ability to resolve increases as θ_1 becomes smaller. A more appropriate designation for θ_1 is the *minimum angle of resolution*.

15.7. Chromatic Resolving Power of a Prism. An example of the use of this criterion for the resolving power of a rectangular aperture is found in the prism spectroscope, if we assume that the face of the prism limits the refracted beam to a rectangular section. Thus, in Fig. 15J, the minimum angle $\Delta\delta$ between two parallel beams which give rise to images on the limit of resolution is such that $\Delta\delta = \theta_1 = \lambda/b$, where b

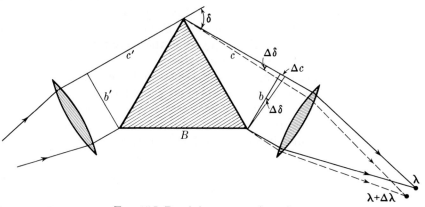

FIG. 15J. Resolving power of a prism.

is the width of the emerging beam. The two beams giving these images differ in wavelength by a small increment $\Delta\lambda$, which is negative because the smaller wavelengths are deviated through greater angles. The wavelength increment is more useful than the increment of angle, and is the quantity that enters in the chromatic resolving power $\lambda/\Delta\lambda$ (Sec. 14.12). To evaluate this for the prism, we first note that, since any optical path between two successive positions b' and b of the wave front must be the same, we can write

$$c + c' = nB \tag{15g}$$

Here n is the refractive index of the prism for the wavelength λ, and B the length of the base of the prism. Now, if the wavelength be decreased by $\Delta\lambda$, the optical path through the base of the prism becomes $(n + \Delta n)B$, and the emergent wave front must turn through an angle $\Delta\delta = \lambda/b$ in order that the image it forms may be just resolved. Since, from the figure, $\Delta\delta = (\Delta c)/b$, this amount of turning increases the length of the upper ray by $\Delta c = \lambda$. It is immaterial whether we measure Δc along the rays λ or $\lambda + \Delta\lambda$, because only a difference of the second order is involved. Then we have

$$c + c' + \lambda = (n + \Delta n)B$$

and, subtracting Eq. 15g,

$$\lambda = B \, \Delta n$$

The desired result is now obtained by dividing by $\Delta\lambda$ and substituting the derivative $dn/d\lambda$ for the ratio of small increments.

$$\frac{\lambda}{\Delta\lambda} = B \frac{dn}{d\lambda} \tag{15h}$$

It is not difficult to show (see Prob. 1) that this expression also equals the product of the angular dispersion and the width b of the emergent beam. Furthermore, we find that Eq. 15h can still be applied when the beam does not fill the prism, in which case B must be the difference in the extreme paths through the prism, and when there are two or more prisms in tandem, when B is the sum of the bases.

15.8. Circular Aperture. The diffraction pattern formed by plane waves from a point source passing through a circular aperture is of considerable importance as applied to the resolving power of telescopes and other optical instruments. Unfortunately it is also a problem of considerable difficulty, since it requires a double integration over the surface

TABLE 15-I

Ring	Circular aperture			Single slit	
	m	I_{max}	I_{total}	m	I_{max}
Central maximum.........	0	1	1	0	1
First dark...............	1.220			1.000	
Second bright...........	1.635	0.01750	0.084	1.430	0.0472
Second dark.............	2.233			2.000	
Third bright............	2.679	0.00416	0.033	2.459	0.0165
Third dark..............	3.238			3.000	
Fourth bright...........	3.699	0.00160	0.018	3.471	0.0083
Fourth dark.............	4.241			4.000	
Fifth bright.............	4.710	0.00078	0.011	4.477	0.0050
Fifth dark..............	5.243			5.000	

of the aperture similar to that mentioned in Sec. 15.5 for a rectangular aperture. The problem was first solved by Airy* in 1835, and the solution is obtained in terms of Bessel functions of order unity. These must be calculated from series expansions, and the most convenient way to express the results for our purpose will be to quote the actual figures obtained in this way (Table 15-I).

* Sir George Airy (1801–1892). Astronomer Royal of England from 1835 to 1881. Also known for his work on the aberration of light (Sec. 19.13). For details of the solution here referred to, see T. Preston, "Theory of Light," 5th ed., pp. 324–327, Macmillan & Co., Ltd., London, 1928.

The diffraction pattern as illustrated in Fig. 15K(a) consists of a bright central disk, known as *Airy's disk*, surrounded by a number of fainter rings. Neither the disk nor the rings are sharply limited but shade gradually off at the edges, being separated by circles of zero intensity. The intensity distribution is very much the same as that which would be obtained with the single-slit pattern illustrated in Fig. 15E by rotating it about an axis in the direction of the light and passing through the principal maximum. The dimensions of the pattern are,

FIG. 15K. Photographs of diffraction images of point sources taken with a circular aperture. (a) One source. (b) Two sources just resolved. (c) Two sources completely resolved.

however, appreciably different from those in a single-slit pattern for a slit of width equal to the diameter of the circular aperture. For the single-slit pattern, the angular separation θ of the minima from the center was found in Sec. 15.3 to be given by $\sin \theta \simeq \theta = m\lambda/b$, where m is any whole number, starting with unity. The dark circles separating the bright ones in the pattern from a circular aperture may be expressed by a similar formula, if θ is now the angular semidiameter of the circle, but in this case the numbers m are not integers. Their numerical values as calculated by Lommel* are given in Table 15-I. This table also includes the values of m for the maxima of the bright rings, and data on their intensities. The column headed I_{max} gives the relative intensities of the maxima, while that headed I_{total} is the total amount of light in the ring, relative to that of the central disk. For comparison, the values of m and I_{max} for the straight bands of the single-slit pattern are also included.

* E. V. Lommel, *Abhandl. Bayer Akad. Wiss.*, **15**, 531, 1886.

15.9. Resolving Power of a Telescope. To give an idea of the linear size of the above diffraction pattern, let us calculate the radius of the first dark ring in the image formed in the focal plane of an ordinary field glass. The diameter of the objective is 4 cm and its focal length 30 cm. White light has an effective wavelength of 5.6×10^{-5} cm, so that the angular radius of this ring is $\theta = 1.220 \dfrac{5.6 \times 10^{-5}}{4} = 1.71 \times 10^{-5}$ rad. The linear radius is this angle multiplied by the focal length and therefore amounts to $30 \times 1.71 \times 10^{-5} = 0.000512$ cm, or almost exactly 0.005 mm. The central disk for this telescope is then 0.01 mm in diameter when the object is a point source such as a star.

Extending Rayleigh's criterion for the resolution of diffraction patterns (Sec. 15.6) to the circular aperture, two patterns are said to be resolved when the central maximum of one falls on the first dark ring of the other. The resultant pattern in this condition is shown in Fig. $15K(b)$. The minimum angle of resolution for a telescope is therefore

$$\theta_1 = 1.220 \frac{\lambda}{D} \tag{15i}$$

where D is the diameter of the circular aperture which limits the beam forming the primary image, or usually that of the objective. For the example chosen above, the angle calculated is just this limiting angle, so that the smallest angular separation of a double star which could be theoretically resolved by this telescope is 1.71×10^{-5} rad, or 3.52 seconds of arc. Since the minimum angle is inversely proportional to D, we see that the aperture necessary to resolve two sources 1 second apart is 3.52 times as great as in the example, or that

$$\text{Minimum angle of resolution in seconds } \theta_1 = \frac{14.1}{D} \tag{15j}$$

D being the aperture of the objective in centimeters. For the largest refracting telescope in existence, that at the Yerkes Observatory, $D = 40$ in. and $\theta_1 = 0.14$ sec. This may be compared with the minimum angle of resolution for the eye, the pupil of which has a diameter of about 3 mm. We find $\theta_1 = 47$ seconds of arc.* Actually the eye of the average person is not able to resolve objects less than about 1 minute apart, and the limit is therefore effectively determined by optical defects in the eye or by the structure of the retina.

With a given objective in a telescope, the angular size of the image as

---

* It might at first appear that the wavelength to be used in this calculation would be that in the vitreous humor of the eye. It is true that the dimensions of the diffraction pattern are smaller on this account, but the separation of two images is also decreased in the same proportion by refraction of the rays as they enter the eye.

seen by the eye is determined by the magnification of the eyepiece. However, increasing the size of the image by increasing the power of the eyepiece does not increase the amount of detail that can be seen, since it is impossible by magnification to bring out detail which is not originally present in the primary image. Each point in an object becomes a small circular diffraction pattern or disk in the image, so that if an eyepiece of very high power is used, the image appears blurred and no greater detail is seen. Thus diffraction by the objective is the one factor that limits the resolving power of a telescope.

The diffraction pattern of a circular aperture, as well as the resolving power of a telescope, can be demonstrated by an experimental arrangement similar to that shown in Fig. 15H. The point sources at S_1 and S_2 consist of a sodium or mercury arc and a screen with several pinholes about 0.35 mm in diameter and spaced from 2 to 10 mm apart. These may be viewed with one of three small holes 1, 2, and 4 mm in diameter, mounted in front of the objective lens to show how an increasing aperture affects the resolution. Under these circumstances the intensity will not be sufficient to show anything but the central disks. In order to observe the subsidiary diffraction rings, the best source to use is the concentrated-arc lamp to be described in Sec. 21.2.

The theoretical resolving power of a telescope will be realized only if the lenses are geometrically perfect and if the magnification is at least equal to the so-called "normal" magnification (Sec. 7.14). To prove the latter statement, we note that two diffraction disks which are on the limit of resolution in the focal plane of the objective must subtend at the eye an angle of at least $\theta_1' = 1.22\lambda/d_e$ in order to be resolved by the eye. Here d_e represents the diameter of the eye pupil. Now according to Eq. 10k the magnification

$$M = \frac{\theta'}{\theta} = \frac{D}{d}$$

where D is the diameter of the entrance pupil (objective) and d that of the exit pupil. At the normal magnification, d is made equal to d_e, so that the normal magnification becomes

$$\frac{D}{d_e} \equiv \frac{1.22\lambda/d_e}{1.22\lambda/D} = \frac{\theta_1'}{\theta_1}$$

Hence, if the diameter d of the exit pupil is made larger than d_e, that of the eye pupil, we have $\theta' < \theta_1'$ and the images will cease to be resolved by the eye even though they are resolved in the focal plane of the objective. In other words, any magnification that is less than the normal one corresponds to an exit pupil larger than d_e, and will not afford the resolution that the instrument could give.

15.10. Brightness and Illuminance of Star Images. It was proved in Sec. 7.13 that regardless of the aperture of an instrument, for magnifications up to the normal magnification the brightness of the image of an extended object remains constant and at most equal to that of the object. If the object is a point source this is no longer true, but instead the brightness increases rapidly for larger apertures. This is because all the light collected by the objective is concentrated in a diffraction pattern at its focal plane, and the area of this pattern varies inversely as the square of the diameter of the objective (Eq. 15i). Assuming normal magnification or greater, all light from the objective is admitted by the eye pupil, and the increase in brightness due to the telescope therefore equals the ratio of the area of the objective to that of the eye pupil. If the magnification is less than the normal, the eye constitutes the aperture stop and the exit pupil, and its image formed by the telescope is the entrance pupil. The ratio of their areas is the square of the magnification of the telescope, which then gives the factor by which the brightness is increased. The area of the retina illuminated remains constant, since it is determined by the diffraction pattern produced by the pupil of the eye.

The illuminance of the image of a point source may be calculated by multiplying the illuminance of the objective by the ratio of its area to that of the central disk of the diffraction pattern it produces, because most of the light entering the objective goes into this disk. Thus the illuminance will be proportional to the area of the objective. It is chiefly for this reason that attempts are constantly being made to increase the diameter of telescope objectives. The 200-in. mirror of the Mt. Palomar telescope permits the photography of much fainter objects than has heretofore been possible.

15.11. Resolving Power of a Microscope. In this case the same principles are applicable. The conditions are, however, different from those for a telescope, in which we were chiefly interested in the smallest permissible angular separation of two objects at a large, and usually unknown, distance. With a microscope the object is very close to the objective, and the latter subtends a large angle $2i$ at the object plane, as shown in Fig. 15L. Here we wish primarily to know the smallest distance between two points O and O' in the object which will produce images I and I' that are just resolved. Each image consists of a disk and a system of rings, as explained above, and the angular separation of two disks when they are on the limit of resolution is $\alpha = \theta_1 = 1.22\lambda/D$. When this condition holds, the wave from O' diffracted to I has zero intensity (first dark ring), and the extreme rays $O'BI$ and $O'AI$ differ in path by 1.22λ. From the insert in Fig. 15L, we see that $O'B$ is longer than OB or OA by $s \sin i$, and $O'A$ shorter by the same amount. The path difference of the extreme rays from O' is thus $2s \sin i$, and upon equating this to 1.22λ, we obtain

$$s = \frac{1.22\lambda}{2 \sin i} \qquad (15k)$$

In this derivation, we have assumed that the points O and O' were *self-luminous* objects, such that the light given out by each has no constant phase relative to that from the other. Actually the objects used in microscopes are not self-luminous but are illuminated with light from a

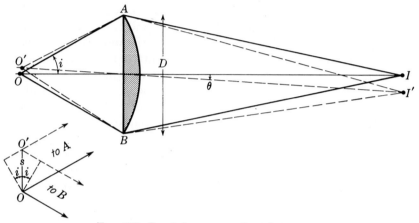

FIG. 15L. Resolving power of a microscope.

condenser. In this case it is impossible to have the light scattered by two points on the object entirely independent in phase. This greatly complicates the problem, since the resolving power is found to depend somewhat on the mode of illumination of the object. Abbe investigated this problem in detail and concluded that a good working rule for calculating the resolving power was given by Eq. 15k, omitting the factor 1.22. In microscopes of high magnifying power, the space between the object and the objective is filled with an oil. Beside decreasing the amount of light lost by reflection at the first lens surface, this increases the resolving power, because when refraction of the rays emerging from the cover glass is eliminated, the objective receives a wider cone of light from the condenser. Equation 15k must then be further modified by substitution of $2ns \sin i$ for the optical path difference, where n is the refractive index of the oil. The result of making these two changes is

$$s = \frac{\lambda}{2n \sin i} \qquad (15l)$$

The product $n \sin i$ is characteristic of a particular objective, and was called by Abbe the "numerical aperture." In practice the largest value of the numerical aperture obtainable is about 1.6. With white light of effective wavelength 5.6×10^{-5} cm, Eq. 15l gives $s = 1.8 \times 10^{-5}$ cm. The use of ultraviolet light, with its smaller value of λ, has recently been applied to still further increase the resolving power. This necessitates the use of photography in examining the image.

One of the most remarkable steps in the improvement of microscopic resolution has been the recent development of the *electron microscope*. As will be explained in Sec. 30.4, electrons behave like waves whose wavelength depends on the voltage through which they have been accelerated. For voltages between 100 and 10,000 volts, λ varies from 1.22×10^{-8} to 1.22×10^{-9} cm, i.e., it lies in the region of a fraction of an angstrom unit. This is more than a thousand times smaller than for visible light. It is possible by means of electric and magnetic fields to focus the electrons emitted from, or transmitted through, the various parts of an object, and in this way details not very much larger than the wavelength of the electrons can be photographed. The numerical aperture of electron microscopes is still much smaller than that of optical instruments, but further developments in this large and growing field of *electron optics* are to be anticipated.*

15.12. Phase Contrast. The eye readily detects differences in amplitude by intensity changes, but it is not able to see changes in phase directly. Thus, as long as the objects on a microscope slide are opaque or absorbing, they appear in the image. If they are transparent, however, and differ only slightly from their surroundings in refractive index or in thickness, they will ordinarily not be visible. It is nevertheless possible to convert the phase changes produced by such objects into amplitude changes in the final image. The so-called *phase-contrast microscope*, devised in 1935 by Zernike,† functions in this way.

To illustrate the basic principle involved here, let us consider how the alternately positive and negative phases in the successive maxima of the single-slit pattern (Fig. 15D) might be rendered visible. Suppose that one were to superimpose on the pattern as it appears on the screen a uniform plane wave that is coherent with the waves forming the pattern, and therefore capable of interfering with them. If this additional wave were to be in phase with the light of the central maximum, we would produce constructive interference and increased intensity of this, and also of the second, fourth, etc., subsidiary maxima. The odd-numbered secondary maxima, however, would be out of phase with it, and the interference would be destructive. Zernike has shown how this effect may be produced experimentally by placing over a fairly wide slit a

---

* See, for example, V. K. Zworykin, G. A. Morton, and others, "Electron Optics and the Electron Microscope," John Wiley & Sons, Inc., New York, 1945.

† F. Zernike (1888–   ). Professor of physics at the University of Groningen, Holland. In 1953 he was awarded the Nobel prize for his discovery of the phase-contrast principle.

much narrower one with semitransparent jaws.   The central maximum due to the latter is made broad enough to spread over the whole pattern caused by the wider slit, and its intensity may be adjusted so that it almost completely eliminates the alternate secondary maxima.   The suppression of these, and the enhancement of the intermediate ones are direct evidence of the phase differences which were present in the original single-slit pattern, and which were otherwise quite unrecognizable to the eye.

The way in which the principle of phase contrast is employed in the microscope is rather involved, and its explanation would require a lengthier discussion than is justified here.*   It must suffice to say that the interference occurs between the direct light which passes unaffected through the uniform parts of the slide and the light which is diffracted by its irregular portions.   The former consists of parallel beams, and is brought to a focus in the secondary focal plane of the objective, while the latter is focused in the plane of the image conjugate to the object.   By placing a quarter-wave retarding plate called the "phase plate" in the secondary focal plane, the phase of the direct light, which is spread uniformly over the image plane, is altered in the proper way to produce an amplitude modulation in this plane which is proportional to the phase modulation caused by the object.   In this way details of transparent biological specimens become visible as increases or decreases of intensity.

PROBLEMS

1. It is a general rule for any spectroscope in which the resolving power is limited by diffraction that

Chromatic resolving power = angular dispersion × width of emerging beam

Using Eq. 23c for the dispersion of a prism at minimum deviation, show that Eq. 15h agrees with this rule.

2. Plane waves of wavelength 5461 Å are incident normally on a slit which has a lens of focal length 40.0 cm behind it.   If the width of the slit is 0.450 mm, find the distance from the principal maximum to the first minimum in the diffraction pattern formed in the focal plane of the lens.   *Ans.* 0.485 mm.

3. A slit 0.20 mm wide is illuminated perpendicularly by an intense parallel beam of white light.   Two meters behind it a small spectroscope is used to explore the spectrum of the diffracted light.   Predict what would be seen when the slit of the spectroscope is displaced in a direction perpendicular to the diffracting slit by a distance of 1 cm from the axis.

4. When diffraction of parallel light by a slit is observed without a lens as in Fig. 15E, the pattern will be essentially a Fraunhofer one when the distance of observation is at least equal to the square of the slit width divided by the wavelength.   According to the description of the conditions used in photographing the pattern of Fig. 15B, how far from the diffracting slit would the plate have to be placed to photograph such a pattern without using the lens L_2?   *Ans.* 1.86 cm.

* A complete discussion of the subject will be found in A. H. Bennett, H. Jupnik, H. Osterberg, and O. W. Richards, "Phase Microscopy," John Wiley & Sons, Inc., New York, 1951.

5. Carry through the derivation of Eq. 15d by the method of complex amplitudes as suggested in the footnote, page 291.

6. Make an accurate plot of the intensity in the Fraunhofer diffraction pattern of a slit in the region of the first subsidiary maximum ($\beta = \pi$ to 2π). From your graph, verify the figures given in Table 15-I for the position and intensity of this maximum. *Ans.* At $\beta = 1.430\pi$, a maximum, of intensity 4.72%.

7. Calculate the approximate intensity of the first weak maximum that appears along the diagonal $\beta/\gamma = l/b$ in the Fraunhofer diffraction pattern of a rectangular aperture.

8. Considering the criterion for the resolution of two diffraction patterns of unequal intensity to be that the drop in intensity between the maxima shall be 20 per cent of the weaker one, find the angular separation required when the intensities are in the ratio 5:1. Express the result in terms of θ_1, the angle required when the intensities are equal. This problem may best be solved graphically, using two plots that may be superimposed with a variable displacement. *Ans.* 1.13θ_1.

9. From the data given in Table 23-I for barium flint glass, calculate the chromatic resolving power of a 60° equiangular prism of this material, if the width of the sides is 6 cm. Make the calculation for the wavelength of the sodium D lines, and for that of the calcium H line.

10. It is desired to resolve a double spectrum line in the ultraviolet, the wavelengths of the components being known to be 3130.326 and 3130.409 Å. A spectrograph containing a crystalline quartz prism with a 10-cm base is available. Such a prism is always made so that the refractive index n_O of Table 26-I is the effective one. Find whether it is theoretically possible for this spectrograph to resolve the doublet. *Ans.* Not resolved.

11. Carry through the differentiation of Eq. 15c and prove that tan $\beta = \beta$ is the condition for maxima.

12. Find the diameter of the first bright ring (secondary maximum) in the focal plane of the 36-in. refractor of the Lick Observatory. The focal length is 56 ft, and the effective wavelength of white light may be taken as 5500 Å. *Ans.* 0.0336 mm.

13. What is the maximum permissible width of the slit source according to the criterion stated at the end of Sec. 15.5 under the following circumstances: source to diffracting slit 50 cm; width of diffracting slit 0.5 mm; wavelength 6000 Å?

14. The pupil of the eye has an average diameter of 2.5 mm in daylight. At what distance would two small orange-colored objects ($\lambda = 6000$ Å) 40 cm apart be barely resolved by the naked eye, assuming the resolution to be limited by diffraction only? *Ans.* 1.37 km.

15. In the projection of a beam of underwater sound for submarine detection, a circular diaphragm 50 cm in diameter is made to oscillate at a frequency of 30,000 cycles/sec. At some distance from such a source, the intensity distribution will be the Fraunhofer pattern for a circular hole of diameter equal to that of the diaphragm. Find the angle between the normal and the first minimum for the given frequency, and also for the audible frequency of 1200 per sec. Assume the velocity of sound to be 1435 m/sec.

16. Find the numerical aperture of the microscope objective that would be required to resolve the lines on a diffraction grating ruled with 14,438 lines to the inch using sodium light. If the objective were to be an immersion one using an oil having $n_D = 1.50$, what would be the required angle of the cone of light to fill the objective? *Ans.* 0.167. 12°49′.

17. Calculate the minimum angle of resolution in seconds of arc for a small galvanometer telescope, the objective of which is 12 mm in diameter. What magnification would be required in order for this resolution to be achieved?

CHAPTER 16

THE DOUBLE SLIT

The interference of light from two narrow slits close together was first demonstrated by Young, and it has already been discussed in Sec. 13.2 as a simple example of the interference of two beams of light. In our discussion of the experiment, the slits were assumed to have widths not much greater than a wavelength of light, so that the central maximum in the diffraction pattern from each slit separately was wide enough to occupy a large angle behind the screen (Figs. 13A and 13B). It is important to understand the modifications of the interference pattern which occur when the width of the individual slits is made greater, until it becomes comparable with the distance between them. This corresponds more nearly to the actual conditions under which the experiment is usually performed. In this chapter we shall discuss the Fraunhofer diffraction by a double slit, and some of its applications.

16.1. Qualitative Aspects of the Pattern. In Fig. 16A(b) and (c) photographs are shown of the patterns obtained from two different double slits in which the widths of the individual slits were equal in each pair, but where the two pairs were different. Referring to Fig. 16B, which shows the experimental arrangement for photographing these patterns, the *slit width* b of each slit was greater for Fig. 16A(c) than for Fig. 16A(b), but the distance between centers $d = b + c$, or the *separation* of the slits, was the same in the two cases. In the central part of Fig. 16A(b) are seen a number of interference maxima of approximately uniform intensity, resembling the interference fringes described in Chap. 13 and shown in Fig. 13D. The intensities of these maxima are not actually constant, however, but fall off slowly to zero on either side and then reappear with low intensity two or three times before becoming too faint to observe without difficulty. The same changes are seen to occur much more rapidly in Fig. 16A(c), which was taken with the slit widths b somewhat larger.

16.2. Derivation of the Equation for the Intensity. Following the same procedure as that used for the single slit in Sec. 15.2, it is merely necessary to change the limits of integration in Eq. 15b to include the

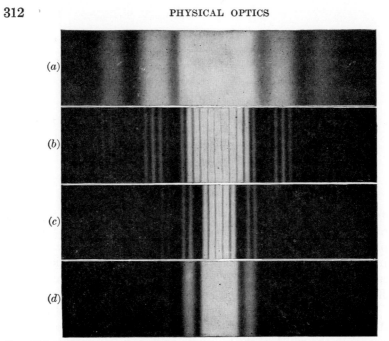

FIG. 16A. Diffraction patterns from (a) a single narrow slit, (b) two narrow slits, (c) two wider slits, (d) one wider slit.

two portions of the wave front transmitted by the double slit.* Thus if we have, as in Fig. 16B, two equal slits of width b, separated by an opaque space of width c, the origin may be chosen at the center of c, and the integration extended from $s = (d/2) - (b/2)$ to $s = (d/2) + (b/2)$. This gives

$$y = \frac{2a}{xk \sin \theta} \left[\sin \left(\frac{1}{2} k(d + b) \sin \theta \right) - \sin \left(\frac{1}{2} k(d - b) \sin \theta \right) \right]$$
$$[\sin (\omega t - kx)]$$

The quantity in brackets is of the form $\sin (A + B) - \sin (A - B)$, and when it is expanded, we obtain

$$y = \frac{2ba}{x} \frac{\sin \beta}{\beta} \cos \gamma \sin (\omega t - kx) \tag{16a}$$

where, as before,

$$\beta = \frac{1}{2} kb \sin \theta = \frac{\pi}{\lambda} b \sin \theta$$

* The result of this derivation is obviously a special case of the general formula for N slits, which will be obtained by the method of complex amplitudes in the following chapter.

$dy_0 =$ spherical wave

$= \dfrac{a\,ds}{x} \sin(\omega t - kx)$

$d_2 = s\sin\theta_2$

$d_1 = s\sin\theta_2$

θ_2

θ_1

x

$d_1 - d_2 = \phi$

If w is very small

effect $= \dfrac{a\,ds}{x} \left[\sin\left(\omega t - kx + \tfrac{1}{2}\phi\right) + \sin\left(\omega t - kx - \tfrac{1}{2}\phi\right) \right]$

$\displaystyle \int_b$

$\dfrac{a\,ds}{x} \left[2\sin 2(\omega t - kx)\cos\phi \right]$

and where

$$\gamma = \frac{1}{2} k(b + c) \sin \theta = \frac{\pi}{\lambda} d \sin \theta \qquad (16b)$$

The intensity is proportional to the square of the amplitude of Eq. 16a, so that, replacing ba/x by A_0 as before, we have

$$I = 4A_0{}^2 \frac{\sin^2 \beta}{\beta^2} \cos^2 \gamma \qquad (16c)$$

The factor $(\sin^2 \beta)/\beta^2$ in this equation is just that derived for the single

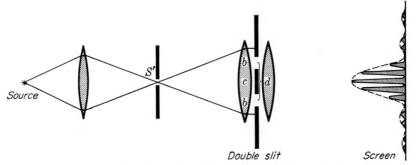

FIG. 16B. Apparatus for observing Fraunhofer diffraction from a double slit. Drawn for the case $2b = c$, that is, $d = 3b$.

slit of width b in the previous chapter (Eq. 15d). The second factor $\cos^2 \gamma$ is characteristic of the interference pattern produced by two beams of equal intensity and phase difference δ, as shown in Eq. 13b of Sec. 13.3. There the resultant intensity was found to be proportional to $\cos^2 (\delta/2)$, so that the expressions correspond if we put $\gamma = \delta/2$. The resultant intensity will be zero when either of the two factors is zero. For the first factor this will occur when $\beta = \pi, 2\pi, 3\pi, \ldots$, and for the second factor when $\gamma = \pi/2$, $3\pi/2, 5\pi/2, \ldots$. That the two variables β and γ are not independent will be seen from Fig. 16C. The difference in path from the two edges

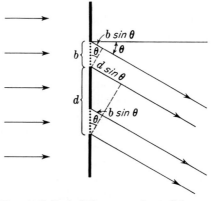

FIG. 16C. Path differences of parallel rays leaving a double slit.

of a given slit to the screen is, as indicated, $b \sin \theta$. The corresponding phase difference is, by Eq. 11f, $(2\pi/\lambda) b \sin \theta$, which equals 2β. The path difference from any two corresponding points in the two slits is, as is illustrated for the two points at the lower edges of the slits, $d \sin \theta$, and the phase difference $\delta = (2\pi/\lambda)d \sin \theta = 2\gamma$. Therefore, in terms of the dimensions of the slits,

$$\frac{\delta}{2\beta} = \frac{\gamma}{\beta} = \frac{d}{b} \tag{16d}$$

16.3. Comparison of the Single-slit and Double-slit Patterns. It is instructive to compare the double-slit pattern with that given by a single slit of width equal to that of either of the two slits. This amounts to comparing the effect obtained with the two slits in the arrangement shown in Fig. 16B with that obtained when one of the slits is entirely blocked off with an opaque screen. If this is done, the corresponding single-slit diffraction patterns are observed, and they are related to the double-slit patterns as shown in Fig. 16$A(a)$ and (d). It will be seen that the intensities of the interference fringes in the double-slit pattern correspond to the intensity of the single-slit pattern at any point. If one or other of the two slits is covered, we obtain exactly the same single-slit pattern in the same position, while if both slits are uncovered the pattern, instead of being a single-slit one with twice the intensity, breaks up into the narrow maxima and minima called interference fringes. The intensity at the maximum of these fringes is four times the intensity of either single-slit pattern at that point, while it is zero at the minima (see Sec. 13.4).

16.4. Distinction between Interference and Diffraction. One is quite justified in explaining the above results by saying that the light from the two slits undergoes interference to produce fringes of the type obtained with two beams, but that the intensities of these fringes are limited by the amount of light arriving at the given point on the screen by virtue of the diffraction occurring at each slit. The relative intensities in the resultant pattern as given by Eq. 16c are just those obtained by multiplying the intensity function for the interference pattern from two infinitely narrow slits of separation d (Eq. 13b) by the intensity function for diffraction from a single slit of width b (Eq. 15d). Thus, the result may be regarded as due to the joint action of interference between the rays coming from corresponding points in the two slits and of diffraction, which determines the amount of light emerging from either slit at a given angle. But diffraction is merely the result of the interference of all the secondary wavelets originating from the different elements of the wave front. Hence it is proper to say that the whole pattern is an interference pattern. It is just as correct to refer to it as a diffraction pattern, since, as we saw from the derivation of the intensity function in Sec. 16.2, it is obtained by direct summing the effects of all of the elements of the exposed part of the wave front. However, if we reserve the term *interference* for those cases in which a modification of amplitude is produced by the superposition of a finite (usually small) number of beams, and *diffraction* for those in which the amplitude is determined by an integration over the infinitesimal elements of the wave front, the double-slit pattern can be said to be due to a combination of interference and diffraction. Interference of the beams from the two slits produces the narrow maxima and minima given by the $\cos^2 \gamma$ factor, and diffraction, represented by $(\sin^2 \beta)/\beta^2$, modulates the intensities of these interference fringes. The student should not be misled by this statement into thinking that diffraction is anything other than a rather complicated case of interference.

16.5. Positions of the Maxima and Minima. Missing Orders. As shown in Sec. 16.2, the intensity will be zero wherever $\gamma = \pi/2, 3\pi/2,$ $5\pi/2, \ldots$ and also when $\beta = \pi, 2\pi, 3\pi, \ldots$ The first of these two sets are the minima for the interference pattern, and since by definition $\gamma = (\pi/\lambda)d \sin \theta$, they occur at angles θ such that

$$d \sin \theta = \frac{\lambda}{2}, \frac{3\lambda}{2}, \frac{5\lambda}{2}, \ldots = \left(m + \frac{1}{2}\right)\lambda \qquad \text{MINIMA} \qquad (16e)$$

m being any whole number starting with zero. The second series of minima are those for the diffraction pattern, and these, since $\beta = (\pi/\lambda)a \sin \theta$, occur where

$$b \sin \theta = \lambda, 2\lambda, 3\lambda, \ldots = p\lambda \qquad \text{MINIMA} \qquad (16f)$$

the smallest value of p being 1. The exact positions of the *maxima* are not given by any simple relation, but their approximate positions may be found by neglecting the variation of the factor $(\sin^2 \beta)/\beta^2$, a justified assumption only when the slits are very narrow and when the maxima near the center of the pattern are considered [Fig. $16A(b)$]. The positions of the maxima will then be determined solely by the $\cos^2 \gamma$ factor, which has maxima for $\gamma = 0, \pi, 2\pi, \ldots$, i.e., for

$$d \sin \theta = 0, \lambda, 2\lambda, 3\lambda, \ldots = m\lambda \qquad \text{MAXIMA} \qquad (16g)$$

The whole number m represents physically the number of wavelengths in the path difference from corresponding points in the two slits (see Fig. $16C$) and represents the *order* of interference.

Figure $16D(a)$ is a plot of the factor $\cos^2 \gamma$, and here the values of the order, of half the phase difference $\gamma = \delta/2$, and of the path difference are indicated for the various maxima. These are all of equal intensity and equidistant on a scale of $d \sin \theta$, or practically on a scale of θ, since when θ is small $\sin \theta \simeq \theta$ and the maxima occur at angles $\theta = 0, \lambda/d,$ $2\lambda/d, \ldots$ With a finite slit width b the variation of the factor $(\sin^2 \beta)/\beta^2$ must be taken into account. This factor alone gives just the single-slit pattern discussed in the last chapter, and is plotted in Fig. 16D(b). The complete double-slit pattern as given by Eq. 16c is the product of these two factors, and therefore is obtained by multiplying the ordinates of curve (a) by those of curve (b) and the constant $4A_0^2$. This pattern is shown in Fig. 16D(c). The result will depend on the relative scale of the abscissas β and γ, which in the figure are chosen so that for a given abscissa $\gamma = 3\beta$. But the relation between β and γ for a given

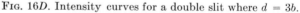

Fig. 16D. Intensity curves for a double slit where $d = 3b$.

angle θ is determined, according to Eq. 16d, by the ratio of the slit width to the slit separation. Hence if $d = 3b$, the two curves (a) and (b) are plotted to the same scale of θ. For the particular case of two slits of width b separated by an opaque space of width $c = 2b$, the curve (c), which is the product of (a) and (b), then gives the resultant pattern. The positions of the maxima in this curve are slightly different from those in curve (a) for all except the central maximum ($m = 0$), because when the ordinates near one of the maxima of curve (a) are multiplied by a factor which is decreasing or increasing, the ordinates on one side of the maximum are changed by a different amount from those of the other, and this displaces the resultant maximum slightly in the direction in which the factor is increasing. Hence the positions of the maxima in curve (c) are not exactly those given by Eq. 16g, but in most cases will be very close to them.

Let us now return to the explanation of the differences in the two patterns (b) and (c) of Fig. 16A, taken with the same slit separation d but different slit widths b. Pattern (c) was taken for the case d = 3b, and is seen to agree with the description given above. For pattern (b), the slit separation d was the same, giving the same spacing for the interference fringes, but the slit width b was smaller, such that d = 6b. In Fig. 13D, d = 14b. This greatly increases the scale for the single-slit pattern relative to the interference pattern, so that many interference maxima now fall within the central maximum of the diffraction pattern. Hence the effect of decreasing b, keeping d unchanged, is merely to broaden out the single-slit pattern, which acts as an envelope of the interference pattern as indicated by the dotted curve of Fig. 16D(c).

If the slit-width b is kept constant and the separation of the slits d is varied, the scale of the interference pattern varies, but that of the diffraction pattern remains the same. A series of photographs taken to illustrate this is shown in Fig. 16E. For each pattern three different exposures are shown, to bring out the details of the faint and the strong parts of the pattern. The maxima of the curves are labeled by the order m, and underneath the upper one is a given scale of angular positions θ. A study of these figures shows that certain orders are missing, or at least reduced to two maxima of very low intensity. These so-called *missing orders* occur where the condition for a maximum of the interference, Eq. 16g, and for a minimum of the diffraction, Eq. 16f, are both fulfilled for the same value of θ, that is for

$$d \sin \theta = m\lambda$$
$$b \sin \theta = p\lambda$$

so that
$$\frac{d}{b} = \frac{m}{p} \qquad (16h)$$

Since m and p are both integers, d/b must be in the ratio of two integers if we are to have missing orders. This ratio determines the orders which are missing, in such a way that when d/b = 2, orders 2, 4, 6, . . . are missing; when d/b = 3, orders 3, 6, 9, . . . are missing; etc. When d/b = 1, the two slits exactly join, and all orders should be missing. However, the two faint maxima into which each order is split can then be shown to correspond exactly to the subsidiary maxima of a single-slit pattern of width 2b.

Our physical picture of the cause of missing orders is as follows: Considering for example the missing order m = 3 in Fig. 16D(c), this point on the screen is just three wavelengths farther from the center of one slit than from the center of the other. Hence we might expect the waves

Fig. 16E. Photographs and intensity curves for double-slit diffraction patterns.

from the two slits to arrive in phase and to produce a maximum. However, this point is at the same time one wavelength farther from the edge of one slit than from the other edge of that slit. Addition of the secondary wavelets from one slit gives zero intensity under these conditions. The same holds true for either slit, so that, although we may add the contributions from the two slits, both contributions are zero and must therefore give zero resultant.

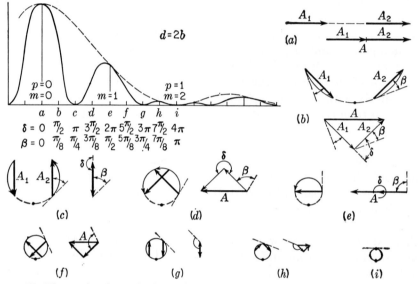

FIG. 16F. Illustrating how the intensity curve for a double slit is obtained by the graphical addition of amplitudes.

16.6. Vibration Curve. The same method as that applied in Sec. 15.4 for finding the resultant amplitude graphically in the case of the single slit is applicable to the present problem. For illustration we take a double slit in which the width of each slit equals that of the opaque space between the two, so that $d = 2b$. A photograph of this pattern appears in Fig. 16E at the top. A vector diagram of the amplitude contributions from one slit gives the arc of a circle, as before, the difference between the slopes of the tangents to the arc at the two ends being the phase difference 2β between the contributions from the two edges of the slit. Such an arc must now be drawn for each of the two slits, and the two arcs must be related in such a way that the phases (slopes of the tangents) differ for corresponding points on the two slits by 2γ, or δ. In the present case, since $d = 2b$, we must have $\gamma = 2\beta$ or $\delta = 4\beta$. Thus in Fig. 16F(b) showing the vibration curve for $\beta = \pi/8$, both arcs subtend an angle of $\pi/4$ ($= 2\beta$), the phase difference for the two edges of each slit, and the arcs are separated by $\pi/4$ so that corresponding points on the two arcs differ by $\pi/2(= \delta)$. Now the resultant contributions from the two slits are represented in amplitude and phase by the chords of these two arcs, that is by A_1 and A_2. Diagrams (a) to (i) give the construction for the points similarly labeled on the intensity curve. The intensity, it will be remembered, is found as the square of the resultant amplitude A, which is the vector sum of A_1 and A_2.

In the example chosen, the slits are relatively wide compared with their separation, and as the phase difference increases the curvature of the individual arcs of the vibration curve increases rapidly, so that the vectors A_1 and A_2 decrease rapidly in length. For narrower slits we obtain a greater number of interference fringes within the central diffraction maximum, because the lengths of the arcs are smaller relative to the radius of curvature of the circle. A_1 and A_2 then decrease in length more slowly with increasing β, and the intensities of the maxima do not fall off so rapidly. In the limit where the slit width a approaches zero, A_1 and A_2 remain constant, and the variation of the resultant intensity is merely due to the change in phase angle between them.

16.7. Effect of Finite Width of Source Slit. A simplification which was made in the above treatment, and which never holds exactly in practice, is the assumption that the source slit (S' of Fig. 16B) is of negligible width. This is necessary in order that the lens shall furnish a single train of plane waves falling on the double slit. Otherwise there will be different sets of waves approaching at slightly different angles, these originating from different points in the source slit. They will produce sets of fringes which are slightly shifted with respect to each other, as illustrated in Fig. 16G(a). In the figure the interference maxima are for simplicity drawn with uniform intensity, neglecting the effects of diffraction. Let P and P' be two narrow lines acting as sources. These may be two narrow slits, or, better, two lamp filaments, since we assume no coherence between them. If the positions of the central maxima of the interference patterns produced by these are Q and Q', the fringe displacement QQ' will subtend the same angle α at the double slit as do the source slits. If this angle is a small fraction of the angular separation λ/d of the successive fringes in either pattern, the resultant intensity distribution will still resemble a true $\cos^2 \gamma$ curve, although the intensity will not fall to zero at the minima. The relative positions of the two patterns, and the sum of the two, in this state are illustrated in Fig. 16G, curves (b). Curves (c) and (d) show the effect of increasing the separation PP'. For (d) the fringes are completely out of step, and the resultant intensity shows no fluctuations whatever. At a point such as Q the maximum of one pattern then coincides with the next minimum of the other, so that the path difference $P'AQ - PAQ = \lambda/2$. In other words, P' is just a half wavelength farther from A than is P. If the intensity of one set of fringes is given by $4A^2 \cos^2 (\delta/2)$ or $2A^2(1 + \cos \delta)$, that of the other is

$$2A^2[1 + \cos (\delta + \pi)] = 2A^2(1 - \cos \delta)$$

The sum is therefore constant and equal to $4A^2$, so that the fringes entirely disappear. The condition for this disappearance of fringes is $\alpha = \lambda/2d$. If PP' is still further increased, the fringes will reappear,

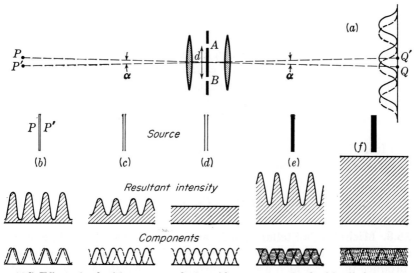

FIG. 16G. Effect of a double source and of a wide source on the double-slit interference fringes.

becoming sharp again when α equals the fringe distance λ/d, disappear when the fringes are again out of register, etc. In general, the condition for disappearance is

$$\alpha = \frac{\lambda}{2d}, \frac{3\lambda}{2d}, \frac{5\lambda}{2d} \cdots \quad \begin{array}{l}\text{DISAPPEARANCE OF FRINGES WITH} \\ \text{DOUBLE SOURCE}\end{array} \quad (16i)$$

where α is the angle subtended by the two sources at the double slit.

Next let us consider the effect when the source, instead of consisting of two separate sources, consists of a uniformly bright strip of width PP'. Each line element of this strip will produce its own set of interference fringes, and the resultant pattern will be the sum of a large number of these, displaced by infinitesimal amounts with respect to each other. Figure 16G(e) illustrates this for $\alpha = \lambda/2d$, that is, for a slit of width such that the extreme points acting alone would give complete disappearance of fringes as in (d). The resultant curve now shows strong fluctuations, and the slit must be still further widened to make the intensity uniform. The first complete disappearance will come when the range covered by the component fringes extends over a whole fringe width, instead of one-half, as above. This case is shown in Fig. 16G(f), for a slit of width subtending an angle $\alpha = \lambda/d$. Widening the slit still further will cause the fringes to reappear, although they never become perfectly distinct again, with zero intensity between fringes. At $\alpha = 2\lambda/d$ they again disappear completely, and the general condition is

$$\alpha = \frac{\lambda}{d}, \frac{2\lambda}{d}, \frac{3\lambda}{d}, \cdots \qquad \begin{array}{l}\text{DISAPPEARANCE OF FRINGES WITH SLIT} \\ \text{SOURCE}\end{array} \qquad (16j)$$

It is of practical importance, in observing double-slit fringes experimentally, to know how wide the source slit may be made in order to obtain intense fringes without seriously impairing the definition of the fringes. The exact value will depend on our criterion for clear fringes, but a good working rule is to permit a maximum discordance of the fringes of about one-quarter of that for the first disappearance. If f' is the focal length of the first lens, this corresponds to a *maximum permissible width* of the source slit

$$PP' = f'\alpha = \frac{f'\lambda}{4d} \qquad (16k)$$

16.8. Michelson's Stellar Interferometer. As was shown in Sec. 15.9, the smallest angular separation that two point sources may have in order to produce images which are recognizable as separate, in the focal plane of a telescope, is $\alpha = \theta_1 = 1.22\lambda/D$. In this equation (Eq. 15i) D is the diameter of the objective of the telescope. Suppose that the objective is covered by a screen pierced with two parallel slits of separation almost equal to the diameter of the objective. A separation of $d = D/1.22$ would be a convenient value. If the telescope is now pointed at a double star and the slits are turned so as to be perpendicular to the line joining the two stars, interference fringes due to the double slit will in general be observed. However, according to Eq. 16i, if the angular separation of the two stars happens to be $\alpha = \lambda/2d$, the condition for the first disappearance, no fringes will be seen. Those from one star completely mask those from the other. Hence one could infer from the nonappearance of the fringes that the star was double with an angular separation $\lambda/2d$ or some multiple of this. (The multiples could be ruled out by direct observation without the double slit.) But this separation is only half as great as the minimum angle of resolution of the whole objective $1.22\lambda/D$ which in this case equals λ/d. In this connection it is instructive to compare, as in Fig. 16H, the dimensions of the diffraction pattern due to a *rectangular* aperture of width b with the interference pattern due to two narrow slits whose separation d is equal to b. The central maximum is only half as wide in the second case. Hence it is sometimes said that the resolving power of a telescope may be increased twofold by placing a double slit over the objective. This statement needs two important qualifications, however. In the first place the stars are not "resolved" in the sense of producing separate images, but their existence is merely inferred from the behavior of the fringes. In the second place, a partial blurring of the fringes, without complete disappearance, can be observed for separations much less than $\lambda/2d$, showing the existence of two stars, and from this point of view the minimum resolvable separation is

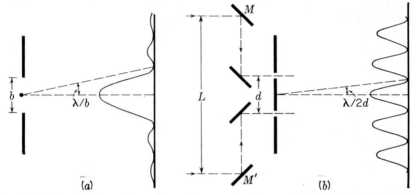

Fig. 16*H*. Fraunhofer pattern from (*a*) a rectangular aperture and (*b*) double slit of separation equal to the width of the aperture in (*a*). In (*b*) are shown the four auxiliary mirrors used in the actual stellar interferometer.

considerably smaller than that indicated by the above statement. In practice it is about one-tenth of this.

The actual measurement of the separation of a given close double star is made by having the slit separation d adjustable. The separation is increased until the fringes first disappear; then, by measuring d, the angular separation is obtained as $\alpha = \lambda/2d$. The effective wavelength λ of the starlight must, of course, be also estimated or measured. Separations of double stars are not often determined by this method, because the advantage over the direct method is not very great, and observations on the Doppler effect (Sec. 11.6) afford an even more sensitive means of detection and measurement. On the other hand, the method of double-slit interference was, until recently,* the only way of measuring the diameter of the disk of a single star, and in 1920 this method was successfully applied by Michelson for this purpose.

From the discussion of the preceding section, it will be seen that if a source such as a star disk subtends a finite angle, disappearance of the fringes would be expected from this cause when the separation of the double slit on a telescope is made great enough. Michelson first demon-

*See R. H. Brown and R. Q. Twiss, *Nature*, **178**, 1447, 1956.

strated the practicability of this method by measuring the diameters of Jupiter's moons, which subtend an angle of about one second. The values of d for the first disappearance are only a few centimeters in this case, and the measurement could be made by a double slit of variable separation over the objective of a telescope. Owing to the fact that the source is a circular disk instead of a rectangle, a correction must be applied to the equation $\alpha = \lambda/d$ for a slit source. This correction may be found by the same method that is used in finding the resolving power of a circular aperture, and gives the same factor. It is found that $\alpha = 1.22\lambda/d$ gives the first disappearance for a disk source. Estimating the angular diameters of the nearer fixed stars of known distance by assuming they are the same size as the sun, one obtains angles less than 0.01 second. The separations of the double slit required to detect a disk of this size are from 20 to 40 ft. Clearly no telescope in existence could be used in the way described above for the measurement of star diameters. Another drawback would be that the fringes would be so fine that it would be difficult to separate them.

Since the blurring of the fringes is the result of variations of the phase difference between the light arriving at the two slits from various points on the source, Michelson realized that it was possible to magnify this phase difference without increasing d. This was done by receiving the light from a star on two plane mirrors M and M' [Fig. 16$H(b)$] and reflecting it into the slits by these and two other mirrors. Then a variation of α in the angle of the incoming rays will cause a difference of path to the two slits of $L\alpha$, where L is the distance MM' between the outer mirrors. The fringes will now disappear when this difference equals 1.22λ, and so the sensitivity is magnified in the ratio L/d. In the actual measurements, M and M' were two 6-in. mirrors mounted on a girder in front of the 100-in. Mt. Wilson reflector so that they could be moved apart symmetrically. In the case of the star Arcturus, for example, the first disappearance of fringes occurred at $L = 24$ ft, indicating an angular diameter $\alpha = 1.22\lambda/L$ of only 0.02 second. From the known distance of Arcturus, one then finds that its actual diameter is 27 times that of the sun.*

16.9. Wide-angle Interference. Nothing has thus far been said as to whether there is any limit to the angle between the two interfering beams as they leave the source. Consider, for example, the double-slit arrangement shown in Fig. 16$I(a)$. The source S could be a narrow slit, but to ensure that there is no coherence between the light leaving various points on it, we shall assume that it is a self-luminous object. It is found experimentally that the angle ϕ may be made fairly large without spoil-

---

* Details of these measurements will be found in A. A. Michelson, "Studies in Optics," chap. 11, University of Chicago Press, Chicago, 1927.

ing the interference fringes, provided the width of the source is made correspondingly small. Just how small it must be is seen from the fact that the path difference from the extreme edges of the source to any given point on the screen such as P must be less than $\lambda/4$. Now if we call s the width of the source, the discussion given in Sec. 15.11 shows that this path difference will be $2s \sin \phi/2$. Hence, for a divergence of 60°, s cannot exceed one-quarter of a wavelength, or 1.3×10^{-5} cm for green light. If the width is made greater than this the fringes disappear completely when the path difference is λ, reappear, and then disappear again at 2λ, etc., just as in the stellar interferometer. By using as a source an

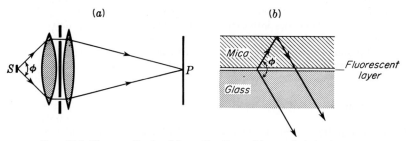

FIG. 16I. Two methods of investigating wide-angle interference.

extremely thin filament, Schrödinger could still detect some interference at an angular divergence ϕ as large as 57°.

An equivalent experiment which permitted using even larger angles of divergence (up to 180°) was performed by Selenyi in 1911. The essential part of his apparatus, shown in Fig. 16I(b), was a film of a fluorescent liquid only $\frac{1}{20}\lambda$ thick contained between a thin sheet of mica and a plane glass surface. When the film is strongly illuminated it becomes a secondary source of light having a somewhat longer wavelength than the incident light (see Sec. 22.5, ahead). Interference may then be observed in a given direction between the light that comes directly from the film and that which is reflected from the outer surface of the mica. Interesting conclusions about the characteristics of the radiating atoms, in particular whether they radiate as dipoles, quadrupoles, etc., can be drawn from data on the variation of the visibility of the fringes with angle.*

PROBLEMS

1. Prove that Eq. 16c may be reduced, for the case where $d = b$, to the equation for the intensity distribution from a single slit of width $2b$.

2. The widths of the individual slits of a double slit are each 0.17 mm, and the separation between their centers is 0.85 mm. Are there missing orders, and if so

* O. Halpern and F. W. Doermann, *Phys. Rev.*, **52**, 937, 1937.

which ones? What are the approximate relative intensities of the orders $m = 0$ and
$m = 3$?   *Ans.* $m = 5, 10, 15, \ldots$ missing. $1:0.22$.

3. The double slit of Prob. 2 is illuminated by parallel light of wavelength 4358 Å,
and the pattern is focused on a screen by a lens of focal length 60 cm. Make a
qualitative plot of the intensity distribution on the screen similar to Fig. 16$D(c)$,
but using as abscissas the distance in millimeters on the screen. Include the first
14 orders on one side of the central maximum.

4. Draw the appropriate vibration curve for the point where the phase difference
$\delta = 2\pi/3$ in the case of a double slit where the opaque space between the slits is
half the width of the slits themselves. What is the value of β for this point? Obtain
graphically a value for the intensity at the point in question relative to that of the
central maximum.   *Ans.* $\beta = 40°$. $I = 0.212$

5. Make a qualitative sketch of the intensity pattern produced by a double slit
having $d = 2.6b$. Take the intensity of the central maximum as unity, and label
the axis of abscissas with the values of m and p as in Fig. 16$D(c)$.

6. The Fraunhofer pattern from a double slit composed of slits each 0.5 mm wide
and separated by $d = 20$ mm is observed in sodium light on a screen 50 cm behind
the slits. Assuming that the eye can resolve fringes that subtend 1 minute of arc,
what magnification would be required to see them in this case? How many fringes
would occur under the central diffraction maximum? Under one of the side maxima?
                              Ans. $4.9\times$.   79.   39.

7. Derive Eq. 16c by the use of the method of complex amplitudes described in
Sec. 14.8.

8. If $d = 4b$ for a double slit, determine exactly how much the second-order maximum is shifted from the position given by Eq. 16g due to modulation by the diffraction
envelope. The problem may best be solved by plotting the intensities in the neighborhood of the expected maximum. Express the result as a fraction of the separation
of orders.   *Ans.* 0.048 order toward center.

9. On an optical bench are placed two double slits. The first has a slit spacing
$d = 0.2$ mm and has a sodium arc placed immediately in front of it at one end of the
bench. The eye, located close behind the second slit, for which $d = 0.8$ mm, sees
clear double-slit fringes when observing at the far end of the bench. When the eye
and the second double slit are moved together toward the source slits, the fringes
completely disappear at a certain point. Find the largest distance between the
double slits for this to occur.

10. Calculate the value for the visibility (Sec. 13.12) of the double-slit fringes
when the source consists of a double star separated by one-tenth the distance required
for complete disappearance. This is the condition mentioned in Sec. 16.8 as being
just perceptible to the eye.   *Ans.* 98.8%.

11. In making observations on the Fraunhofer pattern from a double slit with
$b = 0.12$ mm, $d = 0.78$ mm, the latter is placed between two lenses as illustrated in
Fig. 16$G(a)$. The lenses have focal lengths of 85 cm. The source slit is illuminated
by light of the green mercury line. According to the usual criterion for clear fringes,
how wide may the source slit be made to obtain the best intensity without appreciable
sacrifice of clearness?

12. Derive a formula giving the number of interference maxima occurring under
the central diffraction maximum of the double-slit pattern, in terms of the slit separation d and the slit width b.   *Ans.* $2(d/b) - 1$.

13. The largest star measured by Michelson with his stellar interferometer was
the red giant Betelgeuse. The effective wavelength of the light from this star may
be taken as 5700 Å. Complete disappearance of the fringes first occurred when the

mirrors were 10 ft 1 in apart.   Compute the angular diameter in seconds of the star disk.

14. Young first performed his famous experiment by observing interference in the light coming through two pinholes close together. Suppose these to be round and 0.4 mm in diameter.   For light of wavelength 5550 Å, how close together would they have to be placed in order for the two Airy disks to overlap by one-half the radius of each when observed 1 m. behind the pinholes?   Make a qualitative sketch of the pattern as it would appear to the eye.   *Ans.* 2.54 mm.   3 interference fringes.

15. With a single tungsten lamp filament as a source, and a collimating lens of 3.5 cm focal length in front of a double slit, various separations of the double slit are tried, increasing them until the fringes no longer appear.   If this occurs for $d = 8$ mm, estimate the diameter of the filament.   Assume $\lambda = 6000$ Å.

16. The interference fringes formed in Selenyi's experiment are evidently neither double-slit nor multiple-reflection fringes.   To which of the various arrangements for producing interference described in Chaps. 13 and 14 is this one most closely related?

Ans. Michelson interferometer.

CHAPTER 17

THE DIFFRACTION GRATING

Any arrangement which is equivalent in its action to a number of parallel equidistant slits of the same width is called a *diffraction grating*. Since the grating is a very powerful instrument for the study of spectra, we shall treat in considerable detail the intensity pattern which it produces. We shall find that the pattern is quite complex in general but that it has a number of features in common with that of the double slit treated in the last chapter. In fact, the latter may be considered as an elementary grating of only two slits. It is, however, of no use as a spectroscope, since in a practical grating many thousands of very fine slits are usually required. The reason for this becomes apparent when we examine the difference between the pattern due to two slits and that due to many slits.

17.1. Effect of Increasing the Number of Slits. When the intensity pattern due to one, two, three, and more slits of the same width is photographed, a series of pictures like those shown in Fig. 17A(a) to (f) is obtained. The arrangement of light source, slit, lenses, and recording plate used in taking these pictures was similar to that described in previous chapters, and the light used was the blue line from a mercury arc. These patterns therefore are produced by *Fraunhofer diffraction*. In fact, it was because of Fraunhofer's original investigations of the diffraction of parallel light by gratings in 1819 that his name became associated with this type of diffraction. Fraunhofer's first gratings were made by winding fine wires around two parallel screws. Those used in preparing Fig. 17A were made by cutting narrow transparent lines in the gelatin emulsion on a photographic plate, as described in Sec. 13.2.

The most striking modification in the pattern as the number of slits is increased consists of a narrowing of the interference maxima. For two slits these are diffuse, having an intensity which was shown in the last chapter to vary essentially as the square of the cosine. With more slits the sharpness of these *principal maxima* increases rapidly, and in pattern (f) of the figure, with 20 slits, they have become narrow lines. Another change, of less importance, which may be seen in patterns (c), (d), and (e) is the appearance of weak *secondary maxima* between the principal

FIG. 17A. Fraunhofer diffraction patterns for gratings containing different numbers of slits.

maxima, their number increasing with the number of slits. For three slits only one secondary maximum is present, its intensity being 11.1 per cent of the principal maximum. Figure 17B shows an intensity curve for this case, plotted according to the theoretical equation 17b given in the next section. Here the individual slits were assumed very narrow.

FIG. 17B. Principal and secondary maxima from a grating of three slits.

Actually the intensities of all maxima are governed by the pattern of a single slit of width equal to that of any one of the slits used. The width of the intensity envelopes would be identical in the various patterns of Fig. 17A if the slits had been of the same width in all cases. In fact there were slight differences in the slit widths used for some of the patterns.

17.2. Intensity Distribution from an Ideal Grating. The procedure used in Secs. 15.2 and 16.2 for the single and double slits could be used here, performing the integration over the clear aperture of the slits, but it becomes somewhat cumbersome. Instead let us apply the more powerful method of adding the complex amplitudes (Sec. 14.8). The situation is simpler than in the case of multiple reflections, because for the grating the amplitudes contributed by the individual slits are all of equal magnitude. We designate this magnitude by a, and the number of slits by N. The phase will change by equal amounts δ from one slit to the next; so the resultant complex amplitude is the sum of the series

$$
\begin{aligned}
A e^{i\theta} &= a(1 + e^{i\delta} + e^{i2\delta} + e^{i3\delta} + \cdots + e^{i(N-1)\delta}) \\
&= a \frac{1 - e^{iN\delta}}{1 - e^{i\delta}}
\end{aligned}
\tag{17a}
$$

To find the intensity, this expression must be multiplied by its complex conjugate, as in Eq. 14i, giving

$$
\begin{aligned}
A^2 &= a^2 \frac{(1 - e^{iN\delta})(1 - e^{-iN\delta})}{(1 - e^{i\delta})(1 - e^{-i\delta})} \\
&= a^2 \frac{1 - \cos N\delta}{1 - \cos \delta}
\end{aligned}
$$

Using the trigonometric relation $1 - \cos \alpha = 2 \sin^2 (\alpha/2)$, we may then write

$$
A^2 = a^2 \frac{\sin^2 (N\delta/2)}{\sin^2 (\delta/2)} = a^2 \frac{\sin^2 N\gamma}{\sin^2 \gamma}
\tag{17b}
$$

where, as in the double slit, $\gamma = \delta/2 = (\pi d \sin \theta)/\lambda$. Now the factor a^2 represents the intensity diffracted by a single slit, and after inserting its value from Eq. 15d we finally obtain for the intensity in the Fraunhofer pattern of an ideal grating

$$
I \sim A^2 = A_0{}^2 \frac{\sin^2 \beta}{\beta^2} \frac{\sin^2 N\gamma}{\sin^2 \gamma}
\tag{17c}
$$

Upon substitution of $N = 2$ in this formula, it readily reduces to Eq. 16c for the double slit.

17.3. Principal Maxima. The new factor $(\sin^2 N\gamma)/(\sin^2 \gamma)$ may be said to represent the *interference* term for N slits. It possesses maximum values equal to N^2 for $\gamma = 0, \pi, 2\pi, \ldots$. Although the quotient becomes indeterminate at these values, this result may be obtained by noting that

$$
\lim_{\gamma \to m\pi} \left(\frac{\sin N\gamma}{\sin \gamma} \right) = \lim_{\gamma \to m\pi} \left(\frac{N \cos N\gamma}{\cos \gamma} \right) = \pm N
$$

These maxima correspond in position to those of the double slit, since for the above values of γ

$$d \sin \theta = 0, \lambda, 2\lambda, 3\lambda, \ldots = m\lambda \qquad \text{PRINCIPAL MAXIMA} \qquad (17d)$$

They are more intense, however, in the ratio of the square of the number of slits. The relative intensities of the different orders m are in all cases governed by the single-slit diffraction envelope $(\sin^2 \beta)/\beta^2$. Hence the relation between β and γ in terms of slit width and slit separation (Eq. 16d) remains unchanged, as does the condition for missing orders (Eq. 16h).

17.4. Minima and Secondary Maxima. To find the minima of the function $(\sin^2 N\gamma)/(\sin^2 \gamma)$, we note that the numerator becomes zero more often than the denominator, and this occurs at the values $N\gamma = 0$, π, 2π, $\ldots$ or, in general, $p\pi$. In the special cases when $p = 0$, N, $2N$, $\ldots$, γ will be 0, π, 2π, $\ldots$; so for these values the denominator will also vanish, and we have the principal maxima described above. The other values of p give zero intensity, since for these the denominator does not vanish at the same time. Hence the condition for a minimum is $\gamma = p\pi/N$, excluding those values of p for which $p = mN$, m being the order. These values of γ correspond to path differences

$$d \sin \theta = \frac{\lambda}{N}, \frac{2\lambda}{N}, \frac{3\lambda}{N}, \ldots, \frac{(N-1)\lambda}{N}, \frac{(N+1)\lambda}{N}, \ldots \qquad \text{MINIMA} \quad (17e)$$

omitting the values 0, $N\lambda/N$, $2N\lambda/N$, $\ldots$, for which $d \sin \theta = m\lambda$ and which according to Eq. 17d represent principal maxima. Between two adjacent principal maxima there will hence be $N - 1$ points of zero intensity. The two minima on either side of a principal maximum are separated by twice the distance of the others.

Between the other minima the intensity rises again, but the secondary maxima thus produced are of much smaller intensity than the principal maxima. Figure 17C shows a plot for six slits of the quantities $\sin^2 N\gamma$ and $\sin^2 \gamma$, and also of their quotient, which gives the intensity distribution in the interference pattern. The intensity of the principal maxima is N^2 or 36, so that the lower figure is drawn to a smaller scale. The intensities of the secondary maxima are also shown. These secondary maxima are not of equal intensity but fall off as we go out on either side of each principal maximum. Nor are they in general equally spaced, the lack of equality being due to the fact that the maxima are not quite symmetrical. This lack of symmetry is greatest for the secondary maxima immediately adjacent to the principal maxima, and is such that the secondary maxima are slightly shifted toward the adjacent principal maximum.

These features of the secondary maxima show a strong resemblance to those of the secondary maxima in the *single-slit* pattern. Comparison of the central part of the intensity pattern in Fig. 17$C(d)$ with Fig. 15D for the single slit will emphasize this resemblance. As the number of

FIG. 17C. Fraunhofer diffraction by a grating of six very narrow slits, and details of the intensity pattern.

FIG. 17D. Intensity pattern for 20 narrow slits.

slits is increased, the number of secondary maxima is also increased, since it is equal to $N - 2$. At the same time the resemblance of any principal maximum and its adjacent secondary maxima to the single-slit pattern increases. In Fig. 17D is shown the interference curve for $N = 20$, corresponding to the last photograph shown in Fig. 17A. In this case there are 18 secondary maxima between each pair of principal maxima, but only those fairly close to the principal maxima appear with appreciable intensity, and even these are not sufficiently strong to show in the photograph. The agreement with the single-slit pattern is here practically complete. The physical reason for this agreement will be discussed in Sec. 17.10, where it will be shown that the dimensions of the pattern correspond to those from a single "slit" of width equal to that of the entire grating. Even when the number of slits is small it may be shown that the intensities of the secondary maxima can be computed by summing a number of such single-slit patterns, one for each order (Prob. 6).

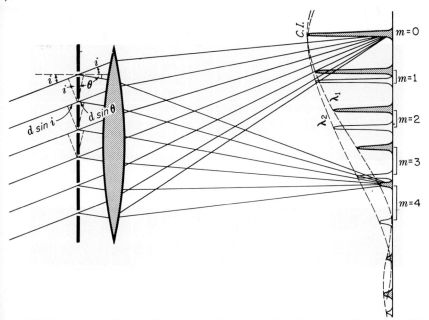

FIG. 17E. Positions and intensities of the principal maxima from a grating, where light containing two wavelengths is incident at an angle i and diffracted at various angles θ.

17.5. Formation of Spectra by a Grating.

The secondary maxima discussed above are of little importance in the production of spectra by a many-lined grating. The principal maxima treated in Sec. 17.3 are called *spectrum lines* because when the primary source of light is a narrow slit they become sharp, bright lines on the screen. These lines will be parallel to the rulings of the grating if the slit also has this direction. For monochromatic light of wavelength λ, the angles θ at which these lines are formed are given by Eq. 17d, which is the ordinary grating equation $d \sin \theta = m\lambda$ commonly given in elementary textbooks. A more general equation includes the possibility of light incident on the grating at any angle i. The equation then becomes

$$d(\sin i + \sin \theta) = m\lambda \qquad \text{GRATING EQUATION} \qquad (17f)$$

since, as will be seen from Fig. 17E, this is the path difference for light passing through adjacent slits. The figure shows the path of the light forming the maxima of order $m = 0$ (called the *central image*), and also $m = 4$ in light of a particular wavelength λ_1. For the central image, Eq. 17f shows that $\sin \theta = - \sin i$, or $\theta = -i$. The negative sign comes from the fact that we have chosen to call i and θ positive when measured on the same side of the normal; i.e., our convention of signs is such that whenever the rays used *cross over* the line normal to the grating, θ is taken as negative. Those intensity maxima which are

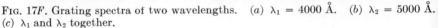

FIG. 17F. Grating spectra of two wavelengths.   (a) $\lambda_1 = 4000$ Å.   (b) $\lambda_2 = 5000$ Å. (c) λ_1 and λ_2 together.

shaded show the various orders of the wavelength λ_1. In the case of the fourth order, for example, the path differences indicated are such that $d(\sin i + \sin \theta) = 4\lambda_1$. The intensities of the principal maxima are limited by the diffraction pattern corresponding to a single slit (broken line) and drop to zero at the first minimum of that pattern, which here coincides with the fifth order. The missing orders in this illustration are therefore $m = 5, 10, \ldots$, as would be produced by having $d = 5b$.

Now if the source gives light of another wavelength λ_2 somewhat greater than λ_1, the maxima of the corresponding order m for this wavelength will, according to Eq. 17f, occur at larger angles θ. Since the spectrum lines are narrow, these maxima will in general be entirely separate in each order from those of λ_1, and we have two lines forming a *line spectrum* in each order. These spectra are indicated by brackets in the figure. Both the wavelengths will coincide, however, for the central image, because for this the path difference is zero for any wavelength. A similar set of spectra occurs on the other side of the central image, the shorter wavelength line in each order lying on the side toward the central image. Figure 17F shows actual photographs of grating spectra corresponding to the diagram of Fig. 17E. If the source gives white light, the central image will be white, but for the orders each will be spread out into *continuous spectra* composed of an infinite number of adjacent images of the slit in light of the different wavelengths present. At any given point in such a continuous spectrum, the light will be very nearly monochromatic because of the narrowness of the slit images formed by the grating and lens. The result is in this respect fundamentally different from that with the double slit, where the images were broad and the spectral colors were not separated.

17.6. Dispersion. The separation of any two colors, such as λ_1 and λ_2 in Figs. 17E and 17F, increases with the order number. To express this separation the quantity frequently used is called the *angular dispersion*, which is defined as the rate of change of angle with change of wavelength. An expression for this quantity is obtained by differentiating Eq. 17f with respect to λ, remembering that i is a constant independent of wavelength. Substituting the ratio of finite increments for the derivative, one has

$$\frac{\Delta\theta}{\Delta\lambda} = \frac{m}{d \cos \theta} \qquad \text{ANGULAR DISPERSION} \qquad (17g)$$

The equation shows in the first place that for a given small wavelength difference $\Delta\lambda$, the angular separation $\Delta\theta$ is directly proportional to the order m. Hence the second-order spectrum is twice as wide as the first order, the third three times as wide as the first, etc. In the second place, $\Delta\theta$ is inversely proportional to the slit separation d, which is usually referred to as the *grating space*. The smaller the grating space, the more widely spread will be the spectra. In the third place, the occurrence of $\cos \theta$ in the denominator means that in a given order m the dispersion will be smallest on the normal, where $\theta = 0$, and will increase slowly as we go out on either side of this. If θ does not become large, $\cos \theta$ will not differ much from unity, and this factor will be of little importance. If we neglect its influence, the different spectral lines in one order will differ in angle by amounts which are directly proportional to their difference in wavelength. Such a spectrum is called a *normal spectrum*, and one of the chief advantages of gratings over prism instruments is this simple linear scale for wavelengths in their spectra.

The *linear dispersion* in the focal plane of the telescope or camera lens is $\Delta l/\Delta\lambda$, where l is the distance along this plane. Its value is usually obtainable by multiplying Eq. 17g by the focal length of the lens. In some arrangements, however, the photographic plate is turned so the light does not strike it normally, and there is a corresponding increase in linear dispersion.   In specifying the dispersion of a spectrograph, it has become customary to quote the so-called *plate factor*, which is the reciprocal of the above quantity and is expressed in angstroms per millimeter.

17.7. Overlapping of Orders.   If the range of wavelengths is large, for instance, if we observe the whole visible spectrum between 4000 and 7200 Å, considerable overlapping occurs in the higher orders.   Suppose, for example, that one observed in the third order a certain red line of wavelength 7000 Å.   The angle of diffraction for this line is given by solving for θ the expression

$$d(\sin i + \sin \theta) = 3 \times 7000$$

where d is in angstrom units.   But at the same angle θ there may occur a green line in the fourth order, of wavelength 5250 Å, since

$$4 \times 5250 = 3 \times 7000$$

Similarly the violet of wavelength 4200 Å will occur in the fifth order at this same place.   The general condition for the various wavelengths that can occur at a given angle θ is then

$$d(\sin i + \sin \theta) = \lambda_1 = 2\lambda_2 = 3\lambda_3 = \cdots \qquad (17h)$$

where λ_1, λ_2, etc., are the wavelengths in the first, second, etc., orders. For visible light there is no overlapping of the first and second orders, since with $\lambda_1 = 7200$ Å and $\lambda_2 = 4000$ Å the red end of the first order falls just short of the violet end of the second.   When photographic observations are made, however, these orders may extend down to 2000 Å in the ultraviolet, and the first two orders do overlap.   This difficulty may usually be eliminated by the use of suitable color filters to absorb from the incident light those wavelengths which would overlap the region under study.   As an example, a piece of red glass transmitting only wavelengths longer than 6000 Å could be used in the above case to avoid the interfering shorter wavelengths of higher order that might disturb observation of λ7000 and lines in that vicinity.

17.8. Width of the Principal Maxima.   It was shown at the beginning of Sec. 17.4 that the first minima on either side of any principal maximum occur where $N\gamma = mN\pi \pm \pi$, or where $\gamma = m\pi \pm (\pi/N)$.   When $\gamma = m\pi$, we have the principal maxima, owing to the fact that the phase difference δ or 2γ, in the light from corresponding points of adjacent slits, is given by $2\pi m$, or a whole number of complete vibrations.   However, if we change the angle enough to cause a change of $2\pi/N$ in the phase difference, reinforcement no longer occurs, but the light from the various slits now interferes to produce zero intensity.   A phase difference of $2\pi/N$ between the maximum and the first minimum means a path difference of λ/N.

To see why this path difference causes zero intensity, consider Fig. 17*G*(*a*), in which the rays leaving the grating at the angle θ form a principal maximum of order *m*. For these, the path difference of the rays from two adjacent slits is $m\lambda$, so that all the waves arrive in phase. The path difference of the *extreme* rays is then $Nm\lambda$, since N is always a very large number in any practical case.* Now let us change the angle of diffraction by a small amount $\Delta\theta$, such that the extreme path difference increases by one wavelength and becomes $Nm\lambda + \lambda$ (rays

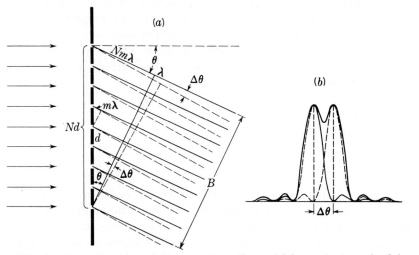

Fig. 17*G*. Angular separation of two spectrum lines which are just resolved by a diffraction grating.

shown by broken lines). This should correspond to the condition for zero intensity, because as is required the path difference for two adjacent slits has been increased by λ/N. It will be seen that the ray from the top of the grating is now of opposite phase from that at the center, and the effects of these two will cancel. Similarly, the ray from the next slit below the center will annul that from the next slit below the top, etc. The cancellation if continued will yield zero intensity from the whole grating, in entire analogy to the similar process considered in Sec. 15.3 for the single-slit pattern.

Thus the first zero occurs at the small angle $\Delta\theta$ on each side of any principal maximum. From the figure, it is seen that

$$\Delta\theta = \frac{\lambda}{B} = \frac{\lambda}{Nd \, \cos\theta} \qquad \begin{array}{l} \text{ANGULAR HALF WIDTH OF PRINCIPAL} \\ \text{MAXIMUM} \end{array} \qquad (17i)$$

* With a small number of slits, it is necessary to use the true value $(N-1)m\lambda$, and the subsequent argument must be slightly modified, but yields the same result (Eq. 17*i*).

It is instructive to note that this is just $1/N$th *of the separation of adjacent orders*, since the latter is represented by the same expression with the path difference $N\lambda$ instead of λ in the numerator.

17.9. Resolving Power. When N is many thousands, as in any useful diffraction grating, the maxima are extremely narrow. The chromatic resolving power $\lambda/\Delta\lambda$ is correspondingly high. To evaluate it, we note first that since the intensity contour is essentially the diffraction pattern of a rectangular aperture, the Rayleigh criterion (Sec. 15.6) may be applied. The images formed in two wavelengths that are barely resolved must be separated by the angle $\Delta\theta$ of Eq. 17i. Consequently the light of wavelength $\lambda + \Delta\lambda$ must form its principal maximum of order m at the same angle as that for the first minimum of wavelength λ in that order [Fig. 17G(b)]. Hence we may equate the extreme path differences in the two cases, and obtain

$$mN\lambda + \lambda = mN(\lambda + \Delta\lambda)$$

from which it immediately follows that

$$\frac{\lambda}{\Delta\lambda} = mN \tag{17j}$$

That the resolving power is proportional to the order m is to be understood from the fact that the *width* of a principal maximum, by Eq. 17i, depends on the width B of the emergent beam and does not change much with order, whereas the *separation* of two maxima of different wavelengths increases with the dispersion, which, by Eq. 17g, increases nearly in proportion to the order. Just as for the prism (Sec. 15.7), we have that

Chromatic resolving power = angular dispersion
$$\times \text{ width of emergent beam}$$

since in the present case

$$\frac{\lambda}{\Delta\lambda} = \frac{\Delta\theta}{\Delta\lambda} \times B = \frac{m}{d \cos\theta} \times Nd \cos\theta = mN$$

In a *given order* the resolving power, by Eq. 17j, is proportional to the total number of slits N, but is independent of their spacing d. However, at *given angles* of incidence and diffraction it is independent of N also, as can be seen by substituting in Eq. 17j the value of m from Eq. 17f.

$$\frac{\lambda}{\Delta\lambda} = \frac{d(\sin i + \sin\theta)}{\lambda} N = \frac{W(\sin i + \sin\theta)}{\lambda} \tag{17k}$$

Here $W = Nd$ is the total width of the grating. At a given i and θ, the resolving power is therefore independent of the number of lines ruled in the distance W. A grating with fewer lines gives a higher order at these given angles, however, with consequent overlapping, and would require some auxiliary dispersion to separate these orders, as does the Fabry-Perot interferometer. The method has nevertheless been recently applied with success in the echelle grating to be described later. Theoretically the maximum resolving power obtainable with any grating

Fig. 17H. Illustrating how the intensity curve for a grating of several slits is obtained by the graphical addition of amplitudes.

occurs when $i = \theta = 90°$, and according to Eq. 17k it equals $2W/\lambda$, or the number of wavelengths is twice the width of the grating. In practice such grazing angles are not usable, however, because of the negligible amount of light. One can only hope to reach about two-thirds of the ideal maximum.

17.10. Vibration Curve. Let us now apply the method of compounding the amplitudes vectorially which was used in Sec. 16.6 for two slits and in Sec. 15.4 for one slit. The vibration curve for the contributions from the various infinitesimal elements of a single slit again forms an arc of a circle, but there are now several of these arcs in the curve, corresponding to the several slits of the grating. In Fig. 17H the diagrams corresponding to the various points (a) to (f) of the intensity plot for six slits are shown. For the central maximum the light from all slits, and from all parts of each slit, is in phase, giving a resultant amplitude A which is N times as great as that from one slit, as shown in (a) of the figure Halfway to the first minimum the condition is as shown in (b). For this point $\gamma = \pi/12$, so that the phase difference from corresponding points in adjacent slits δ equals $\pi/6$ (cf. Fig. 17C).

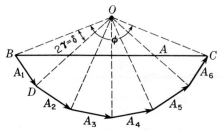

FIG. 17I. Geometrical derivation of the intensity function for a grating.

This is also the angle between successive vectors in the series of six resultants A_1 to A_6 which are the chords of six small equal arcs. Just as for the double slit, the final resultant A is obtained by compounding these vectorially, and the intensity is measured by A^2. With increasing angle the individual resultants become slightly smaller in magnitude as β increases, because it is the arc, not the chord, which is constant in length. Their difference is here small, even for point (f).

The derivation of the general intensity function for the grating, Eq. 17b, can be very simply done by a geometrical method. In Fig. 17I the six amplitude vectors of Fig. 17H are shown with a phase difference somewhat less than in part (b) of the figure. All these have the same magnitude, given by

$$A_n = \frac{\sin \beta}{\beta} A_0 \qquad (17l)$$

since this represents the chord of an arc of length A_0 subtending the angle 2β (see Fig. 15F). Each vector is inclined to the next by the angle $\delta = 2\gamma$, and thus the six form part of a regular polygon. In the figure broken lines are drawn from the ends of each vector to the center O of this polygon. These lines also make the constant angle 2γ with each other. Therefore the total angle subtended at the center is

$$\phi = N\delta = N \times 2\gamma$$

We wish the relation between the resultant amplitude A and the individual ones A_n, which are given by Eq. 17l. By dividing the triangle OBC into two halves with a line from O perpendicular to A, it is seen that

$$A = 2r \sin \frac{\phi}{2}$$

where r represents OB or OC. Similarly, from the triangle OBD as split by a line perpendicular to A_1, we obtain

$$A_n = A_1 = 2r \sin \gamma$$

Dividing this equation into the previous one, we find

$$\frac{A}{A_n} = \frac{2r \sin \dfrac{\phi}{2}}{2r \sin \gamma} = \frac{\sin N\gamma}{\sin \gamma}$$

When we then substitute the value of A_n from Eq. 17*l*, there results, for the amplitude,

$$A = A_0 \frac{\sin \beta}{\beta} \frac{\sin N\gamma}{\sin \gamma}$$

The square of this, which gives the intensity, is seen to be identical with Eq. 17*c*.

The vibration curve as applied to different numbers of slits helps to understand many features of the intensity patterns. For instance, there is the important question of the narrowness of the principal maxima. The adjacent minimum on one side is reached when the vectors first form a closed polygon, as is (*c*) of Fig. 17*H*. It is evident that this will occur for smaller values of δ the larger the number of slits, and this means that the maxima will become sharper. Also one can see at once from the diagram that for this minimum $\delta = 2\pi/N$, or $\gamma = \pi/N$, the condition stated at the beginning of Sec. 17.8. Furthermore, as the number of slits becomes large, the polygon of vectors will rapidly approach the arc of a circle, and the analogy with the pattern due to a single aperture of width equal to that of the grating is thereby seen to be justified. Comparison of Fig. 17*H* with Fig. 15*F* for the single slit will show that for large N the diagrams for the grating will become identical with those for one slit if we replace $N\delta/2$ or $N\gamma$ by β. Since $N\gamma$ is half the phase difference from extreme slits of the grating and β half the phase difference between extreme points in an open aperture, we see the physical reason for the correspondence mentioned in Sec. 17.4.

Finally we note that if the diagrams in Fig. 17*H* are carried further, the first-order principal maximum occurs when the arc representing each interval d forms one complete circle. The chords under these conditions are all parallel and in the same direction as in (*a*), but smaller in magnitude. The second principal maximum occurs when each arc forms two turns of a circle when the resultant chords again line up. These maxima have no analogue in the pattern for a single slit.

17.11. Production of Ruled Gratings. Up to this point we have considered the characteristics of an idealized grating consisting of identical and equally spaced slits separated by opaque strips. Actual gratings

used in the study of spectra are made by ruling fine grooves with a diamond point either on a plane glass surface to produce a *transmission grating* or more often on a polished metal mirror to produce a *reflection grating.*
The transmission grating gives something like our idealized picture,
since the grooves scatter the light and are effectively opaque, while the
undisturbed parts of the surface transmit regularly and act like slits.
The same is true of the reflection grating, except that here the unruled
portions reflect regularly, and the grating equation 17*f* holds equally
well for this case with the same convention of signs for i and θ.

(a)   (b)

FIG. 17*J*. Microphotographs of the rulings on reflection gratings.   (a) Light ruling.
(b) Heavy ruling.   (*After H. D. Babcock.*)

Figure 17*J* shows microphotographs of the ruled surfaces of two different reflection gratings.   The grating shown in (*a*) was ruled lightly, and
the grooves are too shallow to obtain maximum brightness.   That shown
in (*b*) was a high-quality grating having 15,000 lines per inch.   One
or two vertical cross-rulings have been made to show more clearly the
contour of the ruled surface.

Until recently, most gratings were ruled on speculum metal, a very
hard alloy of copper and tin.   Modern practice, however, is to rule on
an evaporated layer of the softer metal aluminum.   Not only does this
give greater reflection in the ultraviolet, but it causes less wear on the
diamond ruling point.   The chief requirement for a good grating is that
the lines shall be as nearly equally spaced as possible over the whole
ruled surface, which in different gratings varies from 1 to 10 in. in width.
This is a difficult requirement to fulfill, and there are very few places
in the world where ruling machines of precision adequate for the production of fine gratings have been constructed.   After each groove has been
ruled, the machine lifts the diamond point and moves the grating forward

by a small rotation of the screw which drives the carriage carrying it. To have the spacing of rulings constant, the screw must be of very constant pitch, and it was not until the manufacture of a nearly perfect screw had been achieved by Rowland,* in 1882, that the problem of successfully ruling large gratings was accomplished.

If ruled gratings are used without any auxiliary apparatus to separate the different orders, the overlapping of these makes it impractical to use values of m above 4 or 5. Hence, to obtain adequate dispersion and resolving power, the grating space must under these circumstances be made very small, and a large number of lines must be ruled. Rowland's engine gave 14,438 per inch, corresponding to $d = 1.693 \times 10^{-4}$ cm, and could produce gratings nearly 6 in. wide. This grating space is about three wavelengths of yellow light, and thus the third order is the highest that can be observed in this color with normal incidence. Correspondingly higher orders can be observed for shorter wavelengths. Even in the first order, however, the dispersion given by such a grating far exceeds that of a prism. From the grating equation one finds that the visible spectrum is spread over an angle of 12°. If it were projected by a lens of 3 m focal length, the spectrum would cover a length of about 60 cm on the photographic plate. In the second order it would be more than a meter long.

The real advantage of the grating over the prism lies not in its large dispersion, however, but in the high resolving power it affords. One can always increase the linear dispersion by using a camera lens of longer focal length, but beyond a certain minimum set by the graininess of the photographic plate no more detail is revealed thereby. With sufficient dispersion, the final limitation is the chromatic resolving power. A 6-in. Rowland grating in the first order gives $\lambda/\Delta\lambda = 6 \times 14,438 \simeq 76,600$. In the orange region two lines only 0.08 Å apart would be resolved, and with the above-mentioned dispersion each line would be only 0.015 mm wide. This separation is only one-eightieth of that of the orange sodium doublet. A glass prism, even though it had the rather large $dn/d\lambda$ of -1200 cm^{-1}, would by Eq. 15h need to have a base 64 cm long to yield the same resolution.

It was first shown by Thorp that fairly good transmission gratings could be made by taking a cast of the ruled surface with some transparent material. Such casts are called *replica gratings*, and may give satisfactory performance where the highest resolving power is not needed. Collodion or cellulose acetate, properly diluted, is poured on the grating

---

* H. A. Rowland (1848–1901). Professor of physics at the Johns Hopkins University, Baltimore. He is famous for his demonstration of the magnetic effect of a charge in motion, for his measurements of the mechanical equivalent of heat, and for his invention of the concave grating (Sec. 17.15).

surface and dried to a thin, tough film which can easily be detached from the master grating under water. It can then be mounted on a plane glass plate or concave mirror. Some distortion and shrinkage is involved in this process, so that the replica seldom functions as well as the master. With modern improvements in the techniques of plastics, however, replicas of high quality are now being made.

17.12. Ghosts. In an actual grating the ruled lines will always deviate to some extent from the ideal of equal spacing. This gives rise to various effects, according to the nature of the ruling error. Three types may be distinguished. (1) The error is *perfectly random* in magnitude and direction. In this case the grating will give a continuous spread of light underlying the principal maxima, even when monochromatic light is used. (2) The error *continuously increases* in one direction. This can be shown to give the grating "focal properties." Parallel light after diffraction is no longer parallel, but slightly divergent or convergent. (3) The error is *periodic* across the surface of the grating. This is the most common type, since it frequently arises from defects in the driving mechanism of the ruling machine. It gives rise to "ghosts," or false lines, accompanying every principal maximum of the ideal grating. When there is only one period involved in the error, these lines are symmetrical in spacing and intensity about the principal maxima. Such ghosts are called *Rowland ghosts*, and may easily be seen in Fig. 21*H*(*g*). More troublesome, though of less frequent occurrence, are the *Lyman** ghosts*. These appear when the error involves two periods that are incommensurate with each other, or else when there is a single error of very short period. Lyman ghosts may occur very far from the principal maximum of the same wavelength.

17.13. Control of the Intensity Distribution among Orders. The relative intensities of the different orders for a ruled grating do not conform to the term $(\sin^2 \beta)/\beta^2$ derived for the ideal case (Eq. 17*c*). Obviously the light reflected from (or refracted by) the sides of the grooves will produce important modifications. In general there will be no missing orders. The *positions* of the spectral lines are uninfluenced, however, and remain unchanged for any grating of the same grating space *d*. In fact, the only essential requirement for a grating is that it impress on the diffracted wave some periodic variation of either amplitude or phase. The relative intensity of different orders is then determined by the angular distribution of the light diffracted by a single element, of width *d*, on the grating surface. In the ideal grating this corresponds to the diffraction from a single slit. In ruled gratings it will usually be a

---

* Theodore Lyman (1874–1954). For many years director of the Physical Laboratories at Harvard University. Pioneer in the investigation of the far ultraviolet spectrum.

complex factor, which in the early days of grating manufacture was considered to be largely uncontrollable.   More recently, R. W. Wood has been able to produce gratings which concentrate as much as 90 per cent of the light of a particular wavelength in a single order on one side.   Thus one of the chief disadvantages of gratings as compared to prisms—the presence of multiple spectra, none of which is very intense—is overcome.

Wood's first experiments were done with gratings for the infrared, which have a large grating space so that the form of the grooves could be easily governed.   These so-called *echelette* gratings had grooves with one optically flat side inclined at such an angle ϕ as to reflect the

(a)   (b)

FIG. 17K. Concentration of light in a particular direction by (a) an echelette or echelle grating and (b) a reflection echelon.

major portion of the infrared radiation toward the order that was to be bright [Fig. 17K(a)].   Of course the light from any one such face is diffracted through an appreciable angle, measured by the ratio of the wavelength to the width b of the face.   When the ruling of gratings oh aluminum was started, it was found possible to control the shape of the finer grooves required for visible and ultraviolet light.   By proper shaping and orientation of the diamond ruling point, gratings are now produced which show a *blaze* of light at any desired angle.

Historically, the first application of the principle of concentrating the light in particular orders was made by Michelson in his *echelon* grating [Fig. 17K(b)].   This instrument consists of 20 to 30 plane-parallel plates stacked together with a constant offset b of about 1 mm.   The thickness t was usually 1 cm so that the grating space is very large and concentration occurs in an extremely high order.   As used by Michelson, echelons were transmission instruments, but larger path differences and higher orders are afforded by the reflection type first made by Williams.*   In either case, the light is concentrated in a direction perpendicular to the fronts of the steps.   At most two orders of a given wavelength appear under the diffraction maximum.   These have such large values of m [about $2t/\lambda$ for the reflection type and $(n-1)t/\lambda$ for the transmission type] that

* W. E. Williams, *Proc. Phys. Soc. (London)*, **45**, 699, 1933.

the resolving power mN is very high, even with a relatively small number N of plates. In this respect the instrument is like an interferometer, and in the same way requires auxiliary dispersion to separate the lines that are being studied. Since it has the same defect of lack of flexibility as does the Lummer-Gehrcke plate, the echelon is little used nowadays.

A more important type of grating called the *echelle*, which is intermediate between the echelette and the echelon, has recently been devel-

Fig. 17L. Echellegram of the thorium spectrum (*After Sumner P. Davis*).

oped.* It has a relatively coarse spacing of the grooves, some 200 to the inch. These are shaped as in Fig. 17$K(a)$, but with a rather steeper slope. The order numbers for which concentration occurs are in the hundreds, whereas for an echelon they are in the tens of thousands. An echelle must be used in conjunction with another dispersing instrument, usually a prism spectrograph, to separate the various orders. If the dispersion of the echelle is in a direction perpendicular to that of the prism, an extended spectrum is displayed as a series of short strips representing adjacent orders, as shown in Fig. 17L.† This is part of a more extensive spectrogram, which covers a large wavelength range with a plate factor

* G. R. Harrison, *J. Opt. Soc. Am.*, **39**, 522, 1949; **43**, 853, 1953.

† The separation of orders, in taking the echellegram of Fig. 17L, was accomplished not by a prism but by an ordinary grating. This accounts for the weaker spectra between the orders marked, which occur in its second order and have echelle orders twice as great.

of only 0.5 Å/mm. Each order contains about 14 Å of the spectrum, the range that is covered by the diffraction envelope of a single groove. This range is sufficient to produce a certain amount of repetition from one order to the next. Thus in Fig. 17L the green mercury line, which has been superimposed as a reference wavelength, appears in the 405th order, and again at the extreme left in the 404th order. The resolving power afforded by the echelle depends only on its total width (Eq. 17k) and can be some fifty times higher than that of the auxiliary spectrograph. Here it is sufficient to resolve the hyperfine structure of the green line. Besides its high resolution and dispersion, the echelle has the advantages of yielding bright spectra, and of registering the spectra in very compact form.

17.14. Measurement of Wavelength with the Grating. Small gratings 1 or 2 in. wide are usually mounted on the prism table of a small spectrometer with collimator and telescope. By measuring the angles of incidence and diffraction for a given spectrum line its wavelength may be calculated from the grating formula (Eq. 17f). For this the grating space d needs to be known, and this is usually furnished with the grating. The first accurate wavelengths were determined by this method, the grating space being found by counting the lines in a given distance with a traveling microscope. Once the absolute wavelength of a single line is known, others may be measured relative to it by using the overlapping of orders. For instance, according to Eq. 17h a sodium line of wavelength 5890 Å in the third order will coincide with another line of $\lambda = \frac{3}{4} \times 5890 = 4417$ Å in the fourth order. Of course no two lines will exactly coincide in this way, but they may fall close enough together so that the small difference can be accurately corrected for. This method of comparing wavelengths is not accurate with the arrangement described above, because the telescope lens is never perfectly achromatic and the two lines will not be focused in exactly the same plane. To avoid this difficulty Rowland invented the *concave grating*, in which the focusing is done by a concave mirror, upon which the grating itself is ruled.

17.15. Concave Grating. If the grating, instead of being ruled on a plane surface, is ruled on a concave spherical mirror of metal, it will diffract and focus the light at the same time, thus doing away with the necessity of using lenses. Beside the fact that this eliminates the chromatic aberration mentioned above, it has the great advantage that the grating may be used for regions of the spectrum which are not transmitted by glass lenses, such as the ultraviolet. A mathematical treatment of the action of the concave grating would be out of place here, but we may mention one of the more important results. It is found that if R is the radius of curvature of the spherical surface of the grating, a circle of *diameter* R (i.e., radius $r = R/2$) may be drawn tangent to the grating at its mid-point which defines the locus of points where the spectrum is in focus, provided the source slit also lies on this circle. This circle is called the *Rowland circle*, and in practically all mountings for concave gratings use is made of this condition for focus.

17.16. Grating Spectrographs. Figure 17*M* shows a diagram of a common form of mounting used for large concave gratings, called the *Paschen mounting*. The slit is set up on the Rowland circle, and the light from this strikes the grating, which diffracts it into the spectra of

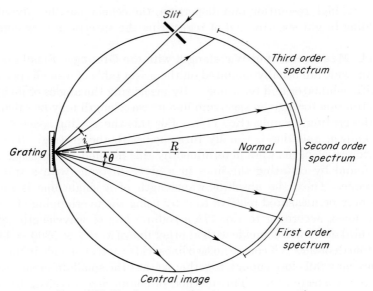

Fig. 17*M*. Paschen mounting for a concave grating.

various orders. These spectra will be in focus on the circle, and the photographic plates are mounted in a plate holder which bends them to coincide with this curve. Several orders of a spectrum can be photographed at the same time in this mounting. The ranges covered by the visible spectrum in the first three orders are indicated in Fig. 17*M* for the value of the grating space mentioned above. In a given order, Eq. 17*g* shows that the dispersion is a minimum on the normal to the grating ($\theta = 0$), and increases on both sides of this point. It is practically constant, however, for a considerable region near the normal, because here the cosine is varying slowly. A common value for R is 21 ft, and a concave grating with this radius of curvature is called a 21-*ft grating*.

Two other common mountings for concave gratings are the *Rowland mounting* and the *Eagle mounting*, illustrated in Fig. 17*N*. In the Rowland mounting, which is now mostly of historical interest, the grating G

and plate holder P are fixed to opposite ends of a rigid beam of length R. The two ends of this beam rest on swivel trucks which are free to move along two tracks at right angles to each other. The slit S is mounted just above the intersection of the two tracks. With this arrangement, the portion of the spectrum reaching the plate may be varied by sliding the beam one way or the other, thus varying the angle of incidence i. It will be seen that this effectively moves S around on the Rowland circle. For any setting the spectrum will be in focus on P, and it will be nearly a normal spectrum (Sec. 17.6) because the angle of diffraction $\theta \simeq 0$. The track SP is usually graduated in wavelengths since, as may be easily

FIG. 17N. (a) One of the earliest and (b) one of the commonest forms of concave-grating spectrograph. (c) Mounting for plane reflection grating.

shown from the grating equation, the wavelength in a given order arriving at P is proportional to the distance SP.

The Eagle mounting, because of its compactness and flexibility, has largely replaced the Rowland and Paschen forms. Here the part of the spectrum is observed which is diffracted back at angles nearly equal to the angle of incidence. The slit S is placed at one end of the plateholder, the latter being pivoted like a gate at S. To observe different portions of the spectrum, the grating is turned about an axis perpendicular to the figure. It must then be moved along horizontal ways, and the plateholder turned, until P and S again lie on the Rowland circle. The instrument can be mounted in a long box or room where the temperature is held constant. Variations of temperature displace the spectrum lines owing to the change of grating space which results from the expansion or contraction of the grating. With a grating of speculum metal it can be shown that a change of temperature of 0.1°C shifts a line of wavelength

5000 Å in any order by 0.013 Å. The Eagle mounting is commonly used in *vacuum spectrographs* for the investigation of ultraviolet spectra in the region below 2000 Å. Since air absorbs these wavelengths, the air must be pumped out of the spectrograph, and this compact mounting is convenient for the purpose. The Paschen mounting is also frequently used in vacuum spectrographs with the light incident on the grating at a practically grazing angle. The *Littrow mounting*, also shown in Fig. 17N, is the only common method of mounting large plane reflection gratings. In principle it is very much like the Eagle mounting, the main difference being that a large achromatic lens renders the incident light parallel and focuses the diffracted light on P, so that it acts as both collimator and telescope lenses at once.

One important drawback of the concave grating as used in the mountings described above is the presence of strong astigmatism. It is least in the Eagle mounting. This defect of the image always occurs when a concave mirror is used off axis. Here it has the consequence that each point on the slit is imaged as two lines, one located on the Rowland circle perpendicular to its plane, the other in this plane and at some distance behind the circle. If the slit is accurately perpendicular to the plane, the sharpness of the spectrum lines is not seriously impaired by astigmatism. Because of the increased length of the lines, however, some loss of intensity is involved. More serious is the fact that it is impossible to study the spectrum of different parts of a source, or to separate Fabry-Perot rings, by projecting an image on the slit of the spectrograph. For this purpose, a *stigmatic mounting* is required. The commonest of these is the Wadsworth mounting, in which the concave grating is illuminated by parallel light. The light from the slit is rendered parallel by a large concave mirror, and the spectrum is focused at a distance of about one-half the radius of curvature of the grating.

PROBLEMS

1. Derive Eq. 17c, as suggested in Sec. 17.2, by integrating Eq. 15b over the proper limits.

2. An ideal transmission grating has $d = 3b$. Described the condition of the vibration curve at a point corresponding to the first missing order.

Ans. Curve for each slit makes a closed circle.

3. Make qualitative sketches of the intensity patterns for (a) four slits having $d/b = 7$, and (b) nine slits having $d/b = 3$. Label several points on the axis of abscissas with the corresponding values of β and γ.

4. Prove that the intensity formula for the ideal grating reduces to that for the double slit in the special case $N = 2$. (HINT: Apply the trigonometric formula for the sine of the double angle.)

5. Seven sources of microwaves ($\lambda = 3$ cm) are placed side by side, 8 cm apart. Describe the radiation pattern observed at a distance sufficient to ensure Fraunhofer diffraction. Compute the angular half width of the central maximum. Find also the angular separation of the principal maxima and of the subsidiary maxima.

6. Prove that the intensity pattern for N slits can be represented as the sum over all orders of a number of single-slit patterns of the type that would be produced by an aperture of width Nd. (The general proof, though exact, is difficult. Try summing the numerical values of the secondary maxima for a specific case, say, $N = 4$, and compare with the values calculated from the grating formula.)

7. Let light of two wavelengths, 5200 and 5500 Å, fall on a plane transmission grating having 3500 lines per centimeter. The emerging parallel light is to be focused on a screen by a lens of 1.5 m focal length. Find the distance on the screen in centimeters between the two spectrum lines (*a*) in the first order, (*b*) in the third order.

8. Find the minimum number of lines that a diffraction grating would need to have in order to resolve in the first order the red doublet given by a mixture of hydrogen and deuterium. The wavelength difference is 1.8 Å at $\lambda 6563$. *Ans.* 3,647.

9. Compare, with regard to chromatic resolving power and angular dispersion (*a*) a diffraction grating ruled with a total of 40,000 lines in a distance of 5 cm, when used in the first order at $\lambda 6250$, and (*b*) a glass prism 5 cm on each side, the glass having $n = 1.5900$ at $\lambda 6000$ and $n = 1.5880$ at $\lambda 6500$.

10. Calculate the angular dispersion in degrees per angstrom for a diffraction grating having 14,438 lines per inch, when used in the third order at 4200 Å. Assume normal incidence. *Ans.* $0.014°/\text{Å}$.

11. Describe the characteristics that would be desired for a filter to remove the other orders that overlap the region $\lambda 3000$ in the third order of a grating spectrum.

12. It is desired to study the structure of a band in the neighborhood of 4300 Å, using a 6-in. plane grating having 30,000 lines per inch, and mounted in the Littrow system. Find (*a*) the highest order that can be used, (*b*) the angle of incidence required to observe it, (*c*) the smallest wavelength interval resolved, and (*d*) the plate factor, if the lens has a focal length of 3 m.
Ans. (*a*) $m = 3$. (*b*) $49°37\frac{1}{2}'$. (*c*) 0.008 Å. (*d*) 0.609 Å/mm.

13. A transmission grating having $d = 1.65 \times 10^{-4}$ cm is illuminated at various angles of incidence by light of wavelength 6000 Å. Make a plot of the deviation of the first-order diffracted beam from the direction of the incident light, using the angle of incidence from 0 to 90° as abscissas.

14. What would be the order number and resolving power for a reflection echelon having 30 plates each 12 mm thick, if it were illuminated by light of the mercury resonance line, $\lambda 2537$? *Ans.* 94,600. 2.84×10^6.

15. An echelette grating has 1200 lines per inch, and is ruled for concentration at a wavelength of 6 μ in the first order. (*a*) Find the angle of the ruled faces to the plane of the grating. (*b*) Find the angular dispersion at this wavelength, assuming normal incidence. (*c*) If this grating were illuminated by the green mercury line, what order or orders would be observed?

16. Prove that one can express the resolving power of an echelle grating as $\lambda/\Delta\lambda = (2B/\lambda)[r^2/(1 + r^2)]^{\frac{1}{2}}$, where B is the width of the grating, and $r = t/b$ the ratio of the depth of the steps to their width. It is assumed that the light is incident and diffracted normal to the faces of width b. (HINT: Use the principle that the resolving power equals the number of wavelengths in the path difference between the rays from opposite edges of the grating.)

17. Investigate the deviation from linear dispersion in the case of a concave grating of 15 ft radius used in the Rowland mounting. If the photographic plate is 18 in. long, by what per cent does the dispersion at one end differ from that at the center? What error in angstroms would be made by computing a wavelength at the end of the plate by using the dispersion at the center? Assume that λ3660 in the first order occurs at the center and that the grating has 15,000 lines per in.

18. A concave grating of 21 ft radius is incorporated in an Eagle mounting. The grating has 15,000 lines per inch, and is $5\frac{1}{4}$ in. wide. If the angle of incidence is 37°, find what wavelength in the second order falls next to the slit. Compute the resolving power and plate factor, also in the second order, at a point on the plate that is 20 cm from the slit along the Rowland circle, in the direction of the grating normal.

Ans. 10,191 Å.   157,500.   1.12 Å/mm.

CHAPTER 18

FRESNEL DIFFRACTION

The diffraction effects obtained when either the source of light or the observing screen, or both, are at a finite distance from the diffracting aperture or obstacle come under the classification of *Fresnel diffraction.* These effects are the simplest to observe experimentally, the only apparatus required being a small source of light, the diffracting obstacle, and a screen for observation. In the Fraunhofer effects discussed in the preceding chapters, lenses were required to render the light parallel, and to focus it on the screen. Now, however, we are dealing with the more general case of divergent light which is not altered by any lenses. Since Fresnel diffraction is the easiest to observe, it was historically the first type to be investigated, although its explanation requires much more difficult mathematical theory than that necessary in treating the plane waves of Fraunhofer diffraction. In this chapter we consider only some of the simpler cases of Fresnel diffraction, which are amenable to explanation by fairly direct mathematical and graphical methods.

18.1. Shadows. One of the greatest difficulties in the early development of the wave theory of light lay in the explanation of the observed fact that light appears to travel in straight lines. Thus if we place an opaque object in the path of the light from a point source, it casts a shadow having a fairly sharp outline of the same shape as the object. It is true, however, that the edge of this shadow is not absolutely sharp and that when examined closely it shows a system of dark and light bands in the immediate neighborhood of the edge. In the days of the corpuscular theory of light, attempts were made by Grimaldi and Newton to account for such small effects as due to the deflection of the light corpuscles in passing close to the edge of the obstacle. The correct explanation in terms of the wave theory we owe to the brilliant work of Fresnel. In 1815 he showed not only that the approximately rectilinear propagation of light could be interpreted on the assumption that light is a wave motion, but also that in this way the diffraction fringes could in many cases be accounted for in detail.

To bring out the difficulty encountered in explaining shadows by the wave picture, let us consider first the passage of divergent light through

an opening in a screen.   In Fig. 18*A* the light originates from a small
pinhole *H*, and a certain portion *MN* of the divergent wave front is
allowed to pass the opening.   According to Huygens' principle, we may
regard each point on the wave front as a source of secondary wavelets.
The envelope of these at a later instant gives a divergent wave with *H*
as its center and included between the lines *HE* and *HF*.   This wave as
it advances will produce strong illumination in the region *EF* of the screen.
But also part of each wavelet will travel into the space behind *LM* and
NO, and hence might be expected to produce some light in the regions

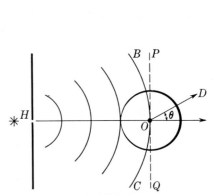

Fig. 18*A*. Huygens' principle applied to secondary wavelets from a narrow opening.

Fig. 18*B*. The obliquity factor for Huygens' secondary wavelets.

of the geometrical shadow outside of *E* and *F*.   Common experience
shows that there is actually no illumination on these parts of the screen,
except in the immediate vicinity of *E* and *F*.   According to Fresnel,
this is to be explained by the fact that in the regions well beyond the
limits of the geometrical shadow the secondary wavelets arrive with
ohase relations such that they interfere destructively and produce practically complete darkness.

The secondary wavelets cannot have uniform amplitude in all directions, since if this were so, they would produce an equally strong wave
in the backward direction.   In Fig. 18*A* the envelope on the left side
of the screen would represent a reverse wave converging toward *H*.
Obviously such a wave does not exist physically, and hence one must
assume that the amplitude at the back of a secondary wave is zero.
The more exact formulation of Huygens' principle to be mentioned later
(Sec. 18.17) justifies this assumption, and also gives quantitatively the
variation of the amplitude with direction.   The so-called *obliquity factor*,
as is illustrated in Fig. 18*B*, requires an amplitude varying as $1 + \cos \theta$,

where θ is the angle with the forward direction.   At right angles, in the directions P and Q of the figure, the amplitude falls to one-half, and the intensity to one-quarter, of its maximum value.   Another property that the wavelets must be assumed to have, in order to give the correct results, is an advance of phase of one-quarter period ahead of the wave that produces them.   The consequences of these two rather unexpected properties, and the manner in which they are derived, will be discussed later.

18.2. Fresnel's Half-period Zones.   As an example of Fresnel's approach to diffraction problems, we first consider his method of finding the effect that a slightly divergent spherical wave will produce at a point

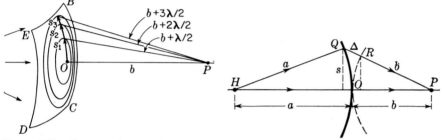

FIG. 18C. Construction of half-period zones on a spherical wave front.

FIG. 18D. Path difference Δ at a distance s from the pole of a spherical wave.

ahead of the wave.   In Fig. 18C let $BCDE$ represent a spherical wave front of monochromatic light traveling toward the right.   Every point on this sphere may be thought of as the origin of secondary wavelets, and we wish to find the resultant effect of these at a point P.   To do this, we divide the wave front into *zones* by the following construction: Around the point O, which is the foot of the perpendicular from P, we describe a series of circles whose distances from O, measured along the arc, are s_1, s_2, s_3, . . . , s_m and are such that each circle is a half wavelength farther from P.   If the distance $OP = b$, the circles will be at distances $b + \lambda/2$, $b + 2\lambda/2$, $b + 3\lambda/2$, . . . , $b + m\lambda/2$ from P.

The areas S_m of the zones, i.e., of the rings between successive circles, are practically equal.   In proving this, we refer to Fig. 18D, where a section of the wave spreading out from H is shown with radius a.   If a circle of radius b is now drawn (broken circle) with its center at P and tangent to the wave front at its "pole" O, the path HQP is longer than HOP by the segment indicated by Δ.   For the borders of the zones, this path difference must be a whole multiple of $\lambda/2$.   To evaluate it, we note first that in all optical problems the distance s is small compared with a and b.   Then s may be considered as the vertical distance of Q above the axis, and Δ may be equated to the sum of the sagittas of the two arcs OQ and OR. By the sagitta formula we then have

$$\Delta = \frac{s^2}{2a} + \frac{s^2}{2b} = s^2 \frac{a+b}{2ab} \tag{18a}$$

The radii s_m of the Fresnel zones are such that

$$m\frac{\lambda}{2} = s_m{}^2 \frac{a+b}{2ab} \tag{18b}$$

and the area of any one zone becomes

$$S_m = \pi(s_m{}^2 - s_{m-1}{}^2) = \pi \frac{\lambda}{2}\left(\frac{2ab}{a+b}\right) = \frac{a}{a+b}\pi b\lambda \tag{18c}$$

To the approximation considered, it is therefore constant and independent of m. A more exact evaluation would show that the area increases very slowly with m.

By Huygens' principle we now regard every point on the wave as sending out secondary wavelets in the same phase. These will reach P with different phases, since each travels a different distance. The phases of the wavelets from a given zone will not differ by more than π, and since each zone is on the average $\lambda/2$ farther from P, it is clear that the successive zones will produce resultants at P which differ by π. This statement will be examined in more detail in Sec. 18.6. The difference of half a period in the vibrations from successive zones is the origin of the name *half-period zones*. If we represent by A_m the resultant amplitude of the light from the mth zone, the successive values of A_m will have alternating signs, because changing the phase by π means reversing the direction of the amplitude vector. Calling the resultant amplitude due to the whole wave A, it may be then written as the sum of the series

$$A = A_1 - A_2 + A_3 - A_4 + \cdots + (-1)^{m-1}A_m \tag{18d}$$

There are three factors which determine the magnitudes of the successive terms in this series: First, because the area of each zone determines the number of wavelets it contributes, the terms should be approximately equal but should increase slowly; second, since the amplitude decreases inversely with the average distance from P of the zone, the magnitudes of the terms are reduced by an amount which increases with m; and third, because of the increasing obliquity, their magnitudes should decrease. Thus we may express the amplitude due to the mth zone as

$$A_m = \text{const.} \cdot \frac{S_m}{d_m}(1 + \cos\theta) \tag{18e}$$

where d_m is the average distance to P and θ the angle at which the light leaves the zone. It appears in the form shown because of the obliquity factor assumed in the preceding section. Now an exact calculation of the S_m's shows that the factor b in Eq. 18c must be replaced by $b + \Delta$, where Δ is the path difference for the middle of the zone. Since at the same time $d_m = b + \Delta$, we find that the ratio S_m/d_m is a constant, independent of m. Therefore we have left only the effect of the obliquity factor $1 + \cos \theta$, which causes the successive terms in Eq. 18d to decrease very slowly. The decrease is least slow at first, because of the rapid change of θ with m, but the amplitudes soon become nearly equal.

With this knowledge of the variation in magnitude of the terms, we may evaluate the sum of the series by grouping its terms in the following two ways. Supposing m to be odd,

$$
\begin{aligned}
A &= \frac{A_1}{2} + \left(\frac{A_1}{2} - A_2 + \frac{A_3}{2}\right) + \left(\frac{A_3}{2} - A_4 + \frac{A_5}{2}\right) + \cdots + \frac{A_m}{2} \\
&= A_1 - \frac{A_2}{2} - \left(\frac{A_2}{2} - A_3 + \frac{A_4}{2}\right) - \left(\frac{A_4}{2} - A_5 + \frac{A_6}{2}\right) - \cdots \\
&\qquad\qquad\qquad\qquad\qquad\qquad\qquad - \frac{A_{m-1}}{2} + A_m \quad (18f)
\end{aligned}
$$

Now since the amplitudes A_1, A_2, . . . do not decrease at a uniform rate, each one is smaller than the arithmetic mean of the preceding and following ones. Therefore the quantities in parentheses in the above equations are all positive, and the following inequalities must hold:

$$
\frac{A_1}{2} + \frac{A_m}{2} < A < A_1 - \frac{A_2}{2} - \frac{A_{m-1}}{2} + A_m
$$

Because of the fact that the amplitudes for any two adjacent zones are very nearly equal, it is then possible to equate A_1 to A_2, and A_{m-1} to A_m. The result is

$$
A = \frac{A_1}{2} + \frac{A_m}{2} \quad (18g)
$$

If m is taken to be even, we find by the same method that

$$
\frac{A_1}{2} - \frac{A_m}{2} = A
$$

Hence the conclusion is that the resultant amplitude at P due to m zones is either half the sum or half the difference of the amplitudes contributed by the first and last zones. If we allow m to become large enough so that the entire spherical wave is divided into zones, θ approaches $180°$ for the last zone. Therefore the obliquity factor causes A_m to become negligible, and the amplitude due to the whole wave is just half that due to the first zone acting alone.

Figure 18E shows how these results may be understood from a graphical construction. The vector addition of the amplitudes A_1, A_2, A_3, . . . , which are alternately positive and negative, would normally be performed by drawing them along the same line, but here for clarity they are separated in a horizontal direction. The tail of each vector is put at the same height as the head of the previous one. Then the resultant amplitude A due to any given number of zones will be the height of the final arrowhead above the horizontal base line. In the figure, it is shown for 12 zones, and also for a very large number of zones.

Fig. 18E. Addition of the amplitudes from half-period zones.

18.3. Diffraction by a Circular Aperture.

Let us examine the effect upon the intensity at P (Fig. 18C) of blocking off the wave by a screen pierced by a small circular aperture as shown in Fig. 18F. If the radius of the hole $r = OR$ is made equal to the distance s_1 to the outer edge of the first half-period zone,* the amplitude will be A_1 and this is twice the amplitude due to the unscreened wave. Thus the intensity at P is four times as great as if the screen were absent. Increasing the radius of the hole until it includes the first two zones, the amplitude is $A_1 - A_2$, or practically zero. The intensity has actually fallen to almost zero by increasing the size of the hole. A further increase of r will cause the intensity to pass through maxima and minima each time the number of zones included becomes odd or even.

The same effect is produced by moving the point of observation P

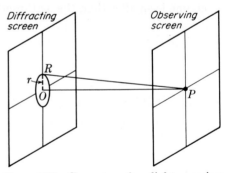

Fig. 18F. Geometry for light passing through a circular opening.

continuously toward or away from the aperture along the perpendicular. This varies the size of the zones, so that if P is originally at a position such that $PR - PO$ of Fig. 18F is $\lambda/2$ (one zone included), moving P toward the screen will increase this path difference to $2\lambda/2$ (two zones), $3\lambda/2$ (three zones), etc. We thus have maxima and minima along the axis of the aperture.

* We are here assuming that the radius of curvature of the wave striking the screen is large, so that distances measured along the chord may be taken as equal to those measured along the arc.

The above considerations give no information about the intensity at points off the axis. A mathematical investigation, which we shall not discuss because of its complexity,* shows that P is surrounded by a system of circular diffraction fringes. Several photographs of these fringes are illustrated in Fig. 18G. These were taken by placing a photographic plate some distance behind circular holes of various sizes, illuminated by monochromatic light from a distant point source. Starting at the upper left of the figures, the holes were of such sizes as to expose one, two, three, etc., zones. The alternation of the center of the pattern from

Fig. 18G. Diffraction of light by small circular openings. (*Original photographs by Hufford.*)

bright to dark illustrates the result obtained above. The large pattern on the right was produced by an aperture containing 71 zones.

18.4. Diffraction by a Circular Obstacle. When the hole is replaced by a circular disk, Fresnel's method leads to the surprising conclusion that there should be a bright spot in the center of the shadow. For a treatment of this case, it is convenient to start constructing the zones at the edge of the disk. If, in Fig. 18F, $PR = d$, the outer edge of the first zone will be $d + (\lambda/2)$ from P, of the second $d + (2\lambda/2)$, etc. The sum of the series representing the amplitudes from all the zones in this case is, as before, half the amplitude from the first exposed zone. In Fig. 18E it would be obtained by merely omitting the first few vectors. Hence the intensity at P is practically equal to that produced by the unobstructed wave. This holds only for a point on the axis, however, and off the axis the intensity is small, showing faint concentric rings. In Fig. 18$H(a)$ and (*b*), which shows photographs of the bright spot, these rings are unduly strengthened relative to the spot by overexposure. In (*c*) the source, instead of being a point, was a photographic negative of a portrait of

* See T. Preston, "Theory of Light," 5th ed., pp. 324–327, The Macmillan Company, New York, 1928.

Woodrow Wilson on a transparent plate, illuminated from behind. The disk acts like a rather crude lens in forming an image, since for every point in the object there is a corresponding bright spot in the image.

The complete investigation of diffraction by a circular obstacle shows that, besides the spot and faint rings in the shadow, there are bright circular fringes bordering the outside of the shadow. These are similar in

(a) (b) (c)

FIG. 18H. Diffraction by a circular obstacle. (a) and (b) Point source. (c) A negative of Woodrow Wilson as a source. (*After Hufford.*)

origin to the diffraction fringes from a straight edge to be investigated in Sec. 18.11.

The bright spot in the center of the shadow of a 1-cent piece may be seen by examining the region of the shadow produced by an arc light several meters away, preferably using a magnifying glass. The spot is very tiny in this case, and difficult to find. It is easier to see with a smaller object, such as a ball bearing.

18.5. Zone Plate. This is a special screen designed to block off the light from every other half-period zone. The result is to remove either

(a) (b)

FIG. 18I. Zone plates.

all the positive terms in Eq. 18d or all the negative terms. In either case the amplitude at P (Fig. 18C) will be increased to many times its value in the above cases. A zone plate can easily be made in practice by drawing concentric circles on white paper, with radii proportional to the square roots of whole num-

bers (see Fig. 18I). Every other zone is then blackened, and the result is photographed on a reduced scale. The negative, when held in the light from a distant point source, produces a large intensity at a point on its axis at a distance corresponding to the size of the zones and the wavelength of the light used. The relation between these quantities is contained in Eq. 18b, which for the present purpose may be written

$$m\frac{\lambda}{2} = \frac{s_m{}^2}{2}\left(\frac{1}{a} + \frac{1}{b}\right) \tag{18h}$$

Hence we see that, for given a, b, and λ, the zones must have $s_m \sim \sqrt{m}$.

The bright spot produced by a zone plate is so intense that the plate acts much like a lens. Thus suppose that the first 10 odd zones are exposed, as in the zone plate of Fig. 18I(a). This leaves the amplitudes A_1, A_3, A_5, . . . , A_{19} (see Fig. 18E), the sum of which is nearly ten times A_1. The whole wave front gives $\frac{1}{2}A_1$, so that, using only 10 exposed zones, we obtain an amplitude at P which is 20 times as great as when the plate is removed. The intensity is therefore 400 times as great. If the odd zones are covered, the amplitudes A_2, A_4, A_6, . . . will give the same effect. The object and image distances obey the ordinary lens formula, since, by Eq. 18h,

$$\frac{1}{a} + \frac{1}{b} = \frac{m\lambda}{s_m{}^2} = \frac{1}{f}$$

the focal length f being the value of b for $a = \infty$, namely,

$$f = \frac{s_m{}^2}{m\lambda} = \frac{s_1{}^2}{\lambda} \tag{18i}$$

There are also fainter images corresponding to focal lengths $f/3$, $f/5$, $f/7$, . . . , because at these distances each zone of the plate includes 3, 5, 7, . . . Fresnel zones. When it includes three, for example, the effects of two of them cancel but that of the third is left over.

18.6. Vibration Curve for Circular Division of the Wave Front. Our consideration of the vibration curve in the Fraunhofer diffraction by a single slit (Sec. 15.4) was based upon the division of the plane wave front into infinitesimal elements of area which were actually strips of infinitesimal width parallel to the length of the diffracting slit. The vectors representing the contributions to the amplitude from these elements were found to give an arc of a circle. This so-called *strip division* of the wave front is appropriate when the source of light is a narrow slit and the diffracting aperture rectangular. The strip division of a divergent wave front from such a source will be discussed below (Sec. 18.8). The method of dividing the spherical wave from a point source appropriate to any case of diffraction by circular apertures or obstacles involves infinitesimal circular *zones*.

Let us consider first the amplitude diagram when the first half-period zone is divided into eight subzones, each constructed in a manner similar to that used for the half-period zones themselves. We make these subzones by drawing circles on the wave front (Fig. 18C) which are distant

$$b + \frac{1}{8}\frac{\lambda}{2}, \, b + \frac{2}{8}\frac{\lambda}{2}, \, b + \frac{3}{8}\frac{\lambda}{2}, \, \ldots , \, b + \frac{\lambda}{2}$$

from P. The light arriving at P from various points in the first subzone will not vary in phase by more than $\pi/8$. The resultant of these may be represented by the vector a_1 in Fig. 18K(a). To this is now added a_2, the resultant amplitude due to the second subzone, then a_3 due to the third subzone, etc. The magnitudes of these vectors will decrease very slowly as a result of the obliquity factor. The phase difference δ between each successive one will be constant and equal to $\pi/8$. Addition of all eight subzones yields the vector AB as the resultant amplitude from the first half-period zone. Continuing this process of subzoning to the second half-period zone, we find CD as the resultant for this zone, and AD as that for the sum of the first two zones. These vectors correspond to those of Fig. 18E. Succeeding half-period zones give the rest of the figure, as shown.

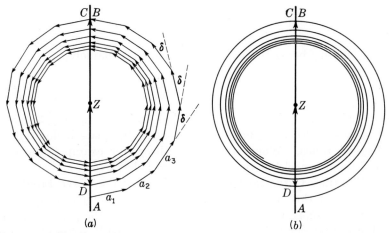

Fig. 18J. Vibration spiral for Fresnel half-period zones of a circular opening.

The transition to the vibration curve of Fig. 18J(b) results from increasing indefinitely the number of subzones in a given half-period zone. The curve is now a *vibration spiral*, eventually approaching Z when the half-period zones cover the whole spherical wave. Any one turn is very nearly a circle, but does not quite close because of the slow decrease in the magnitudes of the individual amplitudes. The significance of the series of decreasing amplitudes, alternating in sign, used in Sec. 18.2 for the half-period zones, becomes clearer when we keep in mind the curve of Fig. 18J(b). It has the additional advantage of allowing us to determine directly the resultant amplitude due to any fractional number of zones. It should be mentioned in passing that the resultant amplitude AZ, which is just half the amplitude due to the first half-period zone, turns out to be, from this treatment, 90° in phase *behind* the light from the center of the zone system. This cannot be true, since it is impossible to alter the resultant phase of a wave merely by the artifice of dividing it into zones and then recombining the effects of these. The discrepancy is a defect of Fresnel's theory resulting from the approximations made therein, and does not occur in the more rigorous mathematical treatment (see Sec. 18.17).

18.7. Apertures and Obstacles with Straight Edges. If the configuration of the diffracting screen, instead of having circular symmetry, involves straight edges like those of a slit or wire, it is possible to use as a source a slit rather than a point. The slit is set parallel to these edges, so that the straight diffraction fringes produced by each element of its length are all lined up on the observing screen. A considerable gain of intensity is achieved thereby. In the investigation of such cases, it is possible to regard the wave front as cylindrical, as shown in Fig. 18K.

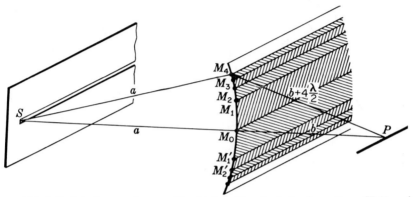

Fig. 18K. Cylindrical wave from a slit which is illuminated coherently. Half-period strips are marked on the wave front.

It is true that to produce such a cylindrical envelope to the Huygens wavelets emitted by various points on the slit these must emit *coherently*, and in practice this will not usually be true. Nevertheless, when intensities are added, as is required for noncoherent emission, the resulting pattern is the same as would be produced by a coherent cylindrical wave. In the following treatment of problems involving straight edges, we shall therefore make the simplification of assuming the source slit to be illuminated by a parallel monochromatic beam, so that it emits a truly cylindrical wave.

18.8. Strip Division of the Wave Front. The appropriate method of constructing half-period elements on a cylindrical wave front consists in dividing the latter into strips, the edges of which are successively one-half wavelength farther from the point P (Fig. 18K). Thus the points M_0, M_1, M_2, . . . on the circular section of the cylindrical wave are at distances b, $b + (\lambda/2)$, $b + (2\lambda/2)$, . . . from P. M_0 is on the straight line SP. The half-period strips M_0M_1, M_1M_2, . . . now stretch along the wave front parallel to the slit. We may call this procedure *strip division* of the wave front.

In the Fresnel zones obtained by circular division, the areas of the zones were very nearly equal. With the present type of division this is by no means true. The areas of the *half-period strips* are proportional to their widths, and these decrease rapidly as we go out along the wave front from M_0. Since this effect is much more pronounced than any variation of the obliquity factor, the latter need not be considered.

The amplitude diagram of Fig. 18L(a) is obtained by dividing the strips into substrips in a manner analogous to that described in Sec. 18.6 for circular zones. Dividing the first strip above M_0 into nine parts,

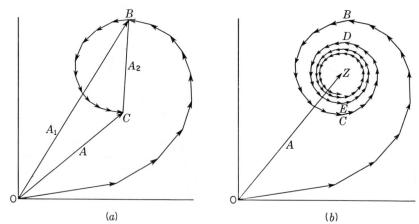

(a)   (b)

Fig. 18L. Amplitude diagrams for the formation of Cornu's spiral.

we find that the nine amplitude vectors from the substrips extend from O to B, giving a resultant $A_1 = OB$, for the first half-period strip. The second half-period strip similarly gives those between B and C, with a resultant $A_2 = BC$. Since the amplitudes now decrease rapidly, A_2 is considerably smaller than A_1, and their difference in phase is appreciably greater than π. A repetition of this process of subdivision for the succeeding strips on the upper half of the wave gives the more complete diagram of Fig. 18L(b). Here the vectors are spiraling in toward Z, so that the resultant for all half-period strips above the pole M_0 becomes OZ.

18.9. Vibration Curve for Strip Division. Cornu's Spiral. When we go over to elementary strips of infinitesimal width, we obtain the vibration curve as a smooth spiral, part of which is shown in Fig. 18M. The complete curve representing the whole wave front would be carried through many more turns, ending at the points Z and Z'. Only the part from O to Z was considered above. The lower half, $Z'O$, arises from the contributions from the half-period strips below M_0.

This curve, called *Cornu's* spiral*, is characterized by the fact that the

* A. Cornu (1841–1902). Professor of experimental physics at the École Polytechnique, Paris.

angle δ it makes with the x axis is proportional to the *square* of the distance v along the curve from the origin. Remembering that, in a vibration curve, δ represents the phase lag in the light from any element

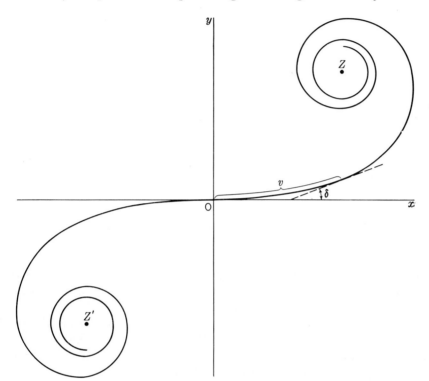

Fig. 18*M*. Cornu's spiral, drawn to include five half-period zones on either side of the pole.

of the wave front, we obtain this definition of the curve by using Eq. 18*a* for the path difference, as follows:

$$\delta = \frac{2\pi}{\lambda} \Delta = \frac{\pi(a + b)}{ab\lambda} s^2 = \frac{\pi}{2} v^2 \qquad (18j)$$

Here we have introduced a new variable for use in plotting Cornu's spiral, namely,

$$v = s \sqrt{\frac{2(a + b)}{ab\lambda}} \qquad (18k)$$

It is defined in such a way as to make it dimensionless, so that the same curve may be used for any problem, regardless of the particular values of a, b, and λ.

18.10. Fresnel's Integrals. The x and y coordinates of Cornu's spiral may be expressed quantitatively by two integrals, and a knowledge of these will permit accurate plotting and calculations. They are derived most simply as follows: Since the phase difference δ is the angle determining the slope of the curve at any point (see Fig. 18M), the changes in the coordinates for a given small displacement dv along the spiral are given by

$$dx = dv \cos \delta = \cos \frac{\pi v^2}{2} dv$$

$$dy = dv \sin \delta = \sin \frac{\pi v^2}{2} dv$$

where the value of δ from Eq. 18j has been introduced. Thus the coordinates of any point (x,y) on Cornu's spiral become

$$x = \int_0^v \cos \frac{\pi v^2}{2} dv \tag{18l}$$

$$y = \int_0^v \sin \frac{\pi v^2}{2} dv \tag{18m}$$

These are known as *Fresnel's integrals*. They cannot be integrated in closed form, but yield infinite series which may be evaluated in several ways.* Although the actual evaluation is too complicated to be given here, we have included a table of the numerical values of the integrals (Table 18-I). Later on, in Sec. 18.14, the method of using these in accurate computations of diffraction patterns is explained.

Let us first examine some features of the quantitative Cornu's spiral of Fig. 18N, which is a plot of the two Fresnel integrals. The coordinates of any point on the curve give their values for a particular upper limit v in Eqs. 18l and 18m. The scale of v is marked directly on the curve, and has equal divisions along its length. Particularly useful to remember are the positions of the points $v = 1$, $\sqrt{2}$, and 2 on the curve. They represent one-half, one, and two half-period strips, respectively, as may be verified by computing the corresponding values of δ from Eq. 18j. More important, however, are the coordinates of the end points Z' and Z. They are $(-\frac{1}{2}, -\frac{1}{2})$ and $(\frac{1}{2}, \frac{1}{2})$, respectively.

As with any vibration curve, the amplitude due to any given portion of the wave front may be obtained by finding the length of the chord of the appropriate segment of the curve. The square of this length then gives the intensity. Thus the Cornu's spiral of Fig. 18N may be used for the graphical solution of diffraction problems, as will be illustrated below. It is to be noted at the start, however, that the numerical values of intensities computed in this way are *relative to a value of 2 for the unobstructed wave*. Thus, if A represents any amplitude obtained

* For the methods of evaluating Fresnel's integrals, see R. W. Wood, "Physical Optics," 2d ed., p. 247, The Macmillan Company, New York, 1921.

TABLE 18-I. TABLE OF FRESNEL INTEGRALS

v	x	y	v	x	y
0.00	0.0000	0.0000	4.50	0.5261	0.4342
0.10	0.1000	0.0005	4.60	0.5673	0.5162
0.20	0.1999	0.0042	4.70	0.4914	0.5672
0.30	0.2994	0.0141	4.80	0.4338	0.4968
0.40	0.3975	0.0334	4.90	0.5002	0.4350
0.50	0.4923	0.0647	5.00	0.5637	0.4992
0.60	0.5811	0.1105	5.05	0.5450	0.5442
0.70	0.6597	0.1721	5.10	0.4998	0.5624
0.80	0.7230	0.2493	5.15	0.4553	0.5427
0.90	0.7648	0.3398	5.20	0.4389	0.4969
1.00	0.7799	0.4383	5.25	0.4610	0.4536
1.10	0.7638	0.5365	5.30	0.5078	0.4405
1.20	0.7154	0.6234	5.35	0.5490	0.4662
1.30	0.6386	0.6863	5.40	0.5573	0.5140
1.40	0.5431	0.7135	5.45	0.5269	0.5519
1.50	0.4453	0.6975	5.50	0.4784	0.5537
1.60	0.3655	0.6389	5.55	0.4456	0.5181
1.70	0.3238	0.5492	5.60	0.4517	0.4700
1.80	0.3336	0.4508	5.65	0.4926	0.4441
1.90	0.3944	0.3734	5.70	0.5385	0.4595
2.00	0.4882	0.3434	5.75	0.5551	0.5049
2.10	0.5815	0.3743	5.80	0.5298	0.5461
2.20	0.6363	0.4557	5.85	0.4819	0.5513
2.30	0.6266	0.5531	5.90	0.4486	0.5163
2.40	0.5550	0.6197	5.95	0.4566	0.4688
2.50	0.4574	0.6192	6.00	0.4995	0.4470
2.60	0.3890	0.5500	6.05	0.5424	0.4689
2.70	0.3925	0.4529	6.10	0.5495	0.5165
2.80	0.4675	0.3915	6.15	0.5146	0.5496
2.90	0.5624	0.4101	6.20	0.4676	0.5398
3.00	0.6058	0.4963	6.25	0.4493	0.4954
3.10	0.5616	0.5818	6.30	0.4760	0.4555
3.20	0.4664	0.5933	6.35	0.5240	0.4560
3.30	0.4058	0.5192	6.40	0.5496	0.4965
3.40	0.4385	0.4296	6.45	0.5292	0.5398
3.50	0.5326	0.4152	6.50	0.4816	0.5454
3.60	0.5880	0.4923	6.55	0.4520	0.5078
3.70	0.5420	0.5750	6.60	0.4690	0.4631
3.80	0.4481	0.5656	6.65	0.5161	0.4549
3.90	0.4223	0.4752	6.70	0.5467	0.4915
4.00	0.4984	0.4204	6.75	0.5302	0.5362
4.10	0.5738	0.4758	6.80	0.4831	0.5436
4.20	0.5418	0.5633	6.85	0.4539	0.5060
4.30	0.4494	0.5540	6.90	0.4732	0.4624
4.40	0.4383	0.4622	6.95	0.5207	0.4591

from the plot, the intensity I, expressed as a fraction of that which would exist were no screen present, which we shall call I_0, is

$$\frac{I}{I_0} = \tfrac{1}{2}A^2 \tag{18n}$$

To verify this statement, we note that according to the discussion of Sec. 18.8 a vector drawn from O to Z gives the amplitude due to the upper

FIG. 18N. Cornu's spiral, a plot of the Fresnel integrals.

half of the wave. Similarly, one from Z' to O gives that due to the lower half. Each of these has a magnitude $1/\sqrt{2}$, so that when they are added, and the sum is squared to obtain the intensity due to the whole wave, we find that $I_0 = 2$, with the conventional scale of coordinates used in Fig. 18N.*

* It will be noticed that the phase of the resultant wave is 45°, or one-eighth period behind that of the wave coming from the center of the zone system (the Huygens' wavelet reaching P from M_0 in Fig. 18K). A similar phase discrepancy, this time of one-quarter period, occurs in the treatment of circular zones in Sec. 18.6. The difference results from the fact that in the representation of a cylindrical wave, to be used in the Kirchhoff integral (Sec. 18.17), there occurs an additional phase constant of $\pi/4$ as compared to that for a spherical wave. The result of the integration over the

18.11. The Straight Edge.   The investigation of the diffraction by a single screen with a straight edge is perhaps the simplest application of Cornu's spiral.   Figure $180(a)$ represents a section of such a screen, having its edge parallel to the slit S.   In this figure the half-period strips corresponding to the point P being situated on the edge of the geometrical shadow are marked off on the wave front.   To find the intensity at P, we note that since the upper half of the wave is effective, the amplitude is a straight line joining O and Z (Fig. $18P$) of length $1/\sqrt{2}$.   The square of this is $1/2$, so that the intensity at the edge of the shadow is just *one-fourth* of that found above for the unobstructed wave.

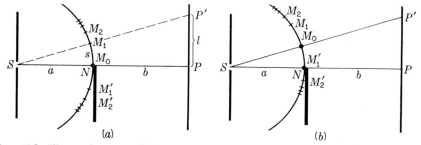

Fig. 180. Illustrating two different positions of the half-period strips relative to a straight edge N.

Consider next the intensity at the point P' [Fig. $180(a)$] at a distance l above P.   To be specific, let P' lie in the direction SM_1, where M_1 is the upper edge of the first half-period strip.   For this point, the center M_0 of the half-period strips lies on the straight line joining S with P', and the figure must be reconstructed as in Fig. $180(b)$.   The straight edge now lies at the point M_1', so that not only all the half-period strips above M_0 are exposed but also the first one below M_0.   The resultant amplitude A is therefore represented on the spiral of Fig. $18P$ by a straight line joining B' and Z.   This amplitude is more than twice that at P, and the intensity A^2 more than four times as great.

Starting with the point of observation P at the edge of the geometrical shadow (Fig. 180), where the amplitude is given by OZ, if we move the point steadily upward, the tail of the amplitude vector moves to the left along the spiral, while its head remains fixed at Z.   The amplitude will evidently go through a maximum at b', a minimum at c', another maximum at d', etc., approaching finally the value $Z'Z$ for the unobstructed wave.   If we go downward from P, into the geometrical shadow, the tail

---

entire surface is, as explained in Sec. 18.17, to bring the phase of the resultant in both cases into agreement with that of the direct wave.   For a discussion of the phase discrepancy in Cornu's spiral, see R. W. Ditchburn, "Light," 1st ed., p. 214, Interscience Publishers, Inc., New York, 1953.

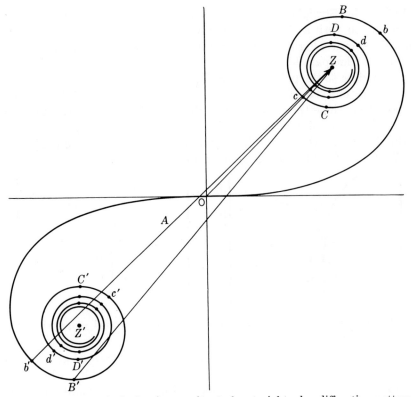

FIG. 18P. Cornu's spiral, **showing** resultants for straight-edge diffraction pattern.

FIG. 18Q. Amplitude and intensity contours for Fresnel diffraction at a straight edge.

of the vector moves to the right from O, and the amplitude will decrease steadily, approaching zero.

To obtain quantitative values of the intensities from Cornu's spiral, it is only necessary to measure the length A for various values of v. The square of A gives the intensity. Plots of the amplitude and the intensity against v are shown in Figs. 18$Q(a)$ and (b), respectively. It will be seen that at the point O, which corresponds to the edge of the geometrical shadow, the intensity has fallen to one-fourth that for large negative values of v, where it approaches the value for the unobstructed wave. The other letters correspond with points similarly labeled on the spiral, B', C', D' . . . , representing the exposure of one, two, three, etc., half-period strips below M_0. The maxima and minima of these *diffraction fringes* occur a little before these points are reached. For instance, the

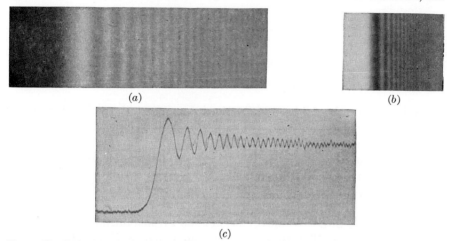

(a)

(b)

(c)

FIG. 18R. Straight-edge diffraction patterns photographed with (a) visible light of wavelength 4300 Å and (b) X rays of wavelength 8.33 Å. (c) Microphotometer trace of (a).

first maximum at b' is given when the amplitude vector A has the position shown in Fig. 18P. Photographs of the diffraction pattern from a straight edge are shown in Fig. 18$R(a)$ and (b). Pattern (a) was taken with visible light from a mercury arc, and (b) with X rays, $\lambda = 8.33$ Å. Figure 18$R(c)$ is a density trace of the photograph (a), directly above, and was made with a microphotometer.

Perhaps the most common observation of the straight-edge pattern, and certainly a very striking one, occurs in viewing a distant street lamp through rain-spattered spectacles. The edge of each drop as it stands on the glass acts like a prism, and refracts into the pupil of the eye rays which otherwise would not enter it. Beyond the edge the field is therefore dark, but the crude outline of the drop is seen as an irregular bright patch bordered by intense diffraction fringes such as those shown in Fig. 18R. The fringes are very clear, and a surprising number may be seen, presumably because of the achromatizing effect of the refraction.

18.12. Rectilinear Propagation of Light. When we investigate the *scale* of the above pattern for a particular case, the reason for the apparently rectilinear propagation of light becomes clear. Let us suppose that in a particular case $a = b = 100$ cm, and $\lambda = 5000$ Å. From Eq. 18k, we then have

$$s = v \sqrt{\frac{ab\lambda}{2(a + b)}} = 0.0354v \text{ cm}$$

This is the distance along the wave front [Fig. 18$O(a)$]. To change it to distances l on the screen, we note from the figure that

$$l = \frac{a + b}{a} s = v \sqrt{\frac{b\lambda(a + b)}{2a}} \tag{18o}$$

For the particular case chosen, therefore,

$$l = 2s = 0.0708v \text{ cm}$$

Now in the graph of Fig. 18$Q(b)$ the intensity at the point $v = +2$ is only 0.025 or one-eightieth of the intensity if the straight edge were absent. This point has $l = 0.142$ cm, and therefore lies only 1.42 mm inside the edge of the geometrical shadow. The part of the screen below this will lie in practically complete darkness, and this must be due to the destructive interference of the secondary wavelets arriving here from the upper part of the wave.

18.13. Single Slit. We next consider the Fresnel diffraction of a single slit with sides parallel to a narrow source slit S [Fig. 18$S(a)$]. By

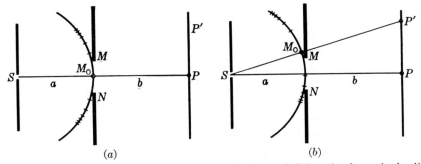

Fig. 18S. Showing division of the wave front for Fresnel diffraction by a single slit.

the use of Cornu's spiral we wish to determine the distribution of the light on the screen PP'. With the slit located as shown, each side acts like a straight edge to screen off the outer ends of the wave front. We have already seen in Sec. 18.11 how to investigate the pattern from a single straight edge, and the method used there is readily extended to the present case. With the slit in the central position of Fig. 18$S(a)$, the only light arriving at P is that due to the wave front in the interval $\Delta s = MN$. In terms of Cornu's spiral we must now determine what length Δv corresponds to the slit width Δs. This is done by Eq. 18k, using Δv for v and Δs for s. Let $a = 100$ cm, $b = 400$ cm, $\lambda = 4000$ Å $= 0.00004$ cm, and the slit width $\Delta s = 0.02$ cm. Substituting in Eq. 18k, we obtain $\Delta v = 0.5$. The resultant amplitude at P is then given

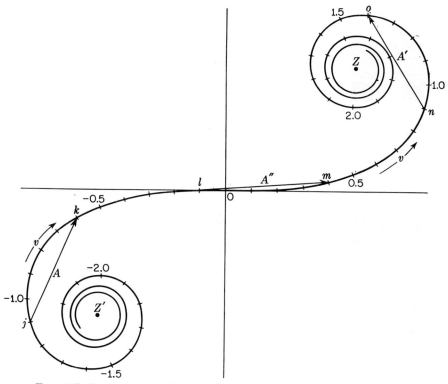

FIG. 18T. Cornu's spiral, showing the chords of arcs of equal lengths Δv.

by a chord of the spiral, the arc of which has a length $\Delta v = 0.5$. Since the point of observation P is centrally located, this arc will start at $v = -0.25$ and run to $v = +0.25$. This amplitude $A \simeq 0.5$ when squared gives the intensity at P.

If we now wish the intensity at P' [Fig. 18$S(b)$], the picture must be revised by redividing the wave front as shown. With the point of observation at P', the same length of wave front, $\Delta s = 0.02$ cm, is exposed, and therefore the same length of the spiral, $\Delta v = 0.5$, is effective. This section on the lower half of the wave front will, however, correspond to a new position of the arc on the lower half of the spiral. Suppose that it is represented by the arc jk in Fig. 18T. The resultant

amplitude is proportional to the chord A, and the square of this gives
the relative intensity. Thus to get the variation of intensity along the
screen of Fig. 18S, we slide a piece of the spiral of *constant* length $\Delta v = 0.5$
to various positions and measure the lengths of the corresponding chords
to obtain the amplitudes. In working a specific problem, the student
may make a straight scale marked off in units of v to tenths, and measure
the chords on an accurate plot such as Fig. 18N, using the scale of

FIG. 18U. Fresnel diffraction of visible light by narrow slits. (*X-ray pattern after Kellstrom.*)

v on the spiral to obtain the constant length Δv of the arc. The results
should then be tabulated in three columns, giving v, A, and A^2. The
value of v to be entered is that for the *central* point of the arc whose
chord A is being measured. For example, if the interval from $v = 0.9$
to $v = 1.4$ is measured (Fig. 18T), the average value $v = 1.15$ is tabulated against $A = 0.43$.

Photographs of a number of Fresnel diffraction patterns for single
slits of different widths are shown in Fig. 18U with the corresponding
intensity curves beside them. These curves have been plotted by the
use of Cornu's spiral. It is of interest to note in these diagrams the
indicated positions of the edges of the geometrical shadow of the slit
(indicated on the v axis). Very little light falls outside these points.
For a very narrow slit like the first of these where $\Delta v = 1.5$, the pattern

greatly resembles the Fraunhofer diffraction pattern for a single slit. The essential difference between the two (cf. Fig. 15D) is that here the minima do not come quite to zero except at infinitely large v. The small single-slit pattern at the top was taken with X rays of wavelength 8.33 Å, while the rest were taken with visible light of wavelength 4358 Å. As the slit becomes wider, the fringes go through very rapid changes, approaching for a wide slit the general appearance of two opposed straight-edge diffraction patterns. The small closely spaced fringes superimposed on the main fringes at the outer edges of the last figure are clearly seen in the original photograph and may be detected in the reproduction.

18.14. Use of Fresnel's Integrals in Solving Diffraction Problems. The tabulated values of Fresnel's integrals in Table 18-I may be used for higher accuracy than that obtainable with the plotted spiral. For an interval $\Delta v = 0.5$, for example, the two values of x at the ends of this interval are read from the table and subtracted algebraically to obtain Δx, the horizontal component of the amplitude. The corresponding two values of y are also subtracted to obtain Δy, its vertical component. The relative intensity will then be obtained by adding the squares of these quantities, since

$$I \sim A^2 = (\Delta x)^2 + (\Delta y)^2 \qquad (18p)$$

The method is accurate, but may be tedious. This is especially so if good interpolations are to be made in certain parts of Table 18-I. Some problems, such as that of the straight edge, are simplified by the fact that the number of zones on one end of the interval is not limited. The values of both x and y will be $\frac{1}{2}$ at this end. Another example of this type will now be considered.

18.15. Diffraction by an Opaque Strip. The shadow cast by a narrow object with parallel sides, such as a wire, may also be studied by the use of Cornu's spiral. In the case of a single slit, treated in Sec. 18.13, it was shown how the resultant diffraction pattern is obtained by sliding a fixed length of the spiral, $\Delta v = $ const., along the spiral and measuring the chord between the two end points. The rest of the spiral out to infinity, i.e., out to Z or Z' on each side of the element in question, was absent owing to the screening by the two sides of the slit. If now the opening of the slit in Fig. 18$S(a)$ is replaced by an object of the same size, and the slit jaws taken away, we have two segments of the spiral to consider. Suppose the obstacle is of such a size that it covers an interval $\Delta v = 0.5$ on the spiral (Fig. 18T). For the position jk the light arriving at the screen will be due to the parts of the spiral from Z' to j and from k to Z. The resultant amplitude due to these two sections is obtained by adding their respective amplitudes as vectors. The lower section gives an amplitude represented by a straight line from Z' to j, with the arrowhead at j. The amplitude for the upper section is represented by a straight line from k to Z with the arrowhead at Z. The vector sum of these two gives the resultant amplitude A and A^2 gives the intensity for a point v halfway between j and k. Photographs of three diffraction patterns produced by small wires are shown in Fig. 18V, accompanied by the corresponding theoretical curves.

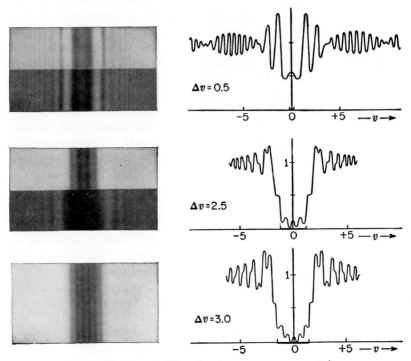

FIG. 18V. Fresnel diffraction by narrow opaque strips.

18.16. Diffracting Screens of Other Shapes. Babinet's Principle. From the foregoing examples, the method should be clear for investigating any problem, however complex, in which all edges of the screen are parallel to the source slit. The student will find it instructive, for example, to work out a double-slit pattern in Fresnel diffraction. Care must always be taken to get the proper direction for any individual amplitude vector obtained as a chord of the Cornu spiral. Since the spiral is made up of infinitesimal amplitude vectors starting at Z' and ending at Z (Sec. 18.8), the arrowhead of any vector must be at the end nearer *on the spiral* to Z.

Screens having straight edges which are not parallel, as, for example, a triangle or a polygon, will not produce clear diffraction patterns unless illuminated by a point source. Cornu's spiral is therefore not applicable to them, and recourse must be had to the more general theory mentioned below. A striking feature of such patterns is the appearance of *light fans* spreading out in both directions perpendicular to any straight edge of the screen.* Thus a point source when viewed through a small opening in the shape of an equilateral triangle looks like a six-pointed star.

There is a generalization known as *Babinet's principle* which relates the diffraction patterns produced by two complementary screens. The term complementary here signifies that the opaque spaces in one screen are replaced by transparent spaces in the other, and vice versa. An opaque strip, for example, is complementary to a slit of the same width. In its most general form, the principle states that the vector amplitude produced at a given point by one screen, when added to that produced by the other screen, gives the amplitude due to the unscreened wave. In effect it says that the whole is the sum of its parts. Thus we may write the vector equation

$$\mathbf{A}_1 + \mathbf{A}_2 = \mathbf{A}_0 \qquad (18q)$$

where the subscripts 1 and 2 refer to the complementary screens, and 0 to the absence of any screen. The truth of the principle may be verified with Cornu's spiral by dividing it into the appropriate parts, although it is applicable to all other types of diffraction as well.

Babinet's principle is not very useful in dealing with Fresnel diffraction, except as it may furnish a short-cut in obtaining the pattern for a particular screen from that of its complement. In Fraunhofer diffraction, however, it has an interesting consequence. Here the unscreened wave yields intensity zero over the whole field except at the image of the source itself. Thus $\mathbf{A}_0 = 0$, and we have $\mathbf{A}_2 = -\mathbf{A}_1$. When these amplitudes are squared to obtain the intensities, we find that *the diffraction patterns due to complementary screens are identical.* That this statement is far from true in a typical case of Fresnel diffraction may be seen by comparing Figs. 18U and 18V. It would apply to the case of a fine wire stretched over the objective of an astronomical telescope, where there would be produced in the image plane a faint single-slit pattern in the corresponding orientation. Finally, it should be mentioned that Babinet's principle is not perfectly rigorous, but involves approximations,† as does the rest of the Huygens-Fresnel treatment thus far discussed.

18.17. More General Treatments of Diffraction. The original application of Huygens' principle to diffraction, although it gave results

---

* Excellent photographs of diffraction patterns due to openings of various shapes will be found in G. Z. Dimitroff and J. G. Baker, "Telescopes and Accessories," appendix VIII, The Blakiston Division, McGraw-Hill Book Company, Inc, New York, 1945.

† See E. T. Copson, *Proc. Roy. Soc. (London)*, **186**, 116, 1946, where its limits of applicability are discussed. The principle is not even approximately true in the case of a perfectly reflecting screen.

agreeing with experiment in problems like those discussed earlier in this chapter, contained certain assumptions which were definitely incorrect. Fresnel took the obliquity factor as cos θ, since it seemed reasonable that the surface element of the wave might radiate according to Lambert's law. He neglected the fact that the phase of the resultant wave came out wrong, since he was interested only in predicting intensities. A more important question, however, is whether an error is not made in assuming uniform amplitude and phase over the wave front in the clear part of the diffracting screen, and zero amplitude behind the opaque parts. The more refined mathematical theories* developed since Fresnel's time have given the correct answers to these questions, and have also shown where the limitations of his method lie.

The first important advance was made by Kirchhoff in 1876, who showed that the light wave at any point in space could be expressed as an integral over a closed surface surrounding that point. The Huygens secondary wavelets appear in this theory as the differential contributions from the surface elements, and when part of the surface coincides with the wave front, their amplitude is found to vary as $1 + \cos \theta$, as we assumed in Sec. 18.1. Furthermore, when the integration is extended over the entire surface, one obtains the wave exactly as it would have reached the point directly from the source, i.e., with its correct amplitude and phase. Hence two deficiencies of Fresnel's theory, relating to the obliquity factor and to the phase, are supplied by Kirchhoff's extension.

In principle, the solution of any diffraction problem may be obtained by making part of Kirchhoff's closed surface coincide with the diffracting screen, and evaluating his integral with suitable boundary conditions. To do this, however, one needs to know the values of the complex amplitude, and of its derivative with respect to the normal, over the whole surface. Actually, these are never accurately known, and to solve the problem certain simplifying assumptions must be made, which in the end yield little more than the original Fresnel treatment. The results are in fact identical when the apertures are many wavelengths wide, and the observations are made at any appreciable distance from them. Recently, it has become possible by the use of microwaves of a few centimeters wavelength to measure diffraction patterns right up to the plane of the aperture, and with apertures of width from several wavelengths to only a fraction of the wavelength.† The results show surprisingly good agreement with the approximate Kirchhoff theory, but also indicate the need

---

* A complete and authoritative account will be found in A. Sommerfeld, "Optics," chaps. 5 and 6, Academic Press, Inc., New York, 1954. For a good summary from a more elementary standpoint, see J. Valasek, "Theoretical and Experimental Optics," pp. 172–186, John Wiley & Sons, Inc., New York, 1949.

† C. L. Andrews, *J. Appl. Phys.*, **21**, 761, 1950; *Am. J. Phys.*, **19**, 280, 1951.

for further theoretical and experimental studies of diffraction by these methods. Since the Fresnel approach is adequate in considering diffraction for optical wavelengths, however, we shall not take up these interesting developments.

After the advent of the electromagnetic theory of light, attempts were made to obtain rigorous treatments of certain simple types of diffraction by applying specific boundary conditions to Maxwell's equations (Chap. 20). These conditions involve a knowledge of the electrical properties of the material of the diffracting screen itself. Sommerfeld was successful in solving the one problem of the straight edge, for a screen of infinitesimal thickness and perfect reflectance, by this method. An interesting point came out of this work, which explained an observation that had long puzzled those who studied diffraction experimentally. When the eye is placed in the region of the diffracted light, the diffracting edge or edges appear luminous, even though precautions are taken to avoid reflected or scattered light. Sommerfeld's theory derives the resultant wave arriving at a point on the screen in all detail, including its phase distribution. In the geometrical shadow of the straight edge, it is found to consist of a cylindrical wave apparently originating at the edge. Outside of the shadow there are both the direct wave and this deflected one, and the diffraction fringes observed there can be interpreted as due to the interference of these two. This is, in fact, the original explanation of diffraction fringes given by Thomas Young, an explanation which was until recently regarded as erroneous. It constitutes an alternative interpretation, and one which is mathematically equivalent to that of Kirchhoff, of any Fresnel diffraction phenomenon. The single-slit pattern may be regarded as caused by the interference of the direct wave and two cylindrical waves, one from each edge.*

PROBLEMS

1. Write out the series of terms analogous to those in Eq. 18f when the number of zones is even, and show that in that case the resultant amplitude is $(A_1/2) - (A_m/2)$.

2. Carry the calculation of the areas of the Fresnel zones to a higher order of approximation than that of Eq. 18c. For a plane wave front, by what percentage does the area of the thirtieth zone exceed that of the first? Take $\lambda = 5000$ Å and $b = 20$ cm. *Ans.* 0.0037 %.

3. Make polar plots of the amplitude and intensity of a Huygens secondary wavelet against θ, using the correct obliquity factor. What is the name for the mathematical curve giving the amplitude?

* Nonmathematical discussions of the luminosity of the diffracting edge and of Young's theory will be found in C. F. Meyer. "The Diffraction of Light, X-rays and Material Particles," 1st ed., chap. 7, secs. 10–11, University of Chicago Press, Chicago, 1934, and in R. W. Wood, "Physical Optics," 3d ed., pp. 218–221, The Macmillan Company, New York, 1933.

4. One of the zone plates of Fig. 18I is photographed on such a scale that the first zone, as measured on a comparator, has a radius of 0.390 mm. It is then mounted on an optical bench 42 cm from a pinhole illuminated by the green mercury line, $\lambda5461$. Find the distance from the zone plate of the primary image, and also of the first two subsidiary ones. *Ans.* 82.7. 11.9. 6.4 cm.

5. A parallel beam of microwaves having $\lambda = 3$ cm passes through a circular opening of adjustable radius. If a detector is placed on the axis of the hole 4 m behind it and the opening gradually increased in radius, at what value would the response reach its first maximum? Its second minimum? At the latter radius, give an equation for the positions of the maxima and minima along the axis.

6. Assume that the bright spot in the shadow of a disk is visible when the deviations from a perfectly circular contour do not exceed one-third of the width of a zone. If a 1-cent piece 18.5 mm in diameter is placed in red light (6000 Å) from a distant point source, and its shadow viewed by an eyepiece 1 m behind it, what is the maximum allowable variation of the radius? *Ans.* 0.011 mm.

7. When a star is eclipsed by the moon, find how long a time it would take for the intensity to fall to one-hundredth of its initial value.

8. Using Cornu's spiral, plot the diffraction pattern of a single slit having a width $\Delta s = 1.2$ mm. Assume $a = 100$ cm, $b = 150$ cm, $\lambda = 5000$ Å.

Ans. Plot, with three strong maxima of almost equal intensity, and weaker side maxima.

9. A slit is placed at one end of an optical bench, and is illuminated with sodium light. A holder for diffracting objects is located 60 cm from the slit, and observations are made with a photoelectric cell behind a narrow slit 120 cm from the object holder. What would be the exact intensity, relative to the unobstructed intensity, (a) at the edge of the geometrical shadow of a rod 1.8 mm thick, (b) at the center of the shadow of this rod?

10. In the arrangement of Prob. 9, find the intensity (a) 2 mm inside the edge of the geometrical shadow of a straight edge, (b) 1 mm outside this edge.
Ans. (a) 0.013 I_0; (b) 1.23 I_0.

11. In the arrangement of Prob. 9, find the intensity (a) at one edge of the geometrical shadow of a single slit 1.5 mm wide, (b) at the center of the pattern of a single slit 2.5 mm wide.

12. From the table of Fresnel's integrals, calculate the exact intensity at the points $v = +1.2$ and -2.0 in the diffraction pattern of a straight edge. To what angles of diffraction do these correspond when the source is very distant and the wavelength is (a) 4000 Å, and (b) 5 cm? The observing screen is 5 m behind the straight edge.
Ans. $0.0308I_0$, $0.844I_0$. (a) $0.014°$, $-0.023°$. (b) $4.85°$, $-8.05°$.

13. Use Cornu's spiral to investigate the Fresnel diffraction pattern of a double slit. If $a = b = 100$ cm, $\lambda = 5000$ Å, and the slits are each 0.4 mm wide with their centers 2 mm apart, find the distance from the center of the pattern of (a) the first minimum, (b) the second maximum.

14. Derive, by using Babinet's principle, a simple relation between the intensity at a point in the single-slit diffraction pattern, and the intensity at the same point in the pattern due to the complementary opaque strip.
Ans. $(I/I_0)_{strip} = (I/I_0)_{slit} - \Delta x - \Delta y + 1$. Here Δx and Δy are the components of the amplitude vector for the slit.

15. For the diffraction by an opaque strip, investigate by Cornu's spiral (a) whether a maximum must necessarily occur at the center of the pattern, as it does in the three cases of Fig. 18V; (b) the origin of the "beats" observed outside the geometrical shadow in the case $\Delta v = 0.5$ of Fig. 18V.

16. According to Young's interpretation of diffraction, the fringes inside the geometrical shadow of an opaque strip are to be regarded as interference fringes caused by the two luminous edges. On this hypothesis, how many bright fringes should occur in the shadow of an opaque strip of width $\Delta v = 2.5$ (cf. Fig. $18V$)? In the shadow of the rod of Prob. 9? *Ans.* 3 fringes. 13 fringes.

17. A plane wave of light of wavelength 5000 Å is incident on a screen containing a circular hole 1 mm in diameter. Find the intensity on the axis at a distance of 30 cm behind the screen, expressing it as a fraction of the intensity at the first maximum. The latter is the intensity at the point where the hole just includes the first Fresnel zone.

CHAPTER 19

THE VELOCITY OF LIGHT

In the preceding chapters we have found that the interference and diffraction of light can be successfully explained by assuming that light consists of waves. We now turn to another fundamental property of light waves, their velocity of propagation. It is to be expected that waves having a definite frequency will travel with finite and constant velocity in a given medium. Light waves, or in general, electromagnetic waves, are unique in their ability to move through empty space and here the velocity is the same for all frequencies. Hence the velocity of light in vacuum, c, is an important constant of nature. In the electromagnetic theory, to be discussed in the next chapter, it appears as the ratio of certain units. Furthermore, the discovery that its observed value is independent of motion of either source or observer formed the original basis of the theory of relativity. Our first object will be to describe the various ways in which this characteristic velocity has been accurately measured.

19.1. Römer's Method. Because of the very great velocity of light, it is natural that the first successful measurement was an astronomical one, because here very large distances are involved. In 1676 Römer* studied the times of the eclipses of the satellites of the planet Jupiter. Figure 19A(a) shows the orbits of the earth and of Jupiter around the sun S and that of one of the satellites M around Jupiter. The inner satellite has an average period of revolution T_0 = 42 hr 28 min 16 sec, as determined from the average time between two passages into the shadow of the planet. Actually Römer measured the times of *emergence* from the shadow, while the times of transit of the small black spot representing the shadow of the satellite on Jupiter's surface across the median line of the disk can be still more accurately measured.

A long series of observations on the eclipses of the first satellite permitted an accurate evaluation of the average period T_0. Römer found that if an eclipse was observed when the earth was at such a position as E_1 [Fig. 19A(a)] with respect to Jupiter J_1, and the time of a later

* Olaf Römer (1644–1710). Danish astronomer. His work on Jupiter's satellites was done in Paris, and later he was made astronomer royal of Denmark.

eclipse was predicted by using the average period, it did not in general occur at exactly the predicted time.   Specifically, if the predicted eclipse was to occur about 3 months later, when the earth and Jupiter were at E_2 and J_2, he found a delay of somewhat more than 10 min.   To explain this, he assumed that light travels with a finite velocity from Jupiter to the earth, and that since the earth at E_2 is farther away from Jupiter, the observed delay represents the time required for light to travel the additional distance.   His measurements gave 11 min as the time for light to go a distance equal to the radius of the earth's orbit.

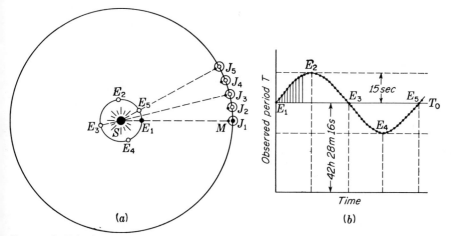

Fig. 19A. Principle of Römer's astronomical determination of the velocity of light from observations on Jupiter's moons.

We now know that 8 min 18 sec is a more nearly correct figure, and combining this with the average distance to the sun 93×10^6 miles, we find a velocity of about 187,000 mi/sec.

It is instructive to inquire how the apparent period of the satellite, i.e., the time between two successive eclipses, is expected to vary throughout a year.   If this time could be observed with sufficient accuracy, one would obtain the curve of Fig. $19A(b)$.   We may regard the successive eclipses as light signals sent out at regular time-intervals of 42 hr 28 min 16 sec from Jupiter.   Now at all points in its orbit except E_1 and E_3 the earth is changing its distance from Jupiter more or less rapidly.   If the distance is increasing, as at E_2, any one signal travels a greater distance than the preceding one and the observed time between them will be increased.   Similarly at E_4 it will be decreased.   The maximum variation from the average period, about 15 sec, is the time for light to cover the distance moved by the earth between two eclipses, which amounts to 2.8×10^6 miles.   At any given position, the total time delay of the eclipse, as observed by Römer, will be obtained by adding the amounts $T - T_0$ [Fig. 19A(b)], by which each apparent period is longer than the average. For instance, the delay of an eclipse at E_2, predicted from one at E_1 using the average period, will be the sum of $T - T_0$ for all eclipses between E_1 and E_2.

19.2. Bradley's* Method.   The Aberration of Light.   Römer's interpretation of the variations in the times of eclipses of Jupiter's satellites was not accepted until an entirely independent determination of the velocity of light was made by the English astronomer Bradley in 1727.

FIG. 19B. Origin of astronomical aberration, when the star is observed perpendicular to the plane of the earth's orbit.

Bradley discovered an apparent motion of the stars which he explained as due to the motion of the earth in its orbit. This effect, known as *aberration*, is quite distinct from the well-known displacements of the nearer stars known as parallax. Because of parallax, these stars appear to shift slightly relative to the background of distant stars when they are viewed from different points in the earth's orbit, and from these shifts the distances of the stars are computed. Since the apparent displacement of the star is opposite to that of the *position* of the earth, the effect of parallax is to cause the star which is observed in a direction perpendicular to the plane of the earth's orbit to move in a small circle with a phase differing by π from the earth's motion. The angular diameters of these circles are very small, being not much over 1 second of arc for the nearest stars. Aberration, which depends on the earth's *velocity*, also causes the stars observed in this direction apparently to move in circles. Here, however, the circles have an angular diameter of about 41 seconds, and they are the same for all stars, whether near or distant. Furthermore, the displacements are always in the direction of the earth's velocity, so that the circular motions are $\pi/2$ different in phase from the earth's motion [Fig. 19B(a)].

Bradley's explanation of this effect was that the apparent direction of the light reaching the earth from a star is altered by the motion of the earth in its orbit. The observer and his telescope are being carried

* James Bradley (1693–1762).   At the time professor of astronomy at Oxford.   He got his ideas about aberration by a chance observation of the changes in the apparent direction of the wind while sailing on the Thames.

along with the earth at a velocity of about 18.5 mi/sec, and if this motion is perpendicular to the direction of the star, the telescope must be tilted slightly toward the direction of motion from the position it would have if the earth were at rest. The reason for this is much the same as that involved when a person walking in the rain must tilt his umbrella forward to keep the rain off his feet. In Fig. 19B(b), let the vector v represent the velocity of the telescope relative to a system of coordinates fixed in the solar system, and c that of the light relative to the solar system. We have represented these motions as perpendicular to each other, as would be the case if the star lay in the direction shown in Fig. 19B(a). Then the velocity of the light relative to the earth has the direction of c', which is the vector difference between c and v. This is the direction in which the telescope must be pointed to observe the star image on the axis of the instrument. We thus see that when the earth is at E_1 the star S has the apparent position S_1, when it is at E_2, the apparent position is S_2, etc. If S were not in a direction perpendicular to the plane of the earth's orbit, the apparent motion would be an ellipse rather than a circle, but the major axis of the ellipse would be equal to the diameter of the circle in the above case.

It will be seen from the figure that the angle α, which is the angular radius of the apparent circular motion, or the major axis of the elliptical one, is given by

$$\tan \alpha = \frac{v}{c} \tag{19a}$$

Recent measurements of this so-called *angle of aberration* give a mean value $\alpha = 20.479'' \pm 0.008$ as the angular radius of the apparent circular orbit. Combining this with the known velocity v of the earth in its orbit, we obtain $c = 186{,}233$ mi/sec, or $299{,}714$ km/sec. This value agrees to within its experimental error with the more accurate results obtained by the latest measurements of the velocity of light by direct methods, the principles of which we shall now describe.

19.3. Fizeau's Terrestrial Method. Fizeau,* in 1849, first succeeded in measuring c by a method not involving astronomical observations, i.e., one in which the light path was on the earth's surface. The principle of his determination was the obvious one of sending out a brief flash of light and measuring the time for this to travel to a distant mirror and back to the observer. This was accomplished with the apparatus shown in Fig. 19C. The cogwheel WF is rotated at high speed so that it cuts the light beam passing through the rim at F into a series of short

---

* H. L. Fizeau (1819–1896). Born of a wealthy French family, he was financially independent to pursue his hobby—the velocity of light. His experiments were carried out in Paris, the light traveling between Montmartre and Suresnes.

flashes. A flash is sent out each time the wheel is in such a position
that the light can pass between two cogs. It is then rendered parallel
by the lens L_2 and focused by L_3 on a plane mirror M. In Fizeau's
experiments the distance MF was 5.36 miles. After reflection from M,
the flash of light retraces its path, and is again focused by L_2 on the rim
of the wheel. If during the time that the light has traveled from F to
M and back the wheel has turned to such a position that a cog is interposed at F, this flash will be cut out, and the same will be true of any
other flash.

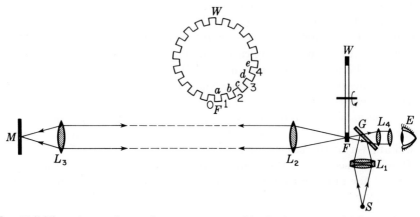

Fig. 19C. Fizeau's experimental arrangement used in the first terrestrial determination
of the velocity of light.

With the wheel at rest in such a position that the light traverses the
opening 0 between two cogs (Fig. 19C, center), the observer at E will
see the image of the light source at F by means of the eyepiece L_4, focused
on F through the half-silvered mirror G. If the wheel is now rotated
with increasing speed, a state will be reached in which the light passing
0 is stopped by a, that passing 1 is stopped by cog b, etc., and the image
will be completely eclipsed. A further increase in speed will cause the
light to reappear when these flashes pass through openings 1, 2, . . . ,
and a second eclipse will occur where they are stopped by b, c, ...
Fizeau's wheel had 720 cogs, and since the light path was 2 × 5.36 or
10.72 miles, the wheel had to turn through $\frac{1}{1440}$ of a revolution in $10.72/c$
sec to produce the first eclipse. Hence the first eclipse should occur at a
speed of $c/(10.72 \times 1440)$ rev/sec, and the others at 3, 5, 7, . . . times
this speed. Fizeau observed the first eclipse at 12.6 rev/sec, giving
c = 194,600 mi/sec or 313,300 km/sec.

That this is appreciably higher than the values obtained by the astronomical methods is not surprising, in view of the difficulties of the
experiment. With Fizeau's arrangement, the determination of the exact

condition of total eclipse caused the principal uncertainty. The experimental conditions were later improved by Cornu, and by Young and Forbes. The latter overcame the above difficulty by placing another lens and mirror, identical with L_3 and M, at a somewhat greater distance. The two images thus formed were observed simultaneously, and instead of measuring the conditions of eclipse or of maximum in either image they measured the speed of the cogwheel at the time the two images appeared to be of equal intensity. The eye is very sensitive to the detection of slight *differences* in intensity of adjacent images, so this

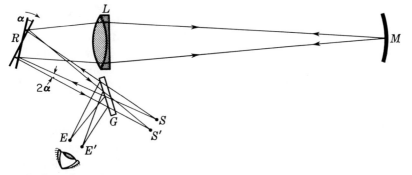

FIG. 19D. Rotating-mirror apparatus used by Foucault in measuring the velocity of light.

measurement could be made more accurately. Their result* was 301,400 km/sec.

19.4. Rotating-mirror Method. This is a second terrestrial method, originally suggested by Arago† and first applied successfully by Fizeau and Foucault‡ independently in 1850. The principle of these early determinations is illustrated in Fig. 19D. Light from the source S traverses the plane glass plate G and, after reflection from the plane mirror R, is focused by the lens L on a stationary concave mirror M. If R is also stationary, the light retraces its path and an image of S is formed at E by partial reflection in G.

If now R is rotated at high speed about an axis perpendicular to the

* For details of the various determinations by Fizeau's method, the reader is referred to T. Preston, "The Theory of Light," 5th ed., p. 534, Macmillan & Co., Ltd., London, 1928.

† D. F. J. Arago (1786–1853). Noted Parisian astronomer and physicist. He is principally known for his work on the interference of polarized light (Chap. 27) and on electromagnetism in conjunction with Ampere.

‡ J. L. Foucault (1819–1868). Between 1845 and 1849 Foucault collaborated with Fizeau, but owing to difference of opinion they afterward worked separately. Foucault is also known for his demonstration of the rotation of the earth by a pendulum and for the Foucault knife-edge test. His researches on the velocity of light in water (Sec. 19.10) constituted his thesis for the doctorate, presented in 1851.

plane of the figure, it will have turned through a small angle α by the time the light has returned from M. The reflected beam will then be turned through 2α, and a displaced image E' will be produced by L. The displacement EE' obviously depends on the angular velocity of R and on the distances RM and RGE, and if these quantities are known the velocity of light may be found.

In the final measurements of Foucault, RM was 20 m and essentially equal to the radius of curvature LM of the mirror M. The displacement EE' was only 0.7 mm but could be measured by the micrometer eyepiece to within 0.005 mm. Foucault's result for the velocity of light was roughly 298,000 km/sec. The accuracy of the determination by the rotating-mirror method was later greatly improved in the experiments of Cornu, Newcomb,* and Michelson. The chief improvement in the later work lay in the use of a greater light path. This was limited in Foucault's arrangement by the loss of intensity in the image when the distance RM was made large. The rotating beam from R is returned by M only during the small fraction of the time that it is sweeping across M. This difficulty was overcome in Michelson's work by using a lens L of larger focal length, and increasing the distance RL until R and M were nearly conjugate foci of L. With S fairly close to R, and a lens L of sufficiently long focus, the mirror M could now be placed several miles away. Another improvement adopted by Newcomb and Michelson was the replacement of the plane mirror R by one having four or more reflecting faces (Fig. 19E). This also resulted in a gain of intensity in the image.†

19.5. Michelson's Later Experiments. We shall not describe the successive experiments in which the determination of c by rotating mirrors was steadily improved. At the present time, it appears that the accuracy of even the best values by this method is surpassed by that of newer devices based on radio-frequency techniques. It will be instructive, however, to consider briefly a classical series of measurements made by Michelson at the Mt. Wilson Observatory in 1926.

The form of the apparatus finally adopted is shown in Fig. 19E. Light from a Sperry arc S passes through a narrow slit and is reflected from one face of the octagonal rotating mirror R. Thence it is reflected from the small fixed mirrors b and c to the large concave mirror M_1 (30-ft focus, 2-ft aperture). This gives a parallel beam of light, which travels 22 miles from the observing station on Mt. Wilson to a mirror M_2, similar to M_1, on the summit of Mt. San Antonio. M_2 focuses the light on a

---

* Simon Newcomb (1835–1909). Distinguished American astronomer, associated with the U.S. Naval Observatory and the Johns Hopkins University.

† For further discussion of these methods, see N. E. Dorsey, *Trans. Am. Phil. Soc.*, **34**, 1, 1944.

small plane mirror f, whence it returns to M_1 and, by reflection from c', b', a', and p, to the observing eyepiece L.

Various rotating mirrors, having 8, 12, and 16 sides, were used, and in each case the mirror was driven by an air blast at such a speed that during the time of transit to M_2 and back (0.00023 sec) the mirror turned through such an angle that the next face was presented at a'. For an octagonal mirror, the required speed of rotation was about 528 rev/sec. The speed was adjusted by a small counterblast of air until the image of the slit was in the same position as when R was at rest. The exact speed of rotation was then found by a stoboscopic comparison with a

FIG. 19E. Michelson's arrangement used for determining the velocity of light (1926).

standard electrically driven tuning fork, which in turn is calibrated with an invar pendulum furnished by the U.S. Coast and Geodetic Survey. This Survey also measured the distance between the mirrors M_1 and M_2 with remarkable accuracy by triangulation from a 40-km base line, the length of which was determined to an estimated error of 1 part in 11 million, or about $\frac{1}{8}$ in.*

The results of the measurements published in 1926 comprised eight values of the velocity of light, each the average of some 200 individual determinations with a given rotating mirror. These varied between the extreme values of 299,756 and 299,803 km/sec and yielded the average value of 299,796 ± 4 km/sec. Michelson also made some later measurements with the distant mirror on the summit of a mountain 82 miles away, but because of bad atmospheric conditions, these were not considered reliable enough for publication.

19.6. Measurements in Vacuum. In the preceding discussion we have assumed that the measured velocity in air is equal to that in a vacuum. That is not exactly true, since the index of refraction $n = c/v$ is slightly greater than unity. With white light the effective value of n for air under the conditions existing in Michelson's experiments was 1.000225. Hence the velocity in vacuum $c = nv$ was 67 km/sec greater than v, the measured value in air. This correction has been applied in the final

* W. Bowie, *Astrophys. J.*, **65**, 14, 1927.

results quoted above. A difficulty which becomes important where measurements as accurate as those of Michelson are concerned is the uncertainty of the exact conditions of temperature and pressure of the air in the light path. Since n depends on these conditions, the value of the correction to vacuum also becomes somewhat uncertain.

To eliminate this source of error, Michelson in 1929 undertook a measurement of the velocity in a long evacuated pipe. The optical arrangement was similar to that described above, with suitable modifications for containing the light path in the pipe. The latter was 1 mile long, and by successive reflections from mirrors mounted at either end the total distance the light traversed before returning to the rotating mirror was about 10 miles. A vacuum as low as $\frac{1}{2}$ mm Hg could be maintained. This difficult experiment was not completed until after Michelson's death in 1931, but preliminary results were published a year later by his collaborators.* The mean of almost three thousand individual measurements was 299,774 km/sec. Because of certain unexplained variations, the accuracy of this result is difficult to assess. It is certainly not as great as that indicated by the computed probable error, and has recently been estimated as ± 11 km/sec.

19.7. Kerr-cell Method. Determinations by this method have equaled if not surpassed the accuracy of those by the rotating mirror. In 1925 Gaviola devised what amounts to an improvement on Fizeau's toothed-wheel apparatus. It is based on the use of the so-called *electro-optic shutter*. This device is capable of chopping a beam of light several hundred times more rapidly than can be done by a cogwheel. Hence a much shorter base line can be used, and the entire apparatus can be contained in one building so that the atmospheric conditions are accurately known. Figure 19$F(a)$ illustrates the electro-optic shutter, which consists of a Kerr cell K between two crossed nicol prisms N_1 and N_2. K is a small glass container fitted with sealed-in metal electrodes and filled with pure nitrobenzene. Although the operation of this shutter depends on certain properties of polarized light to be discussed later (Chap. 29), all that need be known here in order to understand the method is that no light is transmitted by the system until a high voltage is applied to the electrodes of K. Thus by using an electrical oscillator which delivers a radio-frequency voltage, a light beam can be interrupted at the rate of many millions of times per second.

The first measurements based on this principle used two shutters, one for the outgoing and one for the returning light. Except for the shorter distances, the method closely resembled Fizeau's. Subsequent improvements have led to the apparatus shown in Fig. 19$F(b)$, which was used

---

* The final report will be found in Michelson, Pease, and Pearson, *Astrophys. J.*, **82**, 26, 1935.

by W. C. Anderson in 1941.*   To avoid the difficulty of matching the characteristics of two Kerr cells, he used only one and divided the trans-mitted light pulses into two beams by means of the half-silvered mirror M_1.   One beam traversed the shorter path to M_2 and back through M_1 to the detector P.   The other traveled a longer path to M_6 by reflections at M_3, M_4, and M_5, then retraced its course to M_1 which reflected it to P as well.   This detector P was a photomultiplier tube, which responded to the sinusoidal modulation of the light waves.   One may think of the

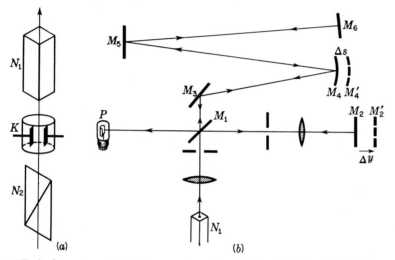

Fig. 19F. Anderson's method of measuring the velocity of light.   (a) Electro-optic shutter.   (b) The light paths.

light wave as the carrier wave, which is amplitude-modulated at the frequency of the oscillator driving the Kerr cell.†   The quotient of the wavelength l of the modulation by the period T of the oscillator thus gives the velocity of light.

   The accurate measurement of l is based on the following principle: If the longer path exceeds the shorter one by a half-integral multiple of l, the sum of the two modulated waves reaching P will give a constant intensity.   The amplifier connected to the photocell was arranged to give zero response under this condition.   The adjustment is made by slight motions Δy of the mirror M_2.   The extra path beyond M_4 could then be cut out by substituting another mirror M_4' which returned the light directly to M_3.   If this extra path (M_4 to M_6 and back) were exactly

* J. Opt. Soc. Am., **31**, 187, 1941.
† Since the shutter transmits at each voltage peak, whether positive or negative, one would expect to use $1/2T$ here.   Actually Anderson applied a d-c bias to the cell so that each cycle gave a single voltage maximum.

a whole number times l, no change in the photocell response would be observed upon cutting it out. As the apparatus was arranged, this was very nearly so, the extra path being about $11l$. By measuring the displacement Δy necessary to reestablish zero response, and applying a correction Δs involved in the substitution of M'_4, the difference from $11l$ of the measured distance could be exactly determined.

The reader will see the resemblance of Anderson's apparatus to a Michelson interferometer for radio waves, since the light pulses have a length essentially equal to the wave length of the radio waves given by the Kerr-cell oscillator. It is not exactly equal, however, because the velocity involved in the experiment is the group velocity of light in air, and not the velocity of radio waves. In his final investigation, Anderson made a total of 2895 observations, and the resulting velocities l/T, after correction to vacuum, yielded an average of $299,776 \pm 6$ km/sec. The chief source of error was in the difficulty of ensuring that both beams used the same portion of the photoelectric surface. A change in the position of the light spot affects the time of transit of the electrons between the electrodes of the photomultiplier tube. The uncertainty involved here was larger than any errors in the length measurements, and in the frequency of the oscillator was known more accurately still—to better than 1 part in 1 million.

In the latest Kerr cell determination by Bergstrand (see Table 19-I) the last-mentioned difficulty is avoided by using only one beam, and locating the maxima and minima through modulation of the detector in synchronism with the source. The result is indicated to be more than ten times as accurate as any previous one by optical methods. It disagrees with the concordant values of Anderson and of Michelson, Pease, and Pearson, seeming to show that Michelson's 1926 value was the more nearly correct. It is difficult to understand how the very thorough work in the period 1930–1940 could have been so far in error, but other recent results, to be described below, certainly put the weight of the evidence in favor of the higher value of c.

19.8. Velocity of Radio Waves. The development of modern radar techniques, and especially the interest in their practical application as navigational aids, has led to renewed attempts to improve our knowledge of the velocity of light. This velocity is of course the same as that for radio waves, when both are reduced to vacuum. There are three methods for using microwaves for an accurate measurement of their velocity, one of which may easily be performed in vacuum. This is to find the length and resonant frequency of a hollow metal cylinder, or cavity resonator. It is analogous to the common laboratory method for the velocity of sound. Measurements of this type were made independently in England, by Essen and Gordon-Smith, and in America, by Bol.* As will be seen from Table 19-I, the results agree with each other and with Bergstrand's precise optical value.

TABLE 19-I. RESULTS OF ACCURATE MEASUREMENTS OF THE VELOCITY OF LIGHT

Date	Investigators	Method	Result, km/sec
1926	Michelson	Rotating mirror	$299,796 \pm 4$
1935	Michelson, Pease, and Pearson	Rotating mirror in vacuum	$299,774 \pm 11$
1940	Hüttel	Kerr cell	$299,768 \pm 10$
1941	Anderson	Kerr cell	$299,776 \pm 6$
1950	Bol	Cavity resonator	$299,789.3 \pm 0.4$
1950	Essen	Cavity resonator	$299,792.5 \pm 3.0$
1951	Bergstrand	Kerr cell	$299,793.1 \pm 0.2$
1951	Aslakson	Radar (shoran)	$299,794.2 \pm 1.9$
1952	Froome	Microwave interferometer	$299,792.6 \pm 0.7$

The other methods involving radio waves are responsible for the last two entries in our table, and have been developed to a comparable accuracy. The radar method consists in the direct measurement of the time of transit of a signal over a known distance in the open air. The microwave interferometer is the Michelson instrument adapted to radio waves. The velocity is found by measuring the wavelength from the motion of a mirror. The details of all the radio methods are interesting and important, but must be omitted here as not falling strictly within the scope of optics.

19.9. Ratio of the Electrical Units. As we shall find in our consideration of the electromagnetic theory (Chap. 20), c may be found from the ratio of the magnitude of certain units in the electromagnetic and electrostatic systems. Two careful measurements of the ratio have been made, and have given results more or less intermediate between the higher and lower values discussed above. Since the accuracy thus far attained is considerably lower than for other methods, these experiments, although they have served to verify the theoretical prediction, have not improved our knowledge of the velocity of light.†

19.10. Velocity of Light in Stationary Matter. The first experiment to measure the velocity of light in a transparent substance much denser

* Valuable summaries of the recent determinations of c, and many original references not given here, will be found in L. Essen, *Nature*, **165**, 583, 1950, and K. D. Froome, *Proc. Roy. Soc. (London)*, **A213**, 123, 1952.

† The indirect measurements all antedate the determinations in Table 19-I. They have been critically reviewed by R. T. Birge, *Nature*, **134**, 771, 1934.

than air was performed in 1850 by Foucault. This was regarded as a crucial experiment to decide between the corpuscular and wave theories of light. Newton's explanation of refraction by the corpuscular theory required that the corpuscles be attracted toward the surface of the denser medium, and therefore that they should travel faster in the medium. On the wave theory, however, it must be assumed that the light waves travel more slowly in the medium.

FIG. 19G. Foucault's apparatus for determining the velocity of light in water.

Foucault's apparatus for this experiment is shown in Fig. 19G. Light coming through a slit is reflected from the plane rotating mirror R to the equidistant concave mirrors M_1 and M_2. When R is in the position (1) the light travels to M_1, back along the same path to R, through the lens L, and by reflection to the eye at E. When R is in the position (2) the light travels the lower path through an auxiliary lens L' and tube T to M_2, back to R, through L to G and then to the eye at E. If now the tube T is filled with water and the mirror R is set into rotation, there will be displacement of the images from E to E_1 and E_2. Foucault observed that the light ray through the tube was the more displaced. This means that it took the light longer to travel the lower path through water than it did the upper path through air. The image observed was due to a fine wire parallel to and stretched across the slit. Since sharp images were desired at E_1 and E_2, the auxiliary lens L' was necessary to avoid the effects of refraction at the ends of the tube T.

Much more accurate measurements were made by Michelson in 1885. Using white light, he found for the ratio of the velocity in air to that in water a value of 1.330. A denser medium, carbon disulfide, gave 1.758. In the latter case he noticed that the final image of the slit was spread out into a short spectrum, which could be explained by the fact that red light travels faster than blue light in the medium. The difference in velocity between "greenish blue" and "reddish orange" light was observed to be 1 or 2 per cent.

According to the wave theory of light, the index of refraction of a medium is equal to the ratio of the velocity of light in vacuum to that in the medium. If we compare the above figures with the corresponding indices of refraction for white light (water 1.334, carbon disulfide 1.635) we find that while the agreement is within the experimental error for water, the directly measured value is considerably higher than the index of refraction for carbon disulfide.

This discrepancy is readily explained by the fact that the index of refraction represents the ratio of the *wave velocities* in vacuum and in the medium ($n = c/v$), while the direct measurements give the *group velocities*. Now in a vacuum the two velocities become identical (Sec. 12.7) and equal to c, so that if we call the group velocity in the medium u, the ratios determined by Michelson were values of c/u, rather than c/v. The two velocities u and v are related by the general Eq. 12p

$$u = v - \lambda \frac{dv}{d\lambda}$$

The variation of v with λ may be found by studying the change of the index of refraction with color (Sec. 23.2), and it is found that v is greater for longer wavelengths, so that $dv/d\lambda$ is positive. Therefore u should be less than v, and this is precisely the result obtained above. Using reasonable values for λ and $dv/d\lambda$ for white light, the difference between the two values for carbon disulfide is in agreement with the theory to within the accuracy of the experiments. For water $dv/d\lambda$ is considerably smaller but nevertheless requires that the measured value of c/u should be 1.5 per cent higher than c/v. That this is not so indicates an appreciable error in Michelson's work. The latest work[*] on the velocity of light in water has given agreement not only as to the magnitude of the group velocity, but also as to its variation with wavelength.

At this point it should be emphasized that all the direct methods for measuring the velocity of light that we have described give the group velocity u and not the wave velocity v. Even though it is not evident in the aberration experiment that the wave is divided into groups, it should be obvious that since all natural light consists of

[*] R. A. Houstoun, *Proc. Roy. Soc. Edinburgh*, **A62**, 58, 1944.

wave packets of finite length, any further chopping or modulation is immaterial. In air the difference between u and v is small but nevertheless amounts to 2.2 km/sec. Michelson apparently did not apply this correction to his 1926 value, which should therefore have been quoted as 299,798 + 4 km/sec.

19.11. Velocity of Light in Moving Matter. In 1859 Fizeau performed an important experiment to determine whether the velocity of light in a material medium is affected by motion of the medium relative to the source and observer. In Fig. 19*H* the light from S is split into two beams, in much the same way as in the Rayleigh refractometer (Sec. 13.15). The beams then pass through the tubes A and B containing

Fɪɢ. 19*H*. Fizeau's experiment for measuring the velocity of light in a moving medium.

water flowing rapidly in opposite directions. On reflection from M, the beams interchange so that when they reach L_1 one has traversed both B and A in the same direction as the flowing water while the other has traversed A and B in the opposite direction to the flow. The lens L_1 then brings the beams together to form interference fringes at S'.

If the light travels more slowly by one route than by the other, its optical path has effectively increased and a displacement of the fringes should occur. Using tubes 150 cm long and a water velocity of 700 cm/sec, Fizeau found a shift of 0.46 of a fringe when the direction of flow was reversed. This corresponds to an increase in the speed of light in one tube, and a decrease in the other, of about half of the velocity of the water.

This experiment was later repeated by Michelson with improved apparatus consisting essentially of an adaptation of his interferometer to this type of measurement. He observed a shift corresponding to an alteration of the velocity of light by 0.434 of the velocity of the water.

19.12. Fresnel Dragging Coefficient. The above results were compared with a formula derived by Fresnel in 1818, using the elastic-solid theory of the ether. On the assumption that the density of the ether in the medium is greater than that in vacuum in the ratio n^2, he showed that the ether is effectively dragged along with a moving medium with a velocity

$$v' = v\left(1 - \frac{1}{n^2}\right) \tag{19b}$$

where v is the velocity of the medium, and n its index of refraction. For water, which has $n = 1.333$ for sodium light, this gives $v' = 0.437v$, in reasonable agreement with Michelson's value for white light quoted in the previous paragraph. The fraction $1 - (1/n^2)$ will be referred to as *Fresnel's dragging coefficient.*

19.13. Airy's Experiment. An entirely different piece of experimental evidence shows that Fresnel's equation must be very nearly correct. In 1872 Airy remeasured the angle of aberration of light (Sec. 19.2), using a telescope filled with water. Upon referring to Fig. 19B(b), it will be seen that if the velocity of the light with respect to the solar system be made less by entering water, one would expect the angle of aberration to be increased. Actually the most careful measurements gave the same angle of aberration for a telescope filled with water as for one filled with air.

This negative result may be explained by assuming that the light is carried along by

FIG. 19*I*. Angle of aberration with a water-filled telescope.

the water in the telescope with the velocity given by Eq. 19b. In Fig. 19*I*, where the angles are of course greatly exaggerated, the velocity now becomes c/n and is slightly changed in direction by refraction. If one is to observe the ordinary angle of aberration α, it is necessary to add to this velocity the extra component v', representing the velocity with which the light is dragged by the water. From the geometry of this figure, it is possible to prove that v' must obey Eq. 19b. The proof will not be given here, however, since a different and simpler explanation is now accepted, based on the theory of relativity (see Sec. 19.17).

19.14. Effect of Motion of the Observer. We have seen that in the phenomenon of aberration the apparent *direction* of the light reaching the observer is altered when he is in motion. One might therefore expect to be able to find an effect of such motion on the *magnitude* of the observed velocity of light. Referring back to Fig. 19B(b), we see that the apparent velocity $c' = v/\sin \alpha$ is slightly greater than the true velocity $c = v/\tan \alpha$. However, α is a very small angle, so that the difference between the sine and the tangent is much smaller than the error of measurement of α. A somewhat different experiment embodying the same principle has been devised, which should be sensitive enough to detect this slight change in the apparent velocity if it exists. Before describing this experiment, however, we consider in more detail the effect of motion of the observer on the apparent velocity of light.

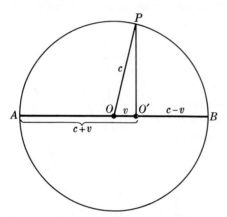

In Fig. 19J, let the observer at O be moving toward B with a velocity v. Let an instantaneous flash of light be sent out at O. The wave will spread out in a circle with its center at O, and after 1 sec the radius of this circle will be numerically equal to the velocity of light c. But during this time the observer will have moved a distance v from O to O'. Hence if the observer were in some way able to follow the progress of the wave, he would find an apparent velocity which would vary with the direction of observation. In the forward direction $O'B$ it would be $c - v$ and in the backward direction $O'A$, $c + v$. At right angles, in the direction $O'P$, he would observe a velocity $\sqrt{c^2 - v^2}$.

FIG. 19J. Velocity of light emitted by a moving source.

It is important to notice that in drawing Fig. 19M we have assumed that the velocity of the light was not affected by the fact that the source was in motion as it emitted the wave. This is to be expected for a wave which is set up in a stationary medium, as for instance a sound wave in the air. The hypothetical medium carrying light waves is the "aether," and if v is the velocity with respect to the aether, the same result is expected. For an experiment performed in air, the Fresnel dragging coefficient $1 - (1/n^2)$ is so nearly zero that it may be neglected. Thus if the observer were moving with the velocity v of the earth in its orbit, these considerations lead us to expect the changes in the apparent velocity of light described above. Effectively the aether should be moving past the earth with a velocity v, and if any effects on the velocity of light were found, they could be said to be due to an aether wind or *aether drift*. It would not be surprising if this drift did not correspond to the velocity of the earth in its orbit, since we know that the solar system as a whole is moving toward the constellation Hercules with a velocity of 19 km/sec and it is more reasonable to expect the aether to be at rest with respect to the system of "fixed stars" than with respect to our solar system.

19.15. The Michelson-Morley Experiment. This experiment, perhaps the most famous of any experiment with light, was undertaken in 1881 to investigate the possible existence of aether drift. In principle it consisted merely of observing whether there was any shift of the fringes in the Michelson interferometer when the instrument was turned through an angle of 90°. Thus in Fig. 19K let us assume that the interferometer is being carried along by the earth in the direction OM_2 with a velocity v with respect to the aether. Let the mirrors M_1 and M_2 be adjusted for parallel light, and let $OM_1 = OM_2 = d$. The light leaving O in the forward direction will be reflected when the mirror is at M'_2 and will return when the half-silvered mirror G has moved to O''. Using the expressions for the velocity derived in the previous section, the time required to travel the path OM'_2O'' will be

FIG. 19K. The Michelson interferometer as a test for aether drift.

$$T_1 = \frac{d}{c + v} + \frac{d}{c - v} = \frac{2cd}{c^2 - v^2}$$

and the time to travel OM_1O'' will be

$$T_2 = \frac{2d}{\sqrt{c^2 - v^2}}$$

Each of these expressions may be expanded into series, giving

$$T_1 = \frac{2cd}{c^2 - v^2} = \frac{2d}{c}\left(1 + \frac{v^2}{c^2} + \frac{v^4}{c^4} + \cdots\right) \simeq \frac{2d}{c}\left(1 + \frac{v^2}{c^2}\right)$$

and $$T_2 = \frac{2d}{\sqrt{c^2 - v^2}} = \frac{2d}{c}\left(1 + \frac{v^2}{2c^2} + \frac{3v^4}{4c^4} + \cdots\right) \simeq \frac{2d}{c}\left(1 + \frac{v^2}{2c^2}\right)$$

Thus the result of the motion of the interferometer is to increase both paths by a slight amount, the increase being twice as large in the direction of motion. The difference in time, which would be zero for a stationary interferometer, now becomes

$$T_1 - T_2 = \frac{2d}{c}\left(1 + \frac{v^2}{c^2}\right) - \frac{2d}{c}\left(1 + \frac{v^2}{2c^2}\right) = d\frac{v^2}{c^3}$$

To change this to path difference we multiply by c, obtaining

$$\Delta = d\,\frac{v^2}{c^2} \qquad (19c)$$

If now the interferometer is turned through 90°, the direction of v is unchanged, but the two paths in the interferometer will be interchanged.

FIG. 19L. Miller's arrangement of the Michelson-Morley experiment to detect aether drift.

This would introduce a path difference Δ in the opposite sense to that obtained before. Hence we expect a shift corresponding to a change of path of $2dv^2/c^2$.

Michelson and Morley made the distance d large by reflecting the light back and forth between 16 mirrors as illustrated in Fig. 19L. To avoid distortion of the instrument by strains, it was mounted on a large concrete block floating in mercury, and observations were made as it was rotated slowly and continuously about a vertical axis. In one experiment d was 11 m, so that if we take $v = 18.6$ mi/sec and $c = 186,000$ mi/sec, we find a change in path of 2.2×10^{-5} cm. For light of wavelength 6×10^{-5}, this corresponds to a change of 0.4λ, so that the fringes should be displaced by two-fifths of a fringe. Careful observations showed that no shift occurred as great as 10 per cent of this predicted value.

This negative result, indicating the absence of an aether drift, was so surprising that the experiment has since been repeated with certain modifications by a number of different investigators. All have confirmed Michelson and Morley in showing that, if a real displacement of the fringes exists, it is at most but a small fraction of the expected value. The most extensive series of measurements has been made by D. C. Miller. His apparatus was essentially that of Michelson and Morley (Fig. 19L) but on a larger scale. With a light path of 64 m, Miller thought he had obtained evidence for a small shift of about one-thirtieth of a fringe, varying periodically with sidereal time. The latest analysis of Miller's data, however, makes it probable that the result is not significant, having been caused by slight thermal gradients across the interferometer.*

19.16. Principle of Relativity. The negative result obtained by Michelson and Morley, and by most of those who have repeated their experiment, forms the basis of the restricted *theory of relativity*, put forward by Einstein† in 1905. The two fundamental postulates on which this theory is based are

1. *Principle of Relativity of Uniform Motion.* The laws of physics are the same for all systems having a uniform motion of translation with respect to one another. As a consequence of this, an observer in any one system cannot detect the motion of that system by any observations confined to the system.

2. *Principle of the Constancy of the Velocity of Light.* The velocity of light in any given frame reference is independent of the velocity of the source. Combined with (1), this means that the velocity of light is independent of the relative velocity of the source and observer.

Returning to our illustration (Fig. 19J) of an observer who sends out a flash of light at O while moving with a velocity v, the above postulates would require that any measurements made by the observer at O' would show that he is the center of the spherical wave. But an observer at rest at O would find that he too is at the center of the wave. The recon-

* R. S. Shankland, S. W. McCuskey, F. C. Leone, and G. Kuerti, *Revs. Mod. Phys.*, **27**, 167, 1955.

† Albert Einstein (1879–1955). Formerly director of the Kaiser Wilhelm Institute in Berlin, Einstein in 1935 came to the Institute for Advanced Study at Princeton. Gifted with one of the most brilliant minds of our times, he has contributed to many fields of physics besides relativity. Of prime importance was his famous law of the photoelectric effect. He received the Nobel prize in 1921.

ciliation of these apparently contradictory statements lies in the fact that the space and time scales for the moving system are different from those for a fixed system. Events separated in space which are simultaneous to an observer at rest do not appear so to one moving with the system.

The first explanation given for the null result of the Michelson-Morley experiment was that the arm of the interferometer that was oriented parallel to the earth's motion was decreased in length because of this motion. The so-called *Fitzgerald-Lorentz contraction* required that, if l_0 is the length of an object at rest, motion parallel to l_0 with a velocity v gives a new length

$$l = l_0 \left(1 - \frac{v^2}{c^2}\right)^{\frac{1}{2}} \tag{19d}$$

This law would satisfy the condition that the difference in path due to aether drift would be just canceled out. Naturally the change in length could not be detected by a measuring stick, since the latter would shrink in the same proportion. A contraction of this kind should, however, bring about changes in other physical properties. Many attempts have been made to find evidence for these, but to no avail. According to the first postulate of relativity, they must fail. The aether drift does not exist, nor is there any contraction for an observer moving along with the interferometer.

Starting from the fundamental postulates of the restricted theory, it is possible to show that in a frame of reference that is moving with respect to the observer there should actually be changes in the observed values of length, mass, and time. The mass of a particle becomes

$$m = m_0 \left(1 - \frac{v^2}{c^2}\right)^{-\frac{1}{2}} \tag{19e}$$

in which m_0 represents the mass when it is at rest with respect to the observer. If light, which has $v = c$, were to be regarded as consisting of particles (see Chap. 30), these would have to have zero rest mass, since otherwise m becomes infinite. Experimental measurements have been made, mostly with high-speed electrons, which quantitatively verify Eq. 19e. Other observable consequences of relativity theory exist, the most striking ones being obtained when it is extended to cover accelerated systems as well as systems in uniform motion.* From this *general theory* of relativity, predictions are made with regard to the deflection of light rays passing close to the sun, and to a decrease in frequency of light emitted

* For a general account of the theory and its consequences, see R. C. Tolman, "Relativity, Thermodynamics and Cosmology," Oxford University Press, New York, 1934. Reprinted, 1949.

by atoms in a strong gravitational field. Accurate measurements of the apparent positions of stars during a total solar eclipse, and of the spectra of very dense (white dwarf) stars, have verified these two optical effects.

These experimental proofs of the theory have been sufficiently convincing to lead to the general acceptance of the correctness of the theory of relativity. While the theory does not directly deny the existence of the aether postulated by Fresnel, it says very definitely that no experiment we can ever perform will prove its existence. For if it were possible to find the motion of a body with respect to the aether, we could regard the aether as a fixed coordinate system with respect to which all motions are to be referred. But it is one of the fundamental consequences of relativity that any coordinate system is equivalent to any other, and no one has any particular claim to finality. Thus, since a fixed aether is apparently not observable, there is no reason for retaining the concept. It cannot be denied, however, that it is historically important and that some of the most important advances in the study of light have come through the assumption of a material aether.

19.17. The Three First-order Relativity Effects. There are three optical effects the magnitude of which depends on the first power of v/c. They are

1. The Doppler effect
2. The aberration of light
3. The Fresnel dragging coefficient

Equations for these effects have been derived on the basis of classical theory in Secs. 11.6, 19.2, and 19.13. Now it is characteristic of the theory of relativity that it yields the same results for first-order effects as does the classical theory. Only in second-order effects, which depend on v^2/c^2, do the predictions of the two theories differ. The Michelson-Morley experiment belongs to this class. Even for the first-order effects listed above, the results from the two theories differ in the small terms of the second and higher power of v/c. In the relativity theory, these equations are derived by applying the *Lorentz transformation*. This is a process of translating the description of a motion in terms of one system of coordinates into a description of the same motion in terms of another system which is in uniform motion with respect to the first. Although it is not practicable to give the mathematics of this process here, we shall state the chief results and discuss them briefly.

When the equation for a periodic wave of frequency ν is rewritten in the coordinates of the observer's frame of reference, the frequency assumes a new value given by

$$\nu' = \nu \frac{\sqrt{1 - (v^2/c^2)}}{1 - (v/c)} = \nu \left(1 + \frac{v}{c} + \frac{1}{2}\frac{v^2}{c^2} + \frac{1}{2}\frac{v^3}{c^3} + \cdots \right) \qquad (19f)$$

This is the Doppler effect for the source and observer approaching each other with a velocity v along the line joining them. Comparison of the series expansion with our previous Eq. 11l shows that the prediction from relativity differs from that of the classical theory only in the terms of second and higher orders. Theoretically these arise from the fact that the rate of a moving clock is slower than that of a stationary one. Ives* has given an elegant demonstration of this fact by comparing the frequency of the radiation emitted by hydrogen atoms in a high-speed beam moving first toward the spectroscope, then away from it. In addition to the large first-order shifts of the line toward higher and lower frequencies respectively in these two cases, he observed and measured a small additional shift which was toward higher frequencies in both cases. Since the term in question contains the square of the velocity, it will be the same for either sign of v. This experiment constitutes another verification of the theory of relativity by observation of a second-order effect which does not exist according to the classical theory. It might also be mentioned that relativity predicts a second-order Doppler shift even when the source is moving at right angles to the line of sight.

The interpretation of the aberration of light and of Airy's experiment is simpler from the relativistic point of view. According to the second fundamental postulate, the velocity of light must always be c to any observer, regardless of his motion. Hence, referring to Fig. 19$B(b)$, the observed velocity labeled c' must now be labeled c. The formula for the angle of aberration, instead of being $tan\ \alpha = v/c$, then becomes

$$\sin \alpha = \frac{v}{c} \tag{19g}$$

It is well known that the sine and the tangent differ only in respect to terms of the third and higher orders. Here the angle is so small that in all likelihood the difference will never be detected. In Airy's experiment, the expectation of observing an increase of the angle when the telescope was filled with water arose from the assumption that the water would decrease the velocity of the light with respect to the solar system, in which the aether was regarded as fixed. But according to the point of view of relativity the only "true" velocity of light is its velocity in the coordinate system of the observer, and this is inclined at the angle α given by Eq. 19g. Hence reducing the magnitude of this velocity by allowing the light to enter water will obviously make no change in its direction.

A positive effect corresponding to Fresnel's aether drag can be observed when the medium is in motion with respect to the observer (Sec. 19.12), but its interpretation by the theory of relativity is entirely different. One result of the Lorentz transformation is that two velocities in coordi-

* H. E. Ives and A. R. Stilwell, *J. Opt. Soc. Am.*, **28**, 215, 1938, **31**, 369, 1941.

nate systems that are in relative motion do not add according the methods used in classical mechanics. For example the resultant of two velocities in the same line is not their arithmetic sum. Let us call V_0 the velocity of light in the coordinate system of a moving medium, and v the velocity of this medium in the observer's coordinate system. Then the resultant velocity V of the light with respect to the observer, instead of being merely $V_0 + v$, must be taken as

$$V = \frac{V_0 + v}{1 + (V_0/c)(v/c)} \tag{19h}$$

The student can easily verify the fact that this equation gives the same velocity V for any observer in motion with the velocity v, in the case that $V_0 = c$, that is, in a vacuum. The expression for the Fresnel dragging coefficient follows at once from Eq. 19h, if one neglects second-order terms. Thus the binomial expansion gives

$$V = (V_0 + v)\left(1 - \frac{V_0}{c} \cdot \frac{v}{c} - \cdots\right)$$
$$= V_0 + v - \frac{V_0^2 v}{c^2} - \frac{v^2 V_0}{c^2} - \cdots$$

The last term is again a quantity of the second order and is to be neglected. Then we obtain, by substituting n for c/V_0,

$$V = \frac{c}{n} + v\left(1 - \frac{1}{n^2}\right) \tag{19i}$$

The velocity as seen by the observer is changed by the fraction $1 - (1/n^2)$, which is just the value required by Eq. 19b. No assumption of any "dragging" is involved in the relativity arguments, nor is the existence of an aether even postulated.

PROBLEMS

1. The innermost satellite of Jupiter has a velocity such that it traverses its own diameter in $3\frac{1}{2}$ min. To what fraction of this time would it be necessary to observe the instant of an eclipse in order to determine the velocity of light to within ± 100 km/sec?

2. Assuming the velocity of light to be 299,793 km/sec, and the radius of the earth's orbit to be 1.4967×10^8 km (in computing its velocity), calculate the exact angle of aberration according to (a) the classical formula, and (b) the relativity formula. Carry through terms of the third order.

Ans. (a) 20.503 seconds of arc. (b) Relativity gives 1.02×10^{-6} seconds greater.

3. At the present time, it is probably more correct to regard the measurements of astronomical aberration as determinations of the earth's velocity than of the velocity of light. Using the value of the angle of aberration given in Sec. 19.2, and Michelson's 1926 value of c, compute the orbital velocity of the earth.

4. In Fizeau's toothed-wheel method let L be the distance from the wheel to the remote mirror, f the frequency of revolution of the wheel, N the number of teeth, and

n the number of the eclipse.   Derive an equation giving c in terms of these quantities, assuming the adjustment to be made for the minimum of light at the nth eclipse.

$$Ans. \ c = LfN/(n - \tfrac{1}{2}).$$

5. Prove that, in Foucault's rotating-mirror arrangement, the intensity of the image is proportional to $\dfrac{u}{v} \dfrac{A}{4\pi r}$, where u is the distance from the source to the lens, v that from the lens to the distant mirror, A the linear aperture of the latter, and r the distance from the source to the rotating mirror.

6. Suppose that 18 m of the distance RM in Foucault's determination (Sec. 19.4) were filled with water.   Using the group velocities of red and blue light ($\lambda = 7200$ and 4000 Å) in water, compute the actual length in millimeters of the spectrum he would observe.   The values of n at these wavelengths are 1.3299 and 1.3432, respectively, and those of $dn/d\lambda - 222$ and -967 cm^{-1}.   *Ans.* 0.023 mm.

7. If the speed of revolution of Michelson's octagonal mirror were exactly 528 rev/sec when the image was reflected to its initial position from an adjacent face, find the distance to the far mirror.

8. In the measurement of the velocity of light in the mile-long evacuated pipe by Michelson, Pease, and Pearson, a mirror with 32 sides was used.   Assuming the total path to have been 13 km, and that there was a perfect vacuum in the pipe, use the result quoted in Table 19-I to find the speed of rotation of the mirror required to obtain the first undisplaced image.   *Ans.* 720.61 rev/sec.

9. If Anderson's Kerr-cell apparatus were arranged so that the distance from M_4 to M_6 and back (Fig. 19F) comprised $11\tfrac{1}{2}$ groups, find this distance.   The frequency of his oscillator was 19.2 Mc/sec.

10. Verify the statement in Sec. 19.11 that a fringe shift of 0.46 fringe in Fizeau's experiment corresponds to a change in the velocity of light by about half the velocity of water flow.   Assuming the effective wavelength and refractive index to be 5500 Å and 1.333, respectively, find what fraction it actually gives.   *Ans.* 0.508v.

11. Assume that, in an experimental measurement of the Fresnel dragging coefficient by the interference method, each tube was 2 m long, and the velocity of the water 6 m/sec.   By what fraction of the fringe would the white-light fringe system ($\lambda 5600$) be displaced upon reversal of the water stream?

12. Carbon disulfide has $n_D = 1.6295$ and $dn/d\lambda = -1820$ per cm at this wavelength.   Find (a) the ratio of the velocity of the light in vacuum to the group velocity in carbon disulfide, and (b) the exact value of the Fresnel dragging coefficient for this substance (see Prob. 14, below).   *Ans.* (a) 1.7367.   (b) 0.6892.

13. Prove from the geometry of Fig. 19I that, in order for the angle of aberration to remain unchanged when the telescope is filled with water, the magnitude of v' must be that given by Eq. 19b.

14. Equation 19b needs a small correction arising from the fact that for the molecules of the moving water the effective frequency is slightly altered by the Doppler effect.   Prove that this may be taken into account by adding a term $-(\lambda/n)(dn/d\lambda)$ to the expression for the dragging coefficient.   Here λ is the wavelength in vacuum. (HINT: Take the refractive index to vary linearly with frequency, and insert the new index, as altered by the Doppler effect, in the equation for the velocity of light in the moving medium.)

15. Suppose a Michelson interferometer having arms of length 50 cm is oriented so that one arm is parallel to the orbital velocity of the earth.   Find the magnitude of the Fitzgerald-Lorentz contraction in centimeters of the arm parallel to the earth's motion.

16. Find the mass of an electron which is moving at 2.0×10^{10} cm/sec.   Find also the mass of a baseball thrown at 200 ft/sec.   The rest masses of the two are 9.106×10^{-28} g and $5\tfrac{1}{2}$ oz, respectively.   *Ans.* 1.222×10^{-27} g. $155.92 + 3.7 \times 10^{-12}$ g.

CHAPTER 20

THE ELECTROMAGNETIC CHARACTER OF LIGHT

Our study of the properties of light has thus far led us to the conclusion that light is a wave motion, propagated with an extremely high velocity. In the explanation of interference and diffraction it was not necessary to make any assumption as to the nature of the displacement y that appears in our wave equations. This is because in these subjects we were concerned only with the interaction of light waves with each other. In the succeeding chapters we are to consider subjects in which the interaction of light with matter plays a part, and here it becomes necessary to specify the physical nature of the quantity y, which is usually termed the *light vector*. Fresnel, who in 1814 first gave the satisfactory explanation of interference and diffraction by the wave theory, imagined the light vector to represent an actual displacement of a material aether, which was conceived as an all-pervading substance of very small density and of high rigidity. This "elastic-solid" theory had considerable success in interpreting optical phenomena and was strongly supported by many leading investigators in the field, such as Lord Kelvin, as late as 1880.

20.1. Transverse Nature of Light Vibrations. The principal objection to the elastic-solid theory lay in the fact that light had been proved to be exclusively a transverse wave motion, i.e., the vibrations are always perpendicular to the direction of motion of the waves. No longitudinal waves of light have ever been detected. The experimental evidence for this comes from the study of the polarization of light (Chap. 24) and is perfectly definite, so that we may here take the fact as established. Now all elastic solids with which we are familiar are capable of transmitting longitudinal as well as transverse waves; in fact, under some circumstances it is impossible to set up a transverse wave without at the same time starting a longitudinal one. Many suggestions were made to overcome this difficulty, but all were highly artificial. Furthermore, the idea of a material aether itself seemed rather forced, inasmuch as its remarkable properties could not be detected by ordinary mechanical experiments.

407

Thus the time was ripe when Maxwell* proposed a theory which not only *required* the vibrations of light to be strictly transverse but also gave a definite connection between light and electricity.   In a paper read before the Royal Society in 1864, entitled "A Dynamical Theory of the Electromagnetic Field," Maxwell expressed the results of his theoretical investigations in the form of four fundamental equations which have since become famous as *Maxwell's equations*.   They were based on the earlier experimental researches of Oersted, Faraday, and Joseph Henry concerning the relations between electricity and magnetism.   They summarize these relations in concise mathematical form, and constitute a starting point for the investigation of all electromagnetic phenomena. We shall show in the following sections how they account for the transverse waves of light.

20.2. Maxwell's Equations for a Vacuum.   The derivation of these equations will not be given here, since it would involve a rather extensive review of the principles of electricity and magnetism.†   Instead we shall in this chapter merely state the equations in their simplest form, applicable to empty space, and then prove that they predict the existence of waves having the properties of light waves.   The modifications that must be introduced in dealing with different kinds of material media will be considered at the appropriate places in the following chapters.

Maxwell's equations may be written as four vector equations, but for those unfamiliar with vector notation we shall express them by differential equations.   In this form the first two equations must be expressed by two sets of three equations each.   For a vacuum these become, using a right-handed set of coordinates,

$$\left.\begin{aligned} \frac{1}{c}\frac{\partial E_x}{\partial t} &= \frac{\partial H_z}{\partial y} - \frac{\partial H_y}{\partial z} \\[2mm] \frac{1}{c}\frac{\partial E_y}{\partial t} &= \frac{\partial H_x}{\partial z} - \frac{\partial H_z}{\partial x} \\[2mm] \frac{1}{c}\frac{\partial E_z}{\partial t} &= \frac{\partial H_y}{\partial x} - \frac{\partial H_x}{\partial y} \end{aligned}\right\} \quad (20a)$$

$$\left.\begin{aligned} -\frac{1}{c}\frac{\partial H_x}{\partial t} &= \frac{\partial E_z}{\partial y} - \frac{\partial E_y}{\partial z} \\[2mm] -\frac{1}{c}\frac{\partial H_y}{\partial t} &= \frac{\partial E_x}{\partial z} - \frac{\partial E_z}{\partial x} \\[2mm] -\frac{1}{c}\frac{\partial H_z}{\partial t} &= \frac{\partial E_y}{\partial x} - \frac{\partial E_x}{\partial y} \end{aligned}\right\} \quad (20b)$$

---

* J. Clerk Maxwell (1831–1879).   Professor of experimental physics at Cambridge University, England.   Contributed a paper to the Royal Society at the age of fifteen. Much of his work on the electromagnetic theory was accomplished while an undergraduate at Cambridge.   His investigations in many fields of physics bear the stamp of genius.   The kinetic theory of gases was given a solid mathematical foundation by Maxwell, whose name is associated with the well-known law of distribution of molecular velocities.

† For an elementary derivation, see F. K. Richtmyer and E. H. Kennard, "Introduction to Modern Physics," 4th ed., chap. 2, McGraw-Hill Book Company, Inc., New York, 1947.

The other two equations may be written

$$\frac{\partial E_x}{\partial x} + \frac{\partial E_y}{\partial y} + \frac{\partial E_z}{\partial z} = 0 \quad (20c) \qquad \frac{\partial H_x}{\partial x} + \frac{\partial H_y}{\partial y} + \frac{\partial H_z}{\partial z} = 0 \quad (20d)$$

These partial differential equations give the relations in space and time between the vector quantities **E**, the electric field strength, and **H**, the magnetic field strength. Thus E_x, E_y, and E_z are the components of **E** along the three rectangular axes, and H_x, H_y, and H_z those of **H**. The electric field is measured in electrostatic units and the magnetic field in electromagnetic units. The system which uses electrostatic units for all electrical quantities and electromagnetic units for all magnetic ones is known as the *Gaussian system* of units. Although not the most convenient one for practical calculations, it is suitable here, and will always be used in what follows. The presence of the important constant c in Eqs. 20a and 20b is of course dependent on our choice of units. It represents the ratio of the magnitudes of the electromagnetic and electrostatic units of current.

Equation 20c merely expresses the fact that no free electric charges exist in a vacuum. The impossibility of a free magnetic pole gives rise to Eq. 20d. Equations 20b express Faraday's law of induced electromotive force. Thus the quantities occurring on the left side of these equations represent the time rate of change of the magnetic field, and the spacial distribution of the resulting electric fields occurs on the right side. These equations do not give directly the magnitude of the emf, but only the rates of change of the electric field along the three axes. In particular problems the equations must be integrated to obtain the emf itself.

20.3. Displacement Current. Maxwell's principal *new* contribution in giving these equations was the statement of Eqs. 20a. These come from an extension of Ampère's law for the magnetic field due to an electric current. The right-hand members give the distribution of the magnetic field H in space, but the quantities on the left side do not at first sight seem to have anything to do with electric current. They represent the time rate of change of the electric field. But Maxwell regarded this as the equivalent of a current, the *displacement current*, which flows as long as the electric field is changing and which produces the same magnetic effects as an ordinary conduction current.

One way of illustrating the equivalence of $\partial E/\partial t$ to an electric current is shown in Fig. 20A. Imagine an electric condenser C to be connected to a battery B by conducting wires, the whole apparatus being in a vacuum with a vacuum between the condenser plates. As the current

i flows for an instant, electric charge accumulates on the plates until the condenser is fully charged to the voltage of the battery. Through the closed surface S, a certain current has been flowing in during this instant, but none has apparently been flowing out. By considerations of continuity, Maxwell was led to assume that as much current should flow out of such a surface as flows in. But no current of the ordinary sort is flowing between the plates of the condenser. The condition of continuity can be satisfied only by regarding the change of the electric field in this space as the equivalent of a displacement current, the current density j of which is proportional to $\partial E/\partial t$. In our system of units this current is given by $j = 1/4\pi$ times $\partial E/\partial t$. It will be noticed that the displacement current "flows" in a vacuum, but stops as soon as $\mathbf{E}$ becomes constant.

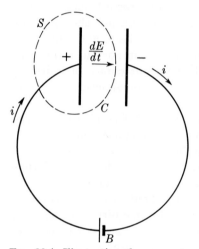

FIG. 20A. Illustrating the concept of displacement current.

One sees at once the analogy between Eqs. 20b and 20a. By Eqs. 20b a changing magnetic field produces an emf. This was observed by Faraday and is very simple to verify experimentally. By Eqs. 20a a changing electric field should produce a magnetic field ("magnetomotive force"). This is a much less familiar idea and cannot be proved by any simple experiment. The reason for the difference is that no substance conducts magnetism as a wire conducts electricity. The peculiarity that some substances possess of being conductors for electricity is the only reason why Eqs. 20b were discovered before Eqs. 20a. The proof of the correctness of Eqs. 20a lies in the remarkable success of Maxwell's equations in accounting for phenomena of nature. It should be noted that Maxwell's equations 20a and 20b may be written in terms of the displacement current j by replacing the x component $(1/c)(\partial E_x/\partial t)$ by $4\pi j_x$ and the other components by similar expressions.

20.4. The Equations for Plane Electromagnetic Waves. Consider the case of plane waves traveling in the x direction, so that the wave fronts are planes parallel to the y,z plane. If the vibrations are to be represented by variations of E and H, we see that in any one wave front they must be constant over the whole plane at any instant, and their partial derivatives with respect to y and z must be zero. Therefore Eqs. 20a to 20d take the form

$$\frac{1}{c}\frac{\partial E_x}{\partial t} = 0$$
$$\frac{1}{c}\frac{\partial E_y}{\partial t} = -\frac{\partial H_z}{\partial x} \qquad (20e)$$
$$\frac{1}{c}\frac{\partial E_z}{\partial t} = \frac{\partial H_y}{\partial x}$$

$$-\frac{1}{c}\frac{\partial H_x}{\partial t} = 0$$
$$-\frac{1}{c}\frac{\partial H_y}{\partial t} = -\frac{\partial E_z}{\partial x} \qquad (20f)$$
$$-\frac{1}{c}\frac{\partial H_z}{\partial t} = \frac{\partial E_y}{\partial x}$$

$$\frac{\partial H_x}{\partial x} = 0 \qquad (20g)$$

$$\frac{\partial E_x}{\partial x} = 0 \qquad (20h)$$

Considering the first equation of Eqs. 20e and Eq. 20h together, it appears that the longitudinal component E_x is constant in both space and time. Similarly from the top line of Eqs. 20f and from Eq. 20g, H_x is also constant. These components can therefore have nothing to do with the wave motion, but must represent constant fields superimposed on the system of waves. For the waves themselves, we may therefore write

$$E_x = 0 \qquad H_x = 0$$

This means, of course, that the waves are transverse, as stated above.

Of the four remaining equations, we see that the second equation 20e and the third equation 20f involve E_y and H_z, while the third equation 20e and the second equation 20f involve E_z and H_y. Let us assume, for example, that E_y represents the light vector, so that we are dealing with a plane-polarized wave with vibrations in the y direction. We should then have to put $E_z = H_y = 0$, and consider the two remaining equations

$$\frac{1}{c}\frac{\partial E_y}{\partial t} = -\frac{\partial H_z}{\partial x}$$
$$-\frac{1}{c}\frac{\partial H_z}{\partial t} = \frac{\partial E_y}{\partial x} \qquad (20i)$$

We now differentiate the first equation with respect to t and the second with respect to x. This gives

$$\frac{1}{c}\frac{\partial^2 E_y}{\partial t^2} = -\frac{\partial^2 H_z}{\partial x \, \partial t}$$
$$-\frac{1}{c}\frac{\partial^2 H_z}{\partial t \, \partial x} = \frac{\partial^2 E_y}{\partial x^2}$$

Eliminating the derivatives of H_z, we find

$$\frac{\partial^2 E_y}{\partial t^2} = c^2 \frac{\partial^2 E_y}{\partial x^2} \qquad (20j)$$

In a similar way, by differentiation of the first equation 20i with respect to x and the second with respect to t, we find

$$\frac{\partial^2 H_z}{\partial t^2} = c^2 \frac{\partial^2 H_z}{\partial x^2} \qquad (20k)$$

Now Eqs. 20j and 20k have just the form of the wave equation for plane waves (Eq. 11b), with E_y and H_z, respectively, playing the part of the displacement y in the two cases. For both, comparison with the wave equation shows that the velocity

$$v = c \tag{20l}$$

Thus we see that two of the four equations in Eqs. 20e and 20f predict the existence of a wave of the electric vector, plane-polarized in the x,y plane, and an accompanying wave of the magnetic vector, plane-polarized in the x,z plane. In the form of Eq. 11a they would be represented by

$$E_y = f(x \pm ct) \qquad H_z = f(x \pm ct) \tag{20m}$$

The two waves are interdependent; neither can exist without the other. Both are transverse waves, and are propagated in a vacuum with the velocity c, the ratio of the electrical units (Sec. 20.2).

If we had started with the other two equations in Eqs. 20e and 20f, we would have obtained another pair of waves, plane-polarized with the electric vector in the x,z plane. This pair is quite independent of the other, and can exist separately from the other pair. A mixture of the two pairs, vibrating at right angles to each other, and with no constant phase relation between E_y and E_z, represents unpolarized light.

20.5. Pictorial Representation of an Electromagnetic Wave. The simplest type of electromagnetic wave is one in which the function f in Eq. 20m is a sine or cosine. This is a plane-polarized monochromatic plane wave. The three components of **E**, and the three of **H**, may for such a wave be written

$$\begin{matrix} E_x = 0 & E_y = A \sin(\omega t - kx) & E_z = 0 \\ H_x = 0 & H_y = 0 & H_z = A \sin(\omega t - kx) \end{matrix} \left.\begin{matrix}\\\\\end{matrix}\right\} \tag{20n}$$

By substituting the derivatives of these quantities in Eqs. 20a to 20d, it is easily verified that they represent a solution of Maxwell's equations.

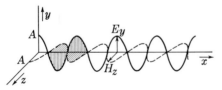

Figure 20B shows a plot of the values of E_y and H_z along the x axis, according to Eq. 20n. In a set of plane waves the values of E_y and H_z at any particular value of x are the same all over the plane

Fig. 20B. Distribution of the electric and magnetic vectors in a plane-polarized monochromatic wave.

$x = $ const.; so this figure merely represents the conditions for one particular value of y and z.

Two important points are to be noticed about Fig. 20B. In the first place, the electric and magnetic components of the wave are *in phase* with each other; i.e., when E_y has its maximum value, H_z is also a maximum. The relative directions of these two vectors, as indicated in the figure, agree with Eqs. 20n. The second point to be noted is that the amplitudes of the electric and magnetic vectors are equal. That these two are numerically equal in the system of units used here is shown by the fact that, in Eqs. 20n, A is the amplitude of each wave.

20.6. Light Vector in an Electromagnetic Wave. The dual character of the electromagnetic wave raises the question as to whether it is the electric vector or the magnetic vector which is to be the light vector. This question has little meaning, since we could assume either one to represent the "displacements" we have been using in previous chapters. In every interference or diffraction phenomenon, the electric waves will mutually influence each other in exactly the same way as the magnetic waves. In one respect, however, the electric component plays a dominant part. It will be proved in Chap. 25 that it is the electric vector that affects the photographic plate and causes fluorescent effects. Presumably also the electric vector is the one that affects the retina of the eye. In this sense, therefore, the electric wave is the part that really constitutes "light," and the magnetic wave, though no less real, is less important.

20.7. Energy and Intensity of an Electromagnetic Wave. The intensity of mechanical waves was shown in Chap. 11 to be proportional to the square of the amplitude. The same result follows from the electromagnetic equations. It can be shown* that in vacuum the electromagnetic field has an energy density given by

$$\text{Energy per unit volume} = \frac{E^2 + H^2}{8\pi} = \frac{E^2}{4\pi} \qquad (20o)$$

where E and H are the instantaneous values of the fields, which here are equal. Half the energy is associated with the electric vector and half with the magnetic vector. The magnitudes of these vectors vary from point to point in any wave; so, in order to obtain the energy in any finite volume, it is necessary to evaluate the average value of E^2 (or H^2). For the plane wave of Eq. 20n, one finds that $E^2 = \frac{1}{2}A^2$, the factor $\frac{1}{2}$ being the average of the square of the sine over all angles. Hence an electromagnetic wave has an energy density $A^2/8\pi$, where A is the amplitude of either the electric or the magnetic component.

The intensity of the wave will merely be the product of the above expression by the velocity c, since this represents the volume of the wave

* L. Page and N. I. Adams, Jr., "Principles of Electricity," 2d ed., p. 564, D. Van Nostrand Company, Inc., New York, 1949.

that will stream through unit area per second.   We therefore have

$$I = \frac{c}{8\pi} A^2 \tag{20p}$$

The reader should be reminded that the above statements are applicable only to a wave traveling in vacuum.   In matter, not only will the velocity be different, but also the magnitudes of E and H will no longer be equal. Aside from factors of proportionality, however, the intensity is still given by the square of the amplitude of either wave (Sec. 23.9).

20.8. Radiation from an Accelerated Charge.   A convenient method of representing an electric or magnetic field is by the use of lines of force. These are familiar to anyone who has studied elementary electricity and magnetism.   Each line of force indicates the direction of the field at every point along the line, and this is such that a tangent to the line of force at any point gives the direction of the force on a small charge or pole placed at that point.   That is, this tangent gives the direction of the electric or magnetic field at that point.

Consider a small positive electric charge at rest at the point A [Fig. 20C(a)].   The lines of force are straight lines diverging in every direction from the charge and are uniformly distributed in space.   The same picture would hold if the charge were moving in the direction AB with constant velocity, assuming this velocity to be not too large.   In these two cases—charge at rest and charge in uniform motion—there is no radiation of electromagnetic waves.

In order to produce electromagnetic radiation, it is necessary to have *acceleration* of the charge.   A particularly simple case is represented in Fig. 20C(b).   Let the charge, originally at rest at A, be accelerated in the direction AC.   The acceleration a lasts only until the charge reaches the point B, and from that point on the charge moves with a constant velocity.   In this case we may obtain some information about the form of the lines of force radiating from the charge at some later time.   Let the time of the acceleration from A to B be Δt, and let the time of the uniform motion from B to C be t.   When the charge has reached C, at a time $t + \Delta t$ after it starts, the parts of the original lines of force lying beyond the arc RR', drawn about A with the radius $c(t + \Delta t)$, cannot have been disturbed in any way.   This follows from the fact that any electromagnetic disturbance is propagated with the velocity c.   At the point C the velocity is uniform and the lines of force as far as the arc QQ', drawn about B with the radius ct, must be uniform and straight, since the charge has had a uniform velocity during the time t.   Consequently we see that in order to have continuous lines of force they must be connected through the region between RR' and QQ' somewhat as shown in the figure.   This gives a pronounced "kink" in each line.   The exact form of the kink will depend upon the type of acceleration existing between A and B, that is, whether it is uniform or some type of nonuniform acceleration.

What is the significance of such a kink in a line of force? If we select some point P lying on the kink [Fig. 20C(c)], the vector E drawn tangent to the line at P gives the actual direction of the field at that point. This may be regarded as the resultant of the field E_0 which would be produced

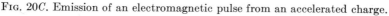

Fig. 20C. Emission of an electromagnetic pulse from an accelerated charge.

by the charge at rest, and a *transverse* field E_t. It is the vector E_t which represents the electric vector of the electromagnetic wave, referred to in the foregoing sections. If we carry out this construction for various points along the kink, we obtain the variations indicated in Fig. 20C(d). This is obviously not a periodic wave form, but merely a pulse. There will be a similar pulse of the H vector at right angles to E_t.

Several important features about the production of electromagnetic radiation are illustrated by this example. Most important is the fact that E_t exists only when the charge is *accelerated*. No radiation is produced if there is no acceleration of charge, and, conversely, an accelerated charge will always radiate to a greater or less extent. Also, the example shows how the electric field of the radiation can be transverse to the direction of propagation. The magnitude of the vector E_t obtained by the construction of Fig. 20C(d), i.e., the amplitude of the wave, obviously depends on the steepness of the kink, and this is determined by how rapidly the charge was accelerated from A to B. It can be shown theoretically that the rate of radiation of energy from an accelerated charge is proportional to the square of the acceleration. Finally, we also find that the amplitude of the radiation varies with angle in such a way that it is a maximum in directions perpendicular to the line AC and falls to zero in both directions along AC. The amplitude is easily shown to be proportional to the sine of the angle between AC and the direction considered.

20.9. Radiation from a Charge in Periodic Motion. If the charge in Fig. 20C, instead of undergoing a single acceleration, is caused to execute a periodic motion, the radiation will be in the form of continuous waves

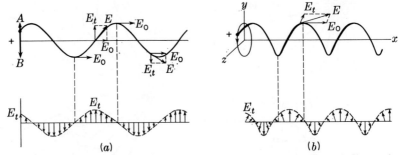

FIG. 20D. Emission of electromagnetic waves from a charge in periodic motion.

instead of a single isolated pulse. Any periodic motion involves accelerations, and hence will cause the charge to radiate. We shall here consider only two especially simple cases, that of linear simple periodic motion and that of uniform circular motion. If the positive charge of Fig. 20$D(a)$ is moved with simple harmonic motion between the limits A and B, any line of force will be bent into the form of a sine curve. Let the upper curve of Fig. 20$D(a)$ represent one such line, say the one running out perpendicular to AB. At the particular instant shown, the electric force E at various points along the line has the direction of the tangent at those points. Resolving it into the undisturbed field E_0 and the transverse component E_t, we find the various values E_t shown just below. These also take the form of a sine curve and represent the variation of the electric vector along the wave sent out. This is a plane-polarized wave.

In part (b) of the figure, the positive charge is revolving counterclockwise in a circle, in the y,z plane shown in perspective. The same construction now gives values of E_t which are constant in magnitude, but vary in direction along the wave. The heads of the arrows lie on a spiral similar to that of the line of force, but displaced one-quarter of a wavelength along the direction of propagation, which here is the x axis.

This screwlike arrangement of the vectors is characteristic of a circularly polarized wave. It is worth pointing out here that, if the radiation along the y or z axes were examined, it would be found to be plane-polarized in the y,z plane. Actual observation of these two cases is possible in the Zeeman effect (Sec. 29.1).

20.10. Hertz's Verification of the Existence of Electromagnetic Waves. We have seen that, starting with a set of equations governing the phenomena of electromagnetism, Maxwell was able to show the possibility of electromagnetic waves and to make definite statements about the production and properties of the waves. Thus he could say that they are generated by any accelerated charge, that they are transverse waves, and that they travel with the velocity c in free space. The experimental production and detection of the waves predicted by Maxwell were achieved by Heinrich Hertz.* In 1887 he began a remarkable series of experiments which constitute the first important experiments on radio

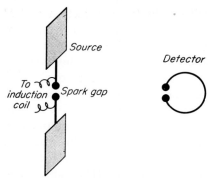

FIG. 20*E*. Source and detector of electromagnetic waves used by Hertz.

waves, i.e., electromagnetic waves of long wavelength. The essential features of Hertz's method are illustrated in Fig. 20*E*. Two plane brass plates are connected to a spark gap *SG* and sparks are caused to jump across the gap by charging the plates to high voltage with an induction coil. It is known that the discharge of the plates by the spark is an oscillatory one. Each time the potential difference between the knobs of the gap reaches the point where the air in the gap becomes conducting, a spark passes. This represents a sudden surge of electrons across the gap, and the signs of the charges on the two plates become reversed. But since the air is still conducting, this will produce a return surge, another reversal of sign, and the process repeats until the energy is dissipated as heat by the resistance of the gap. The frequency of these oscillations depends on the inductance and capacity of the circuit. These were very small for Hertz's oscillator, and the frequency correspondingly high. In some of his experiments it reached 10^9 per sec. Thus we have an electric charge undergoing very rapid accelerations, and electromagnetic waves should be radiated.

* Heinrich Hertz (1857–1894). These experiments were carried on while he was professor of physics at the Technical High School at Karlsruhe, Germany, in 1885–1889. He was then given a professorship at the University of Bonn, which he held until his untimely death.

In Hertz's experiment the presence of electromagnetic waves was detected at some distance from the oscillator by a resonating circuit consisting of a circular wire broken by a very narrow spark gap of adjustable length. The changing magnetic field in the wave induced an alternating emf in the circular wire, whose dimensions were such that the natural frequency of its oscillations was the same as that of the source. Thus the induced oscillations built up by resonance in the detector until they were sufficient to cause sparks to jump the gap.

It was a simple matter to show that the waves were plane-polarized with **E** in the y direction and **H** in the z direction. If the loop was turned through 90° so that it lay in the x,z plane, the sparks ceased to occur. Hertz performed many other experiments with these waves, showing among other things that the waves could be reflected and focused by curved metal reflectors, and that they could be refracted in passing through a large 30° prism of pitch. In these respects they therefore showed the same behavior as light waves.

20.11. Velocity of Electromagnetic Waves in Free Space. The most convincing proof of the reality of Hertz's electromagnetic waves lay in the demonstration that their velocity was that predicted by the theoretical equation (Eq. 20l). The velocity was measured not directly but indirectly by measuring the wavelength. Then from the known frequency of the oscillations the velocity could be found by the relation $v = \nu\lambda$. To measure the wavelength, standing waves were produced by interference of the direct waves with those reflected from a plane metal reflector. The positions of the nodes could be located by the fact that the detector ceased to spark at these points. With a frequency of 5.5×10^7 per sec, λ was found to be about 5.4 m, which gives v very close to 3×10^{10} cm/sec. The determination could not be made accurately, because the oscillations were highly damped, only three or four occurring after each spark, and the wavelength was therefore not accurately defined. More recent work by Mercier with undamped waves produced by a vacuum-tube oscillator gave the result 2.9978×10^{10} cm/sec. We have already seen, in Sec. 19.8, how the increased precision obtainable with cavity resonators has added another significant figure to the velocity of light.

According to Eq. 20l, this observed velocity should equal c, the ratio of the emu to the esu of current. As has been mentioned (Sec. 19.9), this ratio has been accurately measured by different methods, the most recent value being 2.99781×10^{10} cm/sec. But this is just the measured velocity of electromagnetic waves and also agrees exactly with the latest measurements of the velocity of light by Michelson and others. For air or other gases at atmospheric pressure, a slight modification in the equations is necessary (Chap. 23), but the predicted velocity differs only slightly from that in vacuum.

Hence we are forced to conclude that light consists of electromagnetic waves of extremely short wavelength. Beside the evidence of polarization, which proves that light waves are transverse waves, there is much other evidence of this identity. Spectroscopy has shown that the atoms contain electrons and that by assuming the acceleration of these electrons as they move in orbits around the nucleus one can account for the polarization and intensity of the spectrum lines. Furthermore, as mentioned in. Chap. 11, it has been shown that radio waves, which are obviously electromagnetic in character, join continuously onto the region of infrared light waves. Thus the explanation of light waves as an electromagnetic phenomenon, which in the hands of Maxwell was merely a very elegant theory, has since proved to be a reality, and we accept the electromagnetic character of light as an established fact. In treating the interactions of light with matter we shall therefore use the fact that light consists of oscillations of an electric field at right angles to the direction of propagation of the waves, accompanied by oscillations of the magnetic field, also at right angles to this direction and to the direction of the electric field.

20.12. Čerenkov Radiation. It was stated in Sec. 20.8 that an electric charge moving with uniform velocity radiates no energy, but merely carries its electromagnetic field along with it. This is true as long as the charge is traveling in vacuum. If on the other hand it moves through a material medium, as, for example, when a high-speed electron or proton enters a piece of glass, it may radiate a small amount of energy even though its velocity be constant. The required condition is that the speed of the charged particle be *greater than the wave velocity* c/n of light in the medium. It then sets up an impulsive wave similar to the shock wave produced by a projectile traveling at a speed greater than that of sound. It is of the same character as the "bow wave" of a boat, which forms when the boat moves faster than do the water waves.

The production of this wave is an excellent illustration of the application of Huygens' principle (Sec. 18.1). In Fig. 20F let e represent an electron moving through glass of index 1.50 with a velocity which is 0.9 of the velocity of light. (To produce such an electron one would have to accelerate it through a potential difference of some 650,000 volts.) The disturbances produced when the electron occupied successively the positions O, O', and O'' are represented as secondary wavelets which have radii OA, $O'A'$, and $O''A''$, proportional to the elapsed time and to their velocity c/n. The resulting wave front is the common tangent to these, and takes the form of a cone of half angle θ. Since OA is normal to the wave front, it will be seen from the figure that θ is given by

$$\sin \theta = \frac{c}{nv} = \frac{1}{n\beta} \qquad (20q)$$

where v is the velocity of the charged particle and $\beta = v/c$. If $\beta = 0.9$ as in our example, θ is about 48°. A substantial part of the radiation is in visible light, and is detectable by the eye or the photographic plate. Because of dispersion, the variation of n with color, Eq. 20q is not perfectly exact.* Furthermore, when n is largest (blue light), the cone is narrower and the outer edge of the conical fan of light *rays* will therefore be blue, while its inner edge will be red.

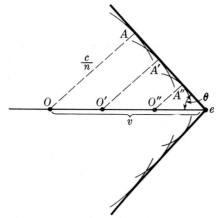

This type of radiation is now commonly observed with the high-speed particles used in nuclear physics. By measuring the angle of the cone, the velocities and energies of the particles may be determined. The light resulting from the passage of a single particle may be made to register a count with a photomultiplier tube. This is the principle of the Čerenkov counter employed by nuclear physicists.

FIG. 20F. Cross section of the conical wave produced in Čerenkov radiation.

PROBLEMS

1. An oscillator of frequency 35 Mc/sec is set up near a plane metal reflector, and the distance between adjacent nodes in the standing waves is found to be 4.28 m. Neglecting the refractive index of air, what does this give for the velocity of light?

2. When a simple harmonic motion is impressed on an electric charge, the lines of force at right angles to the motion take the same form as does a stream of water from the nozzle of a hose undergoing that motion. The nozzle is continuously pointed at right angles to the motion, and gravity is of course neglected. Sketch the form of the line after one complete vibration of the source. Remember to add the velocity of the hose to that of the water at the middle point of the vibration.

Ans. Sine wave starting at the nozzle.

3. Show that Maxwell's equations are satisfied by the solution

$$E_x = 0 \qquad E_y = A \sin(\omega t + kz) \qquad E_z = 0$$
$$H_x = A \sin(\omega t + kz) \qquad H_y = 0 \qquad H_z = 0$$

In which plane is the wave polarized, and in which direction does it travel?

* For the exact equations, see H. Motz and L. I. Schiff, *Am. J. Phys.*, **21**, 258, 1953.

4. Modify Eqs. 20n so that they represent (a) a plane-polarized wave having oscillations of E in the y,z plane, but at 45° to y, and (b) a wave whose oscillations are ellipses in the y,z plane (elliptically polarized wave).

Ans. (a) $E_x = 0$
$\quad E_y = a \sin (\omega t - kx)$
$\quad E_z = a \sin (\omega t - kx)$
$\quad H_x = 0$
$\quad H_y = -a \sin (\omega t - kx)$
$\quad H_z = a \sin (\omega t - kx)$

(b) $E_x = 0$
$\quad E_y = a_1 \sin (\omega t - kx)$
$\quad E_z = a_2 \sin (\omega t - kx + \delta)$
$\quad H_x = 0$
$\quad H_y = -a_2 \sin (\omega t - kx + \delta)$
$\quad H_z = a_1 \sin (\omega t - kx)$

5. Starting with Eqs. 20n, make a list of the values of all partial derivatives occurring in Eqs. 20a to 20d. Show by direct substitution that these derivatives satisfy the latter equations.

6. Prove that the segment of the line of force between Q and R in Fig. 20C(b) is a straight line when the acceleration of the charge has been uniform. From the slope of this segment, show that the ratio E_0/E_t falls off as $1/r$, and hence that at any appreciable distance the transverse component will predominate. (HINT: Remember that E_0 is given by Coulomb's law.)

7. Show that the amplitude of the electromagnetic wave from an accelerated charge varies as $\sin \theta$, where θ is the angle between the direction of observation and the direction of the acceleration. Make a polar plot of the intensity of the radiation vs. angle.

8. Show that the ratio of a charge measured in esu to the same charge measured in emu has the dimensions of a velocity. (HINT: Start from Coulomb's law in each case.)

9. Calculate the amplitude of the electric field strength in a beam of full sunlight, which may be taken as having an intensity of 0.13 watt/cm².

10. The total force F exerted on a charge e that moves in electric and magnetic fields in vacuum is given by

$$F = eE + \frac{evH}{c}$$

where it is assumed that the velocity v is perpendicular to the field H. Find the ratio of an electric force to the magnetic force exerted on an electron in the first Bohr orbit of the hydrogen atom by sunlight which has $E = H = 0.0242$ (Gaussian units).

Ans. 137.

11. Poynting's theorem states that the energy flow in an electromagnetic wave is given by

$$S = \frac{c}{4\pi} [\mathbf{E} \times \mathbf{H}]$$

S is called the *Poynting vector*, and the expression in square brackets represents the vector product. Show that the conclusions of Secs. 20.5 and 20.7 with regard to the direction and magnitude of this flow relative to the directions and magnitudes of **E** and **H** are in agreement with Poynting's theorem.

12. By assuming Einstein's relation between mass and energy, and taking the mass equivalent to an electromagnetic wave to move with the velocity c, derive an expression for the pressure that radiation exerts on a perfectly absorbing surface by virtue of its momentum. *Ans.* $p = I/c = A^2/8\pi$.

13. A beam of protons of energy 340 Mev is passed through a sheet of extra-dense flint glass ($n = 1.88$). The Čerenkov radiation is found to make an angle of 38° with the direction of the proton beam inside the glass. What is the indicated value of β for these protons?

CHAPTER 21

SOURCES OF LIGHT AND THEIR SPECTRA

Since light is an electromagnetic radiation, we should expect that the emission of light from any source results from the acceleration of electric charges. It is now certain that the electric charges involved in the emission of visible and ultraviolet light are the negative electrons in the outer part of the atom. By assuming that vibratory or orbital motions of these electrons cause radiation, many of the characteristics of different light sources may be explained. It should be emphasized, however, that this concept must not be carried too far. In the interpretation of spectra it fails in several important respects. These all involve the discrete or corpuscular nature of light, which is to be discussed later (Chap. 30). For the present, we shall emphasize only those features which can be explained by the assumption that light consists of electromagnetic waves.

21.1. Classification of Sources. Sources of light which are important for optical and spectroscopic experiments may be divided into two main classes: (1) *thermal* sources, in which the radiation is the result of high temperature, and (2) sources depending on the electrical *discharge through gases*. The sun, with its surface temperature of 5000 to 6000°C, is an important example of the first class, but here must also be included such important sources as tungsten-filament lamps, the various electric arcs at atmospheric pressure, and the flame. Under the second class come high-voltage sparks, the glow discharge in vacuum tubes at low pressure, and certain low-pressure arcs like the mercury arc. The distinction between the two classes is not sharp, and we can go continuously from one to the other, for instance by pumping away the air around an electric arc.

21.2. Solids at High Temperature. The majority of practical sources for illuminating purposes use the radiation from a hot solid. In the *tungsten lamp*, the filament is heated to about 2100°C by the dissipation of electrical energy due to its resistance. The filament can be run at temperatures as high as 2300°C but will last for only a short period owing to the rapid vaporization of tungsten. In the *carbon arc* in air, the temperature of the positive pole is about 4000°C and that of the negative pole, 3000°. The positive pole vaporizes and burns away rather rapidly, but it constitutes the brightest thermal source of light available in the laboratory. The heating results chiefly from the bombardment of the positive pole by electrons drawn from the gaseous part of the arc. Relatively little light comes from the gas itself. An interesting type of arc, useful when a very small source of light is needed, is the so-called *concentrated-arc* lamp. A simplified diagram of this device is shown in Fig. 21A(a). The cathode consists of a small metal tube packed with zirconium oxide, and the anode consists of a metal plate containing a hole slightly larger than the end of the cathode. Tungsten, tantalum, or molybdenum, because of their high melting points, are used for the

(a)   (b)

Fig. 21A. The concentrated arc, a close approximation to a "point source."

metal parts. These are sealed into a glass bulb which is filled with an inert gas like argon to a pressure of nearly one atmosphere. The arc runs between the (fused) surface of the zirconium oxide and the surrounding anode, as indicated in part (b) of the figure. The tip of the cathode is heated by ion bombardment to 2700°C or higher, giving it a surface brightness almost equal to that in the carbon arc. The light is observed through the hole in the anode, in the direction shown by the arrow in Fig. 21A(a). Lamps of this type can be made in which the source is as small as 0.007 cm in diameter. A cheaper way of achieving a source of small dimensions is to use a tungsten lamp with a small spiral filament (automobile headlight bulb), run at a voltage somewhat higher than its rated value. This source does not, however, have the smallness and brightness of the concentrated-arc lamp. Other sources of continuous spectra will be considered in Sec. 21.9.

21.3. Metallic Arcs.* When two metal rods connected to a source of direct current are touched together and drawn apart, a brilliant arc forms between them. A resistance of high current capacity must be connected in series with the circuit, and adjusted so that the steady current through the arc is from 3 to 5 amp. Higher currents than this will cause excessive heating and melting of the electrodes. A large self-

* These and other sources for use in spectroscopy as well described in G. R. Harrison, R. C. Lord, and J. R. Loofbourow, "Practical Spectroscopy," 1st ed., chap. 8, Prentice-Hall, Inc., Englewood Cliffs, New Jersey, 1948.

inductance in the circuit will stabilize the arc, and a voltage of 220 is preferable to 110 in this respect. The two poles are held vertically, in line with each other, by clamps with a screw adjustment to vary their separation. In the *iron arc*, the positive pole should be the lower, since then a bead of molten iron oxide collects in the small cavity which soon forms, and this helps the steadiness of the arc. The radiation from an iron, copper, or aluminum arc comes mostly from the gas traversed by the arc, this gas consisting almost entirely of the vapor of the metal. It has been shown that the gas is at a temperature of from 4000 to 7000°C, and it may in cases of very high currents run up to 12,000°C. The equivalent of a metallic arc may be obtained with a carbon arc in which the positive pole has been bored with an axial hole and packed with the salt of a metal, such as calcium fluoride. It is sometimes desirable to run a metallic arc in an atmosphere other than air by enclosing it in an airtight chamber. The arc may then be run at low pressures as well. but this is a difficult procedure.

With the metals of low melting point, the arc may be permanently enclosed in a glass envelope. Of this type are the *mercury arc* and the *sodium arc*, both commonly used in optical laboratories. In the older form of mercury arc, liquid mercury is sealed in a highly evacuated glass container of such a shape that the mercury forms two separate pools. These make electrical connection with two wires sealed through the glass. To start the arc, it is tipped until a thread of mercury connects the two pools for an instant and breaks again. As the arc warms up, the pressure of the mercury vapor increases, and unless a fairly large space is available for cooling and condensation, the arc will go out. With sufficient self-inductance in the circuit, the arc may be run at fairly high temperature and pressure, giving a very intense source. For this purpose the container is made of fused quartz to withstand the higher temperature. Quartz has the advantage that it transmits the ultraviolet light (Sec. 22.3), and quartz arcs are frequently used in spectroscopy and for therapeutic purposes. In using them, great care should be taken not to look at the arc too frequently unless glasses are being worn, as a painful inflammation of the eyes may result. The same is true for the exposed metallic arcs mentioned above.

As is shown in Fig. 21$B(a)$, it is possible to arrange a mercury arc to be self-starting. The type illustrated provides an intense, narrow vertical source of mercury light suitable for illuminating a slit. The arc is formed in a capillary tube of inside diameter 2 mm, and starts a minute or so after connecting the terminals to the 110-volt d-c mains. Before this time, the current is limited to about 1.5 amp by the resistances R_1 and R_2 of 80 and 7 ohms, respectively. R_2 is wound on the lower part of the capillary and encased in cement so that it heats the mercury at that point until a bubble of vapor is formed and the mercury thread breaks.   The resulting arc then generates enough pressure to push the mercury above it up to the point A.   The arc is then confined to the capillary from A to R_2.   The current has now fallen to about 1.0 amp, owing to the additional resistance of the arc itself.

The sodium arc [Fig. $21B(b)$] is always contained in a double-walled envelope made of a special glass that is resistant to blackening by hot

FIG. 21B. (a) Small, self-starting mercury arc.   (b) Sodium arc.

sodium vapor.   The inner envelope contains argon or neon at low pressure, and a small amount of metallic sodium.   The discharge is initiated in the rare gas by electrons emitted from the coiled filament F, and is sustained by a relatively small positive potential applied to the anode. Since the space between the double walls is highly evacuated to prevent heat loss, the interior temperature rises rapidly to the point where the sodium melts and vaporizes into the arc.   The rare-gas spectrum then fades out, being replaced by radiation from the more easily ionized atoms of sodium.   This is nearly all in the yellow sodium doublet, so that the arc yields essentially monochromatic light without the use of filters.   The doublet is so narrow (separation 5.97 Å) that for spectroscopy under low dispersion, and for interference measurements with small path difference, it may be assumed to be a single line with the average wavelength 5892 Å.

Although they are satisfactory sources for use with small gratings and prism spectroscopes, neither of the above arcs yields spectral lines of sufficient sharpness for investigations with very high dispersion. The relatively high pressure, temperature, and current density cause a broadening of the lines, for reasons to be explained in Sec. 21.15. The simplest way to produce sharper lines is to use a discharge through a rare gas with a small admixture of the metal vapor, and to limit the current to a few milliamperes. The discharge may be either a low-voltage arc of the type described above or a glow discharge in a vacuum tube (Sec. 21.6). Very convenient sources of this type, not only for mercury and sodium, but also for cadmium, zinc, and other low-melting metals, may now be purchased commercially. In fact, the ordinary mercury fluorescent lamp is of the kind required to give sharp lines, and would be satisfactory were it not for the coating of fluorescent salt on the inside of the walls.

21.4. Bunsen Flame. When sufficient air is admitted at the base of a bunsen burner, the flame is practically colorless, except for a bluish-green cone bounding the inner dark cone of unburnt gas. The temperature above the cone is in the neighborhood of 1800°C, high enough to cause the emission of light from the salts of certain metals when they are introduced into the flame. The color of the flame and its spectrum are characteristic of the metal and do not depend on which salt is used. The chloride is usually most volatile and gives the most intense coloration. The color of the sodium flame is yellow; of strontium, red; of thallium, green; etc. For introducing the salt into the flame, a common method is to use a loop on the end of a platinum wire, which is first dipped in hydrochloric acid and heated until the sodium yellow disappears. Then, while red-hot, it is touched to the powdered salt, melting a small amount which adheres to the wire. When this is again held in the flame, the color is strong but lasts only a short time. A better method is to mix a fine spray of the chloride solution with the gas before it enters the burner. This is best done with the apparatus shown in Fig. 21C, in case air under pressure is available. Air is forced through the atomizer S, filling the bottle with a fine spray which is carried into the gas at the base of the burner. This gives a very constant light source, and is convenient for the laboratory study of flame spectra. Unfortunately, it can be used for only a limited number of metals, the suitable ones including lithium, sodium, potassium, rubidium, caesium, magnesium, calcium, strontium, barium, zinc, cadmium, indium, and thallium. Other elements may be used in the hotter oxygas flame or oxyhydrogen flame, but these flames are not as convenient to operate.

21.5. Spark. By connecting a pair of metal electrodes to the secondary of an induction coil or high-voltage transformer, a series of sparks can be made to jump an air gap of several millimeters. If there is no capacity in the circuit, the spark is quiet and not very intense, the radiation coming chiefly from the air in the gap.   The spark may be made much more violent and brighter by connecting a condenser (such as a Leyden jar) in parallel across the gap.   We then obtain a *condensed spark*.   This is an extremely bright source, the spectrum of which is very rich in lines characteristic of the metal of the electrodes.   The condensed spark has the drawbacks not only of noisiness and hazard of electric shock, but also of the considerable breadth of the lines it emits. Nevertheless, it furnishes the most intense excitation available, and is the

Fig. 21C. Experimental arrangement for producing spectra by introducing salts of metals into the flame of a bunsen burner.

most efficient source we have for the lines of ionized atoms which have lost one or more electrons.   Such lines are usually called high-temperature, or *spark*, *lines*.

21.6. Vacuum Tube.   This is a source that has become increasingly common, owing to its application to advertising signs.   The familiar red "neon signs" contain pure neon gas at a pressure of about 2 cm Hg. Metal electrodes are sealed through the ends of the tube, and an electric current is caused to traverse the gas by connecting the electrodes to a transformer giving a potential of 5000 to 15,000 volts.   Other colors are produced by introducing a small amount of mercury into a neon or argon tube.   The heat of the discharge vaporizes the mercury, and we obtain the characteristic color and spectrum of mercury vapor.   If the tube is made of colored glass, certain colors of the mercury light are absorbed and various shades of blue and green may be produced.

In the laboratory, this principle can be used on a smaller scale to excite the characteristic radiations of any gas or vapor.   Two common forms of vacuum tube are illustrated in Fig. 21D.   Type (a) is useful where maximum intensity is not required, for instance if the tube is to be operated with a small induction coil.   The electrodes E, E are short pieces of aluminum rod, welded to the ends of tungsten wires, the latter being sealed through the glass.   The light is most intense in the capillary tube C, where the current density is greatest, and it is observed laterally, in the direction indicated by the arrow. Considerably greater intensity can be obtained with the "end-on" type shown in (b). Here the electrodes are of sheet aluminum, rolled up and slipped inside two loosely fitting inner glass tubes, G, G. They are fastened to the tungsten leads by wrapping a small strip of aluminum at one end around the wire and pinching it on tightly. The larger area of the electrodes permits the

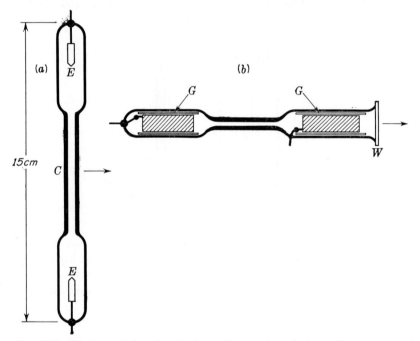

Fig. 21D. Discharge tubes for obtaining the spectra of gases at low pressure.

use of greater currents, usually furnished by a transformer, without overheating of the electrodes. The light is observed through a plane glass window W, which may be fused directly to the tube. The inner glass tubes serve to prevent the deposition of aluminum on the outer walls of the main tube, which occurs rather rapidly when a tube is used at a low pressure.

The exact pressure at which a vacuum tube should be sealed off varies between about 0.5 and 10 mm Hg, according to the gas and to the particular spectrum desired. Only a limited number of gases are suitable for long-continued use in a sealed tube of the above type. Of these, the rare gases neon, helium, and argon are the most satisfactory. Hydrogen, nitrogen, and carbon dioxide tubes will last only a limited time; the gas gradually disappears from the tube, or "cleans up," until a discharge can no longer be maintained. Two processes may be responsible for this. The gas may be decomposed by the discharge and the products deposited on the walls, or removed by chemical combination with the metal electrodes. Or, even with a chemically inert gas, a decrease of pressure may be caused by absorption in the above-mentioned metal layers that are "sputtered" on the walls from the electrodes. Only the main features of the complex phenomena that occur in discharge tubes are well understood, and many interesting effects, such as the formation of striations, have yet to be explained.*

21.7. Classification of Spectra. There are two principal classes of spectra, known as *emission spectra* and *absorption spectra*. In each of these there are three types, *continuous, line,* and *band* spectra. Emission spectra are obtained when the light coming directly from a source is examined with a spectroscope. Absorption spectra are obtained when the light from a source showing a continuous emission spectrum is passed through an absorbing material and thence into the spectroscope. Figures 21G, 21H, and 21J show reproductions of photographed spectra illustrating the three types, both in emission and in absorption. Solids and liquids, with a few rare exceptions,† give only continuous emission and absorption spectra, in which a wide range of wavelengths, without any sharp discontinuities, is covered. Discontinuous spectra (line and band) are obtained with gases. Gases may also, in certain cases, emit or absorb a true continuous spectrum (Sec. 21.9). The three types of emission spectra may be easily observed with a carbon arc. If the spectroscope is pointed at the white-hot pole of the arc, the spectrum is perfectly continuous. If it is pointed at the violet discharge in the gas between the poles, bands in the green and violet are seen, and there are always a few lines, like the sodium lines, owing to impurities in the carbons.

21.8. Emittance and Absorptance. Although in this chapter we are primarily concerned with various sources of light, and hence with emission, it will be well to state here a very important relation which exists between the emissive and absorptive powers of any surface. A solid, when heated, gives a continuous emission spectrum. The amount of radiation in this spectrum and its distribution in different wavelengths

---

* See L. B. Loeb, "Fundamental Processes of Electrical Discharge in Gases," John Wiley & Sons, Inc., New York, 1939.

† Compounds of some of the rare earth metals give line spectra superposed on a continuous spectrum when heated to high temperatures. Their absorption spectra— for example, that of didymium glass—show very narrow regions of absorption, which at liquid-air temperature become sharp absorption lines.

are governed by *Kirchhoff's* law* of radiation. This states that the ratio of the radiant emittance to the absorptance is the same for all bodies at a given temperature. As an equation, this law may be written

$$\frac{W}{a} = \text{const.} = W_B \qquad (21a)$$

The quantity W is the total energy radiated per square centimeter of surface per second, while a represents the fraction of the incident radiation which is not reflected or transmitted by the surface. For the constant representing this ratio, we have used the symbol W_B, because it represents the emittance of a so-called *black body*. This term specifies a body which is perfectly black, i.e., one which absorbs all the radiation falling on its surface. Hence for such an ideal body, $a_B = 1$, and W_B equals the constant ratio W/a for other bodies.

Kirchhoff's law expresses a very general relation between the emission and absorption of radiation by the surface of different bodies. If the absorptance is high, the emittance must also be high. Here it is essential to realize the difference between the term *absorptance*, which measures the amount of light disappearing at a single reflection, and the *absorption* within the body of the material, as measured by the absorption coefficient α (Sec. 11.5). The latter determines the loss of light upon transmission through the material and has no simple connection with the absorptance of the surface. In the case of metals, for example, we shall see (Sec. 25.14) that a very high absorption coefficient is correlated with a high reflectance. But a high reflectance also means a low absorptance. Thus for metals, and in general for smooth surfaces of pure substances, a high absorption coefficient α necessarily means a low absorptance a.

A black body, which is approximated, for example, by a piece of carbon, gives the greatest amount of radiation at a given temperature. Transparent or highly reflecting substances are very poor emitters of visible light, even when raised to high temperatures. Figure 21E shows a practical illustration of the working of Kirchhoff's law. The right-hand picture is a photograph of an ordinary electric iron at room temperature. A few spots of india ink have been made on the surface, and these appear dark since they are regions of high absorptance. The rest of the surface is highly reflecting and hence a poor absorber. The left-hand photograph was taken by the radiation emitted from the iron when heated. The temperature was less than 400°C, so that no visible radiation was emitted. However, with infrared-sensitive photographic plates a successful photograph was obtained, even though the iron was

* Gustav Kirchhoff (1824–1887). Professor of physics at Heidelberg and Berlin. Beside discovering some fundamental laws of electricity, he founded (with Bunsen) the science of chemical analysis by spectra.

invisible to the eye in the dark. In this picture, it will be seen that the spots which were previously dark (good absorbers) have now become brighter than the surroundings, even though they have the same temperature. Hence they also emit radiation most copiously, as Kirchhoff's law requires. Here we are assuming that the ink spots, because they are black by visible light, are also good absorbers for infrared light. It is in fact essential that W and a refer to the same wavelength, or range

(a)   (b)

FIG. 21E. Photographs of an electric iron, illustrating Kirchhoff's law of radiation. (a) Taken with infrared-sensitive plates, with the iron hot but emitting no visible radiation. (b) Taken with ordinary plates and illumination, with the iron at room temperature. For the justification of applying the law at different wavelengths, see text. (*Photographs by H. D. Babcock.*)

of wavelengths. For the radiation within a small wavelength interval we may write

$$\frac{W_\lambda}{a_\lambda} = W_{B\lambda} \qquad (21b)$$

indicating by the subscript the emittance and absorptance at a particular wavelength. This form has important applications to discontinuous spectra (Sec. 21.10).

21.9. Continuous Spectra. The most common sources of continuous emission spectra are solids at high temperature,* and some of these sources were described in Sec. 21.2. Nothing was said there concerning the distribution in different wavelengths of the energy in the continuous spectrum. According to Kirchhoff's law, this depends on the ability of

---

* A good discussion of the experimental methods employed in this field will be found in W. E. Forsythe (ed.), "The Measurement of Radiant Energy," McGraw-Hill Book Company, Inc., New York, 1937.

the surface to *absorb* light of different wavelengths. Thus in a piece of china with a red design glazed upon it, the red parts absorb blue and violet light more strongly than red. When the piece is heated to a high temperature in a furnace and withdrawn, it will be observed that the design will appear bluish by the emitted light, since these portions are the best absorbers and emitters for blue. In general, therefore, the reflectance spectrum of such a solid gives a clue to its emission spectrum.

FIG. 21F. Black-body radiation curves plotted to scale. Abscissas give the wavelengths in angstroms and ordinates the energy in calories per square centimeter per second in a wavelength interval $d\lambda$ of 1 Å. For numerical values, see "Smithsonian Physical Tables," 8th ed., p. 314.

A black body, which absorbs all wavelengths completely, is commonly taken as the standard because it constitutes a particularly simple case with which the radiation from other substances may be compared. Figure 21F shows the energy distribution in the radiation from a black body at seven different temperatures, and Fig. 21G(a) shows photographs of the actual spectra corresponding to these curves.* The curve for 2000°K represents fairly well that for a tungsten filament, while that for 6000°K is closely that of the sun (neglecting the narrow regions of

---

* In comparing the spectra of Fig. 21G(a) with the curves of Fig. 21F it should be borne in mind that photographed spectra do not reproduce the true distribution of intensity in different wavelengths for three reasons: (1) The dispersion of the prism compresses the spectrum at the long-wavelength end. (2) The photographic plate is not equally sensitive to all wavelengths. In particular, the plate used here does not respond at all beyond λ6600. (3) The blackening of the plate is not proportional to the intensity.

absorption due to the Fraunhofer lines). The area under the curve represents the total energy emitted in all wavelengths, and increases rapidly with the absolute temperature. Calling W_B the total energy in ergs emitted from the surface of a black body per square centimeter per

FIG. 21*G*. Continuous spectra. (*a*) Continuous emission spectra of a solid at the three temperatures indicated, taken with a quartz spectrograph. The spectra for 1000°C and 2000°C were obtained from a tungsten filament. That for 4000°C is from the positive pole of a carbon arc. The wavelength scale is marked in hundreds of angstroms. (*b*) Continuous absorption spectra. The upper spectrum is that of the source alone, extending roughly from 4000 to 6500 Å. The others show the effect on this spectrum of interposing three kinds of colored glass.

second, and T the absolute temperature, the *Stefan-Boltzmann* law* states that

$$W_B = \sigma T^4 \qquad (21c)$$

The constant σ has the value 5.669×10^{-5} erg cm^{-2} sec^{-1} °K^{-4}. The wavelength of the maximum of each curve λ_{max} depends on the temperature according to *Wien's†* *displacement law*, which states that

$$\lambda_{max}T = \text{const.} = 0.2898 \text{ cm-deg} \qquad (21d)$$

---

* Ludwig Boltzmann (1844–1906). From 1895 to his death by suicide in 1906, professor of physics at Vienna. The law was originally stated by Josef Stefan (1835–1893) and was independently demonstrated theoretically by Boltzmann. The latter is chiefly known for his contributions to the kinetic theory and the second law of thermodynamics.

† Wilhelm Wien (1864–1928). German physicist, awarded the Nobel prize in 1911 for his work in optics and radiation. He also made important discoveries about cathode rays and canal rays.

where λ_{max} is in centimeters. The shape of the curve itself is given by *Planck's* law*, which may be written

$$W_{B\lambda}\, d\lambda = \frac{c_1}{\lambda^5}\, (e^{c_2/\lambda T} - 1)^{-1}\, d\lambda \qquad (21e)$$

Here e is the base of natural logarithms 2.718, while c_1 and c_2 are constants whose values depend on the unit of λ. For λ in centimeters, $c_1 = 3.7413 \times 10^{-5}$ erg cm^2 sec^{-1} and $c_2 = 1.4388$ cm-deg. These constants are of course connected with those in the Stefan-Boltzmann and Wien laws, because Eq. 21c can be obtained from Eq. 21e by integrating it from $\lambda = 0$ to $\lambda = \infty$, while Eq. 21d is obtained if we differentiate Eq. 21e with respect to λ and equate to zero to obtain the maximum value. Thus, the constant in Eq. 21d is $c_2/4.965$. These equations apply, of course, only to the radiation from an *ideal* black body. This can never be strictly realized experimentally, but it is approximated by a black surface or a hollow cavity with a small opening. The quantity $W_{B\lambda}\, d\lambda$ denotes the emission of unpolarized radiation per square centimeter per second in all directions in a range $d\lambda$.

A source of a continuous spectrum in the ultraviolet region is sometimes desired for the study of absorption spectra in this region. Hot solids are unsuitable for this purpose, because of the relatively small amount of ultraviolet light they emit, even at the highest temperatures available. It has been found that for this purpose a vacuum-tube discharge through hydrogen gas at 5 to 10 mm pressure is very satisfactory. If a current of a few tenths of an ampere is passed through a tube with a rather wide capillary (5 mm diameter) at 2000 volts, a very intense continuous spectrum is obtained. The maximum intensity of this continuum lies in the violet, but it extends far down into the ultraviolet, to about 1700 Å.

21.10. Line Spectra. When the slit of a prism or grating spectroscope is illuminated with the light from a mercury arc, several lines of different color are seen in the eyepiece. Photographs of common line spectra are shown in Fig. 21H(a) to (j). Each of these lines is an image of the slit formed by the telescope lens by light of a particular wavelength. The different wavelengths are deviated through different angles by the prism or grating; hence the line images are separated. It is important to realize that line spectra derive their name from the fact that a *slit* is customarily used, whose image constitutes the line. If a point, a disk, or any other form of aperture were used in the collimator, the spectrum lines would become points, disks, etc., as the case may be. Frequently,

---

* Max Planck (1858–1947). Professor at the University of Berlin. He was awarded the Nobel prize in 1918 for his derivation of the law of black-body radiation and other work in thermodynamics.

FIG. 21H. Line spectra. (a) Spectrum of the iron arc. The emission spectra (a) to (f) were all taken with the same quartz spectrograph. (b) Mercury spectrum from an arc enclosed in quartz. (c) Same, from an arc enclosed in glass. (d) Helium in a glass discharge tube. (e) Neon in a glass discharge tube. (f) Argon in a glass discharge tube. (g) Balmer series of hydrogen in the ultraviolet, λλ3600 to 4000. This is a grating spectrum. The faint lines on either side of the stronger members are false lines called "ghosts" (Sec. 17.12). (h) Flash spectrum, showing the emission spectrum from the gaseous chromosphere of the sun. This is a grating spectrum taken without a slit at the instant immediately preceding a total eclipse, when the rest of the sun is covered by the moon's disk. The two strongest images are the H and K lines of calcium, and show marked prominences, or clouds of calcium vapor. Other strong lines are due to hydrogen and helium. (i) Line absorption spectrum of sodium in the ultraviolet, taken with a grating. The bright lines in the background arise in the source, which here was a carbon arc. Note the slight continuous absorption beyond the series limit. (j) Solar spectrum in the neighborhood of the D lines. The two strong lines are absorbed by sodium vapor in the chromosphere, and together constitute the first member of the series shown in (i).

435

in photographing the spectra from astronomical sources, the collimator is dispensed with entirely, and a prism or grating placed in front of the telescope lens converts the telescope into a spectroscope. In this case, each "line" in the spectrum has the shape of the source. For example, Fig. 21$H(h)$ shows the spectrum of the sun at the instant preceding a total eclipse, when the usual dark-line absorption spectrum is replaced by an emission spectrum from the gases of the solar atmosphere, giving the so-called "flash spectrum." The chief use of a slit is to produce narrow images, so that the images in different wavelengths do not overlap.

TABLE 21-I. WAVELENGTHS, IN ANGSTROMS, OF SOME USEFUL SPECTRAL LINES

Sodium	Mercury	Helium	Cadmium	Hydrogen
5889.95 s	4046.56 m	4387.93 w	4678.16 m	6562.82 s
5895.92 m	4077.81 m	4437.55 w	4799.92 s	4861.33 m
	4358.35 s	4471.48 s	5085.82 s	4340.46 w
	4916.04 w	4713.14 m	6438.47 s	4101.74 w
	5460.74 s	4921.93 m		
	5769.59 s	5015.67 s		
	5790.65 s	5047.74 w		
		5875.62 s		
		6678.15 m		

The most intense sources of line spectra are metallic arcs and sparks, although vacuum tubes containing hydrogen or one of the rare gases are very suitable. Flames are often used, because the spectra they give are in general simpler, being not so rich in lines. All common sources of line emission or line absorption spectra are gases. Furthermore, it is now known that only the *individual atoms* give true line spectra. That is, when a molecular compound is used in the source, such as methane gas (CH_4) in a discharge tube, or sodium chloride in a "cored" carbon arc, the lines observed are due to the elements and not to the molecules. For example, methane gives a strong line spectrum due to hydrogen, and it is well known that sodium chloride gives the yellow sodium lines. Lines due to carbon and chlorine do not appear with appreciable intensity because these elements are more difficult to excite to emission and their strongest lines lie in the ultraviolet and not in the visible part of the spectrum. In Table 21-I are given the wavelengths of the lines in certain commonly used emission spectra, with an indication as to whether they are strong (s), medium (m), or weak (w).

Line *absorption* spectra are obtained only with gases ordinarily composed of individual atoms (monatomic gases). The absorption lines in the solar spectrum are due to atoms which exist as such, rather than combined as molecules, only because of the high temperature and low pressure in the "reversing layer" of the sun's atmosphere [Fig. 21$H(h)$ and (j)]. In the early days of the study of these lines by Fraunhofer, the more prominent ones were designated by letters. The Fraunhofer lines are very useful "bench marks" in the spectrum, for instance in the measurement and specification of refractive indices. Hence we give here, in Table 21-II, their wavelengths and the chemical atoms or molecules to which they are due. The "lines" A, B, and α are really bands, absorbed by the oxygen in the *earth's* atmosphere. It will be seen

TABLE 21-II. THE MOST INTENSE FRAUNHOFER LINES

Designation	Origin	Wavelength, Å	Designation	Origin	Wavelength, Å
A	O_2	7594–7621*	b_4	Mg	5167.343
B	O_2	6867–6884*	c	Fe	4957.609
C	H	6562.816	F	H	4861.327
α	O_2	6276–6287*	d	Fe	4668.140
D_1	Na	5895.923	e	Fe	4383.547
D_2	Na	5889.953	f	H	4340.465
D_3	He	5875.618	G	Fe	4307.906
E_2	Fe	5269.541	G	Ca	4307.741
b_1	Mg	5183.618	g	Ca	4226.728
b_2	Mg	5172.699	h	H	4101.735
b_3	Fe	5168.901	H	Ca^+	3968.468
b_4	Fe	5167.491	K	Ca^+	3933.666

* Band.

that b_4 and G are blends of two lines which are not ordinarily resolved but are due to different elements.

In the laboratory, there are only a few substances which are suitable for observing line absorption spectra, because the absorption lines of most monatomic gases lie far in the ultraviolet. The alkali metals are one exception, and if sodium is heated in an evacuated steel or pyrex-glass tube with glass windows at the ends, the spectrum of light from a tungsten source viewed through the tube will show the sodium lines in absorption [Fig. 21$I(i)$]. They appear as dark lines against the ordinary continuous emission spectrum.

A somewhat simpler experiment to perform, and one which in addition shows the application of Kirchhoff's law to line spectra, is illustrated diagrammatically in Fig. 21I. Here A is a horizontal carbon arc cored with sodium chloride. The arc is run on a fairly large current so that a bright yellow flame F rises above it. If the slit S of the spectroscope is directed at the flame, the sodium D lines are seen in emission. They can now be observed in absorption by placing a concave mirror M in such a position that it casts an image of the bright positive pole of the arc on the slit, the light passing through the flame on its way to the slit. There is a considerable concentration of sodium atoms in the flame, and these are able to absorb, as well as to emit, the particular frequencies corresponding to the D lines. Under these circumstances the lines appear dark in the spectrum, because of the fact that the flame is *at a lower temperature* than the positive pole. This is a consequence of Kirchhoff's law in the form of Eq. 21b. To show this, suppose the absorptance a_λ of the flame for the wavelength of the D lines to be $\frac{1}{4}$, so that one-quarter of this radiation coming from the mirror is removed from the beam. But according to Eq. 21b W_λ for this wavelength is $\frac{1}{4}W_{B\lambda}$, that is, the yellow

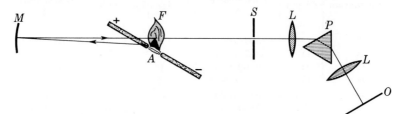

Fɪɢ. 21*I*. Experimental arrangement for showing absorption of the sodium D lines and for illustrating Kirchhoff's law of radiation.

lines are emitted with one-quarter of the intensity of the corresponding portion of the radiation from a black body *at the temperature of the flame.* Hence if the pole of the arc were at the same temperature as the flame, the amount absorbed would be just compensated by the emission, and no line would appear in the spectrum.* The flame, however, is at a considerably lower temperature; hence the amount emitted is not enough to make up for that absorbed, and dark lines are actually observed with the mirror in position. By shifting the mirror so that the image of a cooler part of the pole falls on the slit, the lines can be made to disappear, or to change into bright lines when the temperature of the selected part of the pole is less than that of the flame.

21.11. Theory of the Connection between Emission and Absorption. Kirchhoff's law, as stated in Sec. 21.8, may be proved rigorously by thermodynamical methods. However, it will help more in understanding the above experiment to consider the processes of emission and absorption from the electromagnetic standpoint. We may tentatively picture† the emission of light as due to periodic motions of the electrons in the atoms of the source. These motions would cause electromagnetic

---

* We are assuming here that the pole radiates as a perfect black body.

† That this picture may be only a very approximate one in many instances is indicated later in Sec. 21.14. The correspondence principle of quantum theory shows, however, that it becomes exact for large orbits (high quantum numbers).

waves to be sent out having the same frequencies as the charged particles, just as the sound emitted from a tuning fork has the frequency of the fork. In the case of sodium vapor, each oscillating charge would be regarded as vibrating with a particular frequency, like the tuning fork, and the frequency as that of the yellow sodium light. Now if we consider sodium light to be sent through the vapor, the analogy with the tuning fork would still be valid. It is well known that when sound waves of the right frequency are incident on a tuning fork, the fork will start vibrating and will pick up a considerable amplitude by virtue of resonance. In the same way the sodium atoms respond to the incident electromagnetic waves, and the energy which they absorb from the waves is reemitted as *resonance radiation*. Although all the energy taken from the waves is thus reemitted, resonance radiation is uniformly distributed in all directions and thus will be relatively weaker in the forward direction than if the absorbing atoms were not present.

The connection between the emittance and absorptance of a substance for light of a given wavelength necessarily follows from the above considerations. If a substance absorbs light of one frequency strongly, it must possess a large number of charges whose characteristic frequencies of vibration match that of the light. Conversely, when the substance is caused to emit light, these same vibrations will cause strong emission of the same frequency.

21.12. Series of Spectral Lines. In the spectra of some elements, lines are observed which obviously belong together to form a *series* in which the spacing and intensities of the lines change in a regular manner. For example, in the Balmer series of hydrogen [Fig. 21$H(g)$] the spacing of the lines decreases steadily as they proceed into the ultraviolet toward shorter wavelengths, and their intensities fall off rapidly. Although only the first four lines lie in the visible region, the Balmer series has been traced by photography to 31 members in the spectra of hot stars, where it appears as a series of absorption lines. The absorption spectrum of sodium vapor shows a remarkably long series of lines, each of which is a close doublet [not resolved in Fig. 21$H(i)$], known as the *principal series*. This series also appears in emission from the arc or flame, and the well-known D lines constitute the first doublet of the series. In the sodium spectrum from a flame, about 97 per cent of the intensity in this series is in the first member. The emission spectra of the alkalis also show two other series of doublets in the visible region, known as the *sharp* and *diffuse* series. A fourth weak series in the infrared is called the *fundamental* series. The alkaline earth metals, such as calcium, show two such sets of series—one of single lines, the other of triplets.

A characteristic of any particular series is the approach of the higher series members to a certain limiting wavelength, known as the *limit* or *convergence* of the series. In approaching this limit, the lines crowd closer and closer together, so that there is theoretically an infinite number of lines before the limit is actually reached. Beyond the limit a rather faint continuous spectrum is sometimes observed in emission; in absorption a region of continuous absorption can always be observed if the absorbing vapor is sufficiently dense [Fig. 21H(i)]. The series limits furnish the clue to the identification of the type to which the series belongs. Thus the sharp and diffuse series approach the same limit, while the principal series approaches another limit which for the alkalis lies at shorter wavelengths.

21.13. Band Spectra. The most convenient sources of band spectra for laboratory observation are the carbon arc cored with a metallic salt, the vacuum tube, and the flame. Calcium or barium salts are suitable in the arc or flame, and carbon dioxide or nitrogen in a vacuum tube. As observed with a spectroscope of small dispersion, these spectra present a typical appearance which distinguishes them at once from line spectra [Fig. 21J(a) to (d)]. Many bands are usually observed, each with a sharp edge on one side called the *head*. From the head, the band shades off gradually on the other side. In some band spectra several closely adjacent bands, overlapping to form *sequences*, will be seen [Fig. 21J(b) and (d)], while in others the bands are spaced fairly widely, as in Fig. 21J(c). When the high dispersion and resolving power of a large grating are used, each band is found to be actually composed of many fine lines, arranged with obvious regularity into series called *branches* of the band. In Fig. 21J(e), two branches will be seen starting in opposite directions from a pronounced gap, where no line appears. In (f) the band is double, and the two branches of the left-hand member can be seen running side by side.

Various sorts of evidence point to the conclusion that band spectra arise from *molecules*, i.e., combinations of two or more atoms. Thus it is found that, while the atomic or line spectrum of calcium is independent of which salt we put in the arc, we obtain different bands by using calcium fluoride, calcium chloride, or calcium bromide. Also, the bands appear in those types of sources where the gas receives less violent treatment. Nitrogen in a vacuum tube subjected to an ordinary uncondensed discharge shows only the band spectrum, whereas if a condensed discharge is used, the line spectrum appears. The most conclusive evidence lies in the fact that the absorption spectrum of a gas which is known to be molecular (O_2, N_2) shows bands but no lines, owing to the absence of any dissociation into atoms. Furthermore, it is found that any simple band spectrum, like those described and illustrated above, is due to a *diatomic* molecule. When calcium fluoride (CaF_2) is put into the arc, the bands observed are due to CaF. The violet bands in the uncored carbon arc are due to CN, the nitrogen coming from the air [Fig. 21J(e)]. Carbon dioxide in a vacuum tube gives the spectrum of

FIG. 21J. Band spectra. (a) Spectrum of a discharge tube containing air at low pressure. Four band systems are present: the γ bands of NO (λλ2300 to 2700), negative nitrogen bands (N_2^+, λλ2900 to 3500), second-positive nitrogen bands (N_2, λλ2900 to 5000), and first-positive nitrogen bands (N_2, λλ5500 to 7000). (b) Spectrum of a high-frequency discharge in lead fluoride vapor. These bands, due to PbF, fall in prominent sequences. (c) Spectrum showing part of one band system of SbF, obtained by vaporizing antimony fluoride into "active nitrogen." (b) and (c) were taken with a large quartz spectrograph. (d) Emission and absorption band spectra of BaF. Emission from a carbon arc cored with BaF_2; absorption of BaF vapor in an evacuated steel furnace. The bands are closely grouped in sequences. Second order of 21-ft grating. (e) CN band at λ3883 from an argon discharge tube containing carbon and nitrogen impurities. Second order of grating. (f) Band in the ultraviolet spectrum of NO, obtained from glowing "active nitrogen" containing a small amount of oxygen. Second order of grating. (b) and (c) after G. D. Rochester.

CO, and there are many other examples of this type of dissociation of the more complex molecules into diatomic ones.

21.14. Theory of Line, Band, and Continuous Spectra. The attempt to interpret the various definite frequencies emitted by the atoms of a gas in producing a line spectrum occupied the best minds in physics during the early part of this century, and eventually had most important consequences. Just as the frequencies of vibration of a violin string give sound waves whose frequencies bear the simple ratio of whole numbers to the fundamental note, it was first supposed that the frequencies of the light in the various spectral lines should bear some definite relation to each other, which would furnish the clue to the modes of vibration of the atom and to its structure. This has proved to be the case, though in a very different way than was at first anticipated. The definite relation of frequencies is actually found in spectral series. However, it will be seen at once that the atomic frequencies do not behave like those of a violin string. In the latter the overtones increase steadily toward an infinite frequency (zero wavelength), while the frequencies in a spectral series approach a definite limiting value. The complete explanation of line spectra has now been obtained by developing an entirely new theory, called the *quantum theory*.* Although this theory is in many respects in direct contradiction to the electromagnetic theory, the latter proved an invaluable guide in attacking such problems as the intensity and polarization of spectral lines. It also gave the first clue to the behavior of the lines when the source was placed in a magnetic field (Chap. 29). For the complete explanation of line spectra, however, the quantum theory is absolutely essential. We shall return to this subject in the final chapter.

Band spectra have also required the quantum theory for their complete explanation. Nevertheless, the electromagnetic treatment of the problem of molecular spectra was somewhat more successful. Certain series of bands are observed in the infrared which have frequencies and intensities related very closely like a fundamental and overtones. These are now known to be due to the vibration of the two nuclei in a diatomic molecule along the line joining them. The two branches of an individual band [Fig. 21J(e)] could be explained as due to rotation of the molecule about a direction perpendicular to the above line. Thus the electromagnetic theory predicts two combination frequencies, the sum and the difference of the frequencies of vibration and rotation. This theory, however, required a continuous distribution of frequencies in each branch, and was unable to explain the discrete lines.

That a continuous spectrum is obtained from liquids and solids can be understood from the fact that here the atoms are closer together than in a gas and exert forces on each other. Whereas in a gas the atoms are far apart and able to emit definite frequencies, these are so modified by

---

* For an elementary treatment of atomic spectra see H. E. White, "Introduction to Atomic Spectra," McGraw-Hill Book Company, Inc., New York, 1934. For a discussion of band spectra, see G. Herzberg, "Molecular Spectra and Molecular Structure. I. Diatomic Molecules," D. Van Nostrand Company, Inc., New York, 1950.

the mutual influence of the atoms in a solid that they are spread out into a continuous spectrum. The beginning of this effect is seen in the spectrum of a gas at a fairly high pressure. The lines become broadened because of the more frequent collisions and other influences mentioned below. This broadening increases with pressure, so that finally the lines merge into a continuous spectrum as the gas approaches the liquid state. On the electromagnetic theory, one can understand qualitatively the increase in the radiation from a solid with increase of temperature. The motions of the charged particles increase in amplitude as the substance becomes hotter, with a resultant increase in amplitude of the emitted waves. More rapid accelerations would cause the average wavelength to shift toward higher frequencies as the temperature is raised. Again, however, the quantum theory is required to explain the actual distribution of energy in different wavelengths. In fact, it was the attempt to derive Eq. 21e which first led Planck to make the revolutionary assumptions which constituted the foundations of this theory.

21.15. Breadth of Spectrum Lines. It was emphasized in Sec. 21.10 that lines in a spectrum are images of the slit. Hence narrowing the latter will sharpen the lines, and the sharpening may continue up to the limit set by diffraction (Sec. 15.7). Two causes may, however, prevent this theoretical limit from being reached. One of these is most important for small spectrographs of low dispersion, and the other for those of very high dispersion and resolution. The former cause includes the purely geometrical effects such as aberrations of the lenses, imperfections in the surfaces or in the homogeneity of the glass prisms, etc. But even if by proper design it were possible to eliminate these, and if diffraction were negligible, the lines would never approach an infinitesimal width. There is still a true, or *intrinsic, width* of the lines as emitted by the source, representing a small spread of wavelengths about the mean position of each line. Obviously this will be best revealed by instruments of high resolving power, such as a large grating or a Fabry-Perot interferometer. It is the cause of the decrease of visibility of the fringes in the Michelson interferometer with increasing path difference, which was discussed in Sec. 13.12.

There are three basically different effects contributing to the intrinsic line width:*

1. *Shortening of the wave trains.* As was indicated in Sec. 12.6, shorter trains are equivalent to a greater spread of frequencies. The shortening has two causes:

---

* A more quantitative and detailed discussion of line widths will be found in White, *op. cit.,* chap. 21.

a. Natural damping of the atomic oscillators resulting from the radiation of electromagnetic energy. On classical theory, the width due to this mechanism is 0.000116 Å for a line of any wavelength.

b. Collisions of atoms or molecules, which interrupt the emission of continuous waves.

In the optical region, *b* is usually much more important than *a*. Since collisions become more frequent as the pressure is raised, the broadening from this cause is usually called *pressure broadening*.

2. *Doppler effect*, resulting from the thermal motions of the atoms in the light source. Since the velocities are random in direction, and widely distributed in magnitude, the frequencies will be shifted both up and down by varying amounts. According to the kinetic theory, the width due to this cause is proportional to $\sqrt{T/M}$, where T is the absolute temperature and M the molecular weight. The constant of proportionality is $7.16 \times 10^{-7}\lambda$.

3. *Interatomic fields.* These may be due to the dipole moments of polar molecules, but they are usually the Coulomb fields of the ions in a discharge. In Chap. 29 we shall see that spectrum lines are split into several components by the action of a uniform electric field (Stark effect). Since the interatomic fields are non-uniform in both space and time, their effect is to merely broaden the lines. Sometimes called *Stark broadening*, this effect increases rapidly with the current density in a discharge.

Since a broadening due to any of the above causes is mathematically equivalent to a more rapid interruption of the wave trains, the separation of the second and third effects from the first is justified only by the fact that they are observed to vary in the predicted way with the physical conditions in the source.

PROBLEMS

1. A carbon filament can be run at 2600°C for a short time. Assuming carbon to radiate as a black body, find the wavelength at which the most energy is radiated from a filament at this temperature.

2. Find the total power in watts radiated from a metal sphere 2 mm in diameter, the sphere being maintained at a temperature of 2000°C. Take the absorptance of the surface to be 0.80, and independent of wavelength. *Ans.* 15.21 watts.

3. Consider two bodies in an enclosure at a uniform temperature. The nature and area of their surfaces need not necessarily be the same, and they may be semitransparent. From the experimental fact that they come to the same temperature as the surroundings, show by considering the energy emitted, absorbed, reflected, and transmitted by each that Kirchhoff's law of radiation must hold.

4. A black object becomes barely perceptible to the dark-adapted eye when its temperature reaches 400°C. Find the energy radiated per square centimeter per second in a wavelength interval of 10 Å at 7200 Å under this condition. Find the corresponding energy emitted at white heat (1800°C).

Ans. 2.46 × 10⁻⁴ erg. 1.26 × 10⁵ ergs.

5. Compare the width due to the Doppler effect of the lines due to helium and mercury. Compare also the Doppler widths of either one at 300C° and at the temperature of liquid nitrogen (−196°C).

6. A small prism spectrograph has a theoretical resolving power of 5200 at the wavelength of the sodium D lines. The prism limits the width of the refracted beam to 3.0 cm. The collimator and telescope lenses are each of 30 cm focal length, and the slit width is 0.02 mm. Compare the width of one of the D lines due to diffraction, due to finite slit width, and due to intrinsic width. For the latter, use the Doppler width for a sodium arc at 450°C. *Ans.* 0.012 mm. 0.020 mm. 0.000123 mm.

7. From the kinetic-theory equation for the collision frequency in a gas, compute the average length of the wave trains emitted by iron vapor at 4000°C and at pressures of (*a*) 1 mm Hg, (*b*) 760 mm Hg. Using the approximate relation between coherence length and line width given in Sec. 11.7, find the corresponding line widths at 5000 Å. Assume the effective collision diameter of an iron atom to be 2.5 × 10⁻⁸ cm.

CHAPTER 22

ABSORPTION AND SCATTERING

When a beam of light is passed through matter in the solid, liquid, or gaseous state, its propagation is affected in two important ways. In the first place, the intensity will always decrease to a greater or less extent as the light penetrates farther into the medium. In the second place, the velocity will be less in the medium than in free space. The loss of intensity is chiefly due to absorption, although under some circumstances scattering may play an important part. In this chapter we shall discuss the consequences of absorption and scattering, while the effect of the medium on the velocity, which comes under the term "dispersion," we shall consider in the following chapter. The term absorption as used in this chapter refers to the decrease of intensity of light as it passes through a substance (Sec. 11.5). It is important to distinguish this definition from that of absorptance, which was given in Sec. 21.8. The two terms refer to different physical quantities, but there are certain relations between them, as we shall now see.

22.1. General and Selective Absorption. A substance is said to show *general absorption* if it reduces the intensity of all wavelengths of light by nearly the same amount. For visible light this means that the transmitted light, as seen by the eye, shows no marked color. There is merely a reduction of the total intensity of the white light, and such substances therefore appear to be gray. No substance is known which absorbs all wavelengths equally, but some, such as suspensions of lamp black or thin semitransparent films of platinum, approach this condition over a fairly wide range of wavelengths.

By *selective absorption* is meant the absorption of certain wavelengths of light in preference to others. Practically all colored substances owe their color to the existence of selective absorption in some part or parts of the visible spectrum. Thus a piece of green glass absorbs completely the red and blue ends of the spectrum, the remaining portion in the transmitted light giving a resultant sensation of green to the eye. The colors of most natural objects such as paints, flowers, etc., are due to selective absorption. These objects are said to show pigment or *body color*, as distinguished from *surface color*, since their color is produced

446

by light which penetrates a certain distance into the substance. Then, by scattering or reflection, it is deviated and escapes from the surface, but only after it has traversed a certain thickness of the medium and has been robbed of the colors which are selectively absorbed. In all such cases the absorptance of the body will be proportional to its true absorption and will depend in the same way upon wavelength. Surface color, on the other hand, has its origin in the process of reflection at the surface itself (Sec. 22.7). Some substances, particularly metals like gold or copper, have a higher reflecting power for some colors than for others, and therefore show color by reflected light. The transmitted light here has the complementary color, whereas in body color the color is the same for the transmitted and reflected light. A thin gold foil, for example, looks yellow by reflection and blue green by transmission. As was mentioned in

FIG. 22A. Scattering of light by finely divided particles such as those in smoke.

Sec. 21.8, the body absorption of these materials is very high. This causes a high reflectance and a correspondingly low absorptance.

22.2. Distinction between Absorption and Scattering. In Fig. 22A let light of intensity I_0 enter a long glass cylinder filled with smoke. The intensity I of the beam emerging from the other end will be less than I_0. For a given density of smoke, experiment shows that I depends on the length d of the column according to the exponential law stated in Sec. 11.5, i.e.,

$$I = I_0 e^{-\alpha d} \tag{22a}$$

Here α is usually called the absorption coefficient, since it is a measure of the rate of loss of light from the direct beam. However, most of the decrease of intensity of I is in this case not due to a real disappearance of the light, but results from the fact that some light is *scattered* to one side by the smoke particles and thus removed from the direct beam. Even with a very dilute smoke, a considerable intensity I_s of scattered light may easily be detected by observing the tube from the side in a darkened room. Rays of sunlight seen to cross a room from a window are made visible by the fine suspended dust particles present in the air.

True *absorption* represents the actual disappearance of the light, the energy of which is converted into *heat motion* of the molecules of the absorbing material. This will occur to only a small extent in the above experiment, so that the name "absorption coefficient" for α is not appropriate in this case. In general, we can regard α as made up of two parts, α_a due to true absorption, and α_s due to scattering. Equation 22a then becomes

$$I = I_0 e^{-(\alpha_a + \alpha_s)d} \tag{22b}$$

In many cases either α_a or α_s may be negligible with respect to the other, but it is important to realize the existence of these two different processes and the fact that in many cases both may be operating.

22.3. Absorption by Solids and Liquids. If monochromatic light is passed through a certain thickness of a solid or of a liquid enclosed in a transparent cell, the intensity of the transmitted light may be much smaller than that of the incident light, owing to absorption. If the wavelength of the incident light is changed, the amount of absorption will also change to a greater or less extent. A simple way of investigating the amount of absorption for a wide range of wavelengths simultaneously

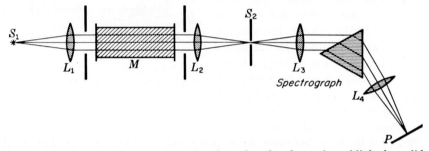

FIG. 22B. Experimental arrangement for observing the absorption of light by solids, liquids, or gases.

is illustrated in Fig. 22B. S_1 is a source which emits a continuous range of wavelengths, such as an ordinary tungsten-filament lamp. The light from this source is rendered parallel by the lens L_1 and traverses a certain thickness of the absorbing medium M. It is then focused by L_2 on the slit S_2 of a prism spectrograph, and the spectrum photographed on the plate P. If M is a "transparent" substance like glass or water, the part of the spectrum on P representing visible wavelengths will be perfectly continuous, as if M were not present. If M is colored, part of the spectrum will be blotted out, corresponding to the wavelengths removed by M, and we call this an *absorption band*. For solids and liquids, these bands are almost always continuous in character, fading off gradually at the ends. Examples of such absorption bands were shown in Fig. 21G(b).

Even a substance which is transparent to the visible region will show such selective absorption if the observations are extended far enough into the infrared or the ultraviolet region. Such an extension involves considerable experimental difficulty when a prism spectrograph is used, because the material of the prism and lenses (usually glass) may itself have strong selective absorption in these regions. Thus flint glass cannot be used much beyond 25,000 Å (or 2.5 μ) in the infrared, nor beyond about 3800 Å in the ultraviolet. Quartz will transmit somewhat farther in the infrared and much farther in the ultraviolet. Table 22-I shows the limits of the regions over which various transparent substances used for prisms will transmit an appreciable amount of light.

Prisms for infrared investigations are usually of rock salt, while for the ultraviolet quartz is most common. In an ultraviolet spectrograph, there is no advantage in using fluorite unless air is completely removed from the light path, because this begins to absorb strongly below 1850 Å. Also, specially prepared photographic plates must be used below this wavelength, since the gelatin of the emulsion by its absorption renders

TABLE 22-I

Substance	Limit of transmission, Å	
	Ultraviolet	Infrared
Crown glass.................	3500	20,000
Flint glass...................	3800	25,000
Quartz (SiO$_2$)...............	1800	40,000
Fluorite (CaF$_2$)..............	1250	95,000
Rock salt (NaCl).............	1750	145,000
Sylvin (KCl)................	1800	230,000
Lithium fluoride..............	1100	70,000

ordinary plates insensitive below about 2300 Å. In the infrared, photography can now be used as far as 13,000 Å, thanks to recently developed methods of sensitizing plates. Beyond this, an instrument based upon measurement of the heat produced, such as a thermopile, is usually used, although as far as 6 μ the *photoconductive cell*, utilizing the change of electrical resistance upon illumination, gives greater sensitivity.

When absorption measurements are extended over the whole electromagnetic spectrum, it is found that no substance exists which does not show strong absorption for some wavelengths. The metals exhibit general absorption, with a very minor dependence on wavelength in most cases. There are exceptions to this, however, as in the case of silver, which has a pronounced "transmission band" near 3160 Å (see Fig. 25N). A film of silver which is opaque to visible light may be almost entirely transparent to ultraviolet light of this wavelength. Dielectric materials, which are poor conductors of electricity, exhibit pronounced selective absorption which is most easily studied when scattering is avoided by having them in a homogeneous condition such as that of a single crystal, a liquid, or an amorphous solid. In a general way, it may be said that such substances are more or less transparent to X rays and γ rays, i.e., light waves of wavelength below about 10 Å. Proceeding toward longer wavelengths, we encounter a region of very strong absorption in the extreme ultraviolet, which in some cases may extend to the visible region, or beyond, and in others may stop somewhere in the near ultraviolet (see Table 22-I). In the infrared, further absorption bands are encountered, but these eventually give way to almost complete transparency in the region of radio waves. Thus for dielectrics we may usually expect three large regions of transparency, one at the shortest wavelengths, one at intermediate wavelengths (perhaps including the visible), and one at very long wavelengths. The limits of these regions vary a great deal in different substances, and one substance, such as water, may be transparent to the visible but opaque to the near infrared, while another, such as rubber, may be opaque to the visible but transparent to the infrared.

22.4. Absorption by Gases. The absorption spectra of all gases at ordinary pressures show narrow, dark lines. In certain cases it is also possible to find regions of continuous absorption (Sec. 21.12), but the outstanding characteristic of gaseous spectra is the presence of these sharp lines. If the gas is monatomic like helium or mercury vapor, the spectrum will be a true line spectrum, frequently showing clearly defined series. The number of lines in the absorption spectrum is invariably less than in the emission spectrum. For instance, in the case of the vapors of the alkali metals, only the lines of the principal series are observed under ordinary circumstances [Fig. $21H(i)$]. The absorption spectrum is therefore simpler than the emission spectrum. If the gas consists of diatomic or polyatomic molecules, the sharp lines form the rotational structure of the absorption bands characteristic of molecules. Here again the absorption spectrum is the simpler, and fewer bands are observed in absorption than in emission from the same gas [Fig. $21J(d)$].

22.5. Resonance and Fluorescence of Gases.* Let us consider what happens to the energy of incident light which has been removed by the gas. If true absorption exists, according to the definition of Sec. 22.2, this energy will all be changed into heat, and the gas will be somewhat warmed. Unless the pressure is very low, this is generally the case. After an atom or molecule has taken up energy from the light beam, it may collide with another particle, and an increase in the average velocity of the particles is brought about in such collisions. The length of time that an energized atom can exist as such before a collision is only about 10^{-7} or 10^{-8} sec, and unless a collision occurs before this time, the atom will get rid of its energy as radiation. At low pressures, where the time between the collisions is relatively long, the gas will become a secondary

---

* A comprehensive discussion of the various aspects of this subject is given in A. C. G. Mitchell and M. W. Zemansky, "Resonance Radiation and Excited Atoms," The Macmillan Company, New York, 1934.

source of radiation, and we do not have true absorption. The reemitted light in such cases usually has the same wavelength as the incident light, and is then termed resonance radiation (Sec. 21.11). This radiation was discovered and extensively investigated by R. W. Wood.* The origin of its name is clear, since as has been mentioned the phenomenon is analogous to the resonance of a tuning fork. Under some circumstances the reemitted light may have a longer wavelength than the incident light. This effect is called *fluorescence*. In either resonance or fluorescence, some of the light is removed from the direct beam and dark lines will be produced in the spectrum of the transmitted light. Resonance and fluorescence are not to be classed as scattering. This distinction will be made clear in Sec. 22.12.

Resonance radiation from a gas can readily be demonstrated by the use of a sodium-arc lamp. A small lump of metallic sodium is placed in a glass bulb connected to a vacuum pump. The sodium is distilled from one part of the bulb to another by heating with a bunsen burner, thus liberating the large quantities of hydrogen always contained in this metal. After a high vacuum is attained, the bulb is sealed off and the light of the arc is focused by a lens on the bulb. The bulb must of course be observed from the side in a dark room. On gently warming the sodium with the flame, a cone of yellow light defining the path of the incident light will be seen. At higher temperatures, the glowing cone becomes shorter, and eventually is seen merely as a thin bright skin on the inner surface of the glass.

Fluorescence of a gas is most easily shown with iodine vapor, which consists of diatomic molecules, I_2. White light from a carbon arc will produce a greenish cone of light when focused in a bulb containing iodine vapor in vacuum at room temperature. A still more interesting experiment can be performed by using monochromatic light from a mercury arc, as shown in Fig. 22C. The source of light is a long horizontal arc A, which is enclosed in a box with a long slot cut in the top parallel to the arc. Immediately above this is a glass tube B filled with water. This acts as a cylindrical lens to concentrate the light along the axis of tube C, containing the iodine vapor in vacuum. The fluorescent light from the vapor is observed with a spectroscope pointed at the plane window on the end of tube C. The other end is tapered and painted black to prevent reflected light from entering the spectroscope, and a screen with a circular hole placed close to the window helps in this respect. A polished reflector R laid over C increases the intensity of

* R. W. Wood (1868–1955). Professor of experimental physics at the Johns Hopkins University. He pioneered in many fields of physical optics and also became one of the most colorful figures in American physics. His discoveries in optics are contained in his excellent text "Physical Optics."

illumination. If B contains a solution of potassium dichromate and neodymium sulfate, only the green line of mercury, $\lambda5461$, is transmitted. Figure $22D(b)$ and (c) were reproduced from a spectrogram taken in this way, though with water in the tube B. Beside the lines of the ordinary mercury spectrum (marked by dots in the figure) which are present as a result of ordinary reflection or Rayleigh scattering (Sec. 22.10), one observes a series of almost equally spaced lines extending toward the red from the green line. These represent the fluorescent light of modified wavelength.

FIG. 22C. Experimental arrangement for observing the fluorescence of iodine vapor with excitation by monochromatic light.

22.6. Fluorescence of Solids and Liquids. If a solid or a liquid is strongly illuminated by light which it is capable of absorbing, it may reemit fluorescent light. According to *Stokes' law*, the wavelength of the fluorescent light is always longer than that of the absorbed light. A solution of fluorescein in water will absorb the blue portion of white light and will fluoresce with light of a greenish hue. Thus a beam of white light traversing the solution becomes visible through emission of green light when observed from the side but is reddish when looked at from the end. Certain solids show a persistence of the reemitted light, so that it lasts several seconds or even minutes after the incident light is turned off. This is called *phosphorescence*.

Very striking fluorescent effects may be produced by illuminating various objects with ultraviolet light from a mercury arc. A special nickel oxide glass can be obtained which is almost entirely opaque to visible light but transmits freely the strong group of mercury lines near $\lambda3650$. If only this light from the arc comes through the glass, many organic as well as inorganic substances are rendered visible almost exclusively by their fluorescent light. The teeth when illuminated by ultraviolet light will appear unnaturally bright, but artificial teeth look perfectly black.

22.7. Selective Reflection. Residual Rays. Substances are said to show selective reflection when certain wavelengths are reflected much more strongly than others. This usually occurs at those wavelengths for which the medium possesses very strong absorption. We are speaking now of dielectric substances, i.e., those which are nonconductors of

FIG. 22D. Photographs of (a) mercury-arc spectrum; (b) fluorescence spectrum of iodine; (c) enlarged section of (b); (d) Raman spectrum of hydrogen (*after Rasetti*); (e) Raman spectrum of liquid carbon tetrachloride (*after M. Jeppeson*); (f) mercury arc.

electricity. The case of metals is rather different and will be considered later in Chap. 25. That there is an intimate connection between selective reflection, absorption, and resonance radiation may be seen from an interesting observation made by R. W. Wood with mercury vapor. At a pressure of a small fraction of a millimeter, mercury vapor shows the phenomenon of resonance radiation when illuminated by λ2536 from a mercury arc. As the pressure of the vapor is increased, the resonance radiation becomes more and more concentrated toward the surface of the vapor where the incident radiation enters, i.e., on the inner wall of the enclosing vessel. Finally, at a sufficiently high pressure, the secondary radiation ceases to be visible except when viewed at an angle corresponding to the law of reflection. At this angle fully 25 per cent of the incident light is reflected in the ordinary way, the remainder having been absorbed and transformed into heat by atomic collisions.   However, this high reflection, which is comparable to that of metals in this region, exists only for the particular wavelength λ2536.   Other wavelengths are freely transmitted.   In this experiment we evidently have a continuous transition from resonance radiation to selective reflection.

A few solids which have strong absorption bands in the visible region also show selective reflection.   The dye fuchsine is an example.   Such substances have a peculiar metallic sheen by reflected light and are strongly colored.   Their color is due to the very high reflection of a

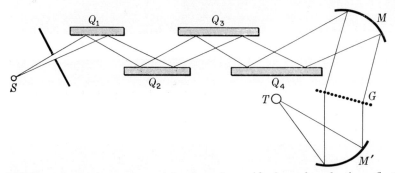

Fig. 22E. Experimental arrangement for observing residual rays by selective reflection.

certain band of wavelengths—so high that it is frequently termed "metallic" reflection.   It is this type of reflection that is responsible for surface color (Sec. 22.1).

The most important application of selective reflection has been its use in locating absorption bands which lie far in the infrared.   For example, quartz is found to reflect 80 to 90 per cent of radiation having a wavelength of about 8.5 μ, or 85,000 Å.   The method of *residual rays* for isolating a narrow band of wavelengths is based upon this fact.*   In Fig. 22E, S is a thermal source of radiation, giving a continuous spectrum. After reflection from the four quartz plates Q_1 to Q_4, the radiation is analyzed by means of a wire grating G and thermopile T.   It is found to consist almost entirely of the wavelength 8.5 μ.   Supposing this wavelength to be 90 per cent reflected at each quartz surface, and other wavelengths 4 per cent reflected, we have, after four reflections $(0.9)^4 = 0.66$ of the former remaining, but only $(0.04)^4 = 0.0000026$ of the latter.   The wavelengths of the residual rays of many substances have been measured in this way.   Among the longest wavelengths measured are those from sodium chloride, potassium chloride, and rubidium chloride at 52 μ, 63 μ, and 74 μ, respectively.

* For more extensive material on this subject, see R. W. Wood, "Physical Optics," 3d ed., pp. 516–519, The Macmillan Company, New York, 1934.

22.8. Theory of the Connection between Absorption and Reflection.
In Sec. 21.11 we mentioned briefly the mechanism postulated in the
electromagnetic theory for the production of resonance radiation. It is
assumed that light waves are incident upon matter which contains
bound charges capable of vibrating with a natural frequency equal to
that of the impressed wave. Thus a charge e is acted upon by the
electric field **E** with a force eE, and if **E** varies with a frequency exactly
matching that with which the charged particle would normally vibrate,
a large amplitude may be produced. As a result, the charged particle
will reradiate an electromagnetic wave of the same frequency. In a
gas at low pressure, where the atoms are relatively far apart, the frequency which can be absorbed will be sharply defined, and there will
be no systematic relation between the phases of the light reemitted from
different particles. The observed intensity from N particles will then
be just N times that due to one particle (Sec. 12.4). This is the case
with resonance radiation.

If, on the other hand, the particles are close together and interacting
strongly with each other, as in a liquid or solid, the absorption will not
be limited to a sharply defined frequency but will spread over a considerable range. The result is that the phases of the reemitted light
from adjacent particles will agree. This will give rise to regular reflection, since the various secondary waves from the atoms in the surface
will cooperate to produce a reflected wave front traveling off at an angle
equal to the angle of incidence. In fact, this is just the conception used
in applying Huygens' principle to prove the law of reflection. Hence
selective reflection is also a phenomenon of resonance, and occurs strongly
near those wavelengths corresponding to natural frequencies of the bound
charges in the substance. The substance will not transmit light of these
wavelengths; instead it reflects strongly. True absorption, or the conversion of the light energy into heat, may also occur to a greater or less
extent because of the large amplitudes of the vibrating charges which
are here involved. If absorption were entirely absent, the reflecting
power would be 100 per cent at the wavelengths in question.

22.9. Scattering by Small Particles. The lateral scattering of a beam
of light as it traverses a cloud of fine suspended matter was mentioned
in Sec. 22.2. That this phenomenon is closely connected both with
reflection and with diffraction may be seen by consideration of Fig. 22F.
In (a) is shown a parallel beam consisting of plane waves advancing
toward the right and striking a small plane reflecting surface. The successive wave fronts drawn are one wavelength apart, so that here the
size of the reflector is somewhat greater than a wavelength. The light
coming off from the surface of the reflector is produced by the vibration
of the electric charges in the surface with a definite phase relation, and

the spherical wavelets produced by these vibrations cooperate to produce short segments of plane wave fronts. These are not sharply bounded at their edges by the reflected rays from the edges of the mirror (dotted lines) but spread out somewhat, owing to diffraction. In fact, the distribution of the intensity of the reflected light with angle is just that derived in Sec. 15.2 for the light transmitted by a single slit. The width of the reflector here takes the place of the slit width, so that we shall have greater spreading the smaller the width of the reflector relative to the wavelength.

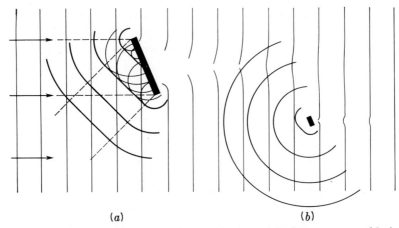

(a)　　　　　　　　　　　　　　　(b)

Fig. 22F. The reflection and diffraction of light by small objects comparable in size with the wavelength of light.

In (b) of the figure, the reflector is much smaller than a wavelength, and here the spreading is so great that the reflected waves differ very little from uniform spherical waves. In this case the light taken from the primary beam is said to be scattered, rather than reflected, since the law of reflection has ceased to be applicable. Scattering is therefore a special case of diffraction. The wave scattered from an object much smaller than a wavelength of light will be spherical, regardless of whether or not the object has the plane form assumed in Fig. 22F(b). This follows from the fact that there can be no interference between the wavelets emitted by the several points on the surface of the scattering particle, inasmuch as the extreme points are separated by a distance much less than the wavelength.

The first quantitative study of the laws of scattering by small particles was made in 1871 by Rayleigh,* and such scattering is frequently called

* Several interesting papers laying the foundation of the theory will be found in "The Scientific Papers of Lord Rayleigh," vols. 1 and 4, Cambridge University Press, New York, 1912.

Rayleigh scattering. The mathematical investigation of the problem gave a general law for the intensity of the scattered light, applicable to any particles of index of refraction different from that of the surrounding medium. The only restriction is that the linear dimensions of the particles be considerably smaller than the wavelength. As we might expect, the scattered intensity is found to be proportional to the incident intensity and to the square of the volume of the scattering particle.

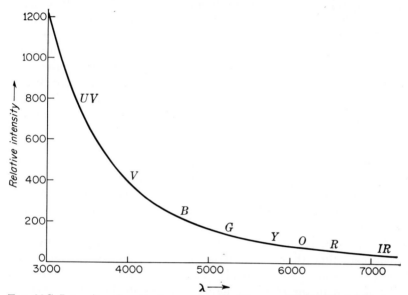

FIG. 22G. Intensity of scattering vs. wavelength according to Rayleigh's law.

The most interesting result, however, is the dependence of scattering on wavelength. With a given size of the particles, long waves would be expected to be less effectively scattered than short ones, because the particles present obstructions to the waves which are smaller *compared with the wavelength* for long waves than for short ones. In fact, as will be proved in Sec. 22.13, the intensity is proportional to $1/\lambda^4$. Since red light, $\lambda7200$, has a wavelength 1.8 times as great as violet light, $\lambda4000$, the law predicts $(1.8)^4$ or 10 times greater scattering for the violet light from particles much smaller than the wavelength of either color. Figure 22G gives a quantitative plot of this relation.

If white light is scattered from sufficiently fine particles, such as those in tobacco smoke, the scattered light always has a bluish color. If the size of the particles is increased until they are no longer small compared to the wavelength, the light becomes white, as a result of ordinary diffuse reflection from the surface of the particles. The blue color seen with very small particles, and its dependence on the size of the particles, were first studied experimentally by Tyndall,* and his name is often associated with the phenomenon. Chalk dust from an eraser, falling across a beam of light from a carbon arc, will illustrate very effectively the white light scattered by large particles.

22.10. Molecular Scattering. Blue Color of the Sky. If a strong beam of sunlight is caused to traverse a pure liquid which has been carefully prepared to be as free as possible of all suspended particles of dust, etc., observation in a dark room will show that there is a small amount of bluish light scattered laterally from the beam. Although some of this light is still due to microscopic particles in suspension, which seem to be almost impossible to eliminate entirely, a certain amount appears to be attributable to the scattering by individual molecules of the liquid. At first sight it is surprising to find that the scattering from liquids is so feeble, in view of the large concentration of molecules present. It is, in fact, much weaker than the scattering from the same number of molecules of a gas. In the latter, the molecules are randomly distributed in space, and in any direction except the forward one the waves scattered by different molecules have perfectly random phases. Thus for N molecules the resultant intensity is just N times that scattered from any individual one (see Sec. 12.4). In a liquid, and even more so in a solid, the spacial distribution has a certain degree of regularity. Furthermore, the forces between molecules act to destroy the independence of phases (Sec. 22.8). The result is that the scattering from liquids and solids in directions other than forward is very weak indeed. The forward-scattered waves are strong and play an essential part in determining the velocity of light in the medium, as we shall see in the following chapter.

Lateral scattering from gases is also weak, but here the weakness is due to the relatively smaller number of scattering centers. When a great thickness of gas is available, however, as in our atmosphere, the scattered light is easily observed. It has been shown by Rayleigh that practically all the light that we see in a clear sky is due to scattering by the molecules of air. If it were not for our atmosphere, the sky would look perfectly black. Actually, molecular scattering causes a considerable amount of light to reach the observer in directions making an angle with that of the direct sunlight, and thus the sky appears bright. Its blue color is the result of the greater scattering of short waves. Rayleigh measured the relative amount of light of different wavelengths in sky light and found rather close agreement with the $1/\lambda^4$ law. The same phenomenon is responsible for the red color of the sun and surrounding sky at sunset. In this case, the scattering removes the blue

---

* John Tyndall (1820–1893). British "natural philosopher," after 1867 superintendent of the Royal Institution and colleague of Faraday. Tyndall was outstanding for his ability to popularize and clarify physical discoveries.

rays from the direct beam more effectively than the red, and the very great thickness of the atmosphere traversed gives the transmitted light its intense red hue. An experiment demonstrating both the blue of the sky and the red of the sun at sunset is described in Sec. 24.15.

22.11. Raman* Effect. This is a scattering with change of wavelength somewhat similar to fluorescence. It differs from fluorescence, however, in two important respects. In the first place, the light which is incident on the scattering material must have a wavelength that does not correspond to one of the absorption lines or bands of the material. Otherwise we obtain fluorescence, as in the experiment of Sec. 22.5, where the green line of mercury is absorbed by the iodine vapor. In the second place, the intensity of the light scattered in the Raman effect is much less intense than most fluorescent light. For this reason the Raman effect is rather difficult to detect, and observations must usually be made by photography.

The apparatus illustrated in Fig. 22C is well adapted to observations of the Raman effect.† For this purpose, a liquid or gas which is transparent to the incident light must be used in the tube C. It is convenient to fill tube B with a saturated solution of sodium nitrite, since this absorbs the ultraviolet lines of the mercury arc but transmits the blue-violet line $\lambda4358$ with great intensity. Figure $22D(e)$ shows the Raman spectrum of CCl_4. It will be seen that the same pattern of Raman lines is excited by each of the strong mercury lines. Figure $22D(d)$ illustrates the Raman spectrum of gaseous hydrogen, showing two sets of lines on the side toward the red of the exciting line, which in this case was $\lambda2536$. Occasionally still fainter lines are seen on the violet side, two of which are visible in (d) and three in (e). This is also sometimes observed in the case of fluorescence. Since the modified light in these lines has a shorter wavelength than the incident light, they represent a violation of Stokes' law (Sec. 22.6) and are called *anti-Stokes* lines.

22.12. Theory of Scattering. When an electromagnetic wave passes over a small elastically bound charged particle, the particle will be set into motion by the electric field **E**. In Sec. 22.8 we considered the case where the frequency of the wave was equal to the natural frequency of free vibration of the particle. We then obtain resonance and fluorescence under certain conditions, and selective reflection under others. In both cases there may exist a considerable amount of absorption. Scattering,

---

* C. V. Raman (1888–   ). Professor at the University of Calcutta. He was awarded the Nobel prize in 1930 for his work on scattering and for the discovery of the effect that bears his name.

† For a description of the most efficient ways of observing Raman spectra, see G. R. Harrison, R. C. Lord, and J. R. Loofbourow, "Practical Spectroscopy," 1st ed., Prentice-Hall, Inc., Englewood Cliffs, New Jersey, 1948.

on the other hand, takes place for frequencies not corresponding to the natural frequencies of the particles. The resulting motion of the particles is then one of *forced vibration.* If the particle is bound by a force obeying Hooke's law, this vibration will have the same frequency and direction as that of the electric force in the wave. Its amplitude, however, will be very much smaller than that which would be produced by resonance. Hence the amplitude of the scattered wave will be much less, and this accounts for the relative faintness of molecular scattering. The phase of the forced vibration will differ from that of the incident wave, and this fact is responsible for difference of the velocity of light in the medium from that in free space. Thus scattering forms the basis of dispersion, which is to be discussed in the following chapter.

The electromagnetic theory is also capable of giving a qualitative picture of the changes of wavelength which occur in the Raman effect and in fluorescence. If the charged oscillator is bound by a force which does not obey Hooke's law, but some more complicated law, it will be capable of reradiating not only the impressed frequency, but also various combinations of this frequency with the fundamental and overtone frequencies of the oscillator. For the complete explanation of these phenomena, however, the electromagnetic theory alone is not adequate. It cannot explain the actual magnitudes of the changes in frequency nor the fact that these are predominantly toward lower frequencies. For this, the quantum theory is required.

Rayleigh scattering yields a characteristic distribution of intensity in different directions with respect to that of the primary beam. The scattered light is also strongly polarized. These features are in general agreement with the predictions of the electromagnetic theory. We shall not discuss them, however, until we have taken up the subject of polarization (see Sec. 24.15).

22.13. Scattering and Refractive Index. The fact that the velocity of light in matter differs from that in vacuum is a consequence of scattering. The individual molecules scatter a certain part of the light falling on them, and the resulting scattered waves *interfere* with the primary wave, bringing about a change of phase which is equivalent to an alteration of the wave velocity. This process will be discussed in more detail in the chapter which follows, but here some simplified considerations may be used to show the connection between scattering and refractive index.

In Fig. 22H plane waves are shown striking an infinitely wide sheet of a transparent material, the thickness of which is small compared to the wavelength. Let the electric vector in this incident wave have unit amplitude, so that in the exponential notation (Sec. 14.8) it may be represented at a particular time by $E = e^{ikx}$. If the fraction of the wave that is scattered is small, the disturbance reaching some point P will be essentially the original wave, plus a small contribution due to the light scattered by all the atoms in the thin lamina. To evaluate the latter, we note that its intensity is proportional to the coefficient α_s of Eq. 22b. This measures the fractional decrease of intensity by scattering in traversing the small thickness t, to which the scattered intensity must be proportional. We therefore have

FIG. 22H. Geometry of scattering by a thin lamina.

$$-\frac{dI}{I} = \alpha_s t \sim I_s \quad (22c)$$

The intensity scattered by a single atom, since there are Nt atoms per unit area of the lamina, becomes

$$I_1 \sim \frac{\alpha_s t}{Nt} = \frac{\alpha_s}{N}$$

and the amplitude

$$E_1 \sim \sqrt{\frac{\alpha_s}{N}}$$

These relations hold if the scattered waves from the different centers are noncoherent, as is true for the smoke particles discussed in Sec. 22.2. The present case of Rayleigh scattering in the forward direction must be taken as *coherent*, however, so that all waves leave the scatterer in phase with each other. Then we must add amplitudes instead of intensities, and the total scattered amplitude

$$E_s \sim Nt \sqrt{\frac{\alpha_s}{N}} = t \sqrt{\alpha_s N}$$

The complex amplitude at P is obtained by integrating this quantity over the surface of the lamina, and adding it to the amplitude of the primary wave. The resultant then becomes

$$E + E_s = e^{ikR_0} + t \sqrt{\alpha_s N} \int_0^\infty \frac{2\pi r \, dr}{R} e^{ikR}$$

where the factor $1/R$ enters because of the inverse-square law. Now since $R^2 = R_0{}^2 + r^2$, we have $r \, dr = R \, dR$, and the integral may be written

$$\int_0^\infty \frac{2\pi}{R} e^{ikR} r \, dr = 2\pi \int_{R_0}^\infty e^{ikR} \, dR = \frac{2\pi}{ik} [e^{ikR}]_{R_0}^\infty$$

Since the wave trains always have a finite length, the scattering as $R \rightarrow \infty$

can contribute nothing to the coherent wave. Substituting the lower limit of the integral, we find

$$E + E_s = e^{ikR_0} - t \sqrt{\alpha_s N} \frac{\lambda}{i} e^{ikR_0}$$

$$= e^{ikR_0} + t \sqrt{\alpha_s N} \, i\lambda e^{ikR_0}$$

$$= e^{ikR_0}(1 + i\lambda t \sqrt{\alpha_s N})$$

By our original assumption, the second term in parentheses is small compared with the first. These will be recognized as the first two terms in the expansion of $e^{i\lambda t \sqrt{\alpha_s N}}$, and may here be equated to it, giving

$$E + E_s = e^{ikR_0} e^{i\lambda t \sqrt{\alpha_s N}} = e^{i(kR_0 + \lambda t \sqrt{\alpha_s N})}$$

Thus the phase of the wave at P has been altered by the amount $\lambda t \sqrt{\alpha_s N}$. But we know (Sec. 13.15) that the presence of a lamina of thickness t and refractive index n gives a phase retardation of $(2\pi/\lambda)(n - 1)t$. Hence

$$\lambda t \sqrt{\alpha_s N} = \frac{2\pi}{\lambda}(n - 1)t$$

and finally

$$n - 1 = \frac{\lambda^2}{2\pi} \sqrt{\alpha_s N} \qquad (22d)$$

This important relation contains Rayleigh's law of scattering (Sec. 22.9). Since, by Eq. 22c, I_s is proportional to α_s, this scattered intensity varies as $1/\lambda^4$, assuming n to be independent of wavelength. In our derivation no absorption has been considered, so that the equation is valid only for wavelengths well away from any absorption bands. In the next chapter we shall see how the refractive index behaves as the wavelength approaches that of an absorption band.

PROBLEMS

1. A certain medium has absorption and scattering coefficients α_a and α_s of 0.070 and 0.023 m^{-1}, respectively. What fraction of the incident light is transmitted by 50 m of the medium, and what fraction appears as scattered light?

2. A tube of smoke 30 cm long transmits 60 per cent of the incident light. After precipitation of the smoke particles, it transmits 92 per cent. Calculate the values of the absorption and scattering coefficients. *Ans.* 0.0028 cm^{-1}. 0.0142 cm^{-1}.

3. The average lifetime of a sodium atom in the excited state ^2P, from which it emits the sodium resonance lines, is 1.6×10^{-8} sec. When nitrogen is added to sodium vapor at low pressure, the resonance radiation is quenched by collisions. If the effective collision diameter of a sodium atom with a nitrogen molecule is 7.0×10^{-8} cm, at what pressure does the time between collisions become equal to the above mean lifetime?

4. According to the data given in this chapter, are the residual rays from potassium chloride transmitted by rock salt? *Ans.* No.

5. Calculate the ratio of the intensities of Rayleigh scattering for the two mercury lines λ2536 and λ5461.

6. Photographers know that a yellow filter will "cut" the bluish haze of scattered light and give better contrast in a landscape. Assuming the spectral composition shown in Fig. 22G, what fraction of the scattered light is removed by a filter that absorbs all wavelengths below 4500 Å? Transmission of the camera lens and film sensitivity limit the normal spectral range of the camera to 3900 to 6000 Å.

Ans. About 49%.

7. Calculate the lateral dimensions of the two objects illustrated in Fig. 22F, assuming that the waves have the value of λ appropriate to the green mercury line.

8. The residual rays after five reflections from a certain crystal are 7×10^4 times stronger than radiation of adjacent wavelengths. Taking the reflectance at the latter wavelengths to be 3.5 per cent, what must be its value at the center of the absorption band? *Ans.* 32.6%.

9. The common material for green eyeshades looks red when doubled over so that one is observing through twice the normal thickness. This effect, known as *dichromatism*, is due to the presence of two absorption bands with different absorption coefficients. Where would these absorption bands have to lie in the above case, and which must have the greater coefficient?

10. Equation 22d is frequently written in terms of the *scattering cross section* $\sigma = \alpha_s/N$, which represents the area of a single atom or molecule that is effective in scattering light. Taking the refractive index n_D for carbon dioxide under standard conditions to be 1.00045, compute the value of σ for CO_2. *Ans.* 9.18×10^{-28} cm².

11. According to Eq. 22d, how should the intensity of the light scattered by a gas depend on the pressure of the gas, at constant temperature? Assume the Lorentz-Lorenz law (Sec. 13.15) for the dependence of n on density.

12. The simplest form of dispersion theory, which postulates the existence in each atom of a single oscillating charge e of mass m and natural frequency ν_0, yields

$$n - 1 = \frac{N}{2\pi} \frac{e^2/m}{\nu_0^2 - \nu^2}$$

Assuming Rayleigh's scattering law, find the scattering coefficient α_s at λ5000 for a gas under standard conditions, if the wavelength corresponding to its natural frequency is 1500 Å. *Ans.* 2.09×10^{-8} cm⁻¹.

13. According to the electromagnetic theory, the theoretically significant quantity measuring the energy scattered in all directions per unit energy density of the incident beam is $8\pi\alpha_s/3$. Compute this "scattering coefficient" for helium at 100 atm, given that $n - 1$ is 3.6×10^{-3} and $\lambda = 5892$ Å.

DISPERSION

The subject of dispersion concerns the velocity of light in material substances, and its variation with wavelength. Since the velocity is c/n, any change in refractive index n entails a corresponding change of velocity. We have seen in Sec. 1.7 that the dispersion of color which occurs upon refraction at a boundary between two different substances is direct evidence of the dependence of the n's on wavelength. In fact, measurements of the deviations of several spectral lines by a prism furnish the most accurate means of determining the refractive index, and hence the velocity, as a function of wavelength.

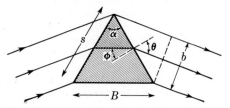

FIG. 23A. Refraction by a prism at minimum deviation.

23.1. Dispersion of a Prism. When a ray traverses a prism, as shown in Fig. 23A, we can measure with a spectrometer the angles of emergence θ of the various wavelengths. The rate of change, $d\theta/d\lambda$, is called the *angular dispersion* of the prism. It can be conveniently represented as the product of two factors, by writing

$$\frac{d\theta}{d\lambda} = \frac{d\theta}{dn}\frac{dn}{d\lambda} \qquad (23a)$$

The first factor may be evaluated by geometrical considerations alone, while the second is a characteristic property of the prism material, usually referred to simply as its *dispersion*. Before considering the latter quantity, let us evaluate the geometrical factor $d\theta/dn$ for a prism, in the special case of minimum deviation.

For a given angle of incidence on the second face of the prism, we may differentiate Snell's law of refraction $n = \sin \theta/\sin \phi$, regarding $\sin \phi$ as a constant. We obtain

$$\frac{d\theta}{dn} = \frac{\sin \phi}{\cos \theta}$$

This is not, however, the value to be used in Eq. 23a, which requires the rate of change of θ for a fixed direction of the rays incident on the *first* face. Because of the symmetry in the case of minimum deviation, it is obvious that equal deviations occur at the two faces, so that the total rate of change of will be just twice the above value. We then have

$$\frac{d\theta}{dn} = \frac{2 \sin \phi}{\cos \theta} = \frac{2 \sin (\alpha/2)}{\cos \theta}$$

where α is the refracting angle of the prism. The result becomes still simpler when expressed in terms of lengths rather than angles. Designating by s, B, and b the lengths shown in Fig. 23A, we may write

$$\frac{d\theta}{dn} = \frac{2s \sin (\alpha/2)}{s \cos \theta} = \frac{B}{b} \tag{23b}$$

Hence the required geometrical factor is just the ratio of the base of the prism to the linear aperture of the emergent beam, a quantity not far different from unity. The angular dispersion becomes

$$\frac{d\theta}{d\lambda} = \frac{B}{b} \frac{dn}{d\lambda} \tag{23c}$$

In connection with this equation, it is to be noted that the equation for the chromatic resolving power (Eq. 15h) follows very simply from it upon the substitution of λ/b for $d\theta$.

23.2. Normal Dispersion. In considering the second factor in Eq. 23a, let us start by reviewing some of the known facts about the variation of n with λ. Measurements for some typical kinds of glass give the results shown in Table 23-I. If any set of values of n is plotted against wave-

TABLE 23-I. REFRACTIVE INDICES AND DISPERSIONS FOR SEVERAL COMMON TYPES OF OPTICAL GLASS (UNIT OF DISPERSION, $1/\text{Å}$)

Wave-length, λ, in Å	Telescope crown		Borosilicate crown		Barium flint		Vitreous quartz	
	n	$-\dfrac{dn}{d\lambda}$	n	$-\dfrac{dn}{d\lambda}$	n	$-\dfrac{dn}{d\lambda}$	n	$-\dfrac{dn}{d\lambda}$
C 6563	1.52441	0.35×10^{-5}	1.50883	0.31×10^{-5}	1.58848	0.38×10^{-5}	1.45640	0.27×10^{-5}
6439	1.52490	0.36×10^{-5}	1.50917	0.32×10^{-5}	1.58896	0.39×10^{-5}	1.45674	0.28×10^{-5}
D 5890	1.52704	0.43×10^{-5}	1.51124	0.41×10^{-5}	1.59144	0.50×10^{-5}	1.45845	0.35×10^{-5}
5338	1.52989	0.58×10^{-5}	1.51386	0.55×10^{-5}	1.59463	0.68×10^{-5}	1.46067	0.45×10^{-5}
5086	1.53146	0.66×10^{-5}	1.51534	0.63×10^{-5}	1.59644	0.78×10^{-5}	1.46191	0.52×10^{-5}
F 4861	1.53303	0.78×10^{-5}	1.51690	0.72×10^{-5}	1.59825	0.89×10^{-5}	1.46318	0.60×10^{-5}
G' 4340	1.53790	1.12×10^{-5}	1.52136	1.00×10^{-5}	1.60367	1.23×10^{-5}	1.46690	0.84×10^{-5}
H 3988	1.54245	1.39×10^{-5}	1.52546	1.26×10^{-5}	1.60870	1.72×10^{-5}	1.47030	1.12×10^{-5}

length, a curve like one of those in Fig. 23B is obtained. The curves found for prisms of different optical materials will differ in detail but will all have the same general shape. These curves are representative

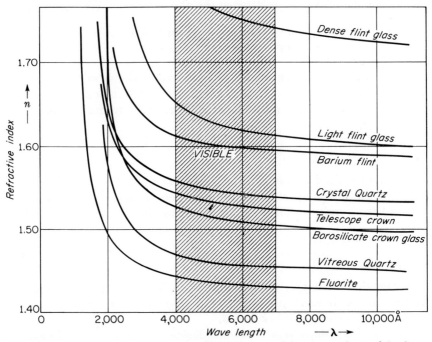

FIG. 23B. Dispersion curves for several different materials commonly used for lenses and prisms.

of *normal dispersion*, for which the following important facts are to be noted:

1. *The index of refraction increases as the wavelength decreases.*
2. *The rate of increase becomes greater at shorter wavelengths.*
3. *For different substances the curve at a given wavelength is usually steeper the larger the index of refraction.*
4. *The curve for one substance cannot in general be obtained from that for another substance by a mere change in the scale of the ordinates.*

The first of these facts agrees with the common observation that in refraction by a transparent substance the violet is more deviated than the red. The second fact can also be expressed by saying that the dispersion increases with decreasing wavelength. This follows because the dispersion, $dn/d\lambda$ is the slope of the curve (its negative sign is usually disregarded), which increases regularly toward smaller λ. An important consequence of this behavior of the dispersion is that in the spectrum formed by a prism the violet end of the spectrum is spread out on a much larger scale than the red end.   The spectrum is therefore far from being a normal spectrum (Sec. 17.6).   This will be clear from Fig. 23C, in which the spectrum of helium is shown diagrammatically as given by flint- and crown-glass prisms and by a grating used under the proper conditions to give a normal spectrum.   In the prism spectra the wavelength scale is compressed toward the red end, as can be seen by comparison with the uniform scale of the normal spectrum.

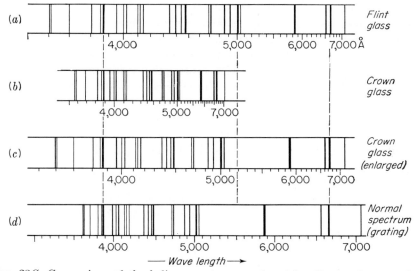

FIG. 23C. Comparison of the helium spectrum produced by flint- and crown-glass prism spectrographs with a normal spectrum.

The third fact stated above requires that for a substance of higher index of refraction, the dispersion $dn/d\lambda$ shall also be greater.   Thus, comparing (a) and (b) in Fig. 23C, the flint glass has the higher index of refraction, and gives a longer spectrum because of its greater dispersion. To compare the *relative* spacing of the lines in (b) with those in (a), the spectrum from crown glass has been enlarged, in (c), to have the same over-all length between the two lines λ3888 and λ6678.   When this is done, it is seen that there is not complete agreement with the lines of (a).   In fact, the spectra from prisms of different substances will never agree exactly in the relative spacing of their spectrum lines.   This is a consequence of the fourth of the above facts, according to which the shape of the dispersion curve is different for every substance.   The curve for flint glass in Fig. 23B has a greater slope at the violet end, relative to that in the red, than does the curve for crown glass.   Consequently, the dispersion of different substances is said to be *irrational*, since there is no simple relation between the different curves.

All transparent substances which are not colored show normal dispersion in the visible region. The magnitude of the index of refraction may be quite different in various substances, but its change with wavelength always shows the characteristics described above.   In general, the greater the density of the substance the higher its index of refraction and its dispersion. For example, flint glass has a density around 2.8, considerably higher than 2.4 for ordinary crown glass. Water has a smaller n and $dn/d\lambda$, while in a very light substance like air n is practically unity and $dn/d\lambda$ very nearly zero.   For air $n = 1.000276$ for red light (Fraunhofer's C line), rising to only 1.000279 for blue light (F line).   This rule relating density to index of refraction is only a qualitative one, and many exceptions are known. For instance, ether has a higher index than water (1.36 as compared with 1.33), yet it is less dense, as is shown by the fact that ether floats on the surface of water. Similarly, the correlation of high dispersion with high index is only rough, and there are exceptions to the third rule listed above.   Diamond has a density of 3.52 and one of the highest known indices of refraction, varying from 2.4100 for the C line to 2.4354 for the F line. The difference in these values, which is a measure of the dispersion, is only 0.0254, whereas a dense flint glass may give as much as 0.05 for the same quantity.

23.3. Cauchy's Equation.   The first successful attempt to represent the curve of normal dispersion by an equation was made by Cauchy in 1836. His equation may be written

$$n = A + \frac{B}{\lambda^2} + \frac{C}{\lambda^4}$$

where A, B, and C are constants which are characteristic of any one substance. This equation represents the curves in the visible region, such as those shown in Fig. 23B, with considerable accuracy. To find the values of the three constants, it is necessary to know values of n for three different λ's. Then three equations may be set up which, when solved as simultaneous equations, give A, B, and C. For some purposes it is sufficiently accurate to include only the first two terms and the two constants can be found from values of n at only two λ's. The two-constant Cauchy equation is, then,

$$n = A + \frac{B}{\lambda^2} \qquad (23d)$$

from which the dispersion becomes, by differentiation

$$\frac{dn}{d\lambda} = -\frac{2B}{\lambda^3} \qquad (23e)$$

This shows that the dispersion varies approximately as the inverse cube of the wavelength. At 4000 Å it will be about eight times as large as at 8000 Å. The minus sign corresponds to the usual negative slope of the dispersion curve.

The theoretical reasoning on which Cauchy based his equation was later shown to be false, so that it is to be considered essentially as an empirical equation. Nevertheless it holds very satisfactorily for cases of normal dispersion and is a useful equation from a practical standpoint. We shall show later that it is a special case of a more complete equation, which does have a sound theoretical foundation.

23.4. Anomalous Dispersion. If measurements of the index of refraction of a transparent substance like quartz are extended into the infrared

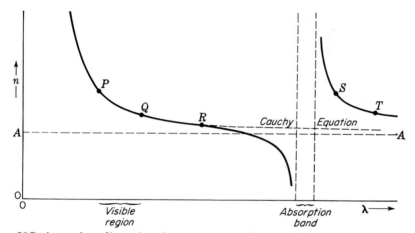

FIG. 23D. Anomalous dispersion of a transparent substance like quartz in the infrared.

region of the spectrum, the dispersion curve begins to show marked deviations from the Cauchy equation. The deviation is always of the type illustrated in Fig. 23D, where, starting at the point R, the index of refraction is seen to fall off more rapidly than required by a Cauchy equation that represents the values of n for visible light (between P and Q) quite accurately. This equation predicts a very gradual decrease of n for large values of λ (broken curve), the index approaching the limiting value A as λ approaches infinity (Eq. 23d). In contrast to this, the measured value of n first decreases more and more rapidly as it approaches a region in the infrared where light ceases to be transmitted at all. This is an absorption band (Sec. 22.3), i.e., a region of selective absorption, the position of which is characteristic of the material. Within the absorption band, n cannot usually be measured because the substance will not transmit radiation of this wavelength. On the long-wavelength side of the absorption band the index is found to be very high, decreasing at first rapidly and then more slowly as we go farther beyond the absorption band. Over the range from S to T, the Cauchy equation will again represent the data, but with different constants. In particular, the constant A will be larger.

The existence of a large discontinuity in the dispersion curve as it crosses an absorption band gives rise to *anomalous dispersion*. The dispersion is anomalous because in this neighborhood the longer wavelengths have a higher value of n and are more refracted than the shorter ones. The phenomenon was discovered with certain substances such as the dye fuchsine and iodine vapor whose absorption bands fall in the visible region. A prism formed of such a substance will deviate the red rays more than the violet, giving a spectrum which is very

FIG. 23E. Experimental arrangement for observing the anomalous dispersion of sodium vapor.

different from that formed by a substance having normal dispersion. When it was later discovered that transparent substances like glass and quartz possess regions of selective absorption in the infrared and ultraviolet, and therefore show anomalous dispersion in these regions, the term "anomalous" was seen to be inappropriate. No substance exists which does not have selective absorption at some wavelengths, and hence the phenomenon, far from being anomalous, is perfectly general. The so-called "normal" dispersion is found only when we observe those wavelengths which lie between two absorption bands, and fairly far removed from them. Nevertheless, the term "anomalous dispersion" has been retained, although it has little more than historical significance.

A very striking experiment showing the anomalous dispersion of sodium vapor in the neighborhood of the yellow D lines was devised by R. W. Wood in 1904. White light when passed through sodium vapor undergoes strong selective absorption at these lines, which form a close doublet of wavelengths 5890 and 5896 Å. At wavelengths far removed from these values, the index of refraction is only very slightly greater than unity, as we expect for a gas. With sodium vapor of appreciable density, the index of refraction in the neighborhood of the D lines passes through a region of anomalous dispersion (strictly speaking, two regions very close together) of the type shown in Fig. 23D. As the D lines are approached from the side of shorter wavelengths, n begins to decrease rapidly, becoming much less than unity as we get very close to them.

On the other side, it is at first very high, dropping off rapidly toward unity as λ increases further.

To show this in a direct way, Wood made use of the fact that we can produce the equivalent of a prism of sodium vapor by vaporizing the metal in a partially evacuated tube, if the tube is heated from the bottom. The arrangement is shown in Fig. 23E. A number of lumps of metallic sodium are placed along the bottom of a steel tube provided with water-cooled glass windows at the ends and an outlet for pumping.   White light from a narrow horizontal slit S_1 is rendered parallel by the lens L_1 and after passing through the tube, forms a horizontal image S_1' on the vertical slit S_3 of an ordinary prism spectro-scope.   When the sodium tube is cold, S_1' will be a sharp, white image, illuminating one point of the spec-troscope slit, and this will be spread out into a narrow horizontal contin-uous spectrum in the focal plane of the spectroscope camera.   If the tube is evacuated to about 2 cm pressure, and the sodium is heated by the row of gas burners, it will va-porize slowly, the vapor diffusing upward through the residual gas in the tube.   A density gradient is set up, the vapor being densest at the bottom and rarest at the top of the tube.   This is equivalent to a prism of vapor, the refracting edge of the

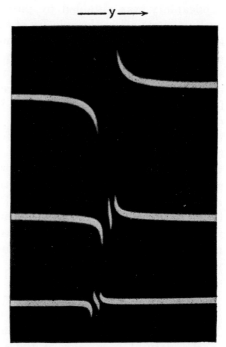

$\longrightarrow$ y $\longrightarrow$

FIG. 23F. Anomalous dispersion of sodium vapor at three different gas densities. (*After Cario.*)

prism being perpendicular to the plane of the figure, and its thick-ness increasing downward. This prism will form an anomalous spec-trum on S_3, in which the wavelengths shorter than the yellow (i.e., on the green side) are deviated upward, since their n is less than 1, and the longer ones (on the orange side) will be deviated downward.   As a result, we might expect to observe in the spectroscope that the spectrum is deviated upward on the green side of the D lines, and downward on the red side.   (The directions are actually reversed because the spectro-scope inverts the image of the slit.)   Three actual photographs of the resulting spectra with different densities of the vapor are shown in Fig. 23F.   As a consequence of the inversion mentioned above, the photographs form qualitatively a plot of n against λ, as in Fig. 23D.   In the practical performance of this experiment, several refinements are desirable, of which an important one is the introduction of an auxiliary diaphragm S_2 to select that portion of the vapor where the density gradient is most uniform.*

23.5. Sellmeier's Equation. We have seen that the Cauchy equation is not capable of representing the dispersion curve in a region of anomalous dispersion. The first success in deriving a formula of more general applicability was obtained by postulating a mechanism by which the medium could affect the velocity of the light wave. It was assumed that the medium contains particles bound by elastic forces, so that they are capable of vibrating with a certain definite frequency ν_0. This is the so-called *natural frequency*, i.e., one with which the particles will vibrate in the absence of any periodic force, and is identical with the natural frequency mentioned in Sec. 22.8 in connection with absorption and selective reflection. Passage of the light waves through the medium is then assumed to exert a periodic force on the particles, which causes them to vibrate. If the frequency ν of the light wave does not agree with ν_0, the vibrations will be forced vibrations of relatively small amplitude, and of frequency ν. As the frequency of the light approaches ν_0, the response of the particles will be greater, and a very large amplitude will be built up by resonance when $\nu = \nu_0$ exactly. These vibrations will in turn react upon the light wave and alter its velocity. A mathematical investigation of this mechanism was made in 1871 by Sellmeier, who obtained the equation

$$n^2 = 1 + \frac{A\lambda^2}{\lambda^2 - \lambda_0^2} \tag{23f}$$

This equation contains two constants, A and λ_0, the latter being related to the natural frequency of the particles by the equation $\nu_0\lambda_0 = c$. Hence λ_0 is the wavelength in vacuum corresponding to ν_0. To allow for the possibility of the existence of several different natural frequencies, the equation can be written with a series of terms,

$$n^2 = 1 + \frac{A_0\lambda^2}{\lambda^2 - \lambda_0^2} + \frac{A_1\lambda^2}{\lambda^2 - \lambda_1^2} + \cdots = 1 + \sum_i \frac{A_i\lambda^2}{\lambda^2 - \lambda_i^2} \tag{23g}$$

in which λ_0, λ_1, . . . correspond to the possible natural frequencies. The constants A_i are proportional to the number of oscillators capable of vibrating with these frequencies.

Figure 23G is a plot of n against λ according to Eq. 23g, assuming two natural frequencies. As λ approaches λ_0 or λ_1, n goes to $-\infty$ or $+\infty$

---

* Further details of the experimental procedure will be found in R. W. Wood, "Physical Optics," 3d ed., pp. 492–496, The Macmillan Company, New York, 1934.

on the short-wavelength or long-wavelength side, since the denominator of one of the terms in Eq. 23g goes to zero. Other important characteristics of the curve to be noted are that n approaches unity as λ approaches zero, and that at $\lambda = \infty$, n^2 takes the value $1 + \sum_i A_i$.

Sellmeier's equation represents a great improvement over that of Cauchy and is in fact identical with that derived from the electromagnetic theory (Sec. 23.10) with certain simplifying assumptions. Not only

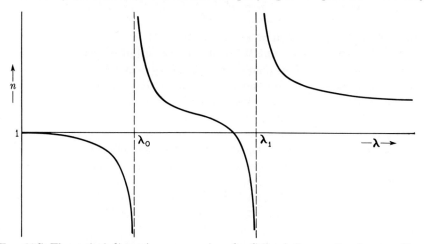

FIG. 23G. Theoretical dispersion curves given by Sellmeier's equation for a medium having two natural frequencies.

does it take account of anomalous dispersion, but it also gives a more accurate representation of n in regions far from absorption bands than does a Cauchy equation with the same number of constants. That Cauchy's equation is an approximation to Sellmeier's can be seen by writing Eq. 23f in the form

$$n^2 = 1 + \frac{A}{\left(1 - \frac{\lambda_0^2}{\lambda^2}\right)}$$

On expanding by the binomial theorem, we find

$$n^2 = 1 + A\left(1 + \frac{\lambda_0^2}{\lambda^2} + \frac{\lambda_0^4}{\lambda^4} + \cdots\right)$$

For that part of the dispersion curve where λ is considerably greater than λ_0, the higher powers of λ_0/λ will be small and may be neglected. This gives

$$n^2 = 1 + A + A\frac{\lambda_0^2}{\lambda^2}$$

Writing M for $1 + A$, and N for $A\lambda_0{}^2$,

$$n = (M + N\lambda^{-2})^{\frac{1}{2}}$$

Expanding again,

$$n = M^{\frac{1}{2}} + \frac{N}{2M^{\frac{1}{2}}\lambda^2} + \frac{N^2}{8M^{\frac{3}{2}}\lambda^4} + \cdots$$

and neglecting higher powers of $1/\lambda$,

$$n = P + \frac{Q}{\lambda^2} + \frac{R}{\lambda^4}$$

This is Cauchy's equation as given in Sec. 23.3.

An instructive experiment to illustrate the origin of dispersion can be performed with a simple pendulum, to the bob of which is attached a light rubber band. If the end of the rubber band is held in the hand and moved to and fro, a periodic force is exerted on the pendulum similar to the action of the light wave on one of the oscillators in the medium. If the frequency motion of the hand is very high compared to the natural frequency of the pendulum, the bob will remain practically motionless. This corresponds to a wave of high frequency and short wavelength, the velocity of which is practically uninfluenced by the presence of the oscillators. In Fig. 23G it will be seen that n approaches unity as λ approaches zero, so the velocity becomes the same as in free space.

If, now, the hand is moved with a frequency only slightly greater than that of the pendulum, it will be found that the pendulum swings 180° out of phase with the motion of the hand. Under these conditions, the rubber band is considerably stretched when the displacements of the hand and bob are in opposite directions and so exerts its maximum force on the hand, tending to pull it back to the central position. This corresponds to an increased restoring force on the "aether" which propagates the wave, and hence to an *increase* in the velocity of the wave (Sec. 11.4). Thus in Fig. 23G, n becomes considerably less than 1 at a wavelength slightly less than λ_0. Finally when the frequency of motion of the hand is made less than the natural frequency, the pendulum will follow the hand, practically in phase with it. In this case the rubber band exerts only small forces on the hand, since the displacements of the pendulum are in the same direction. The forces are less than if the pendulum were at rest, so this corresponds to a decreased restoring force on the aether. The velocity of the wave is therefore *decreased*, and n is greater than one, on the long-wavelength side of λ_0.

The large discontinuity in the dispersion curve at λ_0 is thus seen to be a consequence of the abrupt change of phase by 180° of the oscillator relative to the impressed vibration as the latter passes through resonance frequency. This effect may be demonstrated very directly by hanging three pendulums side by side from a horizontal rod clamped at one end. The center pendulum is a heavy one and corresponds to the aether wave while the other two are very light, one being slightly longer and the other slightly shorter than the heavy pendulum. When the center pendulum is set swinging, the two light ones will swing in opposite phases, the shorter one nearly agreeing in phase with the impressed vibration.

23.6. Effect of Absorption on Dispersion. Although Sellmeier's equation represents the dispersion curve very successfully in regions not too close to absorption bands, it fails completely at those wavelengths where the medium has appreciable absorption. This may be seen directly from the fact that the curve of Fig. 23G goes to infinity on either side of each λ_i. Not only is this physically impossible, but the form of the curve near λ_i does not agree with experiment. It has been possible to measure the dispersion curve right through an absorption band, although this is a difficult matter because practically all the light is absorbed. By using prisms of very small refracting angle, or thin films of the material with a Michelson interferometer (Sec. 13.15), the indices of refraction of a few dyes, such as cyanine, which have an absorption band in the visible, have been carefully measured. The resulting curve resembles one of those shown by a heavy solid line in Fig. 23H. The true form of the curve in the neighborhood of λ_i is seen to be very different from that required by Sellmeier's equation.

This discrepancy was first shown by Helmholtz[*] to be due to the fact that Sellmeier's equation takes no account of the absorption of energy of the wave. In the above discussion, and in the suggested mechanical analogy, it was assumed that the oscillator does not experience any frictional resistance to its vibration. Such a resistance is necessary if energy is to be taken continuously from the wave by the oscillator. Helmholtz assumed a frictional force directly proportional to the velocity of the oscillator, and he therefore derived an equation for the index of refraction which takes account of absorption. As a measure of the strength of the absorption, we could use the absorption coefficient α defined in Eq. 11k, but the equations are simpler when expressed in terms of a constant κ_0, which is related to α as follows:

$$\kappa_0 = \frac{\alpha\lambda}{4\pi} \tag{23h}$$

[*] H. L. F. von Helmholtz (1821–1894). German physicist who contributed in almost every field of science. His work in physiological optics alone, or in sound, would have made him famous. He is regarded as one of the discoverers of the law of conservation of energy.

Here λ is the wavelength measured in vacuum. The physical significance of κ_0 is best expressed by the fact that the intensity falls to $1/e^{4\pi\kappa_0}$ of its initial value in going the distance λ through the medium. The disper-

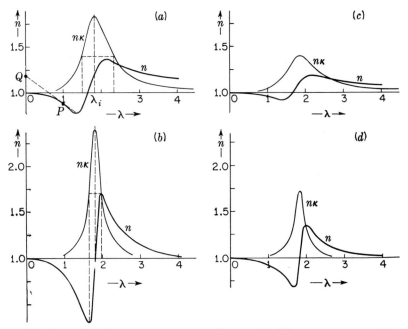

FIG. 23H. Ideal dispersion curves for an oscillator with different amounts of friction and absorption. (a) Strong absorption, strong friction. (b) Strong absorption, weak friction. (c) Weak absorption, strong friction. (d) Weak absorption, weak friction.

sion equations resulting from this purely mechanical theory of Helmholtz may be written

$$\left. \begin{aligned} n^2 - \kappa_0{}^2 &= 1 + \sum_i \frac{A_i \lambda^2}{(\lambda^2 - \lambda_i{}^2) + g_i\lambda^2/(\lambda^2 - \lambda_i{}^2)} \\ 2n\kappa_0 &= \sum \frac{A_i \sqrt{g_i}\,\lambda^3}{(\lambda^2 - \lambda_i{}^2)^2 + g_i\lambda^2} \end{aligned} \right\} \qquad (23i)$$

The constant g_i is a measure of the strength of the frictional force. These equations should now hold for all wavelengths, including those within an absorption band. In regions far from absorption bands, κ_0 and g_i are both essentially zero, and the first of the equations reduces to Sellmeier's equation 23g. Figure 23H(a) is a plot of n and of $n\kappa_0$, the latter of which by Eq. 23h is a measure of the absorption coefficient α, for a case of large friction ($g = 1.96 \times 10^{-3}$). It shows quantitatively the course of dispersion and absorption curves through a region of absorption with a maximum at $\lambda_i = 0.1732$ μ. It will be seen that n no longer goes to infinity, as in Fig. 23G, but remains finite at $\lambda = \lambda_i$. The other curves of Fig. 23H are drawn to show the effects of changing both the strength of the absorption and the frictional damping. The former is determined by the total number of oscillators causing the absorption, while the latter depends on the magnitude of the various effects responsible for the breadth of spectral lines (Sec. 21.15). It should be noted in (b) and (d) that the maxima and minima of the refractive index curves come exactly at the points where the absorption is half its maximum value.

The pendulum experiments described above may be modified to include the effect of frictional damping and to give some insight into the physical reason for the resulting change in the form of the dispersion curve. Thus if the smaller pendulum, which represents the oscillator, has a wire attached to it which dips in water or oil, we have the desired condition. Two important changes in the response of the pendulum to the impressed vibrations will now be apparent. In the first place, the amplitude will not become nearly as large when the impressed frequency is exactly equal to the natural frequency of the pendulum. With no friction, the amplitude produced by resonance is theoretically infinite (in the final equilibrium state), and the corresponding value of n goes to infinity also. The effect of friction, however, limits this maximum amplitude, and this accounts for the fact that only moderate variations of n are actually observed. In the second place, the change of relative phase between the pendulum and the impressed vibrations when the latter pass through the natural frequency is no longer abrupt, but takes place more or less gradually. This accounts for the fact that there is no longer a sharp discontinuity in the dispersion curve, but that it is rounded off into a continuous curve. The phase change becomes more and more gradual as the friction is made greater, for instance by dipping the wire farther into the water, or by using a more viscous liquid.

23.7. Wave and Group Velocity in the Medium. In the curves of Figs. 23G and 23H, the abscissas are wavelengths in vacuum $\lambda = c/\nu$ and the ordinates are the ordinary indices of refraction $n = c/v$, where v is the wave velocity in the medium. For those parts of the curve where $n < 1$, the wave velocity is greater than the velocity c of light in vacuum. This is at first sight a contradiction to one of the fundamental results of the theory of relativity, according to which c is the highest attainable velocity. There is actually no contradiction here, however, since relativity applies to the velocity with which *energy* (a light signal) is transmitted, and this is always less than c.   Remembering that the energy travels with the group velocity u, we require that it is c/u that shall be greater than unity, rather than c/v.   Now u and v are related by Eq. 12p, which may be transformed (see Prob. 7) to read

$$\frac{c}{u} = n - \lambda \frac{dn}{d\lambda} \tag{23j}$$

where λ is the wavelength in vacuum.   Thus the geometrical construction of Sec. 12.8 may also be applied to refractive indices.   If in Fig 23$H(a)$ we draw a tangent to the dispersion curve, it will intersect the axis of n at a point Q whose ordinate is c/u.   That is, while the ordinate of P is n, or c/v, for that wavelength, the ordinate of Q is the corresponding values of c/u for the same wavelength.

This geometrical construction shows, then, that for any point on the curve where it is descending toward the right, the corresponding c/u is

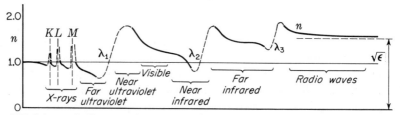

FIG. 23I. Schematic diagram of a complete dispersion curve for a substance transparent to the visible spectrum.

greater than unity, even though n itself may be less than unity.   Therefore the group velocity is less than c, and there is no violation of the principle of relativity.   An exception to this statement appears to occur in the region within the absorption band, where the curve slopes up steeply to the right.   However, in this region we have strong absorption, so that the amplitude of the wave drops practically to zero in a fraction of a wavelength.   In this event, the wave velocity and group velocity no longer have any meaning, but other considerations show that in this case also the relativity requirement is fulfilled.

23.8. The Complete Dispersion Curve of a Substance.   Although the curve of the refractive index against wavelength is different for every different substance, the curves for all optical media, i.e., substances more or less transparent in the visible region, possess certain general features in common.   To illustrate these, let us consider the schematic curve of Fig. 23I, which represents the variation of n from $\lambda = 0$ to several kilometers for an ideal substance.   Starting at $\lambda = 0$, the index of refraction is unity, as stated in Sec. 23.5.   For the very short waves (γ rays and hard X rays), the index is slightly less than 1. Siegbahn* proved this fact experimentally by refracting X rays through a prism. It was found that the beam was deflected very slightly *away from* the base of the prism, as would be the case if the waves travel faster in the prism than in air. It has also been demonstrated that X rays can be totally reflected from a solid substance by using grazing incidence so that the X rays strike the surface at an angle greater than the critical angle. This property of X rays has been used by A. H. Compton† and others to measure the wavelengths of X rays by diffracting them from an ordinary ruled grating used at grazing incidence.

The first absorption is encountered in the X-ray region at a wavelength depending upon the atomic weight of the heaviest element in the material. For silicon it reaches its maximum at 6.731 Å, and for uranium at 0.1075 Å. This absorption rises rapidly to a maximum, and then falls off sharply at the so-called "K-absorption limit" of the element. It gives rise to a relatively narrow region of strong anomalous dispersion, marked K in Fig. 23I. Beyond this will lie other absorption discontinuities of this element, called L, M, . . . limits, as well as the K, L, M, . . . limits of other elements present. Therefore for any actual optical medium there will be many of these sharp discontinuities. For simplicity only three are indicated in the figure.

From the X-ray region the curve descends more rapidly toward longer wavelengths, eventually reaching the broad region λ_1 of strong absorption and anomalous dispersion in the ultraviolet (Sec. 22.3). For most substances this completely covers the region between the soft X rays and the near ultraviolet. The descending course of the curve in the visible region, characteristic of normal dispersion, is seen to be connected with the existence of this ultraviolet absorption. In general the curve will have a steeper slope in the visible region, so that the dispersion $dn/d\lambda$ is greater, the nearer this absorption band lies to the visible. Thus fluorite has a very small dispersion for visible light, quartz somewhat greater, and glass still greater (cf. Fig. 23B and Table 22-I). Dense flint glass, which gives the highest dispersion, frequently has a yellowish color, owing to the fact that the absorption band encroaches slightly on the violet end of the visible.

Somewhere in the near infrared, the curve begins to descend more

* Karl Manne Siegbahn (1886–   ). Director of the Nobel Institute in Stockholm, Sweden, and winner of the Nobel prize in 1924. He is noted for his fine experimental techniques in the measurement of the wavelengths of X rays.

† Arthur H. Compton (1892–   ). Professor of physics at the University of Chicago, and afterward president of Washington University, St. Louis. He received the Nobel prize in 1927, largely for his discovery of the Compton effect in X rays (Sec. 30.2).

steeply, and runs into another absorption band at λ_2. The center of this band is at 8.5 μ for quartz, but the absorption begins to become strong at 4 or 5 μ. Beyond this first absorption band there usually exist one or more others. In passing each of these bands, the index of refraction increases. Thus the index will be higher for certain infrared wavelengths than for any part of the visible. For example, Rubens measured values of n for quartz varying from 2.40 to 2.14 in the region $\lambda = 51$ to 63 μ. An interesting method of isolating radiation of very long wavelengths, called the method of "focal isolation" is based on this fact. Owing to the high value of n, a convex lens will have a much smaller focal length for these long waves than for the shorter waves, and the latter can be screened off with suitable diaphragms. In this way the longest infrared rays ever measured were isolated by Nichols and Tear (Sec. 11.6).

At wavelengths beyond all the infrared bands, the index decreases slowly and more or less uniformly through the region of radio waves, approaching a certain limiting value for infinitely long waves. There are a few narrow regions of absorption in the radio frequencies, but these are always weak. The limiting value will be shown in the following section to be the square root of ϵ, the ordinary dielectric constant of the medium.

23.9. The Electromagnetic Equations for Transparent Media. In Chap. 20 we stated Maxwell's equations as they apply to empty space, and we showed how they predict electromagnetic waves of velocity c. It is now of interest to investigate the characteristics and velocity of such waves in a material substance. For the present we shall consider only nonconducting media, and the more difficult case of conductors will be taken up later in Chap. 25. When a steady electric field acts upon a nonconducting dielectric, there is a small displacement of the bound charges in the atoms, and we say they become *polarized*. The charges do not move continuously along, as in a conductor, but are merely displaced through minute distances and come to rest again in a fashion analogous to the stretching of a spring. As a measure of this *electric displacement* we use the vector quantity $\mathbf{D}$,* and since in an isotropic medium it is proportional to the impressed electric field $\mathbf{E}$, we may write

$$\mathbf{D} = \epsilon\mathbf{E} \tag{23k}$$

Here ϵ is the dielectric constant. To apply Maxwell's equations to such a medium it now becomes necessary to replace $\mathbf{E}$ by $\mathbf{D}$ wherever it occurs in the equations for empty space (Eqs. 20a to 20d). Hence Maxwell's equations for a nonconducting isotropic medium are written:

---

* Strictly speaking, $\mathbf{D}$ itself is not a direct measure of the displacement of the bound charges. The polarization of the medium is usually written $\mathbf{P}$, and $\mathbf{D}$ depends on $\mathbf{P}$ by the relation $\mathbf{D} = \mathbf{E} + 4\pi\mathbf{P}$.

$$\left.\begin{array}{l} \dfrac{\epsilon}{c}\dfrac{\partial E_x}{\partial t} = \dfrac{\partial H_z}{\partial y} - \dfrac{\partial H_y}{\partial z} \\[2mm] \dfrac{\epsilon}{c}\dfrac{\partial E_y}{\partial t} = \dfrac{\partial H_x}{\partial z} - \dfrac{\partial H_z}{\partial x} \\[2mm] \dfrac{\epsilon}{c}\dfrac{\partial E_z}{\partial t} = \dfrac{\partial H_y}{\partial x} - \dfrac{\partial H_x}{\partial y} \end{array}\right\} \quad (23l)$$

$$\left.\begin{array}{l} -\dfrac{1}{c}\dfrac{\partial H_x}{\partial t} = \dfrac{\partial E_z}{\partial y} - \dfrac{\partial E_y}{\partial z} \\[2mm] -\dfrac{1}{c}\dfrac{\partial H_y}{\partial t} = \dfrac{\partial E_x}{\partial z} - \dfrac{\partial E_z}{\partial x} \\[2mm] -\dfrac{1}{c}\dfrac{\partial H_z}{\partial t} = \dfrac{\partial E_y}{\partial x} - \dfrac{\partial E_x}{\partial y} \end{array}\right\} \quad (23m)$$

and

$$\epsilon\left(\frac{\partial E_x}{\partial x} + \frac{\partial E_y}{\partial y} + \frac{\partial E_z}{\partial z}\right) = 0 \qquad (23n)$$

$$\frac{\partial H_x}{\partial x} + \frac{\partial H_y}{\partial y} + \frac{\partial H_z}{\partial z} = 0 \qquad (23o)$$

If we derive the equations for plane waves as was done in Sec. 20.4, starting now with Eqs. 23l and 23m, we find

$$\frac{\partial^2 H_z}{\partial t^2} = \frac{c^2}{\epsilon}\frac{\partial^2 H_z}{\partial x^2}$$

and

$$\frac{\partial^2 E_y}{\partial t^2} = \frac{c^2}{\epsilon}\frac{\partial^2 E_y}{\partial x^2}$$

Comparison with the general wave equation 11b shows the new velocity to be $c/\sqrt{\epsilon}$. The index of refraction becomes

$$n = \frac{c}{v} = \sqrt{\epsilon} \qquad (23p)$$

The solution of Eqs. 23l to 23o for monochromatic plane waves, analogous to Eqs. 20n, is now to be written

$$E_y = A \sin (\omega t - kx)$$
$$H_z = \sqrt{\epsilon}\, A \sin (\omega t - kx)$$

and the magnitude of the electric and magnetic vectors at any instant is such that

$$H_z = \sqrt{\epsilon}\, E_y$$

Therefore in the usual case $\epsilon > 1$ the amplitude of the magnetic wave is greater than that of the electric wave in a ratio equal to the index of refraction (Eq. 23p).

The energy carried by electromagnetic waves in dielectric substances may be found by applying the principles of Sec. 20.7, the only change being the replacement of **E** by **D**. The instantaneous energy densities of the above electric and magnetic waves become $\epsilon E_y^2/8\pi$ and $H_z^2/8\pi$, and are therefore again equal. Their sum may be written as $\sqrt{\epsilon}\, E_y H_z/4\pi$, and when this is multiplied by v from Eq. 23p to obtain the intensity, one finds

$$I = \frac{c}{\epsilon}\frac{\epsilon E_y^2}{4\pi} = \frac{cn}{4\pi} E_y^2 = \frac{cn}{8\pi} A^2 \qquad (23q)$$

As before, the E_y in this equation represents the root-mean-square (rms) value of the electric vector, since the flow of energy is averaged over a time long compared with the period. The result may also be written $cE_yH_z/4\pi$. In this form it represents the expression of a general law of electromagnetism known as Poynting's* theorem, according to which the direction and magnitude of the energy flow are given by the *Poynting vector* $(c/4\pi)[\mathbf{E} \times \mathbf{H}]$, the quantity in brackets being the vector product.

Equation 23p gives very nearly correct values of n for gases, but when we attempt to apply it to denser media, large deviations are found. Thus the dielectric constant for water, measured by placing it between the plates of a condenser charged to a steady potential, is 81, indicating a value of 9 for the index of refraction. For sodium light, the measured index of water is 1.33. For various kinds of glass, ϵ varies from 4 to 9, which would require n to vary from 2 to 3. This again is higher than the observed values for visible light.

We do not have to look far for the cause of this discrepancy. It lies in the fact that the electric field of a light wave is not a steady field, but a rapidly alternating one. For yellow light the frequency is 5×10^{14} per sec. If the dielectric constant of a substance is measured using an alternating potential on the plates in place of a steady one, the result is found to vary with the frequency. From this we see that the index of refraction must also vary with frequency, or wavelength. As the wavelength becomes very large and approaches infinity, the frequency approaches zero. The limiting case of a steady field thus corresponds to zero frequency, and we are led to expect the index of refraction to approach the square root of the dielectric constant for steady fields. That this is in fact the case is shown by the measurements of the index of refraction of water for electromagnetic waves quoted in Table 23-II. The value of $\sqrt{\epsilon}$ measured for steady field is shown for comparison. Clearly the value of n approaches exactly the predicted value for infinitely long waves.

23.10. Theory of Dispersion. In order to explain the variation of n (and hence of $\sqrt{\epsilon}$) with λ by the electromagnetic theory, one must take account of the molecular structure of matter. When an electromagnetic wave is incident on an atom or molecule, the periodic electric force of the wave sets the bound charges into a vibratory motion having the frequency of the wave. The phase of this motion relative to that of the impressed electric force will depend upon the impressed frequency, and will vary with the difference between the impressed frequency and the

---

* J. H. Poynting (1852–1914). Professor of physics at the University of Birmingham, England. He is also known for his accurate work on the measurement of the gravitational constant.

natural frequency of the bound charges in the way discussed in Secs. 23.5 and 23.6. As the wave traverses the empty space between molecules, it will, of course, have the velocity c, and we must now inquire how it is possible that the presence of the oscillating charges in the molecules produces an effective alteration in the rate at which the wave progresses through the medium.

The clue to the explanation of dispersion lies in the secondary waves which are generated by the induced oscillations of the bound charges. These secondary waves are identical with those which give rise to molecular scattering (Sec. 22.10), as in the explanation of the blue color of

TABLE 23-II. VARIATION OF n WITH λ FOR WATER

Wavelength	Frequency	n
5.89×10^{-5} cm	5.1×10^{14}	1.333
12.56	2.9	1.3210
258.	0.116	1.41
800.	0.0375	1.41
0.40 cm	$750. \times 10^8$	5.3
1.75	171.	7.82
8.1	37.	8.10
65.	4.6	8.88
∞	0.	$(9.03 = \sqrt{\epsilon})$

the sky. When a light beam traverses a transparent liquid or solid, the amount of light scattered laterally is extremely small, even though the concentration of scattering centers is much greater than that in the air which gives the sky light. This is due to the fact that the scattered wavelets traveling out laterally from the beam have their phases so arranged that there is practically complete destructive interference. But the secondary waves traveling *in the same direction* as the original beam do not thus cancel out, but combine to form sets of waves moving parallel to the original waves. Now the secondary waves must be added to the primary ones according to the principle of superposition, and the results will depend on the phase difference between the two sets. This interference will modify the phase of the primary waves, and thus is equivalent to a change in their wave velocity. That is, since the wave velocity is merely the rate at which a condition of equal phase is propagated, an alteration of the phase by interference changes the velocity. We have seen that the phase of the oscillators, and hence of the secondary waves, depends on the impressed frequency, so it becomes clear that the velocity in the medium varies with the frequency of the light. This is the physical interpretation of dispersion, expressed in briefest outline.

The foundations for the mathematical treatment of the above mechanism were laid by Rayleigh, who considered the case of mechanical waves, and the theory was later extended to cover the case of electromagnetic waves by Planck, Schuster, and others. We shall not attempt to give this development here. It leads to dispersion formulas similar to that of Helmholtz (Eq. 23i). In fact, there is a close analogy throughout between the electromagnetic and mechanical pictures of the phenomenon. The oscillations of the bound charges must be regarded as damped by a

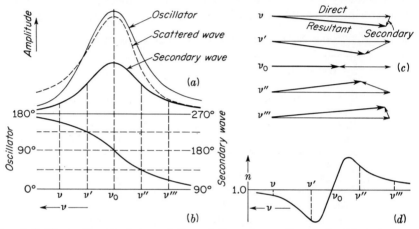

FIG. 23J. Illustrating the interpretation of dispersion as the result of interference of the secondary wave with the direct wave.

frictional force, just as were the particles in Helmholtz's theory. The nature of the damping forces postulated in electromagnetic theory will be briefly discussed in Sec. 23.11.

To show the relative amplitudes and phases of the incident wave, oscillator, and secondary wave, we consider the schematic diagrams of Fig. 23J. The first curve in (a) shows the response of a damped *oscillator* of natural frequency ν_0 to an impressed vibration of frequency ν, the amplitude becoming a maximum when $\nu = \nu_0$. The broken curve shows the amplitude radiated by the oscillator, i.e., of the *scattered wave*. As a consequence of Rayleigh's law that the shorter waves are scattered more effectively, this curve is higher on the sides of higher ν but drops to zero at low frequencies. The third curve gives the amplitude of the *secondary waves* built up from the scattered wavelets. Curve (b), in conjunction with the left-hand scale of ordinates, gives the phase difference between the oscillator and the impressed wave. As pointed out in Sec. 23.6, this changes from 0 to 180° in passing through the natural frequency, but not abruptly because of the damping. At ν_0 it is 90° behind that of the impressed wave. Theory shows, furthermore, that the phase of the scattered waves, and therefore of the secondary waves as well, lags 90° behind that of the oscillators.* This is because electromagnetic radiation is proportional to the rate of change of current, or to the acceleration of a charge [see Sec. 20.8 and Fig. 20$D(a)$]. The current itself, or the velocity of the charge, has the phase that we attribute to the oscillator. Therefore, since in a simple harmonic motion the acceleration is one-quarter period behind the velocity, the phase of the radiated waves is retarded this much behind that of the oscillating source. Taking account of this additional retardation, it will be seen that the right-hand scale of ordinates in Fig. 23$J(b)$ applies to the phase lag of the secondary waves behind the impressed waves.

We now proceed in (c) to compound vectorially the amplitudes of the direct and secondary waves. For the frequency ν, the amplitude of the secondary waves is small [curve (a)] and lags in phase behind the direct waves by nearly 270° [curve (b)]. The vector diaphragm at the top in (c) shows that the resultant amplitude is nearly the same but that the phase is slightly *advanced*, corresponding to a rotation of the vector in a clockwise sense. An advance of phase means an *increase* in velocity, since it will be remembered that the phase increases as we move backward along a wave. Thus in the dispersion curve (d), the index of refraction at ν is slightly less than 1. The second vector diagram, for ν', gives a greater advance of phase, and a considerably smaller resultant amplitude. At $\nu = \nu_0$ there is no change of phase or velocity produced, but merely a reduction of intensity. The energy removed from the resultant forward wave appears in other directions as resonance radiation. Beyond ν_0 there is a retardation instead of an advance of phase, and the velocity of the wave is decreased. Thus it may be seen in a qualitative way how the curve (d), having the form for anomalous dispersion, can result from the mechanism described.

23.11. Nature of the Vibrating Particles and Frictional Forces. In conclusion, we may consider briefly what types of charged particles and damping forces are involved in the various discontinuities of the typical dispersion curve of Fig. 23I. The X-ray absorptions are attributed to the innermost electrons in the atoms, which are assigned to the "shells" K, L, M, etc., of decreasing energy and increasing distance from the nucleus. Because they are deep in the atom, these electrons are shielded from the effects of collisions and electric fields due to neighboring atoms. Hence two of the major causes of line breadth discussed in Sec. 21.15 are not important for X rays, and the absorption discontinuities are sharp, even in solids. It is only in this region that radiation damping makes any appreciable contribution to the line widths.

* See, for example, G. P. Harnwell, "Principles of Electricity and Magnetism," 2d ed., pp. 601–602, McGraw-Hill Book Company, Inc., 1949.

The very broad absorption in the far ultraviolet is due to the outer electrons in the atoms and molecules of the material. These are not shielded, and consequently in solids and liquids an extensive region of continuous absorption is produced. For molecular gases the bands may consist of individual rotational lines that are quite sharp, but these are so numerous that they are usually unresolved. In this region the damping due to collisions begins to become more important than that due to radiation, and at still longer wavelengths it usually predominates. The near-infrared absorption bands represent the various natural frequencies of the atoms as a whole, or even of molecules. Since these vibrators are much heavier than electrons, it is clear why they possess lower vibration frequencies. In the far infrared, other molecular vibrations of lower frequency may be involved. Here the frequencies of rotation of molecules as a whole may also play a part, especially in gases.

PROBLEMS

1. Calculate the dispersion of a sample of glass at a wavelength of 6000 Å, if its refractive indices for the blue and green mercury lines (4358 and 5461 Å) are 1.6130 and 1.6026, respectively. Solve the problem using (a) Cauchy's equation, and (b) Sellmeier's equation.

2. Using the refractive indices for telescope crown glass, as given in Table 23-I, find the values of the constants in a three-term Cauchy equation that fits exactly at 3988, 5086, and 6563 Å. Compare the observed and calculated values at the other wavelengths given.

Ans. $A = 1.51375$, $B = 4.608 \times 10^5$ Å^2, $C = 6.88 \times 10^{10}$ Å^4. Av. deviation = 0.000053, max. deviation = 0.00012.

3. A 60° prism is made of a glass for which the constants in Cauchy's equation are $A = 1.416$ and $B = 1.72 \times 10^6$ Å^2. Find the angular dispersion in radians per angstrom when the prism is set at minimum deviation for a wavelength of 6000 Å.

4. Hartmann has given an empirical dispersion formula, according to which $n = n_0 + b/(\lambda - \lambda_0)$. Test its accuracy, as compared with that of a three-constant Cauchy equation, by finding the constants for telescope crown glass by fitting at the three wavelengths mentioned in Prob. 2. Which equation best represents the data?

Ans. Hartmann; $n_0 = 1.50796$, $b = 80.9528$ Å, $\lambda_0 = 1640.6$ Å; av. deviation = 0.000027, max. deviation = 0.00007.

5. Compare the spectrum formed by a prism giving anomalous dispersion with that formed by an ordinary glass prism. If the absorption maximum of the first prism lies in the green, indicate the relative positions of the other colors as compared with those produced by normal dispersion.

6. Determine graphically from Fig. 23B a value for the group velocity of violet light ($\lambda = 4000$ Å) in borosilicate crown glass. *Ans.* 1.89×10^{10} cm/sec.

7. Starting with Eq. 12p for the relation between the wave and group velocities, derive the expression for the "group index" given in Eq. 23j.

8. From the second of Helmholtz's equations 23i, find the relation between the width of the absorption peak, at half maximum of $n\kappa_0$, and the frictional constant g_i.

$$Ans \ \Delta\lambda = \sqrt{g_i}.$$

9. From the refractive indices of crystal quartz for infrared radiation given in

Sec. 23.8, and assuming that there are no appreciable absorption bands beyond 63 μ, predict a value for the dielectric constant of quartz for static fields. Compare with the value from a table of dielectric constants.

10. A small source emitting a continuous spectrum is placed 60 cm from a crystal quartz lens having a focal length of 40 cm for sodium light. If it is desired to obtain infrared radiation of wavelength 51 μ by the method of "focal isolation," how far behind the lens should a small hole be placed? See Table 26-I and Sec. 23.8 for refractive indices. *Ans.* 20.99 cm.

11. Complete the derivation of the wave equation from Maxwell's equations for a dielectric, as suggested in Sec. 23.9.

12. The refractive index of a certain glass for X rays of wavelength 0.7 Å is 1.60×10^{-6} less than unity. At what maximum angle, measured to the surface, must a beam of X rays strike the glass to undergo total reflection? *Ans.* 0.1025°.

13. A light beam of intensity 2.0 ergs cm^{-2} sec^{-1} in vacuum enters a piece of glass ($n = 1.50$) at normal incidence. Find the amplitudes of the electric and magnetic vectors, and the intensity, inside the glass.

14. According to the electromagnetic theory, the value of A_i is given by

$$\frac{\lambda_i^2 N_i e_i^2}{\pi c^2 m_i}$$

where N_i, e_i, and m_i are the number per unit volume, charge, and mass of the oscillators of frequency c/λ_i. Taking the refractive indices of air as given in Sec. 23.2, and assuming only one absorption band in the ultraviolet, calculate the value of e_i^2/m_i for air. Compare with e^2/m for the electron

Ans. 10.3×10^8 cm^3/sec^2. True value 2.53×10^8.

15. Use a two-constant Cauchy equation which fits the refractive indices of vitreous quartz (Table 23-I) at wavelengths 6563 and 4861 Å to predict the index for the sodium line, 5892 Å. Calculate also a value for the dispersion in radians per centimeter for a 60° prism at the latter wavelength.

CHAPTER 24

THE POLARIZATION OF LIGHT

From the properties of interference and diffraction we are led to conclude that light is a wave phenomenon, and we utilize these properties to measure the wavelength. These effects tell us nothing about the types of waves with which we are dealing—whether they are longitudinal or transverse, or whether the vibrations are linear, circular, or torsional. The electromagnetic theory, however, specifically requires that the vibrations be traverse, being therefore entirely confined to the plane of the wave front. The most general type of vibration is elliptical, of which linear and circular vibrations are extreme cases. Experiments which bring out these characteristics are those dealing with the so-called "polarization of light." Although a longitudinal wave like a sound wave must necessarily be symmetrical about the direction of its propagation, transverse waves may show dissymmetries, and if any beam of light shows such a dissymmetry we say it is polarized.

The present chapter, by way of introduction to the subject of polarization, gives a brief account of the principal ways of producing plane-polarized light from ordinary unpolarized light. Most of the phenomena to be discussed here will be covered in more detail in later chapters. It will be helpful, however, to have a preliminary acquaintance with the experimental methods, and a mental picture of how the various polarizing devices act to separate ordinary light into its polarized components. The common methods used in producing and demonstrating the polarization of light may be grouped under the following heads: (1) reflection, (2) transmission through a pile of plates, (3) dichroism, (4) double refraction, and (5) scattering.

24.1. Polarization by Reflection. Perhaps the simplest method of polarizing light is the one discovered by Malus in 1808. If a beam of white light is incident at one certain angle on the polished surface of a plate of ordinary glass, it is found upon reflection to be plane-polarized. By "plane-polarized" is meant that all the light is vibrating parallel to a plane through the axis of the beam (Sec. 11.2). Although this light appears to the eye to be no different from the incident light, its polarization or asymmetry is easily shown by reflection from a second plate of glass as follows. A beam of unpolarized light, AB in Fig. 24A, is incident at an angle of about 57° on the first glass surface at B. This light is again reflected at 57° by a second glass plate C placed parallel to the first as shown at the left. If now the upper plate is rotated about BC as an axis, the intensity of the reflected beam is found to decrease, reaching zero for a rotation of 90°. Rotation about BC keeps the angle of incidence constant. The experiment is best performed with the back surfaces of the glass painted black. The first reflected beam BC' then appears to be cut off and to vanish at C'. As the upper mirror is rotated further about BC the reflected beam CD reappears, increasing in intensity

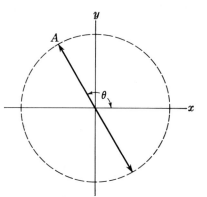

Fig. 24A. Polarization by reflection from glass surfaces.

Fig. 24B. Vibration in a beam of light viewed end-on.

to reach a maximum at 180°. Continued rotation produces zero intensity again at 270°, and a maximum again at 360°, the starting point.

If the angle of incidence on either the lower or upper mirror is not 57°, the twice-reflected beam will go through maxima and minima as before, but the minima will not have zero intensity. In other words there will always be a reflected beam from C. Calling the angle of incidence ϕ in general, the critical value $\bar{\phi}$ which produces a zero minimum for the second reflection is called the *polarizing angle* and varies with the kind of glass used. Before undertaking the explanation of this experiment, it will be worthwhile to consider briefly the accepted ideas as to the nature of the vibrations in ordinary and polarized light.

24.2. Representation of the Vibrations in Light. According to the electromagnetic theory, any type of light consists of transverse waves, in which the oscillating magnitudes are the electric and magnetic vectors. The question as to which of these is to be chosen as constituting the "vibrations" will be deferred until later (Sec. 25.12), but it is immaterial for our present purpose. Let us assume that in a beam of light traveling toward the observer, along the $+z$ axis in Fig. 24B, the electric vector at some instant is executing a linear vibration with the direction and amplitude indicated. If this vibration continues unchanged, we say that the light is *plane polarized*, since its vibrations are confined to the plane containing the z axis and oriented at the angle θ. If on the other hand the light is *unpolarized*, like most natural light, one may imagine that there are sudden, random changes in θ, occurring in time intervals of the order of 10^{-8} sec. Every orientation of A is to be regarded as equally probable so that, as indicated by the dashed circle in Fig. 24B, the average effect is completely symmetrical about the direction of propagation.

This picture of unpolarized light, although a legitimate one, is over-simplified because if there are fluctuations in orientation there should be fluctuations in amplitude as well. Furthermore, linear vibrations are a special case of elliptical ones, and there is no reason for this special type to be preferred. Hence a truer picture is one of elliptical vibrations changing frequently in size, eccentricity, and orientation, but confined to the x,y plane. This complexity presents little difficulty, however, since because

Fig. 24C. Pictorial representations of plane-polarized and ordinary light beams.

all azimuths are equivalent the simpler representation in terms of linear vibrations of constant amplitude and rapidly shifting orientation completely describes the facts. Also, since motion in an ellipse can be regarded as made up of two linear motions at right angles (Sec. 12.9), the two descriptions are in fact mathematically the same.

Still another representation of unpolarized light is perhaps the most useful. If we resolve the vibration of Fig. 24B into linear components $A_x = A \cos \theta$ and $A_y = A \sin \theta$, they will in general be unequal. But when θ is allowed to assume all values at random, the net result is as though we had two vibrations at right angles with equal amplitudes, but with no coherence of phase. Each is the resultant of a large number of individual vibrations with random phases (Sec. 12.4) and because of this randomness a complete incoherence is produced. Figure 24C shows a common way of picturing these vibrations, parts (a) and (b) representing the two plane-polarized components, and part (c) the two together in an unpolarized beam. Dots represent the end-on view of linear vibrations, and double-pointed arrows ones confined to the plane of the paper. Thus (d), (e), and (f) of the figure show how the vibrations in (a), (b), and (c) would appear when looking along the direction of the rays.

24.3. Polarizing Angle and Brewster's Law.   Consider unpolarized light to be incident at an angle ϕ on a dielectric like glass, as shown in Fig. 24$D(a)$.   There will always be a reflected ray OR and a refracted ray OT.   An experiment like the one described in Sec. 24.1, and shown in Fig. 24A, shows that the reflected ray OR is partially plane-polarized and that only at a certain definite angle, about 57° for ordinary glass, is it plane-polarized.   It was Brewster who first discovered that at this polarizing angle $\bar{\phi}$ the reflected and refracted rays are just 90° apart.

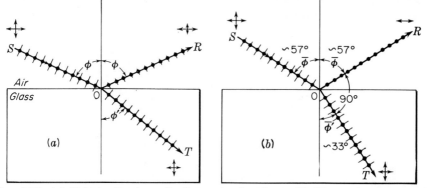

Fig. 24D. (a) Polarization by reflection and refraction.   (b) Illustrating Brewster's law for the polarizing angle.

This remarkable discovery enables one to correlate polarization with the refractive index

$$\frac{\sin \phi}{\sin \phi'} = n \qquad (24a)$$

Since at $\bar{\phi}$ the angle $ROT = 90°$, we have $\sin \bar{\phi}' = \cos \bar{\phi}$, giving

$$\frac{\sin \bar{\phi}}{\sin \bar{\phi}'} = \frac{\sin \bar{\phi}}{\cos \bar{\phi}} = n = \tan \bar{\phi} \qquad (24b)$$

This is *Brewster's law*, which shows that the angle of incidence for maximum polarization depends only on the refractive index.   It therefore varies somewhat with wavelength, but for ordinary glass the dispersion is such that the polarizing angle $\bar{\phi}$ does not change much over the whole visible spectrum.   This fact is readily verified by calculating $\bar{\phi}$ for several wavelengths, using the values of n from Table 23-I, as suggested in one of the problems at the end of this chapter.

It is not difficult to understand the physical reason why the light vibrating in the plane of incidence is not reflected at Brewster's angle. The incident light sets the electrons in the atoms of the material into oscillation, and it is the reradiation from these that generates the reflected beam.   Now when the latter is observed at 90° to the refracted beam, only the vibrations that are perpendicular to the plane of incidence can contribute. Those in the plane of incidence have no component traverse to the 90° direction and hence cannot radiate in that direction. The reason is the same as that which causes the radiation from a horizontal radio-transmitter antenna to drop to zero along the direction of the wires. If the student keeps this picture in mind, and remembers that light waves are strictly transverse, he will have no trouble remembering which of the two components is reflected at the polarizing angle.

24.4. Polarization by a Pile of Plates. Upon examining the refracted light in Fig. 24D(a) for polarization, it is found to be partially polarized

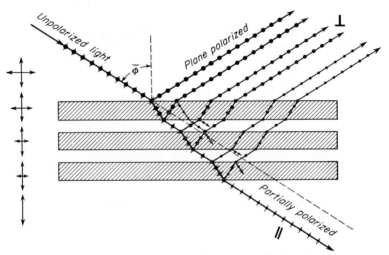

Fig. 24E. Polarization of light by a pile of glass plates.

for all angles of incidence, there being no angle at which the light is completely plane-polarized. The action of the reflecting surface may be described somewhat as follows: Let the ordinary incident light be thought of as being made up of two mutually perpendicular plane-polarized beams of light as shown in Sec. 24.2. Of those waves vibrating in the plane of incidence, i.e., in the plane of the page, part are reflected and part refracted for all angles with the single exception of the polarizing angle ϕ, for which all of the light is refracted. Of the waves vibrating perpendicular to the plane of incidence, some of the energy is reflected and the rest refracted for any angle of incidence. Thus the refracted ray always contains some of both planes of polarization. For a single surface of glass with $n = 1.50$, it will be shown later [Sec. 25.1 and Fig. 25B(a)] that at the polarizing angle 100 per cent of the light vibrating parallel to the plane of incidence is transmitted, whereas for the perpendicular vibrations only 85 per cent is transmitted, the other 15 per cent being reflected.

Obviously the degree of polarization of the transmitted beam is small for a single surface.

If a beam of ordinary light is incident at the polarizing angle on a pile of plates as shown in Fig. 24E, some of the vibrations perpendicular to the plane of incidence are reflected at each surface and all those parallel to it are refracted. The net result is that the reflected beams are all plane-polarized in the same plane, and the refracted beam, having lost more and more of its perpendicular vibrations, is partially plane-polarized. The larger the number of surfaces, the more nearly plane-polarized is this transmitted beam. This is illustrated by the vibration figures at the left in Fig. 24E. In a more detailed treatment of polarization by

Polarizer   Analyzer
(a)   (b)

FIG. 24F. Glass plates mounted at the polarizing angle $\bar{\phi}$.

reflection and refraction (see Chap. 25), the polarizing angle for *internal* reflection is shown to correspond exactly to the angle of refraction $\bar{\phi}'$ in Fig. 24D(b). This means that light internally reflected at the angle $\bar{\phi}'$ will also be plane-polarized.

The degree of polarization P of the transmitted light can be calculated by summing the intensities of the parallel and perpendicular components. If these intensities are called I_p and I_s, respectively, it has been shown* that

$$P = \frac{I_p - I_s}{I_p + I_s} = \frac{m}{m + \left(\dfrac{2n}{1 - n^2}\right)^2} \tag{24c}$$

where m is the number of plates (i.e., $2m$ surfaces) and n their refractive index. This equation shows that by the use of enough plates the degree of polarization can be made to approach unity, or 100 per cent. Better methods of producing a wide beam of polarized light are now available, and will be described below. The pile of plates may be used, however, to illustrate a common arrangement in the production and analysis of polarized light.

Figure 24F shows two such piles, the polarizer (a) and the analyzer

---

* F. Provostaye and P. Desains, *Ann. chim. et phys.*, **30**, 159, 1850. The calculation takes into account not only the ray going directly through, but also those internally reflected two or more times (see Fig. 24E). It does not, however, include any effects of absorption, which would increase P somewhat above the value given by Eq. 24c.

(*b*), with their planes of incidence parallel. The light emerging at *N* is nearly plane-polarized, and will be transmitted freely by the analyzer. Rotation of the latter by 90° about the line *NM* as an axis will cause the transmitted light to be nearly extinguished, since the vibrations are now perpendicular to the plane of incidence of the analyzer and will be reflected to the side. A further rotation of 90° will restore the light, and in a complete revolution there will be two maxima and two minima. Any arrangement of polarizer and analyzer in tandem is called a *polariscope*, and we shall see has numerous uses.

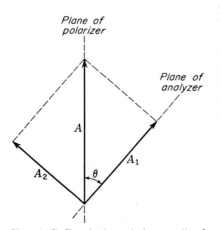

FIG. 24*G*. Resolution of the amplitude of plane-polarized light.

24.5. Law of Malus.[*] This law tells us how the intensity transmitted by the analyzer varies with the angle that its plane of transmission makes with that of the polarizer. In the case of two piles of plates, the plane of transmission is the plane of incidence, and for the law of Malus to hold we must assume that the transmitted light is completely plane-polarized. A better illustration would be the double-reflection experiment of Sec. 24.1, or a combination of two polaroids or nicol prisms (see below), for which the polarization is complete. Then the law of Malus states that the transmitted intensity varies as the *square of the cosine* of the angle between the two planes of transmission.

The proof of the law rests on the simple fact that any plane-polarized vibration—let us say the one produced by our polarizer—may be resolved into two components, one parallel to the transmission plane of the analyzer and the other at right angles to it. Only the first of these gets through. In Fig. 24*G*, let *A* represent the amplitude transmitted by the polarizer for which the plane of transmission intersects the plane of the figure in the vertical dashed line. When this light strikes the analyzer, set at the angle θ, one may resolve the incident amplitude into components A_1 and A_2, the latter of which is eliminated in the analyzer. In the pile of plates, it is reflected to one side. The amplitude of the light that passes through the analyzer is therefore

$$A_1 = A \cos \theta \qquad (24d)$$

* Étienne Malus (1775–1812). French army engineer. His discovery of polarization by reflection was made by accident when looking through a calcite crystal at the light reflected from the windows of the Luxembourg Palace.

and its intensity

$$I_1 = A_1{}^2 = A^2 \cos^2 \theta$$
$$= I_0 \cos^2 \theta \qquad (24e)$$

Here I_0 signifies the intensity of the incident polarized light. This is, of course, one-half of the intensity of the unpolarized light striking the polarizer, provided one neglects losses of light by absorption in traversing it. There will also be losses in the analyzer. For polaroids or nicols there will be some light that is removed from the beam by reflection at the surfaces. Although these effects are neglected in deriving Eq. 24e,

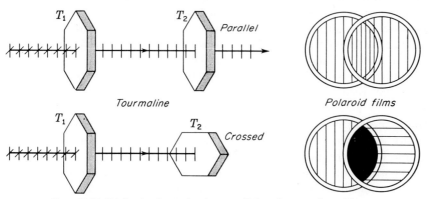

FIG. 24H. Dichroic sheets in the parallel and crossed positions.

it will be noticed that they change only the constant in the equation and do not spoil the dependence of the *relative* intensity on $\cos^2 \theta$. Thus Malus' law is rigorously true and applies for example to the intensity of the twice-reflected light in the experiment of Sec. 24.1, even though its maximum value is only a small fraction of the original intensity. In such cases, the I_0 in Eq. 24e is merely the intensity when the analyzer is parallel to the polarizer.

24.6. Polarization by Dichroic Crystals. These crystals have the property of selectivity absorbing one of the two rectangular components of ordinary light. Dichroism is exhibited by a number of minerals and by some organic compounds. Perhaps the best known of the mineral crystals is *tourmaline*. When a pencil of ordinary light is sent through a thin slab of tourmaline like T_1, shown in Fig. 24H, the transmitted light is found to be polarized. This can be verified by a second crystal T_2. With T_1 and T_2 parallel to each other the light transmitted by the first crystal is also transmitted by the second. When the second crystal is rotated through 90°, no light gets through. The observed effect is due to a selective absorption by tourmaline of all light rays vibrating in one particular plane (called, for reasons explained below, the O vibrations) but not those vibrating in a plane at right angles (called the *E* vibrations). Thus in the figures shown, only the *E* vibrations parallel to the long edges of the crystals are transmitted so that no light will emerge from the crossed crystals. Since tourmaline crystals are somewhat colored, they are not used in optical instruments as polarizing or analyzing devices.

Attempts to produce polarizing crystals of large aperture were made by Herapath* in 1852. He was successful in producing good but small crystals of the organic compound iodosulfate of quinine (now known as herapathite) which completely absorbs one component of polarization and transmits the other with little loss. One variety of the so-called *polaroid film* contains crystals of this substance. Polaroid was invented in 1932 by Land,† and has found uses in many different kinds of optical instruments. These films consist of thin sheets of nitrocellulose packed with ultramicroscopic polarizing crystals with their optic axes all parallel. In more recent developments the lining-up process is accomplished somewhat as follows: Polyvinyl alcohol films are stretched to line up the complex molecules and then are impregnated with iodine. From X-ray diffraction studies of these dichroic films, it can be seen that the iodine is present in polymeric form, i.e., as independent long strings of iodine atoms all lying parallel to the fiber axis, with a periodicity in this direction of about 3.10 Å. Films prepared in this way are called H-Polaroid. Land and Rogers found further that, when an oriented transparent film of polyvinyl alcohol is heated in the presence of an active dehydrating catalyst such as hydrogen chloride, the film darkens slightly and becomes strongly dichroic. Such a film becomes very stable and, having no dyestuffs, is not bleached by strong sunlight. This so-called K-Polaroid is very suitable for polarizing films for uses such as automobile headlights and visors.

24.7. Double Refraction. The production and study of polarized light over a wider range of wavelengths than is afforded by polaroid use the phenomenon of double refraction in crystals of *calcite* and *quartz*. Both of these crystals are found in nature to be transparent to visible as well as to ultraviolet light. Calcite, which chemically is calcium carbonate ($CaCO_3$) occurs in nature in a great variety of crystal forms (in the rhombohedral class of the hexagonal system), but it breaks readily into simple cleavage rhombohedrons of the form shown at the left in Fig. 24*I*. Each face of the crystal is a parallelogram whose angles are 78°5′ and 101°55′. If struck a blow with a sharp instrument, each crystal may be made to cleave or break along cleavage planes into two or more smaller

---

* W. B. Herapath, *Phil. Mag.*, **3**, 161, 1852.

† A good summary of the development of sheet polarizers is given by E. H. Land, *J. Opt. Soc. Am.*, **41**, 957, 1951.

crystals which always have faces that are parallelograms with these same angles.

Quartz crystals, on the other hand, are found in their natural state to have many different forms, one of the more complicated of which is shown at the right in Fig. 24*I*. Unlike cal-
cite, quartz crystals will not cleave along crystal planes but will break into irregular pieces when given a sharp blow. Quartz is pure silica (SiO_2). Further details concerning these crystals will be given in this as well as in the three following chapters.

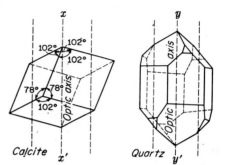

When a beam of ordinary unpolar-
ized light is incident on a calcite or quartz crystal, there will be, in ad-
dition to the reflected beam, two refracted beams in place of the usual single one observed, for example, in

Fig. 24*I*. Calcite and quartz crystal forms. The direction of the optic axis is indicated.

glass. This phenomenon, shown in Fig. 24*J* for calcite, is called *double refraction*. Upon measuring the angles of refraction ϕ' for different angles of incidence ϕ, one finds that Snell's law of refraction

$$\frac{\sin \phi}{\sin \phi'} = n \tag{24f}$$

holds for one ray but not for the other. The ray for which the law holds is called the *ordinary* or *O ray* and the other is called the *extraordinary* or *E ray*.

Fig. 24*J*. Illustrating double refraction of light in a calcite crystal.

Since the two opposite faces of a calcite crystal are always parallel, the two refracted rays emerge parallel to the incident beam and there-
fore parallel to each other. Inside the crystal the ordinary ray is always to be found in the plane of incidence. Only for special directions through the crystal is this true for the extraordinary ray. If the incident light is normal to the surface the extraordinary ray will be refracted at some angle that is not zero and will come out parallel to, but displaced from, the incident beam; the ordinary ray will pass straight through without

deviation. A rotation of the crystal about the O ray will in this case cause the E ray to rotate around the fixed O ray.

24.8. Optic Axis. Calcite and quartz are examples of *anisotropic* crystals, or ones in which the physical properties vary with direction. All crystals except those belonging to the cubic system are anisotropic to a greater or less degree. Furthermore, the two examples chosen show the simple type of anisotropy which characterizes *uniaxial* crystals. In these there is a single direction called the *optic axis*, which is an axis of symmetry with respect to both the crystal form and the arrangement of atoms. If any property, such as the heat conductivity, is measured for different directions, it is found to be the same along any line perpendicular to the optic axis. At other angles it changes, reaching a maximum or a minimum along the axis. The directions of the optic axes in calcite and quartz are shown in Fig. 24*I*.

The double refraction in uniaxial crystals disappears when the light is made to enter the crystal so that it travels along the optic axis. That is, there is no separation of the O and E rays in this case. This is also true in directions at right angles to the axis, but here the O and E rays behave differently in a less obvious respect, namely, they differ in velocity. The consequences of the latter difference will be examined in Chap. 27.

The direction of the optic axis in calcite is determined by drawing a line like xx' through a *blunt corner* of the crystal, so that it makes equal angles with all faces. A blunt corner is one where three obtuse face angles come together, and there are only two such corners more or less opposite each other. In quartz the optic axis yy' runs lengthwise of the crystal, its direction being parallel to the six side faces, as shown. It should be emphasized that the optic axis is not a particular line through the crystal but a *direction*. That is, for any given point in the crystal an optic axis may be drawn which will be parallel to that for any other point.

24.9. Principal Sections and Principal Planes. In specifying the positions of crystals, and also the directions of rays and vibrations, it is convenient to use the principal section, made by a plane containing the optic axis and normal to any cleavage face. For a point in calcite, there are therefore three principal sections, one for each pair of opposite crystal faces. A principal section always cuts the surfaces of a calcite crystal in a parallelogram with angles of 71° and 109°, as shown at the left in Fig. 24*J*. An end view of a principal section cuts the surface in a line parallel to AB, shown as a dotted line in the right-hand figure. All other planes through the crystal parallel to the plane represented by AB are also principal sections. These are represented by the other dotted lines.

The principal section, as so defined, does not always suffice in describing the directions of vibrations. Here we make use of the two other planes, the *principal plane of the ordinary ray*, a plane containing the optic axis and the ordinary ray, and the *principal plane of the extraordinary ray*, one containing the optic axis and the extraordinary ray. The ordinary ray always lies in the plane of incidence. This is not generally true for the extraordinary ray. The principal planes of the two refracted rays do not coincide except in special cases. The special cases are those for which the plane of incidence is a principal section as shown in

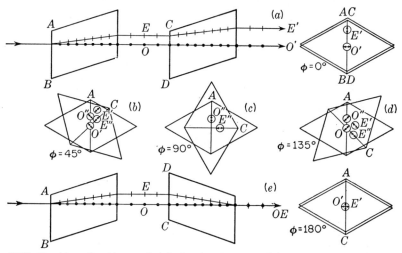

FIG. 24*K*. Double refraction and polarization in two calcite crystals with their principal sections making different angles.

Fig. 24*J*. Under these conditions the plane of incidence, the principal section, and the principal planes of the *O* and *E* rays all coincide.

24.10. Polarization by Double Refraction. The polarization of light by double refraction in calcite was discovered by Huygens in 1678. He sent a beam of light through two crystals as shown at the top of Fig. 24*K*. If the principal sections are parallel, the two rays *O'* and *E'* are separated by a distance equal to the sum of the two displacements found in each crystal if used separately. Upon rotation of the second crystal each of the two rays *O* and *E* is refracted into two parts, making four as shown by an end-on view in (*b*). At the 90° position (*c*) the original *O'* and *E'* rays have faded and vanished and the new rays *O''* and *E''* have reached a maximum of intensity. Further rotation finds the original rays appearing and eventually, if the crystals are of equal thickness, these come together into a single beam in the center for the 180° position shown at the bottom, the rays *O''* and *E''* having now vanished.

Thus, merely by using two natural crystals of calcite, Huygens was able to demonstrate the polarization of light. The explanation of the movement of the light rays is one simply of deviation by refraction and easily understood. The varying intensity of the spots, however, involves the polarization of the two light beams leaving the first crystal. In brief the explanation is somewhat as follows: Ordinary light upon entering the first calcite crystal is broken up into two plane-polarized rays, one, the O ray, vibrating perpendicular to the principal plane, which is here the same as the principal section, and the other, the E ray, vibrating in the principal section. In other words, the crystal resolves the light into two components by causing one type of vibration to travel one path and the other vibration to travel another path.

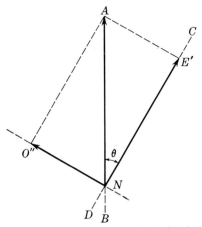

Consider more in detail now what happens to one of the plane-polarized beams from the first crystal when it passes through the second crystal oriented at some arbitrary angle θ. Let A in Fig. 24L represent the amplitude of the E ray vibrating parallel to the principal section of the first crystal just as it strikes the face of the second crystal. This second crystal, like the first, transmits light vibrating in its principal section along one path and light vibrating at right

Fig. 24L. Resolution of polarized light into components by double refraction.

angles along another path. The E ray is therefore split up into two components E' with an amplitude $A \cos \theta$ and O'' with an amplitude $A \sin \theta$. These emerge from the second crystal with relative intensities given by $A^2 \cos^2 \theta$ and $A^2 \sin^2 \theta$. At $\theta = 90°$ E' vanishes and O'' reaches a maximum intensity of A^2. At all positions the sum of the two components, $A^2 \sin^2 \theta + A^2 \cos^2 \theta$, is just equal to A^2, the intensity of the incident beam.

The same treatment holds for the splitting up of the O beam from the first crystal into two plane-polarized beams O' and E''.

24.11. Nicol Prism. This very useful polarizing device is made from a calcite crystal, and derives its name from its inventor.* The nicol prism is made in such a way that it removes one of the two refracted rays by total reflection, as is illustrated in Fig. 24M. There are several different

* William Nicol (1768–1851). Scotch natural philosopher, who became very skillful in cutting and polishing gems and crystals. He devised his prism in 1828, and it is reported that he himself did not completely understand how it worked.

forms of nicol prism,* but we shall describe here one of the commonest ones. First a crystal about three times as long as it is wide is taken, and the ends cut down from 71° in the principal section to a more acute angle of 68°. The crystal is then cut apart along the plane $A'D'$ perpendicular to both the principal section and the end faces. The two cut surfaces are ground and polished optically flat and then cemented together with Canada balsam. Canada balsam is used because it is a clear transparent

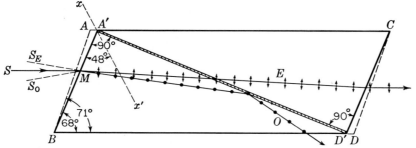

FIG. 24M. Detailed diagram of a nicol prism, showing how it is made from a calcite crystal.

substance with an index of refraction about midway between the index of the O and E rays. For sodium light,

Index of O ray.................... $n_O = 1.65836$
Index of Canada balsam.......... $n_B = 1.55$
Index of E ray.................... $n_E = 1.48641$

Optically the balsam is more dense than the calcite for the E ray, and less dense for the O ray. The E ray therefore will be refracted into the balsam and on through the calcite crystal, whereas the O ray for large angles of incidence will be totally reflected. The critical angle for total reflection of the O ray at the first calcite to balsam surface is about 69° and corresponds to a limiting angle SMS_0 in Fig. 24M of about 14°. At greater angles than this, some of the O ray will be transmitted. This means that a nicol should not be used in light which is highly convergent or divergent.

The E ray in a nicol also has an angular limit, beyond which it will be totally reflected by the balsam. This is due to the fact that the index of refraction of calcite is different for different directions through the crystal. In the next chapter it will be seen that the index $n_E = 1.486$, as it is usually given, applies only in the special case of light traveling at

* Very complete descriptions of polarizing prisms will be found in A. Johannsen, "Manual of Petrographic Methods," 2d ed , pp. 158–164, McGraw-Hill Book Company, Inc., New York, 1918.

right angles to the optic axis. Along the optic axis the E ray travels with the same speed as the O ray and it therefore has the same index of 1.658. For intermediate angles the effective index lies between these two limits 1.486 and 1.658. There will therefore be a maximum angle SMS_E beyond which the balsam will be optically less dense than the calcite, and there will be total reflection of the E vibrations. The prism is so cut that this angle likewise is in the neighborhood of 14°. The direction of the incident light on a nicol therefore is limited on the one side to avoid having the O ray transmitted and on the other side to

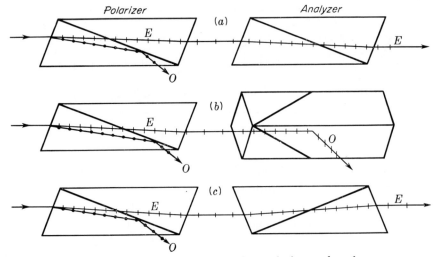

Fig. 24N. Two nicol prisms mounted as polarizer and analyzer.

avoid having the E ray totally reflected. In practice, it is important to keep this limitation in mind.

Polarizing prisms are sometimes made with end faces cut perpendicular to the sides so that the light enters and leaves normal to the surface. The most popular one of this type, the *Glan-Thompson prism*, has an angular tolerance or aperture approaching 40°, hence much larger than that of the nicol. But this prism must be cut with the optic axis parallel to the end faces and is wasteful of calcite, large crystals of which are expensive and difficult to obtain. In another type the halves are held together so that there is a film of air between them instead of balsam. This device, called the *Foucault prism*, will transmit ultraviolet light. It has an angular aperture of only about 8°, however, and some difficulty is experienced with interference occurring in the air film.

24.12. Parallel and Crossed Nicols. When two nicol prisms are lined up one behind the other, as shown in Fig. 24N, they form as good polariscope (Sec. 24.4). Positions (a) and (c) are referred to as "parallel nicols," and for them the E ray is transmitted. A loss of some 10 per cent of the incident light is caused by reflection at the prism faces and absorption in the balsam layer, so that the over-all transmission of a nicol for incident unpolarized light is about 40 per cent. Position (b) in the figure represents one of the two positions called "crossed nicols." Here the E ray from the first nicol becomes an O ray in the second, and is totally reflected to the side. For intermediate angles, the incident E vibrations from the first nicol are broken up into components as shown by the vector diagram in Fig. 24L, where θ is the angle between the principal sections of the two nicols. The E' component is transmitted by the second nicol with the intensity $A^2 \cos^2 \theta$ and the O'' component is totally reflected.

24.13. Refraction by Calcite Prisms. Calcite prisms are sometimes cut from crystals for the purpose of illustrating double refraction and dispersion simultaneously as well as single refraction along the optic axis.

FIG. 24O. Double and single refraction of white light by prisms cut from calcite crystals.

Two regular prisms of calcite are shown in Fig. 24O, the first cut with the optic axis parallel to the refracting edge A, and the other with the axis also parallel to the base and perpendicular to the refracting edge. In the first prism there is double refraction for all wavelengths and hence two complete spectra of plane-polarized light, one with the electric vector parallel to the plane of incidence and the other with the electric vector perpendicular to it. An interesting demonstration of this polarization is accomplished by inserting a polarizer* into the incident or refracted beams. Upon rotation of the polarizer, first one spectrum is extinguished and then the other.

In the second prism, Fig. 24O(b), only one spectrum is observed as is the case with glass prisms. Here the light travels along the optic axis, or very nearly so, so that the two spectra are superposed. In this case a polarizer, when rotated, will not affect the intensity as it does with

---

* Although nicol prisms give the most complete polarization of any of the devices commonly found in laboratories, polaroid films or a pile of glass plates mounted as in Fig. 24F are quite suitable for nearly all experimental demonstrations.

the first prism. The more detailed treatment of double refraction in Chap. 26 will clarify these experimental observations.

24.14. Rochon and Wollaston Prisms. It is often desirable to split a light beam into two plane-polarized components, retaining both of them for a later comparison of their intensities. For this purpose other types of prisms have been designed, the most satisfactory of which are the Rochon and Wollaston prisms. These optical devices, sometimes called double-image prisms, are made of quartz or calcite, cut at certain definite angles and cemented together with glycerine or castor oil.

In the Rochon prism [Fig. 24$P(a)$] the light, entering normal to the surface, travels along the optic axis of the first prism and then undergoes

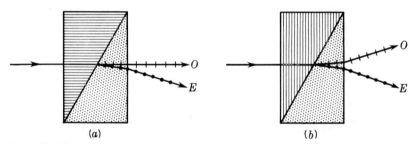

Fig. 24P. Diagrams of (a) Rochon and (b) Wollaston prisms made from quartz.

double refraction at the boundary of the second prism. The optic axis of the second prism is perpendicular to the plane of the page, as is indicated by the dots. In the Wollaston prism [Fig. 24$P(b)$] the light enters normal to the surface and travels perpendicular to the optic axis until it strikes the second prism, where double refraction takes place. The essential difference between the two is shown in the figures by the directions of the two refracted rays. The Rochon prism transmits the O vibrations without deviation, the beam being achromatic. This is frequently desired in optical instruments where only one plane-polarized beam is desired. The E beam, which is chromatic, is readily screened off at a sufficiently large distance from the prism.

The Wollaston prism deviates both rays and consequently yields greater separation of the two slightly chromatic beams. It is commonly used where a comparison of intensities is desired. These intensities will of course be equal for unpolarized light, but will differ if the light is polarized in any way. It should be noted that in the Rochon prism the light should always enter from the left, in order for it to travel first along the optic axis, as shown in the figure. If it is sent in the other direction, the different wavelengths will emerge vibrating in different planes because of a phenomenon known as rotatory dispersion (see Sec. 28.2). This phenomenon, as well as the directions taken by the doubly refracted beams in quartz, will be treated in detail in the following chapters.

24.15. Polarization by Scattering. Scattering is not a practical means of polarizing light because the polarization is usually incomplete and the intensity quite low. The study of polarization effects in the light scattered by small particles does, however, give interesting information on the nature of the particles and of the light itself. If one looks at the blue sky through a nicol or polaroid, observing at right angles to the direction of the sun, i.e., along the line QP of Fig. 24$Q(a)$, the intensity will

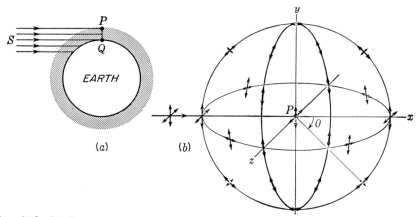

(a) (b)

FIG. 24Q. (a) Scattering of light by the earth's atmosphere. (b) Polarization by scattering from a single particle.

vary considerably as the analyzer is rotated. Thus the light of the sky is at least partially polarized by scattering.

This polarization is direct evidence of the transverse character of light waves. In Fig. 24$Q(b)$ let P represent a small charged particle, say, an electron in an atom or molecule. Unpolarized electromagnetic waves are incident from the left, and cause the particle to execute forced vibrations having the frequency of the waves. These vibrations will generate spherical scattered waves the amplitude and polarization of which will vary with direction as indicated in the figure. The amplitude is proportional to the *projection* of the amplitude of the oscillator perpendicular to the line of sight. Thus for forced vibrations in the y direction of Fig. 24$Q(b)$ the scattered amplitude in the x,y plane will vary as $\cos \theta$, going to zero at right angles, i.e., along the y axis. For those in the z direction it will remain constant for any direction in the x,y plane, but will decrease in the x,z plane to zero along the z axis. The intensity of Rayleigh scattering of incident unpolarized light is proportional to the sum of the squares of the two scattered amplitudes, and hence to $1 + \cos^2 \theta$. It reaches its maximum value in the forward and backward directions.

In any direction at right angles to the primary beam, the scattered light on this simple picture should be completely plane-polarized. It will be seen that this is a consequence of the absence of any longitudinal component (along x) in the light acting on P. At other angles θ the light should be partially polarized, the degree of polarization approaching zero as θ approaches 0° or 180°. As it is usually observed, for example, in the light from the sky, the polarization at 90° is not complete. Any one of three causes may be responsible for this:

1. *Multiple scattering.* If the light reaching the observer has been scattered two or more times, the space relations are more complicated and the conclusions are different.
2. *Molecular anisotropy.* In many molecules the displacement of the electron is not in the same direction as the impressed field. This is the principal reason why the sky light is not completely polarized.
3. *Size of the particles.* Only where Rayleigh scattering is applicable, namely, when the particles are much smaller than a wavelength, is complete polarization expected. This is the only condition under which we can treat the radiation from the individual oscillators as being independent. The larger the particles, the less the degree of polarization.

An interesting experiment to show both the polarization of the scattered light and the origin of the blue sky and red sunset may be performed as shown in Fig. 24R. Light from a bright source S (sunlight or a carbon

FIG. 24R. Experimental arrangement for demonstrating polarization by scattering, and for showing the origin of the blue sky and red sunset.

arc) is made to pass through a lens L_1, a tank of clear water T, a screen with a circular aperture I, a lens L_2, and finally to a screen W. Lens L_1 produces a parallel beam of light in the tank, and L_2 focuses an image of the circular opening I on the screen. About 20 g of photographic fixing powder (hyposulfite of soda) are dissolved in each gallon of water in the tank T. This tank should be from 12 to 24 in. long. If about 1 to 2 cc of concentrated sulfuric acid is now added to the tank, fine microscopic sulfur particles will begin to precipitate slowly. The correct amount of salt and acid to produce the best effect must be determined by trial.   It should take 2 or 3 min for the first visible precipitate to form.

As the particles begin to form, scattered blue light will mark the path of the beam of light through the tank.   Viewed through a nicol prism or other analyzer, from a direction at right angles to the light beam, the light is first found to be plane-polarized and later, after more particles have formed, to be partially polarized, as predicted.   The bright circular image on the screen, representing the sun, will be observed to change slowly from white to yellow then to orange and finally red.   In the latter stages of the experiment multiple scattering causes the whole front end of the tank to be blue.   The other end is yellow and orange since the blue and violet has been scattered out of the beam.   When the demonstration is for an audience where individual analyzers are not to be had, a large nicol or polarizing plate can be inserted at the position P.   Upon rotating this polarizer the scattering is made to appear or disappear with each 90° rotation.   A large mirror M placed directly above the tank will in this case show the beam alternately in the mirror and in the tank.

In performing an experiment of this kind Tyndall was the first to observe another type of scattering when the particles become large enough to scatter white light.   If the white scattered light is viewed through a nicol held in the position for the ordinary extinction of blue scattered light, the blue color appears again with increased brilliancy. This Tyndall called the residual blue.   A theoretical consideration of the phenomenon by Rayleigh shows that this scattering is proportional to ν^8.   With smaller particles the residual blue vanishes and a zero minimum is observed.

PROBLEMS

1. Prove that when light strikes a plane-parallel glass plate at the polarizing angle the refracted beam also falls on the second surface at its polarizing angle.

2. Compute the variation of the polarizing angle through the visible spectrum (4000 to 7200 Å) for the borosilicate crown glass listed in Table 23-I.   Give only the values at the extreme limits and their difference.   *Ans.* 56.75°.   56.43°.   19'15''.

3. The effective intensity of a source is reduced by the use of a polarizer and analyzer whose relative orientation is θ.   To what accuracy, in degrees, must θ be known to obtain an accuracy of 2 per cent in the intensity of the transmitted light, at a setting which reduces the intensity in a ratio of approximately 1:7?

4. Light is reflected from a smooth surface of water at such an angle that the reflected beam is completely plane-polarized.   (*a*) What are the angles of incidence and refraction?   (*b*) Describe what would be seen if the reflected image of the source were viewed through a calcite crystal which is rotated about the direction of the reflected rays.

Ans. (*a*) 53.12°; 36.88°.   (*b*) Two images, E disappearing when principal section of calcite parallel to plane of incidence, O when perpendicular.

5. Natural light is partially polarized by passing it through a single glass plate at the polarizing angle. Assuming 15 per cent reflection of the intensity of the s vibrations at each surface (corresponding to $n = 1.50$), find the degree of polarization (a) if multiple reflections within the plate are neglected, (b) if they are taken into account. Make a similar comparison for 16 plates.

6. Unpolarized light is sent through three dichroic polarizers, the second of which is oriented at 20° with the first, and the third at 40° with the first in the same sense. What intensity gets through the system, relative to that of the incident unpolarized light? *Ans.* $0.39I_0$.

7. Calculate the relative intensities of the four images O', E', O'', and E'' obtained in the two-crystal experiment (Fig. 24K), when the angle between the principal sections is 70°.

8. Find the angular divergence of the beams from a Rochon prism made of calcite, if the refracting angles of the component prisms are 20°. *Ans.* 3.62°.

9. The effective index of refraction for the E ray in a nicol prism, when the ray was traveling along the axis of the latter before entering it, can be computed to be 1.535. Find the angle between the O- and E-wave normals in the nicol.

10. A crystal is placed in a polariscope, the polarizer and analyzer being parallel. The principal section of the crystal makes an angle of 24° with the planes of transmission of the polarizer and analyzer. Find the ratio of the intensities of the O and E beams, (a) as they leave the crystal, (b) after they have passed through the analyzer. *Ans.* (a) 0.198. (b) 0.039.

11. Find the lengths of the two polarized spectra illustrated in Fig. 24O, if they are projected on a screen 2 m from the prism. Take the limiting wavelengths to be the Hg line, λ4046, and the He line, λ7065. Find also the distance between the red line in the two spectra. The refracting angle is 60°, and the refractive indices for calcite may be found in Table 26-I.

12. Calculate the degree of polarization of the light due to Rayleigh scattering at 135° with the direction of the primary beam. Calculate also the intensity of this light relative to that scattered straight backward. *Ans.* 33.3%. 0.75.

13. In the Glan-Thompson prism the optic axis is perpendicular to the longitudinal axis of the prism, and the diagonal dividing plane makes an angle of 22° with the longitudinal axis. The prism halves are usually put together with linseed oil ($n = 1.4896$). Verify the fact that total reflection of the O ray occurs under these conditions. What would happen if the prism halves were cemented with Canada balsam? What disadvantage do you see in cementing with the latter substance?

14. In a Wollaston prism of quartz having refracting angles of 30°, what will be the separation of color (Fraunhofer C to F lines) relative to the separation of the polarized beams (D line)? For refractive indices, see Table 26-I. *Ans.* 0.0142.

15. The absorption coefficient of a sample of tourmaline for the O ray is 3.6 per cm, and for the E ray is 0.8 per cm. What thickness would be required to give a degree of polarization of the transmitted light of 98 per cent?

CHAPTER 25

REFLECTION

Among the subjects touched upon in the last chapter the first to be discussed in greater detail will be related to the sections on polarization by reflection and transmission. There we considered the effects at the particular angle of incidence called the polarizing angle. Going beyond this special case, we shall now investigate the characteristics of the reflected and transmitted light as they depend on wavelength, polarization, and angle of incidence. It will be assumed that the surfaces are optically smooth, which means that any irregularities are small compared with the wavelength. The properties of the reflecting substance play an essential role, and among these absorption is an important one. Metals are in general the best reflectors, a fact which will be found to be related to their ability to conduct electricity, and consequent high absorption. We begin, however, with the simpler case of nonconducting dielectric materials like glass.

25.1. Reflection from Dielectrics. The essential features of reflection from a single glass surface are briefly described as follows: At normal incidence about 4 per cent of the intensity of a beam of unpolarized visible light is reflected, and the other 96 per cent is transmitted. At other angles of incidence the reflecting power increases with angle, at first slowly and then more rapidly until at 90°, i.e., grazing incidence, all the light is reflected.

It was shown at the beginning of the last chapter that there is one angle of incidence for which the reflected light is completely plane-polarized with its electric vector perpendicular to the plane of incidence. At angles different from this the reflected light is only partially polarized. The relations in this case are most easily described in terms of the reflection of the two plane-polarized components of the incident unpolarized light, the vibrations of which are, respectively, parallel and perpendicular to the plane of incidence. In the laboratory this is usually done by examining the reflected light that passes through a nicol or other polarizer (see Fig. 25A). If the nicol is oriented with its principal section parallel to the plane of incidence, the p vibrations, i.e., the vibrations parallel to the plane of incidence, can be measured. Rotation of the nicol through 90° then allows the *s* vibrations perpendicular to the plane of incidence (*s* stands for the German *senkrecht*, meaning "perpendicular") to be measured. The results of such an experiment when plotted against the angle of incidence ϕ are represented by the two solid curves shown in

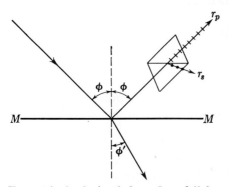

Fig. 25B(a). The ordinates are r_p, the fraction of the incident *p* light reflected, and r_s, the corresponding fraction for the *s* light. These fractions are called the *reflectances* for *p* and *s* light. Part (b) of the figure refers to the amplitudes and will be discussed below.

The curves of Fig. 25B are represented very accurately by theoretical equations which were first derived by Fresnel from the elastic-solid theory and are known as *Fresnel's laws of reflection*. Their

FIG. 25A. Analysis of the reflected light into its two plane-polarized components.

derivation by the electromagnetic theory will be given in Sec. 25.13, but for the present we shall merely state them and show their application to the main features of reflection from dielectrics. The laws may be written

$$\frac{R_s}{E_s} = -\frac{\sin (\phi - \phi')}{\sin (\phi + \phi')} \qquad \frac{R_p}{E_p} = \frac{\tan (\phi - \phi')}{\tan (\phi + \phi')} \tag{25a}$$

$$\frac{E_s'}{E_s} = \frac{2 \sin \phi' \cos \phi}{\sin (\phi + \phi')} \qquad \frac{E_p'}{E_p} = \frac{2 \sin \phi' \cos \phi}{\sin (\phi + \phi') \cos (\phi - \phi')} \tag{25b}$$

Here the symbols E, R, and E' mean the amplitudes of the electric vectors in the incident, reflected, and refracted light, respectively, the subscripts denoting the two planes of vibration. The angles ϕ and ϕ', following our usual notation, are the angles of incidence and refraction.

The fractional amplitudes given by Eqs. 25a and 25b are plotted against the angle of incidence in Fig. 25B(b), the values of ϕ and ϕ' used in the equations corresponding to the index of refraction 1.50. Solid curves represent the amplitudes, both positive and negative, as they are given by the equations, while the absolute magnitudes of the reflected components are shown by broken curves. The negative signs indicate phase changes of π, which will be discussed below. These, however, are immaterial for the intensities since the latter are dependent on the squares of the amplitudes.

The reflectances are given by

$$r_s = \frac{R_s{}^2}{E_s{}^2} \qquad r_p = \frac{R_p{}^2}{E_p{}^2} \tag{25c}$$

and these are the curves in part (a) of the figure. At normal incidence, where $\phi = 0$, the parallel and perpendicular components must be equally reflected because here the plane of incidence is undefined and the two components are not distinguishable. With increasing ϕ, r_p drops and r_s rises until at the polarizing angle their values are zero and 15 per cent, respectively. At grazing incidence both components are totally reflected. Even an unsilvered glass surface becomes a nearly perfect mirror when the light source is viewed very close to the reflecting plane. It is easily

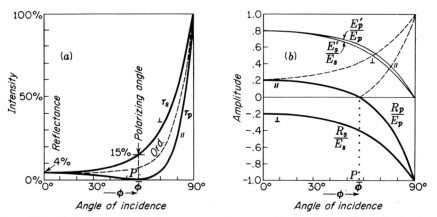

FIG. 25B. Reflectances and the corresponding amplitudes for a dielectric having $n = 1.50$.

verified that the glaze on a page of this book becomes highly reflecting at a grazing angle.

The value of the reflectance at normal incidence does not follow immediately from Eqs. (25a) by setting $\phi = 0$, since this substitution gives an indeterminate result. It can be evaluated, however, as follows: Since both ϕ and ϕ' become small as we approach perpendicular incidence, we may set the tangents equal to the sines, obtaining

$$\frac{R_p}{E_p} = -\frac{R_s}{E_s} = \frac{\sin(\phi - \phi')}{\sin(\phi + \phi')} = \frac{\sin\phi\cos\phi' - \cos\phi\sin\phi'}{\sin\phi\cos\phi' + \cos\phi\sin\phi'}$$

Dividing numerator and denominator of the last expression by $\sin\phi'$ and replacing $\sin\phi/\sin\phi'$ by n, we find that it reduces to

$$\frac{R}{E} = \frac{n\cos\phi' - \cos\phi}{n\cos\phi' + \cos\phi} \simeq \frac{n-1}{n+1} \tag{25d}$$

The approximate equality becomes exact in the limit when the angles become zero. Hence the reflectance at normal incidence is

$$r = \frac{R^2}{E^2} = \left(\frac{n-1}{n+1}\right)^2 \tag{25e}$$

This very useful equation gives the reflectance at $\phi = 0$ for any single clean surface of a dielectric. Thus a glass having $n = 1.50$ has $r = 0.04$, or exactly 4 per cent, as indicated in Fig. 25B(a).

25.2. Intensities of the Transmitted Light. One might expect that the transmitted intensities would be complementary to the reflected ones, so that the two would add to give the incident intensity, but this is not so. The intensity is defined as the energy crossing unit area per second, and the cross-sectional area of the refracted beam is different from that of the incident and reflected beams except at normal incidence. It is the total energy in these beams that is complementary. There are, however, simple relations between the incident, reflected, and transmitted *amplitudes*, which follow, as we shall show later, from the boundary conditions of electromagnetic theory. These are

$$\frac{E'_s}{E_s} - \frac{R_s}{E_s} = 1 \qquad \text{and} \qquad n\frac{E'_p}{E_p} - \frac{R_p}{E_p} = 1 \qquad (25f)$$

In Fig. 25B(b) it will be seen that the curves for E'_s and R_s run parallel to each other. Those for E'_p and R_p are not parallel, but become so if the ordinates of the former curve are multiplied by n. Since Eqs. 25f are simpler than the Fresnel equations 25b, it is sufficient to remember only the former in addition to Eqs. 25a in order to solve problems involving transmitted amplitudes and intensities.

The fraction of the incident intensity that is transmitted, or the transmittance, when light enters a dielectric of refractive index n is not given directly by the square of the relative amplitude. The intensity in the medium according to Eq. 23q also contains a factor n, so that the transmittance becomes $n(E'/E)^2$. Now, as stated above, the sum of this and the reflectance $(R/E)^2$ does not equal unity, as may easily be verified from Eqs. 25a and 25b. The total energy flux in the refracted beam is its intensity times its area, and the latter differs from that of the incident or reflected beams in the ratio $\cos \phi'/\cos \phi$. Conservation of energy is then expressed by the relation

$$\left(\frac{R}{E}\right)^2 + n\left(\frac{E'}{E}\right)^2 \frac{\cos \phi'}{\cos \phi} = 1$$

which applies to either s or p light.

25.3. Internal Reflection. In the above discussion it was assumed that the light strikes the boundary from the side of the optically less dense medium (usually air) so that we were dealing with the so-called rare-to-dense, or *external, reflection*. Fresnel's laws apply equally well to the case of dense-to-rare, or *internal, reflection*. If the same value of n is to be retained for the dense medium, the latter case merely involves the exchange of ϕ and ϕ' in the equations. The resulting curves are plotted in Fig. 25C, the reflectances in (a) and the amplitudes in (b). Up to the critical angle $\phi_c = 41°$ these resemble the curves for external reflection, starting with $r = 4$ per cent at normal incidence and diverging until the polarizing angle $\bar{\phi}$ is reached. This angle, 33°, corresponds to the angle of refraction at the polarizing angle in the external case, since the angle in the rarer medium (57°) must be such as to render the refracted and reflected rays perpendicular to each other.

At the critical angle the refracted ray leaves at a grazing angle, and the internal reflectance becomes 100 per cent just as for external reflection

Fig. 25C. Intensity and amplitude curves for internal reflection. $n = 1.54$.

at grazing incidence. When ϕ exceeds the critical angle, Fresnel's equations contain imaginary quantities but as we shall see may still be used. It will be found that the reflection remains total but that there is a continually changing phase shift.

25.4. Phase Changes on Reflection. Returning for the moment to external reflection where $\phi > \phi'$ through the whole range, we find from Eqs. 25a that the sign of R_s/E_s is always negative. This means that there is an abrupt change of phase of 180° in the process of reflection. We express it by writing $\delta_s = \pi$. For the p light the sign is positive for small ϕ, indicating no phase change, but when the condition $\phi + \phi' = 90°$ is reached, the tangent in the denominator goes to infinity and changes sign. Thus δ_p changes abruptly from zero to π at the polarizing angle. No real discontinuity is involved, however, because at this angle the amplitude of the p light goes through zero [Fig. 25B(b)]. Plots of δ_p and δ_s for the entire range of ϕ are given in Fig. 25D.

The directions in space of the electric vector before and after reflection are shown in Fig. 25E. These are deduced from the signs in Fresnel's equations considered in connection with the conventions adopted in deriving them (Sec. 25.13). It is seen that in case (a), where δ_p is taken as zero, the incident and reflected vectors are in nearly opposite directions.

This apparent contradiction comes from our convention of regarding a displacement as positive or negative according as it is seen looking *against the light* in all cases. If the observer turns from viewing the incident beam to viewing the reflected beam, the rotation occurring in the plane of incidence, he finds that the two arrows maintain the same orientation

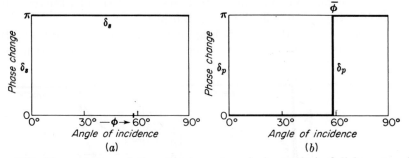

FIG. 25D. Phase change of the electric vector of plane-polarized light externally reflected from a dielectric.

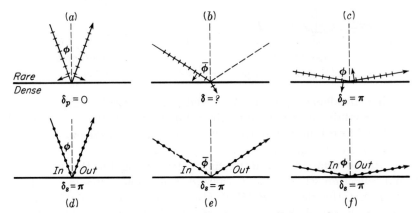

FIG. 25E. Positions in space of the electric vector just before and just after external reflection from a dielectric.

relative to him. It is unfortunate that this convention gives a phase change for the *s* light but none for the *p* light at normal incidence, because at $\phi = 0$ the distinction between *s* and *p* vanishes. Using the opposite convention for *p* would, however, lead to an equally bad inconsistency in case (*c*) of the figure.

The phase changes that occur in internal reflection are, up to the critical angle, exactly the reverse of those at the corresponding angles for external reflection. This is a necessary consequence of Stokes' relations (Eq. 11*p*), according to which there must be a relative difference of π between the two cases. Beyond ϕ_c, in the region of total reflection,

Eqs. 25a lead* to the following expressions for the tangent of half the phase change:

$$\tan \frac{\delta_s}{2} = \frac{\sqrt{n^2 \sin^2 \phi - 1}}{n \cos \phi}$$

$$\tan \frac{\delta_p}{2} = \frac{n \sqrt{n^2 \sin^2 \phi - 1}}{\cos \phi}$$

(25g)

In Fig. 25F are shown separate curves for δ_p and δ_s, and for their difference $\delta = \delta_p - \delta_s$. The δ_p curve rises more steeply than δ_s and at $\phi = 45°$ according to Eqs. 25g is exactly twice as large. Since the curves come together again at $\phi = 90°$, their difference δ passes through a maximum

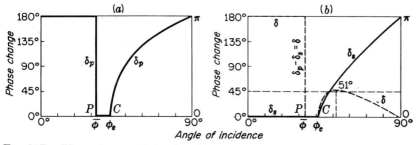

FIG. 25F. Phase changes of the electric vector for internal reflection. $n = 1.51$.

and decreases to zero. The principle of the Fresnel rhomb (Sec. 25.6) is based on this fact.

25.5. Reflection of Plane-polarized Light from Dielectrics. We are now prepared to predict the nature of the reflected light when plane-polarized light is incident on the surface at any angle. Let the light fall on a plate of glass as in Fig. 25G with the plane of vibration making an angle $\psi = 45°$ with the *perpendicular* to the plane of incidence.† This angle we shall call the *azimuth* angle, whether it refers to the light vibrations in the incident, reflected, or refracted beam. The incident light, of amplitude E, may here be resolved into two equal components E_p and E_s and each of these treated separately.

Consider first the case where the angle of incidence ϕ is small, as in diagram (a) of the figure. Referring to Fig. 25B(b), the amplitudes of the two reflected components are found to be small and very nearly equal in magnitude. They are also out of phase by 180°. If the angle ϕ is about 10°, the component R_s is just a little larger than R_p. Taking the vector sum of the reflected components, one finds R in the direction shown. In case (b) the azimuth of the incident light is again 45°, but

---

* See, for example, M. Born, "Optik," p. 43, J. Springer, Berlin, 1933.
† It is customary to measure ψ this way because the "plane of polarization" was originally defined to be at right angles to what we now call the plane of vibration.

the angle of incidence is about 50°. R_p is now quite small and in phase
with E_p, whereas R_s is larger than before and still 180° out of phase with
E_s.   The reflected ray remains plane-polarized, but the plane of vibration has turned farther away from the plane of incidence.   When $\phi = \bar{\phi}$,
as in (c), $R_p = 0$, while R_s is still larger and maintains the same phase.
The resultant amplitude has continued to grow and now stands at right
angles to the plane of incidence.   In diagram (d), where the angle ϕ
approaches 90°, i.e., grazing incidence, the reflected components have

FIG. 25G. Azimuths and amplitudes of plane-polarized light externally reflected from a
glass surface at different angles of incidence.

increased markedly, approaching in magnitude those of the corresponding components in the incident light.   Both these components have now
undergone a phase change of 180°, so that the reflected light approaches
100 per cent in intensity and the plane of vibration approaches the plane
of the incident light.

An equation giving the variation of the plane of vibration of the
reflected light with the angle of incidence is readily obtained by dividing
the two equations 25a.

$$\frac{R_p}{R_s} = -\frac{E_p \cos (\phi + \phi')}{E_s \cos (\phi - \phi')} \tag{25h}$$

This is the tangent of the angle ψ, that is,

$$\frac{R_p}{R_s} = \tan \psi \tag{25i}$$

since the azimuth ψ is the angle between R and R_s.   This angle is plotted in Fig. 25H for the case where the incident light has an azimuth of 45°, making $E_p = E_s$. The heavily drawn curves are for external reflection, while the lighter curves, to be discussed in the following section, are for internal reflection.

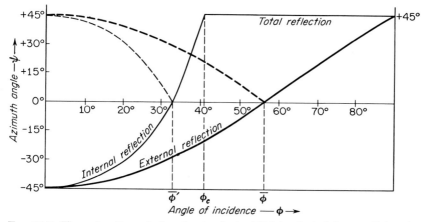

FIG. 25H. The azimuth angle for plane-polarized light reflected from a dielectric.

25.6. Elliptically Polarized Light by Internal Reflection.

Reference to Fig. 25$F(b)$, which gives the phase change for light internally reflected from a glass surface, will show that at an angle of incidence near 50° there is a phase difference of slightly more than 45° between the two components. More exactly, the phase difference for $n = 1.51$ reaches a maximum of 45°56' at $\phi = 51°20'$ and is just 45° at the two angles $\phi = 48°37'$ and 54°37'. This behavior of the phase difference was first tested and confirmed by Fresnel, who constructed a glass rhomb of the form illustrated in Fig. 25I. Plane-polarized light falls normally on the shorter surface of the rhomb with its plane of vibration oriented at 45° to the

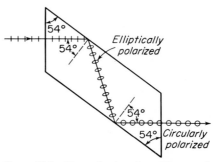

FIG. 25I. Fresnel rhomb. The angle shown is for glass having $n = 1.51$.

plane of the paper. It then strikes the first diagonal surface at an (internal) angle of incidence of 54°37'. Here it is totally reflected with a phase difference of 45° between the two components. Now we have seen in Sec. 12.9 that the result of combining two linear vibrations at right angles is in general an elliptical one, the shape of the ellipse depending on the two amplitudes and on their phase difference δ. Only when δ

is some integral multiple of π is the resultant linear, and the light plane-polarized. This situation exists in all cases of external reflection, and in internal reflection up to the critical angle. But in total reflection one obtains elliptically polarized light as the result of a single internal reflection at $\phi > \phi_c$. The systematic study of elliptical and circular polarization will be taken up in Sec. 27.5.

Circularly polarized light will occur only if the two amplitudes are equal and the phase difference is 90°. In the Fresnel rhomb an additional

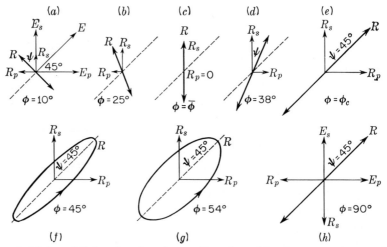

FIG. 25J. Modes of light vibrations internally reflected in glass at various angles of incidence.

phase difference of 45° is produced by a second internal reflection, so that on emergence the p component is 90° ahead in phase. The device is therefore useful in producing and analyzing circularly polarized light, and as we shall see later, there are other somewhat more common methods of doing this.

The polarization of the reflected beam when plane-polarized light undergoes a single internal reflection at various angles of incidence is shown in Fig. 25J. The amplitude of the electric vector in the incident and reflected light, and their components, are designated as was done in Fig. 25G for external reflection. Here, however, they are shown as they would appear to an observer looking against the direction of each beam, with the plane of incidence cutting the plane of the page in a horizontal line. If these diagrams are studied in connection with Figs. 25C, F, and H, their main features should be clear. From $\phi = 0°$ to $\phi = \phi_c$ the reflected light remains plane-polarized, but changes its azimuth steadily and increases in intensity. Beyond ϕ_c the vibration opens out into an ellipse having its maximum width at $\phi = 51°$, then narrows again to a linear vibration at 90°.

25.7. Penetration into the Rare Medium. One might conclude from the fact that internal reflection beyond the critical angle is total that the amplitude of the light drops discontinuously to zero just at the reflecting surface. According to the boundary conditions of electromagnetic theory (Sec. 25.13) this is not possible, however, and furthermore there is experimental evidence that a disturbance capable of producing light exists for a short distance beyond the surface. Suppose that a given surface is totally reflecting an intense beam of light and one brings the edge of a razor blade very close to the surface, or scatters fine particles

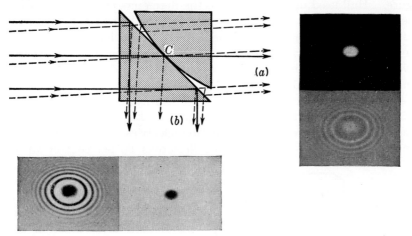

Fig. 25K. Hall's experiment for measuring the penetration that occurs in total reflection.

on it. Observation of the edge of the blade or of the particles with a microscope will show them to be secondary sources of light. In the absence of such foreign matter the electromagnetic theory predicts a disturbance which dies off exponentially beyond the surface,* but which involves no net transfer of energy through it. The energy merely oscillates in and out through the surface. The disturbance is periodic in a direction parallel to the surface but not at right angles to it, and hence cannot properly be called a light wave. When the electromagnetic field is distorted by the presence of denser matter sufficiently close to the surface, however, energy is drained off in the form of light.

An instructive experiment to illustrate this penetration was performed by Hall,† who used it for quantitative measurements of the distance of penetration. The apparatus, as shown in Fig. 25K, consists of two total-reflection prisms, one of which has a slightly convex face. If the two prisms are barely in contact at the point C, and the angle of incidence

---

* Quantitative relations are given, for example, in R. W. Ditchburn, "Light," p. 434, Interscience Publishers, Inc., New York, 1953.

† E. E. Hall, *Phys. Rev.*, **15**, 73, 1902.

exceeds the critical angle, total reflection would send all the light in the direction (b). Actually it is found that in the reflected light there is a dark patch about C, and a corresponding bright one in the transmitted light. Photographs of these are shown in the figure. As the angle of incidence is increased further beyond ϕ_c, the size of the patch shrinks, showing that the distance of penetration decreases. At an angle of incidence just below the critical angle (the rays indicated by broken lines), the complete set of Newton's rings in reflection and transmission appears, as illustrated by the ring patterns at the left and right of the figure. Hall used measurements of the diameters of these rings to measure the thicknesses of the air layers corresponding to different observed diameters of the patch mentioned above. He thus had an accurate measure of the distance of penetration. Both theory and experiment give a decrease of the energy to about $\frac{1}{100}$ in a distance of one wavelength when $\phi = 45°$ and $n = 1.51$. When $\phi = 60°$, it decreases to 1/40,000 in the same distance.

25.8. Metallic Reflection. In general, highly polished metallic surfaces have a higher reflectance than do dielectrics. At normal incidence, for example, silver and aluminum reflect over 90 per cent of all visible

FIG. 25L. Reflection of plane-polarized light from a metal surface to give elliptically polarized light.

light. Experiments show that the reflectance depends not only on the particular metal but on the preparation of the surface and on the wavelength and direction of the incident light. If plane-polarized light is reflected from a metal at other than normal incidence (Fig. 28L), the p and s components of the incident electric vector are reflected with a phase difference and this gives rise to elliptical polarization. It is a general observation for all metals that plane-polarized light is not reflected as plane-polarized light except when it vibrates either in the plane of incidence or perpendicular to it.

In discussing the reflectance of metals it is convenient just as for dielectrics to resolve the incident light vector E into two components E_p and E_s. Curves for the two reflectances as a function of the angle of incidence are shown in Fig. 25M. These are experimental curves obtained by using white light from a tungsten-filament lamp. A comparison with the corresponding curves for a dielectric [Fig. 25B(a)] shows similarities and at the same time striking differences. Metals and dielectrics are similar in that the values for the p and s components start together at normal incidence, separate, and then come together again at grazing incidence. The essential differences are the much higher reflectance of metals at normal incidence and the relatively high minimum at $\bar{\phi}$. This angle for minimum reflection of E_p is called the *principal angle of incidence.*

The reflectance of a metal usually varies considerably with wavelength. In Fig. 25N this variation is shown for a number of typical metals. In spite of irregularities at the shorter wavelengths, all metals reflect very well in the red and infrared. Silver and aluminum are of particular importance for general use because they maintain their high

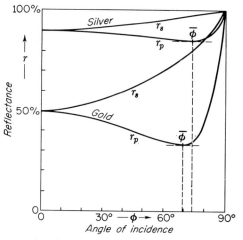

Fig. 25M. Reflectances for plane-polarized white light of gold and silver mirrors.

reflectance throughout the visible spectrum. The development of methods of depositing metal films by evaporation in vacuum has rendered aluminum the most satisfactory substance for mirrors in optical instruments. This is due chiefly to two factors: first, aluminum retains its high reflectance in the near ultraviolet as well as in the visible, and, second, the surface does not easily tarnish even after years of exposure to air. It is now standard practice to coat the mirrors of large reflecting telescopes, such as the 200-in. instrument at Mt. Palomar, with evaporated aluminum. A freshly made silver mirror actually has a slightly greater reflectance in the visible, but it soon tarnishes and becomes poorer than aluminum. For the reflecting surfaces of Fabry-Perot etalons, however, silver is preferred for use in visible and infrared light. For ultraviolet light aluminum, or a mixture of aluminum and magnesium, is better.

Silver is exceptional in showing a narrow region of very low reflectance near 3200 Å. The light of this wavelength that is not reflected may be mostly transmitted if the silver film is sufficiently thin. Such a transmission band is also possessed by the alkali metals at still shorter wavelengths.* A sodium film, for example, can be used as an ultraviolet filter, opaque to all wavelengths except those near 1950 Å.

25.9. Optical Constants of Metals. The optical properties of a dielectric at a particular wavelength are completely described by one constant, the refractive index n at that wavelength. For a metal, however, another constant must be specified which measures the strength of

FIG. 25N. Reflectances at normal incidence of aluminum, silver, gold, copper, and steel.

absorption of light as it enters the metal. Because they contain free electrons, metals have very high absorption, the intensity falling to practically zero in a small fraction of a wavelength. An important quantity used in dealing with the optics of metals is the absorption index κ, which is defined in terms of the absorption coefficients κ_0 and α (Sec. 23.6) as

$$\kappa = \frac{\kappa_0}{n} = \frac{\alpha\lambda}{4\pi n} \tag{25j}$$

The determination of n for a dielectric material is usually accomplished

---

* For details, see R. W. Wood, "Physical Optics," 3d ed., pp. 558–566, The Macmillan Company, New York, 1934.

by refraction measurements, but it can also be done using the reflected light by finding the polarizing angle and applying Brewster's law. With metals the absorption is so strong that measurements are difficult to do with transmitted light. It has been possible, working with very thin samples, to measure rough values of n and κ, but besides their inaccuracy the results may not be strictly applicable to the metal in bulk. Hence accurate values of the optical constants of metals are determined by investigating the reflected light.

Since there are the two constants to be found, n and κ, two measurements are required. In analogy to the measurement of Brewster's angle for dielectrics, one of these may be the principal angle of incidence $\bar{\phi}$ defined above. The other is then the corresponding azimuth, called the *principal azimuth* $\bar{\psi}$. In view of the fact that the light reflected from metals is elliptically polarized, it is not immediately evident what is meant by its azimuth. The definition is made by disregarding the phase difference between the p and s components, which is actually 90° if the light is incident at $\bar{\phi}$, and defining the azimuth in the same way as for dielectrics, namely, by the equation

$$\tan \psi = \frac{R_p}{R_s} \tag{25k}$$

The theory shows that to a fair approximation* the two constants may be found from the relations

$$n \sqrt{1 + \kappa^2} = \sin \bar{\phi} \tan \bar{\phi}$$
$$\kappa = \tan 2\bar{\psi} \tag{25l}$$

The method of measurement of $\bar{\phi}$ and $\bar{\psi}$ will be briefly described below, after we have considered the variation in the character of the reflected light with the angle of incidence.

The values of the optical constants found in the literature show considerable variations because of different preparation of the surfaces, purity of the samples, and accuracy of the equations used. We quote in Table 25-I, however, some typical values, including in the last column the reflectances at normal incidence calculated from Eq. 25s, below. It will be seen that there are large variations of n among the metals, those for the better conductors running considerably below unity. These refractive indices cannot be interpreted in the same way as for dielectrics, since here we are dealing with highly damped waves (see Sec. 23.7).

---

* The theoretical basis for Eqs. 25l will be briefly discussed in Sec. 25.14. Exact equations, including the relations at other angles of incidence, will be found in H. Geiger and K. Scheel, "Handbuch der Physik," Vol. 20, pp. 240–250, Springer-Verlag OHG, Berlin, 1928, which in general follows the work of C. Pfeiffer, "Beitrage zur Kentnisse der Metallreflexion," dissertation, Giessen, 1912.

The value of κ_0 for copper, for instance, corresponds to the intensity falling to $1/e$ when the light penetrates a depth of only one thirty-third of a vacuum wavelength.

TABLE 25-I. OPTICAL CONSTANTS FOR VARIOUS METALS FOR SODIUM LIGHT: $\lambda 5893$

Metal	$\bar{\phi}$	$\bar{\psi}$	n	κ	κ_0	r, %
Steel*............	77° 9'	27°45'	2.485	1.381	3.433	58.4
Cobalt*..........	78° 5'	31°40'	2.120	1.900	4.040	67.5
Copper*..........	71°34'	39° 5'	0.617	4.258	2.630	74.1
Silver*..........	75°35'	43°47'	0.177	20.554	3.638	95.0
Gold.............	72°18'	41°39'	0.37	7.62	2.82	85.1
Sodium..........	71°19'	44°58'	0.005	522.0	2.61	99.7

* After Minor.

25.10. Description of the Light Reflected from Metals. If plane-polarized light is reflected from a metal, the shape and orientation of the elliptical vibration in the reflected light depend on the orientation of the incident vibration, on the magnitude of the reflected p and s components, and on the phase difference between them. The latter factor has not thus far been discussed, and a quantitative treatment of it would require a more extensive mathematical development than would be profitable to include here. We may, however, consider the main results on the behavior of δ ($= \delta_p - \delta_s$) as a function of ϕ.

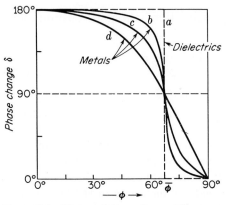

FIG. 25O. Plots of the phase difference $\delta_p - \delta_s$ for a dielectric and for three metals of increasing absorption index κ.

Figure 25O shows plots of the theoretical equations for the phase differences for three different metals b, c, and d, in the order of increasing absorption index κ. It also shows, as the broken line a, the plot for a dielectric, which has $\kappa = 0$. We see that the discontinuous transition of δ from π to zero which occurs at $\bar{\phi}$ for dielectrics becomes for metals a more or less gradual change. We also note that at the principal angle of incidence the value of δ is always exactly 90°.

Knowing the values of R_p/E_p, R_s/E_s, and δ, it is possible to predict the shape of the elliptical vibration reflected at each angle of incidence. Thus suppose, as in Fig. 25P, that the electric vector in the incident plane-polarized light makes an angle of 45° with the plane of incidence.

so that $E_p = E_s$. We have taken the reflecting metal to be steel, which according to Fig. 25N has a reflectance $r = 0.58$ for sodium light at normal incidence. Hence near normal incidence [case (a) of Fig. 25P] we construct the reflected amplitudes $R_p = R_s = 0.76E_p = 0.76E_s$, since $0.76 = \sqrt{0.58}$. Now because of the phase change of π shown in Fig. 25O, we must shift the p vibration in the reflected light 180° ahead of the s vibration, and the result is a linear vibration of amplitude R in the direction shown. This direction is actually opposite in space to that of E

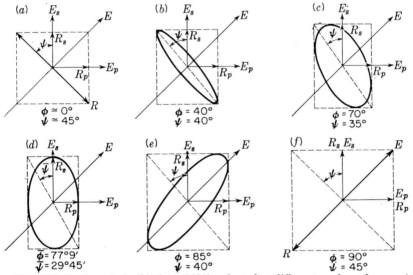

Fig. 25P. Elliptically polarized light ($\lambda5893$) reflected at different angles ϕ from a steel mirror.

[see Fig. 25G(a)]. As the angle of incidence increases from zero, the gradual change in the phase difference causes the vibration to open out into an ellipse which is contained in a rectangle of sides $2R_p$ and $2R_s$. When the angle $\bar{\phi}$ is reached, as in (d) of the figure, we obtain an ellipse symmetrical to the axes, and the one that has the least eccentricity. From then on the ellipse becomes slimmer until finally at grazing incidence, as in (f), we have a linear vibration of the same amplitude as the incident light, but exactly out of phase with it.

The meaning of the azimuth angle ψ is best seen from Fig. 25P. It is the angle that the diagonal of the rectangle makes with R_s. From the figure we see that ψ first diminishes and then increases again in going from $\phi = 0$ to $\phi = 90°$. The minimum value occurs at $\bar{\phi}$, but it is not zero at this angle as it is for a dielectric. The depth of this minimum becomes less for metals of larger κ. This effect may be seen in Fig. 25Q, where the letters a to d have the same significance as in Fig. 25O. In the figure we have marked the value of the principal azimuth $\bar{\psi}$ for the particular metal c.

25.11. Measurement of the Principal Angle of Incidence and Principal Azimuth. The determination of these quantities is a special case of the general problem of the analysis of elliptically polarized light, a problem which will be treated in some detail in Chap. 27. It is not difficult to see,

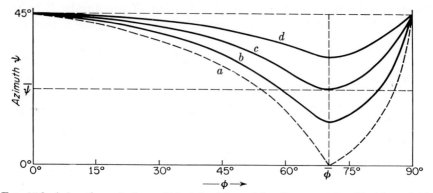

FIG. 25Q. Azimuth angle for a dielectric, (a), and for three metals, (b), (c), and (d).

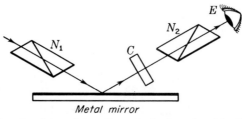

FIG. 25R. Apparatus for determining the principal angle of incidence and principal azimuth for a metal.

however, with the aid of Fig. 25R in connection with Fig. 25$P(d)$, how measurements of $\bar{\phi}$ and $\bar{\psi}$ might be made. Let the nicol N_1 of Fig. 25R be oriented so that the incident vibrations are at 45° to the plane of incidence. In the reflected beam is placed some type of compensator C, which retards the p vibrations by a quarter of a period, or 90°, with respect to the s vibrations. This could be a Fresnel rhomb (Sec. 25.6) but is more commonly a quarter-wave plate or a Soleil compensator (Secs. 27.2 and 27.4). Now at any angle of incidence other than $\bar{\phi}$ the value of δ is different from 90°, so that the phase difference will not be completely removed by the compensator. The light transmitted by C will still be elliptically polarized and cannot be extinguished by rotation of the analyzer N_2. Various angles of incidence are tried until complete extinction becomes possible, and under this condition the light is incident at $\bar{\phi}$.

The fact that it is possible to obtain complete extinction with a nicol means that the compensator has changed the elliptically polarized reflected light into plane-polarized light. In Fig. $25P(d)$ the ellipse is converted into a linear motion along the diagonal of the rectangle by removing the phase difference of 90° that exists between the p and s components. It will therefore be seen that when the condition of extinction has been found the plane of transmission of the analyzer makes the angle ψ with R_p, namely, with the plane of incidence.

25.12. Wiener's Experiments. In Sec. 12.3 we described a classical experiment in which Wiener demonstrated the formation of standing waves of light by reflection from a silver mirror. The object of this

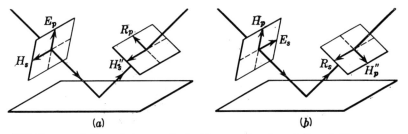

FIG. 25S. Space relations between the incident and reflected **E** and **H** vectors. (a) For p polarization. (b) For s polarization. The angle of incidence is assumed to be less than $\bar{\phi}$.

experiment was not only to reveal the standing waves, but also to tell whether it is the electric or the magnetic vector that produces the observed effects, and hence is to be identified as the "light vector." Now according to the electromagnetic theory the incident and reflected electric vectors are oppositely directed in space for external reflection at normal incidence. With dielectrics the reflected waves have a much smaller amplitude than the incident ones so that the destructive interference is not complete. For metals, however, we should obtain a node of the electric vector at the surface.* As to the magnetic vectors, their relative directions in the incident and reflected light may be found from the fact that **E, H**, and the direction of propagation are related according to the right-hand screw rule (Sec. 23.9). The result is shown in Fig. 25S. If the angle of incidence is made to approach zero, we see that the **H''** and **H** vectors approach the same direction for each polarization. Their superposition should produce an antinode of the standing waves at the surface. Now as was explained before, Wiener observed a node where

* The values of δ_p and δ_s are not exactly 0° or 180° for metals at normal incidence, although their difference is. The only effect of this, however, is to shift the position of the node so that it does not occur exactly at the surface. With silver, for example, the node is located 0.043λ below the surface.

the detecting plate touched the surface. This indicated that the *electric* vector was the important one, at least for photographic action.

One would expect from theory that the electric vector would be more important than the magnetic one in producing the observed effects of light. Wherever it is a question of the action of light on electrons, the electric fields in the wave exert much greater forces than do the magnetic fields. In fact, only two years after Wiener's work Drude and Nernst showed that the same result holds when fluorescence instead of photography is used for detection. In recent years Ives demonstrated it using the photoelectric effect. It is assumed that the electric vector is also responsible for vision.

FIG. 25T. Wiener's experiment at 45° incidence. Interference is observed for the electric vector oriented as in (a), while the corresponding magnetic vector (b) would show none.

An even more convincing demonstration, and one which does not depend on the phase changes, nor on the achievement of perfect contact of the end of the photographic plate with the mirror, was given by Wiener in the following way: Plane-polarized light was reflected at an angle of incidence of exactly 45°. Then the incident and reflected rays are at right angles to each other, and the orientations of the vectors in space are those illustrated in Fig. 25S. We see that for *s* polarization the electric vectors E_s and R_s vibrate along the same line and can interfere. On the other hand E_p and R_p are perpendicular to each other, and no interference is possible. Exactly the reverse is true for the **H** vectors. The experiment is illustrated schematically in Fig. 25T. In part (a) the electric vector is perpendicular to the plane of the figure, a condition which could be achieved by a preliminary reflection from a glass plate at Brewster's angle, and interference can occur along the horizontal planes marked by dots. These planes are $1/\sqrt{2}$ times as far apart as for normal incidence. In the figure the phase change of π on reflection is indicated by the change from solid to broken lines, and vice versa. For the corresponding magnetic vectors, as shown in part (b), there is no phase change on reflection. On the surface at point A the resultant is a linear vibration normal to the surface. Farther up the vibration becomes elliptical, then circular as at a, and finally linear again at B with horizontal vibrations. The reverse sequence is followed to point C, with the points A, B, and C being separated by a distance $\lambda/2$ along the ray. The energy associated with all these vibration forms is the same (Sec. 28.8), and hence, if the magnetic vector were the active one, the test plate should be uniformly blackened. Wiener actually found interference bands in the case illustrated, and uniform blackening when the vibrations in the incident light were turned through 90°.

25.13. Electromagnetic Theory of Dielectric Reflection and Refraction. The treatment of reflection and refraction by the electromagnetic theory involves the application of the so-called *boundary conditions* to Maxwell's equations. When light in one medium like air falls on the surface of a dielectric like glass, the reflected and refracted beams depend for their direction, intensity, and polarization upon the electric and magnetic fields existing on the two sides of the boundary. These fields depend for their magnitude and direction on the dielectric constants of the two media and on the conditions specified for the incident light wave.

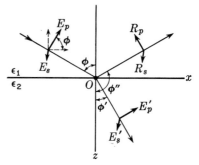

FIG. 25U. Electric vectors used in applying the boundary conditions. (The E_s, R_s, and E'_s vectors are $\perp$ to the page.)

In going from a medium of dielectric constant ϵ_1 to one of dielectric constant ϵ_2, the change in the electric and magnetic fields is continuous and takes place within a thin transition layer at the boundary. It can be shown that, to satisfy the principle of conservation of energy, the boundary condition must be imposed that *the components of the electric and magnetic fields parallel to the surface in one medium are at every point and at every instant equal to the corresponding parallel components immediately on the other side of the boundary.* In other words, the components of **E** and **H** parallel to the surface have no discontinuity at that surface.

To apply these conditions, let a plane wave in a medium of dielectric constant ϵ_1 be incident at an angle ϕ on the surface of a medium of dielectric constant ϵ_2, as shown in Fig. 25U. Let the positive z axis extend downward and the y axis out from the page, with the boundary in the x,y plane. Now let the electric intensity of the incident wave be resolved into two components, the one E_p parallel to the plane of incidence (the x,z plane), and the other E_s perpendicular to the plane of incidence. The component E_p can then be further resolved into two components, one, $E_p \cos \phi$, parallel to the x axis, and the other, $E_p \sin \phi$, antiparallel to the positive z axis. The latter is not required in applying the boundary

conditions and can henceforth be left out of account. Since the magnitude of the electric components varies rapidly with time, we make use
of the wave equation in the form of Eq. 11e and obtain for the two components parallel to the boundary

$$E_{x1} = E_p \cos \phi \sin (\omega t - k_1 a)$$
$$E_{y1} = E_s \sin (\omega t - k_1 a)$$

Here k_1 is the propagation number $2\pi/\lambda_1$ in the first medium, and a is the
distance from the origin measured along the incident ray. For this
distance we have

$$a = x \sin \phi + z \cos \phi$$

Accompanying these electric components there will be the magnetic components of the incident wave, and these will always be in phase with,
but at right angles to, each electric component. The amplitudes of the
magnetic components will, according to Sec. 23.9, be $\sqrt{\epsilon_1}$ times as great
as those of the correlated electric components. These magnetic components are therefore expressed by

$$H_{x1} = - \sqrt{\epsilon_1} E_s \cos \phi \sin (\omega t - k_1 a)$$
$$H_{y1} = \sqrt{\epsilon_1} E_p \sin (\omega t - k_1 a)$$

The negative sign in the first equation comes from the fact that H_p
is in the opposite direction from E_p, and, as will be seen from Fig. 25U,
its component parallel to the surface is directed toward negative x.

The above four relations represent the variation of **E** and **H** parallel
to the boundary due to the incident wave. Since the wave is here partly
reflected, we must add to these the components due to the reflected wave
to obtain the total tangential fields just above the boundary. The
reflected components may be represented by

$$R_{x1} = E_{x1}'' = R_p \cos \phi'' \sin (\omega t - k_1 b)$$
$$R_{y1} = E_{y1}'' = R_s \sin (\omega t - k_1 b)$$
$$H_{x1}'' = - \sqrt{\epsilon_1} R_s \cos \phi'' \sin (\omega t - k_1 b)$$
$$H_{y1}'' = \sqrt{\epsilon_1} R_p \sin (\omega t - k_1 b)$$

where we use the symbol E'' for R to emphasize that it is an electric
component. The distance $b = x \sin \phi'' + z \cos \phi''$, where ϕ'' is the
supplement of the angle of reflection (Fig. 25U).

Below the boundary there are only the fields due to the refracted
wave. Here the components of interest are

$$E_{x2}' = E_p' \cos \phi' \sin (\omega t - k_2 c)$$
$$E_{y2}' = E_s' \sin (\omega t - k_2 c)$$
$$H_{x2}' = - \sqrt{\epsilon_2} E_s' \cos \phi' \sin (\omega t - k_2 c)$$
$$H_{y2}' = \sqrt{\epsilon_2} E_p' \sin (\omega t - k_2 c)$$

where the subscripts (2) refer to the second medium and c is the distance along the refracted ray, namely, $c = x \sin \phi' + z \cos \phi'$.

The laws of reflection and refraction follow at once from the application of the boundary conditions stated above. Thus, if the tangential electric and magnetic fields are to be continuous across the boundary, we must require that just at the surface, $z = 0$, the coefficients of x and t in all the equations be identical. Thus we have

$$\omega t - k_1 x \sin \phi'' = \omega t - k_1 x \sin \phi = \omega t - k_2 x \sin \phi'$$

so that
$$k_1 \sin \phi'' = k_1 \sin \phi = k_2 \sin \phi' \qquad (25m)$$

Now if $\sin \phi'' = \sin \phi$, there are the two possibilities $\phi'' = \phi$ and $\phi'' = \pi - \phi$. The former one has no physical meaning since it would require a reflected wave in the same direction as the incident wave. By reference to Fig. 25U the latter relation is seen to be the usual law of reflection. The second equality in Eqs. 25m contains the law of refraction, because by definition $k = 2\pi/\lambda = 2\pi\nu/v$, and therefore

$$\frac{\sin \phi}{\sin \phi'} = \frac{k_2}{k_1} = \frac{v_1}{v_2} = n$$

To derive Fresnel's laws of reflection, one equates the tangential components of **E** and **H** just above the boundary, each of which is the sum of the two components due to the incident and reflected waves, to those due to the refracted wave just below the boundary. There are thus the four conditions

$$\begin{aligned} E_{x1} + E_{x1}'' = E_{x2}' \qquad H_{x1} + H_{x1}'' = H_{x2}' \\ E_{y1} + E_{y1}'' = E_{y2}' \qquad H_{y1} + H_{y1}'' = H_{y2}' \end{aligned} \Bigg\} \qquad (25n)$$

At the boundary we have seen that each term in these equations contains the same phase factor $\omega t - k_1 x \sin \phi$, and we may therefore write the equations in terms of the corresponding amplitudes. In doing so, we substitute $- \cos \phi$ for $\cos \phi''$, since we have shown that $\phi'' = \pi - \phi$. We then obtain

$$\left. \begin{aligned} (E_p - R_p) \cos \phi = E_p' \cos \phi' \\ E_s + R_s = E_s' \\ \sqrt{\epsilon_1}\,(E_s - R_s) \cos \phi = \sqrt{\epsilon_2}\, E_s' \cos \phi' \\ \sqrt{\epsilon_1}\,(E_p + R_p) = \sqrt{\epsilon_2}\, E_p' \end{aligned} \right\} \qquad (25o)$$

Solution of these equations for R_p and R_s in terms of E_p and E_s then yields Fresnel's equations 25a, while the evaluation of E_p' and E_s' in terms of E_p and E_s yields Eqs. 25b. The only additional relation needed is

$$\frac{\sqrt{\epsilon_2}}{\sqrt{\epsilon_1}} = \frac{n_2}{n_1} = \frac{\sin \phi}{\sin \phi'} \qquad (25p)$$

which was derived as Eq. 23p in the chapter on dispersion. It will be noted that the simple relations for the amplitudes of the transmitted light that were given in Eqs. 25f follow at once by substituting $n = \sqrt{\epsilon_2}/\sqrt{\epsilon_1}$ in Eqs. 25o.

25.14. Theory of Metallic Reflection. The characteristic property which distinguishes metals from dielectrics is their ability to conduct electricity. As was mentioned in Sec. 25.9 the presence of free electrons which can move through the metal under the influence of an electric field is responsible for the rapid damping of the light wave when it enters the metal. The electric field of the wave causes conduction currents which dissipate some of its energy in the form of heat, but these currents also give rise to very strong reflected waves. We have seen in Chap. 23, Dispersion, that whenever the absorption index κ is large the reflectance is also high. Hence metals make the best mirrors,* and it is this property that renders them of importance optically.

The modification of Maxwell's equations that must be made in applying them to metals consists in introducing a conduction current in addition to the displacement current. The latter is still present because metals also contain bound electrons, but its effect is small, especially at long wavelengths. In Chap. 20 the density of the displacement current in vacuum was given as the time rate of change of $\mathbf{E}$ divided by 4π. In matter, this must be multiplied by the dielectric constant. Then if the matter is a conductor, we must add the conduction current. By Ohm's law this is $\sigma\mathbf{E}$, where σ is the specific conductance. The total current density then becomes

$$\mathbf{j} = \sigma\mathbf{E} + \frac{\epsilon}{4\pi}\frac{\partial\mathbf{E}}{\partial t}$$

When this current is resolved into x, y, and z components and substituted in Maxwell's equations in a manner similar to that used in dispersion theory (Sec. 23.9), equations of the following form are obtained:

$$\frac{4\pi\sigma}{c}E_x + \frac{\epsilon}{c}\frac{\partial E_x}{\partial t} = \frac{\partial H_z}{\partial y} - \frac{\partial H_y}{\partial z}, \text{ etc.}$$

and

$$\frac{1}{c}\frac{\partial H_x}{\partial t} = \frac{\partial E_y}{\partial z} - \frac{\partial E_z}{\partial y}, \text{ etc.}$$

In solving these equations† the same boundary conditions imposed

---

* It is interesting that recently surfaces having a higher reflectance than any metal, but composed only of dielectric materials, have been produced. These are the so-called multilayer films (Sec. 14.6), which use the principle of interference. Their high reflectance does not, however, extend over as great a wavelength range as does that of metals.

† For a detailed treatment of the electromagnetic theory of metallic reflection, see P. Drude, "Theory of Optics," English edition, Longman's Green & Co., Inc., New York, 1922; Born, *op. cit.*, p. 261; Geiger and Scheel, *op. cit.*, p. 240. The last reference gives fewer approximate equations.

in the treatment of dielectrics, which must also hold for metals, are introduced at the proper points. These are the four relations $25n$ given in the preceding section. The plane-wave solutions involve complex quantities, yielding expressions of the type

$$E_x = A \sin \omega \left[t - \frac{n}{c} (1 - i\kappa)z \right], \text{ etc.} \tag{25q}$$

Here n and κ are the refractive and absorption indices discussed earlier. The form of this expression is similar to that for a dielectric (Sec. 23.9), except that the previous n is now replaced by a quantity

$$n' = n(1 - i\kappa) \tag{25r}$$

called the *complex refractive index*. This may be substituted for n in the equations for dielectrics to obtain the corresponding relations for metals. For example, Eq. 25d for the amplitude reflected at normal incidence becomes

$$\frac{R}{E} = \frac{n(1 - i\kappa) - 1}{n(1 - i\kappa) + 1}$$

Now to obtain the intensity one multiplies by the complex conjugate, as was explained in Sec. 14.8. Thus i is replaced by $-i$ throughout and the product taken as follows:

$$\frac{R^2}{E^2} = \frac{n(1 - i\kappa) - 1}{n(1 - i\kappa) + 1} \cdot \frac{n(1 + i\kappa) - 1}{n(1 + i\kappa) + 1} = \frac{(n - 1)^2 + \kappa_0^2}{(n + 1)^2 + \kappa_0^2} \tag{25s}$$

where $\kappa_0 = n\kappa$ (see Eq. 25j). This expression evidently reduces to Eq. 25e for dielectrics as the absorption coefficient approaches zero and the refractive index becomes real. It is interesting to note that either a very small n or a large κ_0 can lead to a high reflectance. In the best reflectors both these conditions hold. Study of the values of r in the last column of Table 25-I as related to the figures for n and κ_0 will prove instructive.

PROBLEMS

1. Derive Fresnel's laws of reflection (Eqs. 25a and 25b), starting with the boundary-condition relations (Eqs. 25o).

2. Plot the reflectance curves for external reflection on a flint glass of refractive index 1.60. Give the value of the polarizing angle to 1 minute of arc. *Ans.* 58°0′.

3. Repeat Prob. 2 for internal reflection. Give accurate values of both the polarizing angle and the critical angle.

4. Compute the reflectance at normal incidence of the following substances: (a) fused quartz, $n = 1.470$; (b) flint glass, $n = 1.604$; (c) metallic calcium, $n = 0.290$, $\kappa_0 = 1.64$; (d) electrolytic platinum, $n = 2.63$, $\kappa_0 = 3.54$.
Ans. (a) 0.0362. (b) 0.0538. (c) 0.733. (d) 0.591.

5. Derive an equation for the azimuth of the refracted light in a dielectric. Make a plot of this as is done in Fig. 25H for the reflected light.

6. Plane-polarized light is incident at $\phi = 60°$ on a glass surface with its electric vector vibrating at 20° with the plane of incidence. Calculate the azimuth angle ψ of the reflected plane-polarized light. Assume $n = 1.560$.   *Ans.* 11°15′.

7. Using Fresnel's laws of reflection, verify the fact that the sum of the energy fluxes in the reflected and transmitted beams equals that in the incident beam.

8. From Eqs. 25g for the phase changes on internal reflection in a dielectric, prove that at $\phi = 45°$ the value of δ_p is just twice that of δ_s. (HINT: Apply the formula for the tangent of the half angle.)

9. Plane-polarized light is internally reflected at $\phi = 45°$ from the hypotenuse of a total-reflection prism made of glass of index $n = 1.52$. If the azimuth of the incident light is 45°, calculate the phase difference between the reflected p and s components. Plot to scale the elliptical vibration form as was done in Fig. 25J.

10. Unpolarized light strikes a glass surface ($n = 1.50$) at an angle of incidence of 30°. Calculate the amplitudes and intensities of the reflected p and s components. Calculate also the degree of polarization (Sec. 24.4) of the refracted light. What is the total flux in the refracted beam, expressed as a fraction of that in the incident beam?

Ans. Amplitudes 0.159, −0.241. Reflectances 0.0253, 0.0578. Polarization 1.7%. Flux 0.958.

11. Plot the phase changes on internal reflection in glass having $n = 1.60$ between the critical angle and grazing incidence. Take the difference $\delta = \delta_p - \delta_s$, and find what two angles could be used in designing a Fresnel rhomb of this glass.

12. Explain why, in making the Fresnel rhomb described in Sec. 25.6, it is more desirable to choose the angle 54°37′ rather than the other angle 48°37′, which also gave a phase difference $\delta = 45°$. *Ans.* Phase difference varies more slowly with angle.

13. Beryllium has $n = 2.66$ and $\kappa = 0.89$ for green mercury light. Calculate (a) its reflectance at normal incidence, and (b) its principal angle of incidence and principal azimuth.

14. For a certain metal the principal angle of incidence and principal azimuth are 61.1° and 36.5°, respectively. Determine the optical constants of this metal, and its reflectance at normal incidence.   *Ans.* $n = 0.464$. $\kappa = 3.271$. $r = 0.583$.

15. Suppose that in Hall's experiment the diameter of the bright patch at a particular angle of incidence just matched that of the third bright Newton's ring for sodium light. Find the distance, in centimeters, that the light penetrated into the air layer.

CHAPTER 26

DOUBLE REFRACTION

From the standpoint of physical optics, doubly refracting crystals are classified as either *uniaxial* or *biaxial*. We have seen that in uniaxial crystals the refractive indices, and hence the velocities, of the O and E waves become equal along a unique direction called the optic axis. In biaxial crystals, on the other hand, there are two directions in which the velocity of plane waves is independent of the orientation of the incident vibrations. These two optic axes make a certain angle with each other which is characteristic of the crystal, and depends to some extent on the wavelength. Uniaxial crystals may be thought of as a special case of biaxial crystals where the angle between the axes is zero.

26.1. Wave Surfaces for Uniaxial Crystals. Uniaxial crystals may be divided into two classes, *negative* and *positive*. In a negative crystal like calcite, the extraordinary index of refraction is less than the ordinary index. In quartz, a positive crystal, the index of the extraordinary ray is greater than that of the ordinary ray. A general treatment of the propagation of light in positive and negative crystals is usually given in terms of wave surfaces, which lend themselves so aptly to Huygens' construction.

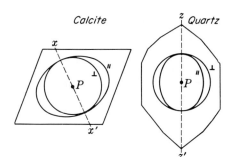

FIG. 26A. Wave-surface diagrams in calcite and quartz.

The wave surface is a wave front (or pair of wave fronts) completely surrounding a point source of monochromatic light. Thus if in one of the crystals of Fig. 26A the source is at P, the circle and ellipse around it represent the traces of the wave fronts, which are the loci of points of *equal phase* in the waves given out by P. If these crystals were isotropic substances such as glass, there would be a single wave surface and this would take the form of a sphere, showing that the velocity of the wave in all directions is the same. In most crystalline substances, however, two wave surfaces are formed, one called the *ordinary wave sur-*

535

face and the other the *extraordinary wave surface.* In both calcite and quartz the ordinary wave surface is a sphere and the extraordinary wave surface an ellipsoid of revolution. The actual three-dimensional surfaces are obtained by rotating the cross-sectional figures of Fig. 26A about the optic axes which, for reasons to be explained, are labeled xx' and zz'. The circle generates a sphere, and the ellipse an ellipsoid of revolution. The three cross sections of these surfaces are shown in Fig. 26B. The eccentricity of the elliptical sections in these figures is exaggerated, the major and minor axes actually differing by only 11 per cent for calcite and 0.6 per cent for quartz.

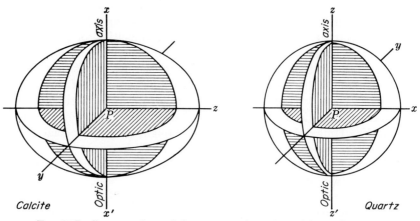

FIG. 26B. Cross sections of the wave surfaces for calcite and quartz.

In calcite the ellipsoid touches the enclosed sphere at the two points where the optic axis through P passes through the surfaces. In quartz the sphere and enclosed ellipsoid do not quite touch at the optic axis through P. The fact that they do not touch gives rise to a whole new phenomenon called optical activity, a subject which will be treated in detail in Chap. 28. The approach of the two surfaces along the optic axis is so close, however, that for the present they will be assumed to touch as they in fact do in other positive crystals like titanium dioxide, zinc oxide, ice, etc. It should be pointed out that owing to the dispersion of all media the wave surfaces shown apply to one wavelength only. Correspondingly smaller or larger surfaces would be drawn for other wavelengths. Furthermore, it is important to remember that the radii drawn from P are proportional to phase velocities and hence do not measure the rate of propagation of energy. The group velocities, which in dispersive media are usually less than phase velocities (Sec. 23.7), would be represented by proportionately smaller surfaces. They would be the same as the wave surfaces described here only in the case of ideal monochromatic light.

The directions of vibration in the two wave surfaces are indicated in Fig. 26A by ⊥ for vibrations perpendicular to the page and by ∥ for vibrations in the plane of the page. These will be more exactly specified after we have considered how the wave surfaces may be applied.

26.2. Propagation of Plane Waves in Uniaxial Crystals. The origin of the double refraction of light at a crystal surface is readily explained in terms of the wave surfaces just described. This is accomplished by the use of Huygens' principle of secondary wavelets. Consider for example a beam of parallel light incident normally on the surface of a crystal like calcite, whose optic axis makes some arbitrary angle with

Fig. 26C. Huygens' construction for a plane wave incident normally on calcite.

the crystal surface (see Fig. 26C). The optic axis has the direction shown by the broken lines. According to Huygens' principle we may now choose points anywhere along the wave front as new point sources of light. Here A, B, and C are chosen just as the wave strikes the crystal boundary. After a short time interval the Huygens wavelets entering the crystal from these points will have the form shown in the figure.

If one now proceeds to find the common tangents to these secondary wavelets, he obtains the two plane waves labeled OO' and EE' in the figure. Since the first is tangent to spherical wavelets, it behaves as would a wave in an isotropic substance, traveling perpendicular to the surface with a velocity proportional to AA', BB', and CC'. We have seen in the last chapter that the vibrations for this O wave are normal to the principal section. The tangent to the ellipsoidal wavelets represents the wave front for the E vibrations, which take place in the principal section. The E rays, connecting the origins of the wavelets with the points of tangency, diverge from the O rays and are no longer perpendicular to the wave front. They represent the direction in which a narrow beam of light would be refracted, which is the direction in which the energy of the E vibrations is transmitted. Its velocity, proportional to Aa, Bb, or Cc, is called the ray velocity. This is greater than the normal velocity, measured by Aa', Bb', or Cc', the velocity with which the wave advances through the crystal in a direction normal to its own plane.

If the normal velocity Aa' is plotted in polar coordinates as a function of the angle between the optic axis and the E-wave normal, we get the dashed ovals of Fig. $26D$. These ovals are of course three-dimensional surfaces symmetrical about the optic axis. Now it is seen that the wave surface, i.e., the ellipsoid of revolution, is really a ray-velocity surface. The normal-velocity surface and the ray-velocity surface for the ordinary vibrations are both represented by the same circle or

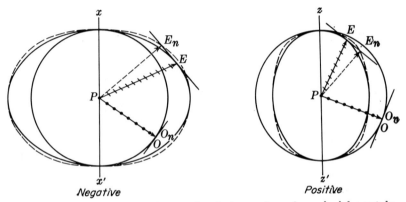

FIG. 26D. Wave surfaces and normal-velocity surfaces for uniaxial crystals.

sphere. Hereafter the ellipsoid of revolution will be referred to as the *wave surface* of the E wave and the oval of revolution as the *normal-velocity surface* of the E wave.

In constructing Fig. $26C$ the optic axis was assumed to be in the plane of the page. In case the optic axis is not in the plane of the page, a plane drawn tangent to the ellipsoidal wavelets will make contact at points in front of or in back of the plane of the page. If the optic axis is either parallel or perpendicular to the surface of the crystal, however, the situation is especially simple. Figure $26E$ illustrates Huygens' construction in these important cases, where the crystal face is cut (1) parallel to the optic axis as in (a) and (b), and (2) perpendicular to the optic axis as in (c). In both cases the ray velocities are equal to the normal velocities, and there is no double refraction. In case (1), however, the E wave travels faster than the O wave. When a difference in these velocities exists, we obtain the phenomenon of interference in polarized light, to be discussed in the following chapter.

It will assist in understanding the rather complex behavior of the velocity of light vibrating in different directions, and described by the wave surface, to note the following facts. The O wave, which vibrates everywhere perpendicular to the optic axis, has the same velocity in every direction. The vibrations of the E wave make a different angle with the axis for each different ray that is drawn from P (Fig. 26D). In particular, for the ray drawn along the optic axis, the vibrations of which are perpendicular to the axis, the velocity becomes equal to that of the O ray, which is also vibrating perpendicular to the axis. These facts suggest that the velocity of light is for some reason dependent on the angle of inclination between the vibrations and the optic axis. In terms

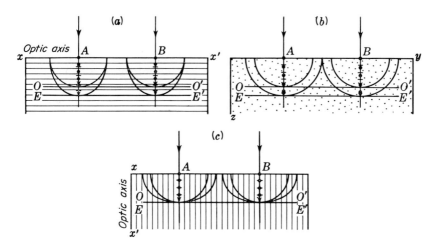

Fig. 26E. Propagation of normally incident plane waves through calcite crystals cut parallel and perpendicular to the optic axis.

of the elastic-solid theory, this could be explained by assuming two different coefficients of elasticity for vibrations parallel and perpendicular to the optic axis. In calcite, for example, the restoring force is taken to be greater for the E ray traveling perpendicular to the optic axis (vibrations parallel to the axis) than for the O ray in the same direction (vibrations perpendicular to the axis). Hence the E wave travels faster in this direction.

26.3. Plane Waves at Oblique Incidence. Continuing the study of the double refraction of light in uniaxial crystals, consider the case of a beam of parallel light incident at an angle on the surface of a crystal whose optic axis lies in the plane of incidence and at the same time makes some arbitrary angle with the crystal surface (see Fig. 26F). At the point A where the light first strikes the boundary, the O-wave surface is drawn with such a radius that the ratio CB/AD is equal to the refractive index of the O ray. The ellipsoidal wave surface is then drawn tangent to the circle at the intersection with the optic axis xx'. The points D and F and the new wave fronts DB and FB are located by draw-

ing tangents from the common point B to the circle and ellipse.   While
the light is traveling from C to B in air, the O vibrations travel from
A to D in the crystal and the E vibrations travel from A to F.   In the
more general case where the optic axis is not in the plane of incidence,

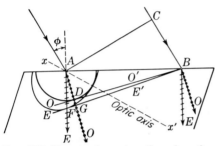

the refracted ray will not lie in the
same plane.   Such cases require
three-dimensional figures and cannot be easily shown.

The principles of Huygens' construction are applied to three special cases in Fig. 26G.   In (a) and
(c), the optic axis, the plane of incidence, and the E and O principal
planes coincide with the plane of the
page.*   In (b) the axis is perpendicular to the plane of incidence, and

Fig. 26F. Huygens' construction when the
optic axis lies in the plane of incidence.

the cross sections of the wave surfaces from A yield two circles.   This
is a case where the two principal planes defining the directions of vibra-

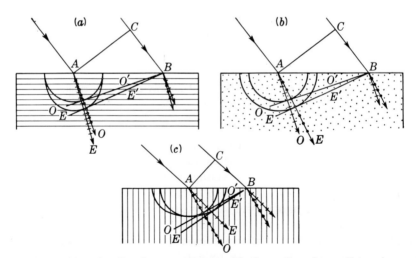

Fig. 26G. Double refraction for crystals cut with the optic axis parallel and perpendicular to the surface.

tions of the O and E rays (Sec. 24.9) are separate from each other and
from the principal section.

* From geometry it may be shown for the special case of Fig. 26G(a), where the
optic axis is in the surface as well as in the plane of incidence, that the directions of the
refracted rays are given by $\tan \phi'_E / \tan \phi'_O = n_E/n_O$.   Here ϕ'_E and ϕ'_O are the angles
of refraction, and n_E and n_O are the principal refractive indices.

26.4. Direction of the Vibrations. In crystals the physical nature of the "vibrations" must be specified more closely than merely as the oscillations of the electric (or magnetic) vector used thus far. For reasons to be discussed below, the direction of the electric displacement **D** (Sec. 23.9) is not in general the same as that of the electric field **E**. The application of Maxwell's equations to anisotropic substances along the lines to be outlined in Sec. 26.9 shows that the vibrations lying in the wave front are those of **D**. The vibrations of **E**, however (i.e., of the electric vector—not to be confused with the symbol E for the extraordinary wave) are perpendicular to the ray, and hence inclined to the wave front. Hence the extraordinary wave is a transverse wave for **D** but not for **E**. In our Figs. 26C and 26D, and in what follows, we indicate as the direction of the vibrations that of the electric displacement **D**.

For uniaxial crystals, the directions of vibration of the O and E rays may be specified in terms of the principal planes for these rays defined in Sec. 24.9. The O vibrations are perpendicular to the principal plane of the O ray, which contains this ray and the optic axis. They are also tangent to the O-wave surface. The E vibrations lie in the principal plane of the E ray and are tangent to the E-wave surface. These definitions may seem unnecessarily complicated in cases like Fig. 26C, where the principal section and the two principal planes all coincide with the plane of the figure, but they are essential in the more general case, where all three of these planes are different. Another way of determining the directions of the vibrations, which holds quite generally for all cases including biaxial crystals, is as follows: The electric displacements associated with one ray (the E ray in uniaxial crystals) are in the direction of the projection of the ray on its wave front. Those associated with the other ray may then be found from the fact that for a given direction of the wave normal the two possible directions of **D** are mutually perpendicular. Inspection of our figures will show agreement with these rules in the simple cases we have considered.

26.5. Indices of Refraction for Uniaxial Crystals. The index of refraction is usually defined as the ratio of the velocity of light *in vacuo* to the velocity in the medium in question. In uniaxial crystals there are two principal indices of refraction, one expressing the velocity of the E wave when traveling normal to the optic axis, and the other the velocity of the O wave. These are related to the two elastic coefficients mentioned in Sec. 26.2. In negative crystals, such as calcite, *the principal index for the extraordinary wave is defined as the velocity of light in vacuo divided by the maximum velocity in the crystal.*

$$n_E = \frac{\text{velocity } in \ vacuo}{\text{maximum velocity of } E \text{ wave}} \qquad (26a)$$

The maximum normal velocity, it should be noted, is equal to the maximum ray velocity. The ordinary index is defined as

$$n_O = \frac{\text{velocity } in \text{ } vacuo}{\text{velocity of } O \text{ wave}} \tag{26b}$$

In positive uniaxial crystals the principal index for the extraordinary wave is defined as

$$n_E = \frac{\text{velocity } in \text{ } vacuo}{\text{minimum velocity of } E \text{ wave}} \tag{26c}$$

The principal indices for calcite and quartz are given in Table 26-I for several wavelengths throughout the visible, ultraviolet, and near infrared spectrum.

TABLE 26-I. THE PRINCIPAL INDICES OF CALCITE AND QUARTZ AT 18°C

Source element	Wave-length	Calcite		Quartz		Fused quartz
		n_O	n_E	n_O	n_E	
Au	2000.60	1.90302	1.57663	1.64927	1.66227	
Cd	2265.03	1.81300	1.54914	1.61818	1.62992	1.52308
Cd	2573.04	1.76048	1.53013	1.59622	1.60714	1.50379
Cd	2748.67	1.74147	1.52267	1.58752	1.59813	1.49617
Sn	3034.12	1.71956	1.51366	1.57695	1.58720	1.48594
Cd	3403.65	1.70080	1.50561	1.56747	1.57738	1.47867
Hg	4046.56	1.68134	1.49694	1.55716	1.56671	1.46968
H$_\gamma$	4340.47	1.67552	1.49428	1.55396	1.56340	1.46690
H$_\beta$	4861.33	1.66785	1.49076	1.54968	1.55898	1.46318
Hg	5460.72	1.66168	1.48792	1.54617	1.55535	1.46013
Hg	5790.66	1.65906	1.48674	1.54467	1.55379	
Na	5892.90	1.65836	1.48641	1.54425	1.55336	1.45845
H$_\alpha$	6562.78	1.65438	1.48461	1.54190	1.55093	1.45640
He	7065.20	1.65207	1.48359	1.54049	1.54947	1.45517
K	7664.94			1.53907	1.54800	
Rb	7947.63			1.53848	1.54739	1.45340
	8007.00	1.64867	1.48212			
O	8446.70			1.53752	1.54640	
	9047.0	1.64579	1.48095			
Hg	10140.6			1.53483	1.54360	
	10417.0	1.64276	1.47982			

Since the E-wave surface touches the O-wave surface at the optic axis, the ordinary index n_O also gives the velocity of the E wave along the axis. Each pair of values of n_O and n_E for a given wavelength therefore determines the ratio between the major and minor axes of the extraordinary wave surfaces for that wavelength of light.

The principal indices for uniaxial crystals are readily determined experi-mentally by refracting light through a prism of known angle. If either of the prisms in Fig. 26H is placed on a spectrometer table, two spectra will be observed. For any given wavelength there will be two spectrum

(a)   (b)

FIG. 26H. Double refraction in prisms cut from a negative uniaxial crystal.

lines and hence two angles of minimum deviation. The O and E indices are then calculated in the usual way (Sec. 2.8) by the formula

$$n = \frac{\sin \frac{1}{2}(\alpha + \delta_m)}{\sin \frac{1}{2}\alpha} \qquad (26d)$$

where δ_m is the angle of minimum deviation and α is the angle of the prism.

At minimum deviation in prism (a) the E ray is traveling essentially perpendicular to the optic axis, the necessary conditions for measuring the principal index n_E. In prism (b) it should be noted that the cross section of the wave surface yields two circles. This means that the velocity of the E ray, as well as that of the O ray, is independent of direction in the plane of the figure and Snell's law of refraction holds for it also.

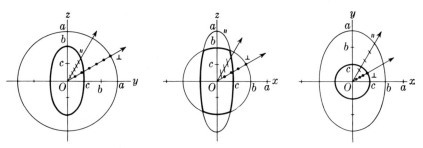

FIG. 26I. Cross sections of wave surfaces for a biaxial crystal.

26.6. Wave Surfaces in Biaxial Crystals. The majority of crystals occurring in nature are biaxial, possessing two optic axes, or directions of single normal velocity. Double refraction in such crystals, just as in calcite and quartz, is most easily described in terms of wave-surface diagrams and Huygens' principle. Three cross-sectional views of the wave surfaces for a biaxial crystal are given in Fig. 26I. As before, the directions of vibration are shown by dots and lines. Each section cuts the two surfaces in one circle and one ellipse, and these are different in the three sections. The figures are drawn for the case where the semiaxes of the intersections of the wave surface with the coordinate planes are, as shown in the figure, $a = 3$, $b = 2$, and $c = 1$. (Such large differences in a, b, and c are never found in nature.)

Of the three cross sections, the center one (that in the x,z plane) is the most interesting, for it contains the four singular points where the outer wave surface (light line) touches the inner surface (heavy line). As

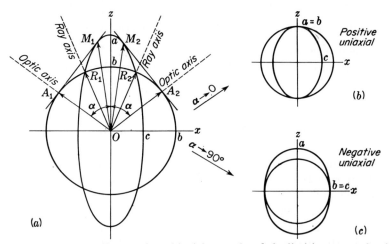

FIG. 26J. Wave-surface diagram for a biaxial crystal and the limiting cases of uniaxial crystals.

shown again in Fig. 26$J(a)$, the rays OR_1 and OR_2 represent directions in which there is but one ray velocity. These are not the optic axes. The optic axes are located by drawing the tangent planes, A_1M_1 and A_2M_2. It is difficult to show in two dimensions that these tangent planes touch the three-dimensional outer surface in circles whose diameters are A_1M_1 and A_2M_2, but such is the case. Since the cross section of one surface is a circle, the lines OA_1 and OA_2 are perpendicular to the tangent planes. They therefore give the same normal velocity for both the ellipse and the circle, so that OA_1 and OA_2 are the optic axes for the point O.

From Fig. 26I it is seen that one can determine the shape of the wave surfaces by specifying three principal indices of refraction. These are determined by the fact that there are three particular velocities, corresponding to vibrations parallel to x, y, and z, respectively. The elastic-solid theory specified three different coefficients of elasticity for these three types of vibration, which gave rise to these three velocities. If the wave surfaces represent the wave fronts after they have traveled a time of 1 sec from the point O, the indices are given by

$$n_a = \frac{V}{a} \qquad n_b = \frac{V}{b} \qquad \text{and} \qquad n_c = \frac{V}{c}$$

where V is the distance light travels in 1 sec in vacuum, and a, b, and c are the semiaxes of the elliptic sections of the wave front. Values of n_a, n_b, and n_c are given for several crystals in Table 26-II.

TABLE 26-II. PRINCIPAL INDICES OF REFRACTION FOR BIAXIAL CRYSTALS (FOR SODIUM LIGHT)

Crystal, formula	n_a	n_b	n_c	Angle between axes, 2α
Negative crystals:				
Mica, $KH_2Al_3(SO_4)_3$....................	1.5601	1.5936	1.5977	138°
Aragonite, $CaO(CO)_2$...................	1.531	1.682	1.686	162°
Stibnite, $Sb_2S_3(\lambda7620)$..................	3.194	4.046	4.303	133°
Positive crystals:				
Sulfur, S..............................	1.950	2.043	2.240	69°
Topaz, $(2AlO)FSiO_2$....................	1.619	1.620	1.627	65°
Turquoise, $CuO3Al_2O_32P_2O_59H_2O$.........	1.520	1.523	1.530	40°

The distinction between positive and negative crystals is made according to whether the angle α of Fig. 26$J(a)$ is less than or greater than 45°. As α approaches zero, it will be seen that a becomes equal to b, and the surface takes the form for a positive uniaxial crystal [Fig. 26$J(b)$]. When on the other hand $\alpha = 90°$, we have $b = c$, and the surface is that of a negative uniaxial crystal, as in (c) of the figure. In terms of the refractive indices these limiting cases are

$$n_a = n_b < n_c \qquad \text{POSITIVE UNIAXIAL CRYSTAL}$$
$$\text{HAVING } n_O = n_a \text{ OR } n_b, \; n_E = n_c$$
$$n_a < n_b = n_c \qquad \text{NEGATIVE UNIAXIAL CRYSTAL}$$
$$\text{HAVING } n_O = n_b \text{ OR } n_c, \; n_E = n_a$$

It is to be noted in Fig. 26I that each coordinate plane contains one circular cross section of the wave surface. This means that one of the two rays refracted into a crystal along any of these planes will obey Snell's law. Prisms may therefore be cut from crystals in such a way as to make use of this fact in determining the principal indices of refraction.

One quadrant of the wave surface for a biaxial crystal is shown in Fig. 26K to illustrate the directions of the electric displacements $\mathbf{D}$, that is, the vibrations in the wave fronts, and also to show the normal velocity surface (dashed lines). The outer sheet touches the inner one at only four points, where it forms "dimples." These are located at points such as R_2, where the surface is intersected by the ray axes. Along the x, y, and z axes the ray velocity is equal to the normal velocity. It will be seen that the vibrations in the wave surface wherever it has a circular section are perpendicular to the coordinate plane, for only under these conditions do they maintain a constant angle with the optic axes.

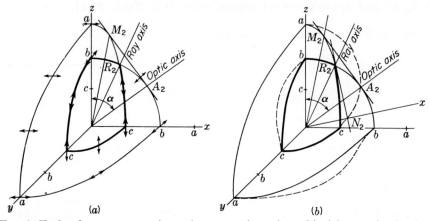

Fig. 26K. Quadrant cross sections of wave surfaces for a biaxial crystal. Dashed lines are normal-velocity surfaces. Arrows show the direction of the electric displacement.

26.7. Internal Conical Refraction. The investigation of refraction in biaxial crystals follows the same lines as that given in the preceding sections for uniaxial crystals. To treat refraction in the x,z plane, for example, we may apply Huygens' construction using secondary wavelets of the form shown in Fig. 26J. One finds in general two plane-polarized refracted rays, so that we have double refraction here also. Two special cases arise, however, in which the behavior of a biaxial crystal is different from the simpler uniaxial type. They correspond to the singular case where light is sent along the optic axis of a uniaxial crystal. One of these, *internal conical refraction*, is observed when a beam is directed alone one of the *optic* axes inside the crystal. In the other, *external conical refraction*, it is sent along one of the *ray* axes.

Internal conical refraction comes about as follows: It has already been mentioned that the tangent plane A_2M_2 [Figs. 26J(a) and 26L(a)] makes contact with the three-dimensional wave surface in a circle of diameter A_2M_2. Suppose now that a plane-parallel plate is cut from a crystal so that its surfaces are perpendicular to an optic axis, and that the crystal has the thickness OA_2 of Fig. 26L(a). Let a ray of unpolarized light be incident normally on the first surface at O. The perpendicular vibrations will travel along the optic axis OA_2 and pass through undeviated. The parallel vibrations will be propagated along OM_2, and will emerge after a second refraction traveling in the same direction as OA_2. Now the incident unpolarized ray contains vibrations in all planes through the ray (Sec. 24.2) and for each particular plane of vibration there is a different direction along which the wave will be propagated with the same normal velocity as along any other ray. In three dimensions these rays will form a cone of light in the crystal spreading out from O. Arriving simultaneously at the second surface A_2M_2 all these

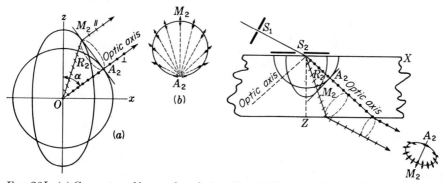

Fig. 26L. (a) Geometry of internal conical refraction. (b) End view of internal conically refracted light, showing the directions of vibration.

Fig. 26M. Internal conical refraction in a biaxial crystal plate.

waves are refracted parallel to each other to form a circular cylinder. Looking at this hollow beam of light end-on, the planes of vibration will be as shown in Fig. 26L(b).

Internal conical refraction was predicted by Sir William Hamilton and at his suggestion is reputed to have first been verified experimentally by Lloyd in 1833. The observations are usually made now with a parallel crystal plate as shown in Fig. 26M. A beam of light, confined to a narrow pencil by two movable pinholes S_1 and S_2, is incident at just such an angle that the light vibrating perpendicular to the plane of incidence is refracted along the optic axis. When the pinhole S_2 is moved around to vary the angle of incidence, there will be only two refracted rays until the correct direction for internal conical refraction is reached. When this happens, the light spreads out from the two spots near A_2 and M_2 into a ring.*

26.8. External Conical Refraction. External conical refraction in biaxial crystals deals with the refraction of an external hollow cone of

* A photograph of internal conically refracted light is given in Max Born, "Optik," p. 240, J. Springer, Berlin, 1933.

light into a narrow pencil or ray of light inside the crystal (Figs. 26*N* and 26*O*). Suppose that a beam of monochromatic light is moving inside a crystal along the ray axis OR_2. From the diagram in Fig. 26*N* two tangents can be drawn at the intersection R_2, one to ellipse and one to the circle.

In the three-dimensional wave surfaces the point R_2 is like a dimple, and there is an infinite number of wave fronts enveloping the obtuse

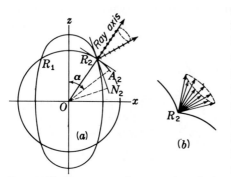

cone. Corresponding to these wave fronts there will be an infinite number of wave normals, each with its own particular direction of vibration [Fig. 26*N*(*b*)], and these will form an acute-angled cone. When these wave fronts, the energy of each one of which travels along the ray axis, arrive at the crystal surface, they will emerge as a cone of rays, since each wave normal inside corresponds to a refracted ray outside. There is thus a cone of wave

Fig. 26*N*. Geometry of external conical refraction.

normals outside as well as inside. By the principle of the reversibility of light rays a hollow cone of polarized light rays from outside a crystal should unite to form one ray inside traveling along the single-ray axis.

Experimentally a solid cone of converging unpolarized light, somewhat larger than necessary, is made to fall on a crystal plate cut as shown in

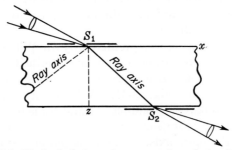

Fig. 26*O*. Method of observing external conical refraction.

Fig. 26*O*. The ray axis is located by moving one of the pinhole apertures S_1 and S_2. From the incident light the crystal picks the hollow cone of rays vibrating in the proper planes that unite to form one ray. The various other rays travel different directions in the crystal and are stopped by the screen S_2. Upon refraction from the second crystal surface a hollow cone of polarized light is observed emerging from S_2. The cone shown in Fig. 26*O* is not the same as the one shown in Fig. 26*N*(*b*), but is the one produced by refraction of the latter.

26.9. Theory of Double Refraction. Maxwell's equations for crystalline media have the same form as those given in Sec. 23.9 for transparent media in general, namely,

$$\frac{1}{c}\frac{\partial D_x}{\partial t} = \frac{\partial H_z}{\partial y} - \frac{\partial H_y}{\partial z} \qquad -\frac{1}{c}\frac{\partial H_x}{\partial t} = \frac{\partial E_z}{\partial y} - \frac{\partial E_y}{\partial z}$$
$$\frac{\partial D_x}{\partial x} + \frac{\partial D_y}{\partial y} + \frac{\partial D_z}{\partial z} = 0 \qquad \frac{\partial H_x}{\partial x} + \frac{\partial H_y}{\partial y} + \frac{\partial H_z}{\partial z} = 0 \tag{26e}$$

Only in the case of an isotropic substance like glass, however, is it permissible to write for the electric displacement $\mathbf{D} = \epsilon\mathbf{E}$, as was done in Sec. 23.9. In anisotropic crystals it is found that the measured values of the dielectric constant ϵ vary with the orientation of the optic axis or axes relative to the electric field $\mathbf{E}$. In the electron theory of dielectric media, the value of the dielectric constant depends on the *polarization* of the atoms under the influence of the electric field. This fact was mentioned in connection with our discussion of dispersion. The effect of the electric field is to produce a slight relative displacement of the positive and negative charges, so that the atom acquires an electric moment. Now the moment generated in a given atom depends on the electric field at that atom, which will be determined in part by the fields from other polarized atoms in its immediate neighborhood. If these other atoms are arranged in a particular way, it is clear that the polarization, and the effective dielectric constant, should depend on the orientation of the electric vector of the waves. In calcite, for example, the oxygen atoms in the CO_3 group are the most easily polarized, and they exert a strong influence on each other. Under this influence, they are more easily polarized by an electric field parallel to the plane of the group than by one perpendicular to it. At a result, we shall find that the refractive index should be greatest for light having its electric vector perpendicular to the trigonal axis.

The fact that ϵ varies with direction in these crystals can be shown by the electromagnetic theory to give rise to double refraction. The direction of $\mathbf{D}$ differs from that of $\mathbf{E}$ except in three singular directions, which are mutually perpendicular. The value of ϵ is a maximum along one of these axes, a minimum along another, and intermediate along the third. Designating them by x, y, and z, we therefore find that, for the three components of $\mathbf{D}$ in Maxwell's equations, we must now write

$$D_x = \epsilon_x E_x \qquad D_y = \epsilon_y E_y \qquad D_z = \epsilon_z E_z \tag{26f}$$

When these values are substituted in Eqs. 26e, and the equation for plane electromagnetic waves derived,* it is found that for any direction

---

* See, for example, P. Drude, "Theory of Optics," English edition, pp. 314–317, Longmans, Green & Co., Inc., New York, 1922.

of the wave front there are two velocities for vibrations of the vector **D** in two mutually perpendicular directions, and this is the fundamental aspect of double refraction.

The most concise way of presenting the results of the electromagnetic theory is by the use of what we may call the *dielectric ellipsoid*. This is an ellipsoid described by the equation

$$\frac{x^2}{\epsilon_x} + \frac{y^2}{\epsilon_y} + \frac{z^2}{\epsilon_z} = 1 \tag{26g}$$

in which ϵ_x, ϵ_y, and ϵ_z are the *principal dielectric constants* of Eqs. 26f. The semiaxes of the ellipsoid are $\sqrt{\epsilon_x}$, $\sqrt{\epsilon_y}$, and $\sqrt{\epsilon_z}$, as shown in Fig. 26P,

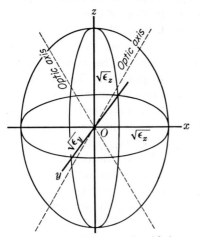

where we have taken $\epsilon_x < \epsilon_y < \epsilon_z$. From the ellipsoid we may obtain the two velocities and the corresponding directions of vibration for a wave traveling in any arbitrary direction through the crystal, as explained below. This mode of representation was first given by Fresnel in terms of the elastic-solid theory of light. Since, in the older theory, the velocity was dependent on the elasticity and density of the ether (Sec. 11.4), Fresnel's ellipsoid could be either an "ellipsoid of elasticity" or an "ellipsoid of inertia." Replacing it by a dielectric ellipsoid, Fresnel's results can be translated directly into the terms of the electromagnetic theory.

FIG. 26P. Dielectric ellipsoid for a biaxial crystal.

Suppose now that ordinary light waves vibrating in all planes are moving through the point O in the crystal in every direction and that we wish to determine the double wave surfaces presented in the preceding sections. In Eq. 23p, the velocity of light was given by

$$v = \frac{c}{\sqrt{\epsilon}} \tag{26h}$$

where c is the velocity *in vacuo*. We therefore have the relations

$$v_a = \frac{c}{\sqrt{\epsilon_x}} \qquad n_a = \sqrt{\epsilon_x}$$

$$v_b = \frac{c}{\sqrt{\epsilon_y}} \qquad n_b = \sqrt{\epsilon_y}$$

$$v_c = \frac{c}{\sqrt{\epsilon_z}} \qquad n_c = \sqrt{\epsilon_z}$$

where $v_a > v_b > v_c$. Now v_a represents the velocity of waves traveling perpendicular to the x axis with their electric displacements parallel to x. Their velocity is therefore determined by ϵ_x. The application of this statement to the other directions of vibration and velocities of propagation along the three coordinate axes may be seen by inspection of Fig. 26Q.

Let us now see how the two velocities in any arbitrary direction may be determined by the use of the dielectric ellipsoid. First we note that the velocities along any one of the coordinate axes are inversely proportional to the major and minor axes of the elliptical section of the ellipsoid made by the coordinate plane that is perpendicular to that axis. In the same way, for any other direction of propagation, we pass a plane through O parallel to the plane of the wave. This will cut the ellipsoid in

Fig. 26Q. Correlation of the velocities and directions of vibration in the waves with the directions of the three principal dielectric constants.

an ellipse with major and minor axes OA and OB, Fig. 26R(a). On the wave normal the distances OM and ON are measured off inversely proportional to OA and OB. The planes M and N parallel to the initial plane represent a later position of the waves vibrating parallel to the

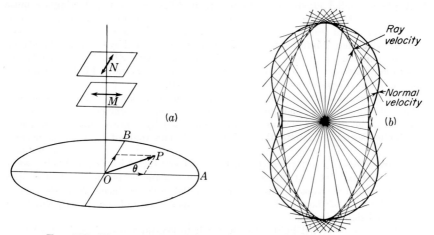

FIG. 26R. Illustrating the construction of a normal-velocity surface.

two axes of the ellipse. If we consider a single vibration in plane AOB making an angle θ with OA, the electric vector OP may be resolved into two components $OP \cos \theta$ and $OP \sin \theta$. These components along the major and minor axes travel with the two different velocities. If now the plane AOB is rotated about O in every possible direction the points M and N will trace out the normal-velocity surfaces (dotted lines) shown in Fig. 26K(b).

For every ellipsoid with three different axes there are two planes only for which the cross sections are circles. For these two planes, OA and OB in Fig. 26R(a) will be equal and the planes M and N will coincide. The directions of the normal for these two circular cross sections of the dielectric ellipsoid give the optic axes of the crystal, i.e., the directions of equal *normal* velocity for all planes of vibration. The envelope of all plane waves at the instant they reach the normal-velocity surface is the wave surface previously described in Sec. 26.6. This envelopment, giving a surface of elliptical section, is illustrated in Fig. 26R(b).

The optical properties of doubly refractive crystals are completely determined when one knows the values of the three principal refractive indices and the directions of two of the principal axes. As was mentioned, these may be measured by cutting the crystal into prisms of different orientation. There exist, however, more powerful and more convenient methods based on the interference effects resulting from the difference in velocity of the two polarized components, and these will be discussed in the next chapter.

PROBLEMS

1. A plane-parallel crystal of sodium nitrate 1.200 mm thick, having its optic axis parallel to the surface, is placed on the stage of a microscope. Focusing first on the top surface of the crystal, and then successively on the two images of a speck on the lower surface, it is found that the focus must be changed by 0.757 and 0.898 mm. The light from the two images is found to be polarized with vibrations perpendicular and parallel, respectively, to the principal section of the crystal. Find the values of n_E and n_O for this crystal, assuming it to be uniaxial.

2. Find by graphical construction how thick a natural calcite crystal would need to be in order that a ray of sodium light incident normally on one cleavage face should emerge from the opposite face as two rays separated by a linear distance of 1 mm. In a principal section of calcite, the optic axis makes an angle of 45° with the normal.
Ans. 9.2 mm.

3. Suppose that a ray strikes the surface of a crystal of ice ($n_O = 1.3090$, $n_E = 1.3104$, for sodium light) at grazing incidence in a plane perpendicular to the optic axis. The crystal is cut so that its axis lies parallel to the surface. Find the separation in millimeters of the O and E rays at the opposite face of the crystal, which is a plane-parallel slab 3 cm thick.

4. A ray of unpolarized light falls on a calcite crystal the optic axis of which is parallel to the surface. The angle of incidence is 34°, and the plane of incidence coincides with the principal section of the crystal. Find the angles of refraction of the O and E rays for the green mercury line. *Ans.* 19°20′. 17°45′.

5. Carry through the geometrical proof of the formula given in the footnote, page 540.

6. Calculate the angles of minimum deviation, and their difference, for a 60° prism of ammonium phosphate which has $n_O = 1.525$ and $n_E = 1.479$. The prism is cut with its optic axis parallel to its refracting edge. *Ans.* 39.37°. 35.37°. 4°0'.

7. By what fraction would the wave surface in quartz have to be increased or decreased in size if it were to apply to group velocities instead of wave velocities? Make the calculation for light of wavelength 4046 Å, using the refractive indices of Table 26-I.

8. Draw to scale the two cross sections of the wave surface of cinnabar (HgS) made by planes (*a*) parallel to the optic axis, (*b*) perpendicular to the axis. Cinnabar has $n_O = 2.854$ and $n_E = 3.201$. Indicate the directions of the vibrations on each diagram. Is cinnabar a positive or a negative crystal? *Ans.* Positive crystal.

9. The angle 2α between the optic axes of a biaxial crystal is given by $\cos \alpha = \sqrt{(b^2 - c^2)/(a^2 - c^2)}$. Find this angle 2α for the following crystals, and hence determine whether they are positive or negative crystals: (*a*) lithargite (PbO), $n_a = 2.510$, $n_b = 2.610$, $n_c = 2.710$; (*b*) anhydrite (CaSO$_4$), $n_a = 1.569$, $n_b = 1.575$, $n_c = 1.613$.

10. The criterion for classifying biaxial crystals as positive or negative is sometimes stated in terms of whether n_b is closer to n_a or closer to n_c, respectively. Using the equation of Prob. 9, show that this criterion is different from the correct one given in the text. Formulate one in terms of the refractive indices that does agree with the correct one. *Ans.* $(1/n_a)^2 - (1/n_b)^2$ less than $(1/n_b)^2 - (1/n_c)^2$ for positive crystals.

11. Draw to scale cross sections in the three coordinate planes of the wave surface of the biaxial crystal stibnite (Sb$_2$S$_3$), which has $n_a = 3.194$, $n_b = 4.046$, and $n_c = 4.303$.

12. Use one quadrant of the x,z section of the wave surface of stibnite (see Prob. 11) to construct the section of the normal velocity surface in this plane. [HINT: Refer to Fig. 26$R(b)$.]

13. Parallel light falls on a crystal of aragonite cut so that the bisector of the acute angle between the optic axes is perpendicular to the surface of the crystal. If the angle of incidence is 45° and the plane of incidence coincides with the plane containing the optic axes, find by Huygens' construction the two angles of refraction. Specify the directions of vibration for each.

14. A crystal of topaz is cut into a 60° prism with its refracting edge perpendicular to the plane containing the optic axes. The angle of minimum deviation is measured for a ray of sodium light polarized with its vibrations parallel to the refracting edge. What value would be expected according to the refractive indices given in Table 26-II? *Ans.* 48°11'.

15. The axis of single ray velocity in a biaxial crystal makes an angle with the z axis the cosine of which is a/b times as large as the value of $\cos \alpha$ given in Prob. 9. Find the apex angle of the cone of internal conical refraction in a crystal of stibnite, using the refractive indices given in Table 26-II.

CHAPTER 27

INTERFERENCE OF POLARIZED LIGHT

The first investigation of the interference of polarized light was made by Arago in 1811. Examining the blue light of the sky with a calcite crystal, he observed that when a thin sheet of clear mica was interposed, the ordinary and extraordinary rays became richly colored. This color effect is produced by nearly all crystals and is due in most cases to the interference of polarized light and in a relatively few to optical activity. The latter subject will be treated in detail in the next chapter, and the phenomena attributed to interference will be considered now.

27.1. Elliptically and Circularly Polarized Light. Suppose that plane-polarized light from a nicol prism N_1, as in Fig. 27A, is incident normally on a thin plate of calcite C cut with faces parallel to the optic axis.

Fig. 27A. Plane-polarized light incident normally on a crystal plate cut parallel to the optic axis.

Fig. 27B. Advance of the E wave ahead of the O wave in a negative crystal plate.

Making use of the wave-surface diagrams and Huygens' construction as in Fig. 26E(a), we can now determine qualitatively the nature of the light emerging from the calcite plate. Upon entering the crystal at P normal to the surface but with the vibrations at an angle with the optic axis, the light will break up into two components E and O (Fig. 27C). As shown in Fig. 27B, the E wave having vibrations parallel to the optic axis will travel faster than the O wave, but along the same path.

To find just how far the E vibrations get ahead of the O vibrations by the time they have traversed the thickness d of the crystal, we take the difference in the *optical paths* (Sec. 1.5) and then convert this into phase difference. The optical path for the O ray is, according to Eq. 1g, merely $n_O d$, and that for the E ray, $n_E d$. The path difference is therefore

$$\Delta = d(n_O - n_E) \tag{27a}$$

The corresponding phase difference, by Eq. 11f, becomes

$$\delta = \frac{2\pi}{\lambda} d(n_O - n_E) \tag{27b}$$

Here d may also represent the distance of penetration into a given crystal, and one sees that the phase differ-ence δ steadily increases in propor-tion to this distance.

Looking end-on against the light beam, as in Fig. 27C, let the plane-polarized light vibrations from the first nicol N_1 meet the first crystal face, making an angle θ with the principal section. If A is the am-plitude of this light, it will be broken up into two components, $E = A \cos \theta$ traveling with the faster velocity v_E and $O = A \sin \theta$ traveling with the slower velocity v_O. After leaving the crystal, the O and E rays will continue in the same straight line and, of course, with their vibrations perpendicular to each other.

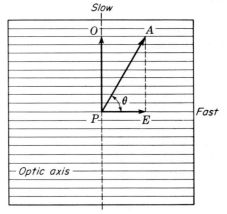

FIG. 27C. Resolution by the crystal of the light incident as in Fig. 27A.

Within the crystal there are, at any given point, two vibrations at right angles having the phase difference δ. They are of the same fre-quency, equal to that of the light outside the crystal. The problem of the composition of such vibrations has already been investigated in Sec. 12.9, where it was shown that the resultant motion is one of the various Lissajous figures for equal frequencies (Fig. 12K). The vibra-tion is therefore an ellipse, a straight line, or a circle. In fact, at steadily increasing distances through the crystal from P towards Q (Fig. 27B), the vibration forms will progress through a whole sequence of figures like those in Fig. 12K and usually will repeat the sequence many times. It is only when the light emerges from the crystal, however, that the type of vibration may be readily observed. Depending on the thickness of the crystal, and on the other quantities in Eq. 27b, this will be some figure enclosed within a rectangle of sides $2A \cos \theta$ and $2A \sin \theta$. For $\delta = 0, 2\pi, 4\pi, \ldots$ the linear incident vibration will emerge unchanged, while for $\delta = \pi, 3\pi, 5\pi, \ldots$ it will be transformed into another linear vibration making an angle 2θ with its original direction. At all intermediate values of δ the motion is in an ellipse, the shape of which is determined by the particular θ and δ according to the principles explained in Sec. 12.9. Such light is termed *elliptically polarized* light, of which linearly polarized* and circularly polarized light are obviously special cases.

Let us consider for a moment what is meant by the statement that the vibrations in a beam of light are elliptical. Since the "vibration" is actually a periodic variation of the electric field in space, it means that at any given point in an elliptically polarized beam *the terminus of the electric vector moves in an ellipse* in a plane perpendicular to the direction of propagation of the light. The vector thus varies continuously in both direction and magnitude, returning to the original values with the frequency of the wave. At other points along the wave the motion is similar but of different phase, so that the vector is in a different part of the ellipse. In a "snapshot" of the wave, the electric vectors would have a screwlike arrangement like that illustrated in Fig. 20D(b).

For the crystal to produce *circularly polarized* light, two conditions must hold. First, the amplitudes of the O and E rays must be equal. This requires that $\sin \theta = \cos \theta$, or that $\theta = 45°$. Second, the phase difference must be either $\pi/2$ or $3\pi/2$. (Addition of any multiple of 2π to either of these is of no consequence.) The difference between the two cases is one of the direction of rotation in the circle, as was explained in Sec. 12.9 in connection with Fig. 12L. Which value of δ gives right circular polarization and which left will depend on whether the plate is made of a positive or of a negative crystal. With calcite, for example, the E wave travels faster, and if $\delta = \pi/2$, a left-handed rotation is produced, looking against the direction of the light. The directions parallel to and perpendicular to the optic axis in a negative crystal are often called the *fast* and *slow* axes of the plate, as is indicated in Fig. 27C. In a positive crystal these designations relative to the axis are of course interchanged.

27.2. Quarter- and Half-wave Plates. The simplest device for producing and detecting circularly polarized light is known as a quarter-wave plate, or $\lambda/4$ plate. Such plates are usually made of thin sheets of split mica, although they can be of quartz cut parallel to the optic axis. The thickness is adjusted so as to introduce a 90° phase change between the O and E vibrations.† The correct thickness for such plates can in the

---

* The terms "plane-polarized" and "linearly polarized" are often used interchangeably. The latter is rather to be preferred when comparisons are made with "elliptically polarized" light.

† Strictly speaking, mica is a negative biaxial crystal of which there are many different forms. The angle between the optic axes may be almost anything from 0 to 42°

case of uniaxial crystals be computed by use of Eq. 27b.   Since the phase difference δ depends upon the wavelength, the principal indices for yellow sodium light, λ5893, are usually used for computing the required thickness for a quarter-wave plate.   When a quarter-wave plate is oriented at an angle of 45° with the plane of the incident polarized light, the emerging light is circularly polarized.   Reasonably good plates can be made by splitting good clear mica into very thin sheets about 0.035 mm thick.   This can be done with a penknife or a needle, using a micrometer caliper for checking the thickness.

Use is often made of plates which introduce a phase difference of 180° between the components and which are therefore called *half-wave* plates. As was mentioned in the previous section, the effect of a plate of this kind is merely to alter the direction of vibration of plane-polarized light by the angle 2θ, where θ is the angle between the incident vibrations and the principal section.   In certain instruments where it is desired to compare two adjacent fields of light polarized at a certain angle with each other, half the field is covered with a half-wave plate.

27.3. Crystal Plates between Crossed Nicols.   As was explained in Sec. 24.12, when the polarizer and analyzer are set at right angles to each other, no light is transmitted by the combination.   Suppose now that a crystal plate cut parallel to the optic axis is inserted between crossed nicols as shown in Fig. 27D.   The observed result is that light will now get through the second nicol.   One way of interpreting this result is to say that the plane-polarized light entering the crystal at *a* emerges as elliptically polarized light at *b* and thus has developed a component parallel to the transmitting plane of the analyzer.   This view is correct and very simple: it is just the component A_1 shown in Fig. 27E that is passed by the analyzer, and the corresponding intensity is proportional to A_1^2.   For purposes of computation, however, it is possible to consider the phenomenon as one of *interference* between the two component vibrations emerging from the plate, part of each being transmitted by the analyzer.   In Fig. 27D, the four lower diagrams represent end-on views of the light (looking *against* the light) at the four points designated by corresponding letters in the diagram above.   In (*a*) the plane vibration is shown as it arrives at the crystal plate with an amplitude *A* and making an angle θ with the optic axis.   This ampli-

---

depending upon the chemical constitution as well as the crystal structure.   The most common mica "muscovite" (pale brown in color) has an angle of 42° (= 180° − 2α) between the optic axes (see Table 26-II).   The cleavage plane along which it splits most easily is the *y,z* plane in Figs. 26*I* and 26*J*.   The difference between the velocities along the *x* axis is therefore very small.   This is an advantage, since then the plates do not have to be made too thin and fragile.   Quartz has no natural cleavage planes and has to be cut and the faces polished to optical flatness.

tude is broken up into two components, $E = A \cos \theta$ along the optic axis, and $O = A \sin \theta$ perpendicular to it. One of these components travels faster in the crystal and, upon emerging, will be ahead of the

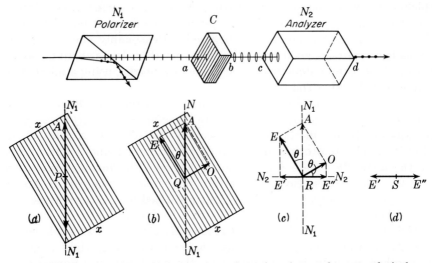

FIG. 27D. Origin of the components brought to interference by crossed nicols.

other in phase. In (c) these two components are shown as they arrive at the second nicol N_2 where only the E vibrations parallel to its principal section $N_2 N_2$ can be transmitted. In other words, only the components E' and E'' get through and they are now vibrating in the same plane. These have the magnitudes

$$E' = E \sin \theta = A \cos \theta \sin \theta \qquad (27c)$$

and

$$E'' = O \cos \theta = A \sin \theta \cos \theta \qquad (27d)$$

This result shows that regardless of the angle θ both components E' and E'' transmitted by the second nicol are equal in magnitude when the nicols are crossed.

These two components are now vibrating in the same plane and have

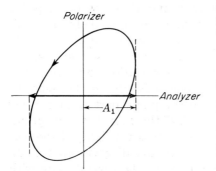

FIG. 27E. Component of elliptically polarized light transmitted by an analyzer that is crossed with the polarizer.

the phase difference given by Eq. 27b. If the thickness of the plate is such that $\delta = 0, 2\pi, 4\pi, \ldots$, the two *destructively interfere*. (Note that for zero thickness $d = 0$, $\delta = 0$, and the components E' and E'' are in opposite directions and hence cancel.) For all other phase angles the resultant of the two vibrations will be transmitted. To find the amplitude and intensity of this transmitted light the two components are combined as shown in Chap. 12, Fig. 12A. The equations for these quantities will be derived in Sec. 27.6.

It should be noted that destructive interference is not produced in front of the second nicol. It is only after the two components are brought into the same plane that interference is brought about. This principle is best expressed by the *Fresnel-Arago laws*, the two most significant of which are

1. Two rays polarized at right angles do not interfere.
2. Two rays polarized at right angles (obtained from the same beam of plane-polarized light) will interfere in the same manner as ordinary light only when brought into the same plane.

27.4. Babinet Compensator. Frequently in the study of the optical phenomena a crystal plate of variable thickness is useful in producing

(a)

(b)

FIG. 27F. Diagrams of (a) Babinet compensator and (b) Soleil compensator.

or analyzing elliptically polarized light. Such a plate, with faces cut parallel to the optic axis, was made by Babinet and is called a *Babinet compensator*. It consists of two wedge-shaped prisms of quartz cut at a very small angle as shown in Fig. 27F(a). The optic axes are parallel and perpendicular, respectively, to the two refracting edges. If plane-polarized light is incident normally on the compensator with the plane of vibration at some arbitrary angle θ to the optic axis, it will be broken up into two components. The E component, parallel to the optic axis in the first crystal, travels slower (since the compensator is made of quartz) than the O component until it reaches the second crystal. At this point the E vibration becomes the O vibration since it is now perpendicular to the axis. At the same point the O vibration from the first crystal becomes the E vibration in the second. In other words, the two vibrations exchange velocities in passing from one prism to the other. The effect is such that one prism tends to cancel the effect of the other. Along the center at C, where both paths are equal, the cancellation is complete and the effect is that of a plate of zero thickness. On each side of C one vibration will be behind or ahead of the other because of the different path lengths.   Thus the effect is that of a plate the thickness of which is zero along the center line and varies linearly in both directions from this line.

The chief disadvantage of a Babinet compensator is that a specified plate thickness or a certain desired retardation is confined to a narrow region along the plate parallel to the refracting edges of the prisms.   A modification which permits a changeable thickness which is the same over a large field consists of two wedges cut and mounted together with axes shown in Fig. 27F(b).   The effective thickness is varied by a calibrated screw which slides the top prism along the other.   By making the prism angles very small a careful adjustment to a λ/4 or λ/2 plate thickness is readily made for any color of light.   This arrangement is called a *Soleil compensator*.

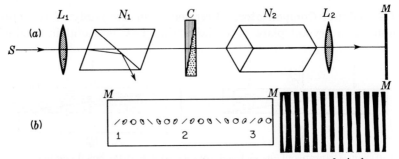

Fig. 27G. Effect of a Babinet compensator between crossed nicols.

The properties of a Babinet compensator are well illustrated by the following experiment: Light from a carbon-arc lamp is polarized by a nicol prism N_1 as shown in Fig. 27G(a).   The compensator C is oriented at about 45° with N_1 and its image focused on a screen MM by means of a lens L_2.   Owing to the effectively variable thickness along the compensator, the light on the screen (with N_2 removed) will be polarized as shown in Fig. 27G(b) (see also Sec. 27.1 and Fig. 12K).   If a second nicol is inserted at N_2 and oriented perpendicular to one set of plane-polarization regions, for example, those marked 1, 2, and 3 in the figure, no light will be transmitted at these points.   The screen will thus be crossed by a set of equidistant parallel dark bands.   With white light the bands are colored and look like Young's double-slit fringes but with the center one black.   Best results are obtained with monochromatic light.   Piles of glass plates mounted in tubes, or polaroid films, may of course be used in place of nicols N_1 and N_2.

27.5. Analysis of Polarized Light.   If one has a beam of light that is completely polarized, linearly, elliptically, or circularly, it will appear to the eye to be no different from ordinary unpolarized light. By using simple auxiliary apparatus, however, its character and vibration form may be easily determined. For this purpose an analyzer, in the form of a nicol or polaroid, is used in conjunction with either a quarter-wave plate or some form of compensator. For many purposes a $\lambda/4$ plate is adequate, and the compensator need be used only where precise measurements of elliptical polarization are required.

To illustrate the use of the $\lambda/4$ plate, suppose, for example, that it is placed in a beam of circularly polarized light. Regardless of the orientation of the optic axis, the circular vibration is equivalent to two linear and mutually perpendicular ones along the slow and fast axes, 90° out of phase with each other. Upon emerging from the plate these two are in phase and recombine to give plane-polarized light vibrating at 45° with the axes of the plate. The plane of the emergent light depends on the direction of rotation of the incident circularly polarized light. In either of the possible cases it can be completely extinguished by the analyzer. If the light to be studied is elliptically polarized, it will be converted into plane-polarized light only when the fast axis of the $\lambda/4$ plate coincides with either the major or the minor axis of the ellipse. The ratio of these axes can then be found as the tangent of the angle that the plane of transmission of the analyzer makes with the fast axis when extinction has been achieved.

The same information may be found with greater accuracy by means of a Babinet compensator, which has the additional advantage of being usable for any wavelength. We have seen that, when the incident light is plane-polarized at 45° to the principal section of one wedge, a dark band occurs at the center. If for some other kind of light the dark band is displaced from this position, a phase difference must exist between the two rectangular components of this light, and this means that it is elliptical to a greater or less degree. Since a phase difference of 2π corresponds to one whole fringe, the actual difference can be found from the fractional fringe displacement. The measurement is done by screwing one wedge over the other until the dark fringe returns to the center, so that the phase difference has been *compensated*. For details of the use of the compensator, the reader should refer to more advanced texts.*

If the light is not completely polarized, but contains some admixture of unpolarized light, it is still possible to completely determine its character by using a $\lambda/4$ plate and an analyzer in the systematic way outlined in Table 27-I. The light is first studied with the analyzer alone. If there is no change in intensity on rotating it, the procedure outlined in

* M. Born, "Optik," p. 244, J. Springer, Berlin, 1933.

TABLE 27-I. ANALYSIS OF POLARIZED LIGHT
A. No Intensity Variation with Analyzer Alone

I. If with λ/4 plate in front of analyzer	II. If with λ/4 plate in front of analyzer one finds a maximum, then	
1. One has no intensity variation,	2. If one position of analyzer gives zero intensity,	3. If no position of analyzer gives zero intensity,
one has	one has	one has
natural unpolarized light	circularly polarized light	mixture of circularly polarized light and unpolarized light

B. Intensity Variation with Analyzer Alone

I. If one position of analyzer gives	II. If no position of analyzer gives zero intensity		
1. Zero intensity,	2. Insert a λ/4 plate in front of analyzer with optic axis parallel to position of maximum intensity		
	(a) If get zero intensity with analyzer,	(b) If get no zero intensity,	
		(1) But the same analyzer setting as before gives the maximum intensity,	(2) But some other analyzer setting than before gives a maximum intensity,
one has	one has	one has	one has
plane-polarized light	elliptically polarized light	mixture of plane-polarized light and unpolarized light	mixture of elliptically polarized light and plane-polarized light

part A of the table is followed. If there is some change of intensity, part B is followed. The seven kinds of light which can be identified in this way represent all the possible conditions of polarization. Other more complicated mixtures can be shown to be equivalent to one or another of these.

To specify quantitatively the state of polarization of a beam of light, it is found that just four numbers are required. These are called the *Stokes parameters*, and can be determined by making four suitably chosen measurements. One of these involves the total intensity, and another requires some phase-shifting device like a $\lambda/4$ plate in conjunction with an analyzer. The remaining two can be made with the analyzer alone.*

27.6. Interference with White Light. Referring to Eq. 27*b*, it is observed that the phase difference between the E and O rays depends upon the wavelength as well as on the thickness of the plate. As for the difference between the principal indices of refraction $(n_O - n_E)$, the values given in Table 26-I show that there is little change throughout the visible region. As the thickness of a crystal plate increases, the phase difference δ between the O and E rays for violet light, $\lambda 4000$, increases nearly twice as fast as the phase difference for red light, $\lambda 6500$, since λ occurs in the denominator of the expression for δ. This fact gives rise to the rich colors frequently observed in thin plates of mica, quartz, calcite, etc., cut parallel to the axis and placed between crossed nicols. The reason for the color is that some one or more parts of the continuous visible spectrum are stopped by the second nicol prism.

Suppose that a thin sheet of mica which introduces a phase change for yellow light of 2π rad, i.e., a full-wave plate, is introduced between crossed nicols and oriented at an angle $\theta = 45°$. The orange and red wavelengths will undergo a phase change less than 2π and the green, blue, and violet more than 2π. Components of all colors but yellow light will therefore get through the second nicol. With yellow absent, the resultant color will be the mixture of red, orange, green, blue, and violet, giving a purple hue.

If, in the above experiment with a mica sheet, the analyzing nicol is replaced with a thick natural calcite crystal, one obtains the ordinary vibrations O' and O'' as well as the extraordinary ones (Fig. 27*H*), but in a different position. This O beam is also colored and is complementary to the E beam containing the components E' and E''. These two beams if made to overlap will give white light, since what is absent in one beam is present in the other. A slight increase or decrease in thickness of the mica plate will change the wavelength or color of the light interfering destructively and hence change the color of each transmitted beam.

To show that these two colors are complementary it must be shown that the sum of the two beams gives the original intensity A^2. For the E beam the components E' and E'' must be combined with their proper phase angle difference.

---

* A summary of the uses of the Stokes parameters, including their application to photons and elementary particles, is given by W. H. McMaster, *Am. J. Phys.*, **22,** 351, 1954.

$$A_1{}^2 = E'^2 + E''^2 + 2E'E'' \cos(\delta + \pi)$$
$$= (A \sin\theta \cos\theta)^2 + (A \sin\theta \cos\theta)^2 + 2A^2 \sin^2\theta \cos^2\theta \cos(\delta + \pi)$$
$$= 2A^2 \sin^2\theta \cos^2\theta (1 - \cos\delta)$$
$$= 4A^2 \sin^2\theta \cos^2\theta \sin^2\frac{\delta}{2}$$

where δ is the phase angle difference given by Eq. 27b, and π is added since E' and E'' are oppositely directed when the plate thickness $d = 0$ (Fig. 27H).

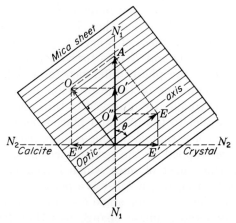

FIG. 27H. Components of plane-polarized light transmitted by a thin doubly refracting plate and an analyzing crystal. The lines N_1 and N_2 indicate the directions of the O and E vibrations in the calcite.

Similarly, for the O beam the two components O' and O'' must be combined.

$$A_2{}^2 = O'^2 + O''^2 + 2O'O'' \cos\delta$$
$$= (A \cos^2\theta)^2 + (A \sin^2\theta)^2 + 2A^2 \sin^2\theta \cos^2\theta \cos\delta$$
$$= A^2 \left[\sin^4\theta + \cos^4\theta + 2 \sin^2\theta \cos^2\theta \left(1 - 2 \sin^2\frac{\delta}{2}\right) \right]$$
$$= A^2 \left[(\sin^2\theta + \cos^2\theta)^2 - 4 \sin^2\theta \cos^2\theta \sin^2\frac{\delta}{2} \right]$$
$$= A^2 - 4A^2 \sin^2\theta \cos^2\theta \sin^2\frac{\delta}{2}$$

When added together, the two intensities yield the original one, since

$$A_1{}^2 + A_2{}^2 = A^2$$

Because of the rapid change of δ with wavelength, if a plate several times as thick as the one described above is inserted between crossed nicols, several narrow bands of the visible spectrum will be absent from the transmitted light. This may be shown experimentally with a crystal plate cut parallel to the axis as follows: A calcite plate about 0.01 to 0.03 mm thick, or a quartz plate 0.2 to 1.0 mm thick, is placed in a beam of plane-polarized light and beyond it a prism spectroscope arrangement as shown in Fig. 27I. With an arc lamp as a source at S, a continuous spectrum will be formed on the screen MM. If the crystal plate axis is oriented at an angle $\theta = 45°$, this light is polarized as shown schematically in the figure. To test this polarization, a second nicol is now inserted between C and S_1. When it is crossed with the polarizer, the intensity will vary sinusoidally through the spectrum, with zeros at

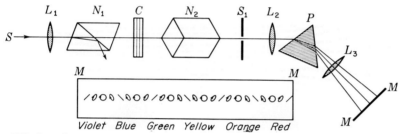

Fig. 27I. Interference of white light produced by a crystal plate between crossed nicols.

those wavelengths for which the light transmitted by C is plane-polarized with vibrations perpendicular to the transmission plane of the second nicol. The thicker the plate the larger the number of dark bands across the spectrum.

With thick plates the combined light of the spectrum will appear white, since the large number of very narrow bands removed all along the spectrum affect the eye only as a lowering of the intensity. If a Soleil compensator is used in place of a fixed plate in the above experiment, any desired number of dark fringes can be introduced across the spectrum. A slow continuous change in thickness will cause the bands to move sideways across the spectrum and at the same time to increase or decrease slowly in number.

27.7. Polarizing Monochromatic Filter. The dark bands produced in the spectrum as described above have been used in an ingenious manner by Lyot[*] to construct a "light filter" which transmits one or more very narrow bands of wavelength. The separation of the bands produced in the spectrum by a single crystal is inversely proportional to the thickness of the crystal. Hence if one uses a thick crystal followed by one exactly half as thick, every other maximum due to the thick one will be suppressed because it will coincide with a minimum for the thinner

[*] B. Lyot, *Compt. rend.*, **197**, 1593, 1933.

one. Still another crystal one-quarter as thick as the first will blot out every other maximum that is transmitted by the first two. Thus it will be seen that, by placing in series a number of quartz plates the thicknesses of which vary in the geometrical progression $1:2:4:8: \ldots$, it is possible to isolate a very few narrow wavelength bands. Then the unwanted ones can be cut out by an ordinary color filter.

In one polarization filter Lyot used six quartz plates varying from 2.221 to 71.080 mm in thickness, with polaroids between each pair. The optic axes of all the plates were perpendicular to the light beam, and parallel

FIG. 27J. Photoelastic effect in a plastic beam loaded at two points. (*After R. W. Clough, Jr.*)

to each other, while the polaroids were set at 45° with the optic axes. This filter transmitted 13 narrow bands only 2 Å wide. Filters of this type have been very valuable to astronomers, since they permit the study of the solar corona and prominences without the necessity of a total eclipse. By varying the temperature of the filter, it is possible to shift the wavelength of the transmitted bands to the desired value, thanks to the expansion of the plates, and decrease of the refractive indices, with rising temperature.

27.8. Applications of Interference in Parallel Light. If the source is sufficiently intense, very small amounts of double refraction can be detected by the restoration of light when the sample is placed between crossed polarizers. If a transparent, isotropic substance like glass is subjected to mechanical stress, it becomes weakly doubly refracting with the effective optic axis in the direction of the stress. Glass blowers examine their finished work in a polariscope to check it for proper annealing. Engineers make models of structures out of a transparent plastic in order to study the distribution of stresses when a load is applied. The stresses are revealed by the distribution of light when the model is placed between crossed polaroids. As a simple example, Fig. 27J shows the interference fringes produced by a rectangular beam when stressed at two points by small rollers.   This field of *photoelasticity* is obviously one of great practical importance.*

Many common transparent substances such as silk fibers, white hair, fish scales, etc., possess a small anisotropy which can be detected by examination in polarized light.   Such substances are often highly colored when viewed in a polariscope.   This fact is made use of in the study of microscopic crystal growths, the color yielding a contrast that permits ready observation of the normally transparent crystals.

These applications are cited merely as examples of the many practical uses of interference in polarized light.   Another is discussed in the following section, and still further ones will be found in Chap. 29.

27.9. Interference in Highly Convergent Light.   Up to this point in our discussion of interference of polarized light we have considered only

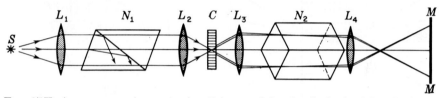

FIG. 27*K*. Arrangement for projecting "rings and brushes" obtained by the interference of highly convergent polarized light.

uniaxial crystals in parallel beams.   In Sec. 27.4 conditions of interference were described in which the thickness of the crystal could be varied continuously, thus altering the phase difference between the O and E rays by any desired amount.   A similar result may be achieved by sending light at different angles through a plate of uniform thickness. In this case a single plane-parallel plate is usually cut with its two faces perpendicular to the optic axis.   Experimentally such a plate is inserted between crossed analyzer and polarizer as shown in Fig. 27*K*. Parallel white light from the polarizer is made highly convergent by one or more short focus lenses at L_2.   After passing through the crystal C, the light is made parallel again by a similar lens L_3.   Beyond the analyzer N_2 another lens L_4 focuses on the screen M all parallel rays leaving C. This lens therefore images the secondary focal plane of L_3 on M.

A detailed diagram of the convergent light passing through a uniaxial crystal is shown in Fig. 27*L*(*a*).   The central ray parallel to the optic axis undergoes no change in phase since both the O and E components travel with the same speed and, in fact, there is no distinction between them. Other rays like P and Q, however, travel a greater distance in the crystal

* Complete descriptions of the methods used are given in M. Frocht, "Photo-elasticity," vol. 1, 1941, vol. 2, 1948, John Wiley & Sons, Inc., New York.

and being at an angle with the optic axis are doubly refracted. As they travel at different speeds, there will be a phase difference between the O and E rays which will increase with increase angle of incidence. Referring to the end view in Fig. 27L(b), all rays entering at points on the circle P, H, Q, G pass through the same thickness of crystal and show the same phase difference upon emergence. The vertical line N_1 represents the plane of vibration of the incident light from the first nicol and N_2 the plane of vibration transmitted by the second.

Consider now any point on the circle of Fig. 27L(b) such as S where the light is not normal to the crystal surface. This light will be broken

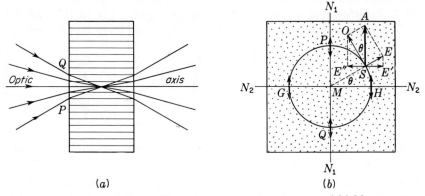

(a)   (b)

Fig. 27L. Resolution of O and E components for interference of highly convergent polarized light.

up into two components O and E. Since the plane of incidence contains the optic axis, the refracted rays will also be in this plane. The E vibrations with amplitude $A \sin \theta$ will lie in the plane of incidence, and the O ray vibrations with amplitude $A \cos \theta$ will be perpendicular to it, as shown. Upon arrival at the second nicol N_2, the components E' and E'' will be transmitted, and will interfere destructively or otherwise depending on the emergent phase relations. Whatever the phase relations for the point S, they will be the same for all other points on the same circle. For points on some other circle the phase will be different. If the plate is of several millimeters thickness, there will be a number of regularly spaced concentric dark circles where the phase difference is some multiple of 2π, so that destructive interference is produced. Thus the transmitted light will give interference rings, as shown in Fig. 27M(a). If white light is used, these fringes will be highly colored because of the various wavelengths present.

The dark cross appearing in these patterns, usually referred to as the "brushes," may be explained by again using Fig. 27L(b). As the point S approaches G or H, the components E' and E'' vanish. At these points the vibrations traverse the crystal as pure O vibrations.   They therefore undergo no change and are stopped by the analyzer.   Similarly the light striking P and Q is transmitted as E vibrations.   Hence the intensity along the directions N_1 and N_2, corresponding to the planes of the two nicols, is zero.   On each bright fringe it rises steadily to a maximum at 45° to these directions.

If the second nicol is parallel to the first, the interference pattern becomes just the complement, in every respect, of the one described.

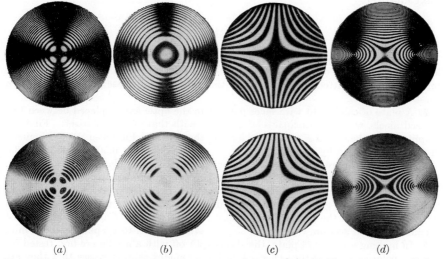

(a)   (b)   (c)   (d)

FIG. 27M. Interference patterns from crystals placed in highly convergent light. Upper photographs for crossed nicols, lower photographs for parallel nicols.   (a) Calcite cut ⊥ to the optic axis.   (b) Quartz cut ⊥.   (c) Quartz cut ‖.   (d) Aragonite cut ⊥ to the bisector of the two optic axes.

This pattern is shown in the lower part of (a) in Fig. 27M.   One sees that this must be true by remembering that any light that is stopped by a crossed nicol will be passed by a parallel one, and vice versa.

It is possible to eliminate the brushes by introducing quarter-wave plates immediately before and behind the crystal.   The light traversing the latter is then circularly polarized, and since there is no preferred direction, there can be no brushes.   The so-called *optical ring sight* is made in this way, using polaroids as the polarizing elements.   Looking through such a combination one sees white-light interference rings, the center of which is exactly on the foot of the perpendicular from the eye. It can therefore be used as a gun sight of great accuracy and convenience.

In the case where the crystal is cut not perpendicular but parallel to the optic axis, the fringes turn out to be hyperbolic instead of circular. Part (c) of the figure shows fringes of this type.   Because in this case the phase difference is not small anywhere in the field, white light cannot be used in observing these fringes. The interference figures produced by biaxial crystals, such as that shown in (d), are more complicated in their explanation, but the same general principles apply. The two "eyes" show the points of intersection of the optic axes with the surface of the crystal. Such figures are of importance in the identification of mineral specimens, and the mineralogist obtains them in a microscope fitted with polarizing attachments.* The bright center of the ring system observed with the uniaxial crystal quartz [photographs (b)] will be explained in the next chapter.

PROBLEMS

1. A quartz plate 1 mm thick is illuminated by plane-polarized red light of wavelength 6563 Å. The optic axis is parallel to the surface. Find (a) the optical paths for the two transmitted components, (b) the difference in phase in degrees between these components.

2. A plate of calcite cut with faces parallel to the optic axis is placed between two crossed nicols, with its principal section at 60° with that of the polarizer. Find the amplitudes of the O and E vibrations leaving the calcite. Find also the components of these transmitted by the analyzer.   *Ans.* 0.866.   0.500.   0.433.   0.433.

3. Calculate the required thickness for a quarter-wave plate made of quartz. Use the refractive indices listed in Table 26-I for the green mercury line.

4. It is desired to make a half-wave plate of the biaxial crystal aragonite. From the refractive indices given in Table 26-II, determine in which plane the crystal should be cut in order that the plate should be least thin and fragile. Calculate the required thickness for this section.   *Ans.* Parallel to y,z plane.   0.037 mm.

5. In making a mica $\lambda/4$ plate, the sheets split off with a needle are first tested for circular polarization and then checked with micrometer calipers to see that they are not $3\lambda/4$ to $5\lambda/4$ plates. What disadvantage do you see in using the latter instead of a $\lambda/4$ plate? How accurately would the calipers have to read to distinguish between these? The appropriate indices are $n_b = 1.5936$ and $n_c = 1.5977$.

6. Sodium light is passed first through a polaroid and then through a sheet of corundum ($n_O = 1.768$, $n_E = 1.760$) oriented with its axis at 40° in a clockwise direction from the electric vector of the incident light. If the sheet is 0.1 mm thick, make a plot similar to one of those in Fig. 12K showing the form of vibration of the transmitted light.

Ans. Ellipse with major axis inclined at 77.1° to right, axial ratio 1.30, counterclockwise rotation.

7. In the above problem, find the intensity of the light transmitted by an analyzer that is crossed with the polarizer. Make the calculation (a) graphically from the component of the ellipse transmitted by the analyzer, and (b) by use of the equation derived in Sec. 27.6. Express the result relative to the intensity of the light incident on the corundum crystal.

8. Into a polariscope set for extinction are inserted side-by-side two half-wave plates with their axes making a small angle α. The fields are of equal intensity when the direction of the incident vibrations bisects the angle α. Find the ratio of their intensities when the analyzer is turned through 1° if α has the values (a) 20°, (b) 5°, and (c) 2°.   *Ans.* 1.51.   5.45.   ∞.

* See the book by Johannsen referred to on p. 501.

9. It is desired to determine the direction of rotation in a beam of circularly polarized light. When a quarter-wave plate is placed in front of the analyzer and the latter set for extinction, it is found that the fast axis of the $\lambda/4$ plate lies in such a position that it must be turned 45° counterclockwise in order to bring it into coincidence with the direction of transmission of the analyzer. Does the light have right or left circular polarization?

10. Compute the value required for the wedge angles of a Babinet compensator made of quartz in order that the interference fringes should be 0.50 mm apart. The comparator is used in the ordinary way, with a sodium source.   *Ans.* 3°42′.

11. When a light beam of unknown polarization is viewed through a nicol prism, its intensity varies upon rotation of the latter, but does not go to zero in any position. A $\lambda/4$ plate is inserted in front of the analyzer when set for a maximum intensity, and the fast axis turned parallel to the plane of transmission of the analyzer. A clockwise rotation of the analyzer by 70° will then completely extinguish the light. (*a*) What is the type of polarization? (*b*) Describe quantitatively the mode of vibration.

12. A plate of the uniaxial crystal beryl is ground and polished with its axis parallel to the surface. Its thickness is measured as 0.740 mm. When this crystal is placed between crossed polarizer and analyzer and the emergent light examined with a spectroscope, dark bands are observed at wavelengths of 4100, 4450, 4900, 5400, 6100, and 7000 Å. What value of the difference between n_O and n_E is indicated by this experiment?   *Ans.* 0.00662.

13. What color would a sheet of mica 0.08 mm thick produce when placed in a polariscope at 45° with the crossed polarizer and analyzer? For the appropriate indices of refraction, see Prob. 5.

14. Devise an arrangement that could be used to produce a beam of elliptically polarized light for which the major axis of the ellipse is vertical, the ratio of the major to minor axis is 2:1, and the direction of rotation counterclockwise. Specify carefully each part of the apparatus and its orientation.

Ans. Polarizer with plane of transmission turned 26°34′ clockwise from vertical, followed by $\lambda/4$ plate with fast axis horizontal.

15. If the light described in the previous problem were passed through a Babinet compensator having its zero line vertical, and were observed through an analyzer, at what angle with the vertical would the plane of transmission of the latter have to be set to obtain maximum contrast in the fringes? How would these fringes lie relative to the zero line?

CHAPTER 28

OPTICAL ACTIVITY

In the preceding chapters on the behavior of polarized light in crystals we have seen that when the light travels along the optic axis there is no double refraction. In this particular direction one expects that any kind of light will be propagated without change. As early as 1811, however, Arago discovered exceptions to this simple rule. He found that certain substances, notably crystalline quartz, will restore the light when placed between crossed nicols even though the optic axis is parallel to the direction of the light. An example of this effect was shown in Fig. 27M(b).

28.1. Rotation of the Plane of Polarization. When a beam of plane-polarized light is directed along the optic axis of quartz, it is found that the plane of polarization turns steadily about the direction of the beam,

Fig. 28A. Rotation of the plane of vibration in an optically active substance.

as shown in Fig. 28A, and emerges vibrating in some other plane than that at which it entered. The amount of this rotation is found experimentally to depend upon the distance traveled in the medium and upon the wavelength of the light. The former fact shows that the action occurs within the medium and not at the surface. This phenomenon of the rotation of the plane of vibration is frequently called *optical activity*, and many substances are now known to exhibit the effect. Some of these are cinnabar, sodium chlorate, turpentine, sugar crystals, sugar in solution, and sulfate of strychnine.

Some quartz crystals and sugar solutions rotate the plane of vibration to the right and some to the left. Substances which rotate to the right are called *dextrorotatory* or *right-handed*, and those which rotate to the left are called *levorotatory* or *left-handed*. By "right-handed rotation" is meant that upon looking *against* the oncoming light the plane of vibration is rotated in a clockwise direction. Left-handed substances rotate the light counterclockwise.*

28.2. Rotatory Dispersion. A striking feature of optical activity is that different colors are rotated by very different amounts. The first accurate measurements of this effect were made by Biot, who found that the rotation was very nearly proportional to the inverse square of the

(a) (b)

Fig. 28B. Rotation for different colors by a plate of quartz 1 mm thick.

wavelength. In other words, there is a rotatory dispersion, violet light being rotated nearly four times as much as red light. This effect is illustrated diagrammatically for quartz in Fig. 28B(a). Let plane-polarized white light be incident normally on a quartz plate and let the direction of its vibration be indicated by AA. Upon passing through 1 mm thickness of the crystal, the violet light is rotated about 50°, the red about 15°, and the other colors by intermediate amounts. More exact values for 15 wavelengths throughout the visible and ultraviolet spectrum are given in Table 28-I.

This rotation for a 1-mm plate, plotted in Fig. 28B(b), is called the *specific rotation*. Careful measurements on quartz and other substances as well show that Biot's inverse-square law is only approximately true. In fact, optical activity is closely enough connected with ordinary dispersion theory for the regular dispersion formulas for refractive index to be applied to rotation. Cauchy's equation (Sec. 23.3), for example, can be used to represent the specific rotation for quartz in the visible

---

* Although the convention used here seems to be the most common, many books will be found which use the opposite convention.

region. Thus we have

$$\rho = A + \frac{B}{\lambda^2} \qquad (28a)$$

where A and B are constants to be determined.

Experimentally, the phenomenon of rotatory dispersion can be illustrated by inserting a quartz plate between crossed analyzer and polarizer

TABLE 28-I. SPECIFIC ROTATION ρ OF PLANE-POLARIZED LIGHT IN QUARTZ

Wavelength, Å	Deg/mm	Wavelength, Å	Deg/mm	Wavelength, Å	Deg/mm
2265.03	201.9	4358.34	41.548	5892.90	21.724
2503.29	153.9	4678.15	35.601	6438.47	18.023
3034.12	95.02	4861.33	32.761	6707.86	16.535
3403.65	72.45	5085.82	29.728	7281.35	13.924
4046.56	48.945	5460.72	25.535	7947.63	11.589

as shown in Fig. 28C. With a monochromatic source at S, some light will get through the analyzer to the screen MM, since in passing through the quartz along the optic axis the plane of vibration has been rotated. This is shown diagrammatically in Fig. 28D(a). After the vibration is rotated from the plane AP to the plane A_1P, a certain component $EP = A_1P \sin \theta$ gets through the analyzer N_2. If now the analyzer

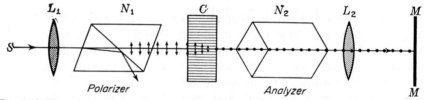

FIG. 28C. Experimental arrangement for studying the rotation produced by a plate C.

is made parallel to A_1P, all the light will be transmitted, whereas if it is normal to A_1P, none will be transmitted.

Suppose that white light is used in place of monochromatic light, so that upon passage through the crystal the different colors are rotated by different amounts as shown in Fig. 28D(b). The new planes of vibration are RP for the red and VP for the violet. On arriving at N_2 the two horizontal components E_RP to E_VP will get through. There being more violet light transmitted than red, the image on the screen will be colored. What has happened is that more of the red light has been eliminated in the second nicol. This may be seen by the following modification of the experiment.

Let the analyzer in Fig. 28C be replaced by a calcite crystal. This will transmit in one beam the E vibrations given by the analyzer alone and, in a separate beam, the O vibrations. The E beam will contain the

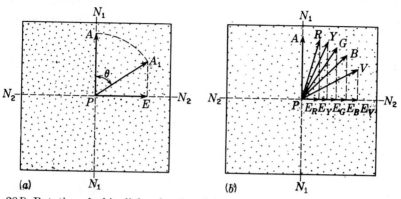

FIG. 28D. Rotation of white light, showing the various colors transmitted by a crossed analyzer.

components E_RP to E_VP (see Fig. 28E) and the O beam the components O_RP to O_VP. In other words, what the E beam does not contain, the O beam does. The two images on the screen MM are therefore the *complementary* colors, and if made partly to overlap, the regions of overlapping will be white. This is an excellent method for demonstrating a series of complementary colors, for if the calcite is turned slowly, varying amounts of the different colors can be thrown into the O or E beams.

Another very striking demonstration of optical activity and rotatory dispersion is achieved by passing plane-polarized light vertically into a clear solution of cane sugar contained in a large glass tube. On observing the tube from the side with a nicol prism, a very fine spiral arrangement of colors, somewhat like a barber-pole, will be seen.

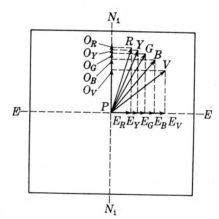

FIG. 28E. Quartz plate between a polarizer N_1 and a calcite crystal E as analyzer.

28.3. Fresnel's Explanation of Rotation. Fresnel proposed an explanation for rotation in crystals like quartz which is based upon the assumption that circularly polarized light is propagated along the optic axis without change. This explanation, while not a theory in the sense of giving the basic cause of the phenomenon, nevertheless gives an admirable account of the facts. It is based upon the elementary principle in mechanics that any simple harmonic motion along a straight line may be described as the resultant of two opposite circular motions.

Fresnel's first assumption in that *plane-polarized light entering a crystal along the optic axis is decomposed into two circularly polarized vibrations rotating in opposite directions with the same frequency.* In a crystal like calcite, which is not optically active, these two circular motions R and L

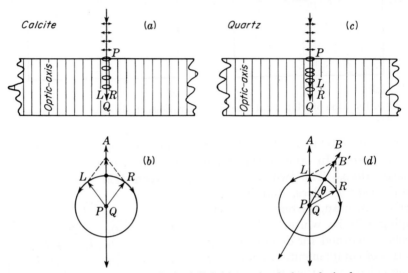

FIG. 28F. Resolution of plane-polarized light into circularly polarized components.

travel with the same speed as shown in Fig. 28F(a). Since both vibrations arrive simultaneously at any given point along their path, their resultant will be a simple harmonic motion in the plane of the original vibration as indicated in (b). Thus, in calcite, a plane-polarized wave along the axis is propagated with its vibrations always in the same plane.

In an optically active crystal, the two circular vibrations move forward with very slightly different velocities. In right-handed quartz, the right-handed or clockwise motion (looking against the light) travels faster, and in left-handed quartz the left-handed or counterclockwise motion travels faster.

Consider now some point Q, in a right-handed crystal, along the path of a plane-polarized incident beam as shown in Fig. 28F(c). Let the amplitude and plane of the incident vibration be represented by AP in Fig. 28F(d). The right circular component R of this vibration arrives at Q first, and as the wave travels on, the displacement turns through an angle θ before the left-handed component L arrives. At this instant, the two circular motions are in opposite senses with the same frequency, the one starting at R and the other at L. The result is that the point B' vibrates along the fixed line BQ with the same amplitude and frequency as the original vibration AP, and this represents the vibration form of the light at Q. Thus in traveling from the crystal face at P to the point Q, the plane of vibration has been rotated through an angle $\theta/2$. It is clear, therefore, that the plane of vibration would under these assumptions rotate continuously as the light penetrates deeper and deeper into the crystal and that the angle of rotation would be proportional to the thickness.

28.4. Double Refraction in Optically Active Crystals.

Since the ability to rotate the plane of polarization is a special property not possessed by many anisotropic crystals, the question arises as to its relation to the ordinary type of double refraction discussed in previous chapters. Optical activity is shown only by a certain type of crystal, but such a crystal will also show double refraction when the light is transmitted in some direction other than that of the axis. Hence the one phenomenon must change continuously into the other as the angle is changed. To

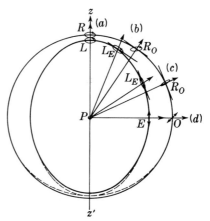

Fig. 28G. Wave-surface diagram for a right-handed quartz crystal, showing the two vibrations associated with different directions of the wave normal.

understand this, we must realize that Fresnel's two velocities for right and left circular light are actually velocities represented by the wave surfaces introduced in Chap. 26 (Fig. 26B). There it was pointed out that the two sheets of the wave surface in quartz do not touch at the optic axis as they do in calcite. In Fig. 28G the wave surfaces for quartz are shown again. In the equatorial plane linear vibrations O and E, perpendicular and parallel, respectively, to the optic axis, are propagated with different velocities but unchanged in form, as shown. Along the axis z, z', right and left circular vibrations R and L are propagated with slightly different velocities. Along intermediate directions like (b) and (c) only *elliptical vibrations* of a definite form can be transmitted unchanged.

In calcite the elliptic wave surface gave a measure of the velocity of *plane*-polarized light in the various directions, and the variation of the velocity, represented by the radius vector of the surface, was due to the varying angle that the vibrations made with the optic axis. In quartz or any

optically active crystal, each of the two surfaces represents the velocity
of various kinds of polarized light, depending on the direction of propagation. For a direction parallel to the axis, the velocity for the outer
surface is that of right circularly polarized light (right-handed quartz),
and that for the inner surface is of left circularly polarized light. For
directions at an angle with this the velocity is that of two elliptically

Fig. 28H. Effects on plane-polarized light of quartz crystals cut in three different
planes.

polarized components. The major axes of the two ellipses are perpendicular to each other, and the ellipses become narrower with increasing
angle from the axis, degenerating into lines (plane-polarized light) for a
direction at right angles to the axis.

The behavior of plane-polarized light when it enters a crystal traveling
either parallel or perpendicular to the optic axis, as in parts (a) and (b)
of Fig. 28H, is easily understood from the above characteristics of
the wave surface. In (a) the incident linear vibrations are resolved,
upon entering the crystal, into two circular vibrations which travel with
different velocities. The resultant of these two gives merely a plane
vibration which rotates by an amount depending on the thickness of the
crystal and the wavelength. In (b) the incident vibrations are again
linear, but are here parallel to the optic axis so that the light is transmitted as an E beam with the velocity determined by the inner sheet

of the wave surface. If the vibrations were perpendicular to the axis, they would travel with the greater velocity of the O beam. In either case the form and direction of vibration would remain unchanged. At other angles for the incident vibrations there would be two linear components moving with different velocities, and these give rise to elliptically polarized light. Hence for light traveling perpendicular to the optic axis quartz behaves precisely as do other uniaxial crystals and gives the interference effects described in the last chapter.

When the axis is not perpendicular to the ray, the effects of optical activity will manifest themselves to a greater or less extent, becoming greatest when the ray moves parallel to the axis. In Fig. 28$H(c)$, where the incident vibrations lie in the principal section, they are decomposed upon entering the crystal into two ellipses L_E and R_O of different size. The major axes are at right angles, and the senses of rotation are opposite. In contrast to the case of nonactive crystals, an incident ray vibrating parallel to the principal section is not transmitted as a single E ray, but instead gives two rays of different intensity. We shall see in the following sections that except when the angle between the ray and the axis is very small the intensity of the ray marked R_O is very low, and L_E is a very slim ellipse. We shall also see that the O wave surface is not strictly spherical, so that R_O is slightly deviated even at normal incidence.

Some biaxial crystals are known to show optical activity. In general the phenomenon is accompanied by double refraction and is somewhat difficult to show. The wave surfaces for such crystals have the same general appearance as those given in Chap. 26 with the exception that the inner and outer surfaces do not quite touch at the ray axes, i.e., at the "dimple" in the outer surface.

28.5. Shape of the Wave Surface in Quartz. In order to explain the polarization effects observed when light is sent through quartz crystals, it is found that the usual spherical and ellipsoidal surfaces for nonactive crystals must be assumed to be distorted, ever so slightly, in the neighborhood of the optic axis. The outer surface is bulged and the inner surface flattened as shown in an exaggerated way at the bottom in Fig. 28G. The dotted lines represent a true circle and ellipse, while the solid lines give the actual wave surface. The exact shape of these two surfaces, however, is not so important optically as is the distance between them. Actually the change from circularly polarized light to almost plane-polarized light takes place within a very small angle of the optic axis, so that except for very small angles quartz acts essentially like an ordinary uniaxial crystal. This is due to the fact that the difference in velocity (or difference in the refractive indices) of the two circularly polarized rays R and L moving parallel to the optic axis is small compared to the difference in velocity of the O and E rays moving perpendicularly. This is best seen from the values given for red and violet light in Table 28-II.

TABLE 28-II. REFRACTIVE INDICES FOR QUARTZ

Wavelength, Å	n_E	n_O	n_R	n_L
3968	1.56771	1.55815	1.55810	1.55821
7620	1.54811	1.53917	1.53914	1.53920

Along the optic axis the separation of the two surfaces as compared to the radius of a spherical surface is as 1:26,000 for red light and 1:14,000 for violet. Perpendicular to the axis the ratios are 1:170 and 1:160, respectively.

Since there are two velocities for circular vibrations along the optic axis, the angle of rotation of plane-polarized light can be calculated from the refractive indices. The phase difference δ between two waves a given distance apart is given by Eq. 27b as

$$\delta = \frac{2\pi}{\lambda} d(n_L - n_R) \tag{28b}$$

where d is the distance traveled in the medium, λ the wavelength of the light, and $n_L - n_R$ the difference in refractive index. If the R circular motion gets δ rad ahead of the L, the plane of vibration will be rotated through $\delta/2$ rad [see Fig. 28$F(d)$].

For a quartz plate 1 mm thick, for example, we get, on substitution in Eq. 28b,

$$\delta = \frac{2\pi}{0.000076 \text{ cm}} 0.1 \text{ cm } (0.00006) = 0.5 \text{ rad}$$

This gives a rotation for red light, $\lambda7600$, of about 14° [see Fig. 28$B(b)$]. It should be pointed out, however, that accurate differences for $n_L - n_R$ are in practice calculated from the observed rotation.

28.6. Fresnel's Multiple Prism. The first experimental demonstration of double refraction into two circularly polarized rays was made by Fresnel. He reasoned that if two circular components travel with different velocities along the optic axis of quartz, they should, upon emerging obliquely from a crystal surface into the air, be refracted at different angles. Upon failing to observe the effect with a single quartz prism, Fresnel constructed a train of right- and left-handed prisms cut and mounted together, as shown in Fig. 28I. With this prism train two circularly polarized beams were observed, one rotating to the right and the other to the left.

The reason the two rays get farther and farther apart at each oblique surface may be explained as follows: With light incident normally on the first crystal surface, the two component circular vibrations travel along the optic axis with different speeds. Upon passing through the first oblique boundary, the R motion which was faster in the first prism becomes the slower in the second. The opposite is true for the L motion. By the ordinary law of refraction, then, the one ray is refracted away from the normal to the boundary and the other toward it. At the second boundary the velocities are again interchanged, so that the ray bent

FIG. 28I. Fresnel multiple prism for demonstrating the circularly polarized components.

toward the normal at the first oblique boundary is now bent away from it. The net result is that the angular separation of the two rays increases at each successive refraction.

If such a prism is available to the student, Fresnel's observations may be repeated by placing it on the table of a small laboratory spectrometer. If the two images in the eyepiece are examined with a nicol prism or other analyzing device, they appear unchanged as the analyzer is rotated. If a quarter-wave plate is inserted in front of the nicol, both circular vibrations become plane-polarized perpendicular to each other. Now the images will disappear alternately with each 90° rotation of the nicol.

28.7. Cornu Prism. The double refraction into circularly polarized light is appreciable even with a single quartz prism cut with the optic axis parallel to the base as in Fig. 28J(a). For sodium light and a 60° prism, the angular separation is only 27 seconds of arc, and hence is greatly exaggerated in the figure. When quartz prisms are to be used in spectrographs, even this small doubling of spectrum lines cannot

FIG. 28J. (a) Simple crystal quartz prism. (b) Cornu prism.

be tolerated, particularly in the instruments of large dispersion. To overcome this effect, Cornu devised a 60° prism made up of right- and left-handed quartz as shown in Fig. 28J(b). Because of the interchange in velocities, light may be transmitted without double refraction if the prism is set at minimum deviation. Practically all 60° quartz prisms used in spectrographs are of this type.

In a Littrow spectrograph only one-half of a Cornu prism is used, and this takes the place of the grating shown in Fig. 17N. In this case the back face AB of, say, the R prism, Fig. 28J(b), is made a reflector by depositing silver or aluminum on the surface. By reflecting the light back the half prism is used a second time, giving the same dispersion as the Cornu prism. The R vibrations approaching the mirror become L vibrations after reflection, thus nullifying the double refraction.

Fused quartz prisms and lenses are sometimes used in optical devices, but not where the best performance is desired. Although fused quartz is transparent and not doubly refracting, manufacturing processes have not yet produced large samples sufficiently free from inhomogeneities to make them useful for precision work.

28.8. Vibration Forms and Intensities in Active Crystals. In Sec. 28.4 the propagation of light in various directions with respect to the optic axis in quartz was briefly described in terms of the wave surface for such a crystal. In right-handed quartz, for example, the outer sheet of the

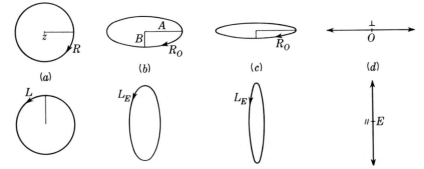

FIG. 28K. Vibrations for light traveling in an optically active crystal at different angles with the optic axis.

wave surface represents the velocity of a right-handed circular vibration traveling along the axis, of an elliptical vibration at some angle to it, and of a linear vibration in the equatorial plane. Looking against the light from the positions (a), (b), (c), and (d) of Fig. 28G, these vibrations would appear as shown in Fig. 28K. All vibrations are confined to planes tangent to the wave surface, with the major axis of each ellipse on the outer sheet perpendicular to the optic axis, and the minor axis of each ellipse on the inner surface also perpendicular to this axis. In left-handed quartz the directions of rotation would be interchanged, but the figures would otherwise remain unchanged.

As has been mentioned, the transition from circularly polarized to essentially linearly polarized light actually occurs within a few degrees of the optic axis.* For example, in quartz the ratio between the axes

---

* Equations giving the difference of velocity as a function of angle are derived in P. Drude, "Theory of Optics," English edition, pp. 408–412, Longmans, Green & Co., Inc., New York, 1922.

of the elliptical vibrations (major to minor axes of each) is already 2.37 for sodium light traveling at 5° to the optic axis. At 10° the ratio has increased to 7.8. These are the ratios used in drawing Fig. 28K(b) and (c).

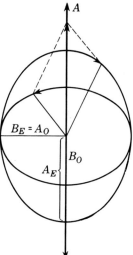

When a quartz plate cut perpendicular to the axis is placed in highly convergent light between analyzer and polarizer, so that the light traverses the crystal at various angles to the axis, the interference figures (see Fig. 27M) are much the same as those obtained with a nonactive crystal like calcite. The essential difference is that the center of the pattern, even with crossed analyzer and polarizer, is nearly always bright instead of dark. A rotation of the vibration plane has the result that some light gets through at the center of the otherwise dark brushes. The effect may be seen in both the photographs shown in part (b) of Fig. 27M.

The intensities of the two elliptically polarized beams derived from an incident *unpolarized* beam will always be equal. The two ellipses, such as those in part (b) of Fig. 28K, are alike except for their orientation. Remembering that an elliptical vibration can be regarded as made up of two linear ones at right angles and 90° out of phase, we find the corresponding intensity in terms of the major and minor semiaxes A and B as

Fig. 28L. Resolution of a linear harmonic vibration into two similar elliptical vibrations.

$$I \sim A^2 + B^2 \qquad (28c)$$

In the limiting case of circularly polarized light having the radius $B = A$, we therefore have

$$I \sim 2A^2 \qquad (28d)$$

and for linearly polarized light ($B = 0$) the usual relation

$$I \sim A^2 \qquad (28e)$$

If each beam is to maintain the same intensity regardless of the eccentricity, the amplitude of the linear vibration must therefore be $\sqrt{2}$ times as large as the radius of the corresponding circular one.

If the incident light is *plane-polarized*, as in the example of Fig. 28H(c), the two ellipses are of different size. Now, in order that they may represent components of the original linear vibration, Fig. 28L shows that the minor axis of the large ellipse must equal the major axis of the smaller one.

Namely, it is necessary that $B_E - A_O = 0$ for the horizontal components to cancel. Furthermore, since for the vertical ones to add up to the initial linear vibration $A_E + B_O = A$, it follows that $A_E/B_E = A_O/B_O$, and the ellipses have the same shape. The ratio of the corresponding intensities will depend on the actual value of either ratio A/B, and will vary from unity in the direction of the optic axis to zero at right angles to it.

For unpolarized light, which is equivalent to two independent linear vibrations at right angles, each of these will yield two counter-rotating ellipses of different size. When one combines the two left-handed ones to obtain another left-handed ellipse, and the two right-handed ones to obtain a right-handed ellipse, it is found that the resultant ellipses have the same size. These are the ones illustrated in Fig. 28K.

28.9. Theory of Optical Activity. The theory of the rotation of plane-polarized light in optically active substances goes back to an early experiment performed by Reusch. He found that when plane-polarized light was incident normally on a pile of thin mica plates cut parallel to the axis, and each plate turned through a small angle to the right of the one preceding it, the plane of vibration rotated to the right. The smaller the angle between successive plates, the more nearly the pile imitated rotation along the axis in quartz.

Reusch's experiment thus suggests that optically active crystals are made up of atomic layers which are twisted slightly one from the other.

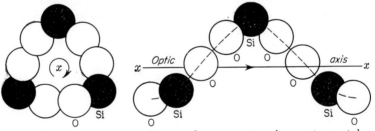

FIG. 28M. Arrangement of silicon and oxygen atoms in quartz crystals.

In right-handed crystals the layers are built up clockwise around the optic axis, and in left-handed crystals, counterclockwise. The known structure of crystalline quartz, which chemically is SiO_2, confirms this. Looking along the axis of a quartz-crystal model, one finds columns of silicon and oxygen atoms built up in spirals, as shown in Fig. 28M. These spirals of atoms form planes which give the effect of rotation along the optic axis. From the diagrams of right- and left-handed crystals in Fig. 28N this twisted formation is suggested by the arrangement of the smaller crystal faces. One crystal, in both its gross and atomic structures, is a mirror image of the other. The above analogy to a pile of plates must not be interpreted to mean that the plane of vibration rotates as fast as the atomic layers, as this would preclude any rotatory dispersion.

The electromagnetic theory of optical activity is due mainly to Born and his collaborators, and has been well summarized by Condon.* In an ordinary dielectric an imposed electric field produces a separation of charges and a resultant polarization of the medium in the direction of E (Sec. 23.9). In an optically active substance, we imagine the charges constrained to move in helical paths, so that in addition to the forward motion producing ordinary polarization there is a circulatory motion of charge which gives rise to magnetic effects. Drude has shown that this may be taken into account by introducing an additional term in one of Maxwell's equations for a dielectric (in the left-hand member of Eq. 23l). The solution of the equations then yields the phenomenon of optical activity. Born assumed that each molecule or crystal unit consisted of a set of oscillators coupled together by electrical forces. The simplest

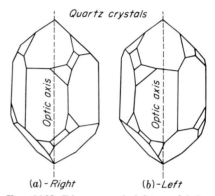

Fig. 28N. Diagrams of right- and left-handed quartz crystals. Each is a mirror image of the other.

such unit, according to him, necessarily contains at least four oscillators arranged in a form that does not have symmetry. A tetrahedron, as an example, has symmetry properties, so that any crystal built on this structure will not show optical activity. If, however, the tetrahedron is twisted slightly out of shape, then optical activity is a natural result. Born's early theoretical treatments have been applied to quartz by Hylleraas† and found to give excellent agreement with observations. It has since been shown by Condon and others that the assumption of coupled oscillators is not essential, and that the desired results can be obtained with a single-oscillator model.

28.10. Rotation in Liquids. The rotation of the plane of vibration by liquids was discovered quite accidentally by Biot in 1811. He found that turpentine behaved like quartz in producing a rotation proportional to the light path through the substance and very nearly proportional to the inverse square of the wavelength. In such cases the rotation is attributable to the molecular structure itself. In fact, most liquids exhibiting rotation are organic compounds involving complex molecules.

* E. U. Condon, *Revs. Modern Phys.*, **9**, 432–457, 1937.
† E. A. Hylleraas, *Z. Physik*, **44**, 871, 1927.

Each molecule of a liquid may be thought of as a small crystal with an optic axis along which plane-polarized light is rotated. Since in a liquid the molecules are oriented at random, the observed rotation is an average effect of all the molecules and therefore the same in any direction through the liquid. One might at first sight think that the random orientation of the molecules would cancel out the rotatory effect entirely. But the molecules has a screwlike arrangement of atoms, and a right-handed screw is always right-handed, no matter from which end it is viewed.

Liquids made up of an optically active substance and an inactive solvent are found to produce a rotation very nearly proportional to the amount of the active substance present. This has led to the very wide use of polarized light in industry as an accurate means of determining the amounts of sugar, an optically active substance, in the presence of nonactive impurities. The *specific rotation* or *rotatory power* is defined as the rotation produced by a 10-cm column of liquid containing 1 g of active substance for every cubic centimeter of solution. This may be written as an equation,

$$[\rho] = \frac{10\theta}{ld} \tag{28f}$$

where $[\rho]$ is the specific rotation, d the number of grams of active substance per cubic centimeter, l the length of the light path in centimeters, and θ the angle of rotation.

In general the rotation in liquids is considerably less than in crystals. For example, 10 cm of turpentine rotates sodium light $-37°$. (The minus sign indicates left-handed or counterclockwise rotation, looking against the direction of propagation.) An equal thickness of quartz, on the other hand, rotates sodium light $2172°$. It is for this reason that the specific rotation for crystals is taken as the angle for a 1-mm path.

Careful determinations of the rotatory power of an optically active substance in various nonactive solvents have given slightly different results. There is a variation not only with solvents but with the concentration of the active substance. From experiment the rotatory power is found to be adequately given by

$$\rho = L + Md + Nd^2 \tag{28g}$$

where L, M, and N are constants and d is the amount of the active material in solution.

Like crystals, active substances in solution give rise to rotatory dispersion quite similar to that shown for quartz in Fig. 28B(b). Just as normal dispersion is a special case of anomalous dispersion observed near absorption bands in ordinary nonactive materials, so normal rotatory dispersion is a special case of anomalous rotatory dispersion known to exist at the absorption bands in optically active substances.

PROBLEMS

1. Find the angular splitting of the right- and left-handed circularly polarized rays when an incident unpolarized ray is refracted by a single 60° quartz prism as in Fig. 28$J(a)$. Make the calculation for green mercury light, obtaining the refractive indices from the data of Tables 26-I and 28-I.

2. Calculate the angular separation for sodium light produced by a Fresnel prism designed as shown in Fig. 28I. Take the angle between the prism faces and the optic axis as 30°.   *Ans.* 6.80 minutes.

3. Find the thickness of a quartz plate cut perpendicular to the axis that is required for it to rotate the plane of polarization of green mercury light by 360°. If such a plate were placed between crossed polarizer and analyzer, what wavelengths would be missing in the transmitted light?

4. The ratio of the axes of each ellipse into which unpolarized light divides when it enters quartz traveling at some angle α with the optic axis is approximately $(R^2 + 1)^{\frac{1}{2}} + R$, where $R = \sin^2 \alpha (n_O - n_E)n_O{}^3/(n_R - n_L)n^3$. Here n is the mean of n_O and n_E. Find the ratio for sodium light at $\alpha = 18°$.   *Ans.* 24.3.

5. From the indices of refraction of quartz for right- and left-handed circularly polarized light of wavelength 7620 Å given in Table 28-II, calculate the rotation of the plane of polarization of this light produced by a plate 0.5 mm thick.

6. Plane-polarized light is incident normally on a plane-parallel plate of quartz cut with its optic axis at an angle of 5° with the normal, as in Fig. 28$H(c)$. Using the axis ratio given in Sec. 28.8, make plots of the vibration forms in the two beams L_E and R_O. If the plate is of such thickness as to produce a phase difference of 90° between these beams, find by graphical composition the resultant vibration form of the emergent light.   *Ans.* Ellipse tilted to right and rotating counterclockwise.

7. In measuring the rotation produced by sugar solutions, the accuracy obtainable by using the ordinary extinction point of an analyzer is not sufficient. Best results are obtained by matching the intensity of two adjacent fields produced by altering the polarizer so that it gives two beams linearly polarized at a small angle α with each other. Investigate the action of such a device by plotting the intensities of the two fields for a complete rotation of the analyzer. Take $\alpha = 5°$.

8. What should be the angle α in Prob. 7 to be able to measure the rotation to 1 minute of arc, supposing that the eye can detect a 2 per cent difference of intensity in the two fields?   *Ans.* 6.63°.

9. A sample of l-glucose is suspected of being impure. If a sample weighing 6.20 g is dissolved in water to give 50 cc of solution, and this is placed in a polarimeter tube 20 cm long, it is found to rotate the plane of polarization of sodium light 11.30° to the left. Find the fraction of the sample that is not glucose. $[\rho] = -51.4$ for l-glucose.

10. An unknown solution is suspected of containing sucrose and does not contain any other optically active substance. If a 12-cm length of this solution rotates sodium light 0.60°, what is the concentration of sucrose? For sucrose $[\rho] = 66.5°$.   *Ans.* 7.5 g/liter.

11. What thickness of right-handed quartz will just annul the rotation of sodium light produced by a 4-cm thickness of turpentine?

12. The specific rotatory power of maltose in water solution is $+138.48 - 1.837d$. Find the rotation in degrees produced by a column of solution 20 cm long and containing 22 g of maltose per 100 cc of solution.   *Ans.* 60.75°.

CHAPTER 29

MAGNETO-OPTICS AND ELECTRO-OPTICS

We have already seen in Chap. 20 and Secs. 23.9, 26.9, and 28.9 that the electromagnetic theory is capable of explaining the main features of the propagation of light through free space and through matter. In further support of the electromagnetic character of light, there is a group of optical experiments which demonstrates the interaction between light and matter when the latter is subjected to a strong external magnetic or electric field. In this group of experiments those which depend for their action on an applied magnetic field are classed under *magneto-optics* and those which depend for their action on an electric field are classed under *electro-optics*. In this chapter the following known optical effects will be treated briefly under these headings:

Magneto-optics	*Electro-optics*
Zeeman effect	Stark effect
Inverse Zeeman effect	Inverse Stark effect
Voigt effect	Electric double refraction
Cotton-Mouton effect	Kerr electro-optic effect
Faraday effect	
Kerr magneto-optic effect	

The four electro-optic effects in the order listed here are respectively the electric analogues of the first four magneto-optic effects.

29.1. Zeeman* Effect. In the year 1896, Zeeman discovered that when a sodium flame is placed between the poles of a powerful electromagnet, the two yellow lines are considerably broadened. Shortly afterward, Lorentz presented a simple theory for these observations, based upon the electron theory of matter, and predicted that each spectrum line when produced in such a field should be split into two components when viewed parallel to the field [Fig. 29A(a)], and into three components when viewed perpendicular to the field [Fig. 29A(b)]. He further

---

* P. Zeeman (1865–1935). Dutch physicist and Nobel prize winner (1902). He held numerous honorary positions in scientific circles and is most famous for his work on the splitting up of spectral lines in a magnetic field. His chief contributions are summarized in his celebrated book "Researches in Magneto-optics," Macmillan & Co., Ltd., London, 1913.

predicted that in the longitudinal direction (a) these lines should be circularly polarized and in the transverse direction (b), plane-polarized. With improved experimental conditions these predictions were later verified by Zeeman, Preston, and others in the case of some spectral lines.

The Lorentz theory assumes that the electrons in matter are responsible for the origin of light waves and that they are charged particles whose motions are modified by an external magnetic field. In the special case of an electron moving in a circular orbit, the plane of which is

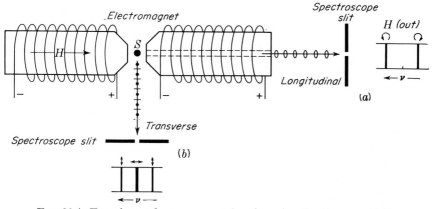

FIG. 29A. Experimental arrangement for observing the Zeeman effect.

normal to the field direction H, the electron should be speeded up or slowed down by an amount proportional to the field strength H. A classical treatment of this problem shows that if ν_0 represents the orbital frequency of the electron in a field-free space, the frequency in the presence of a field will be given by $\nu_0 \pm \Delta\nu$, where

$$\Delta\nu = \frac{eH}{4\pi mc} = 1.40 \times 10^6 \times H \text{ sec}^{-1} \qquad (29a)$$

where c is the velocity of light, m the mass of the electron in grams, e the charge on the electron in electrostatic units, and H the magnetic field strength in oersteds.

In the study of spectrum lines this frequency difference $\Delta\nu$ is most conveniently expressed in wave numbers (Sec. 14.14) by dividing by the velocity of light c:

$$\Delta\sigma = \frac{\Delta\nu}{c} = 4.67 \times 10^{-5} \times H \text{ cm}^{-1} \qquad (29b)$$

In the classical theory of the Zeeman effect we are concerned with an aggregation of atoms in which the electrons are revolving in circular or elliptical orbits oriented at random in space. It will now be shown, however, that this situation is equivalent to having one-third of the electrons vibrating in straight lines along the direction of the magnetic field and two-thirds of them revolving in circular orbits in the plane perpendicular to the field.   Of the latter ones, half are revolving in one sense and half in the opposite sense.   The radius of their orbits is $1/\sqrt{2}$ times the amplitude of the linear vibrations.   To prove these statements, let us select any one of the electrons and resolve its elliptical motion into

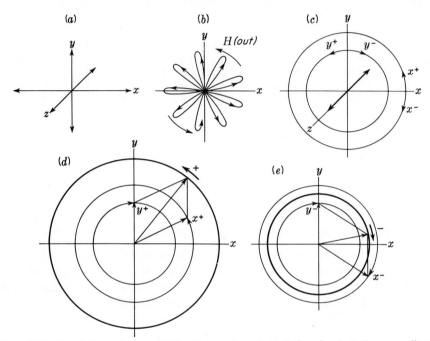

FIG. 29B. Resolution of an orbit for the explanation of the classical Zeeman effect.

three mutually perpendicular linear motions as shown in Fig. 29B(a). For simplicity we shall assume that the electron is bound by an elastic force obeying the law

$$F = -kr \qquad (29c)$$

where r is the displacement from the equilibrium position.   Under this condition the three components are simple harmonic motions, but for any one electron they are not equal in amplitude nor are they in the same phase.

If a magnetic field is now applied in the z direction, the component parallel to z will be uninfluenced, for it is equivalent to a current directed along the lines of force.   The x and y vibrations will each be modified however, since an electron which is moving across a magnetic field experiences a force

$$F_H = \frac{evH}{c} \tag{29d}$$

perpendicular to the field and also perpendicular to its motion. The effect of this force is to change the x and y components into rosette motions such as that shown in Fig. $29B(b)$ for the y component. These can be described to better advantage in terms of circular components, y^+ and y^- for the y motion, and x^+ and x^- for the x motion [diagram (c) of the figure]. In the presence of the field both plus circular components have a higher frequency than the minus ones, so we may combine the x^+ and y^+ motions to get a resultant positive circular motion, as in diagram (d), and x^- and y^- to get a negative one, as in (e). Thus the original elliptical orbit when subjected to a magnetic field is equivalent to a linear motion of unchanged frequency along the field, plus two circular motions, one of higher and one of lower frequency, in the plane at right angles to the field.

Only the circular components will emit light along the field direction, and these give circularly polarized light of two different frequencies. The intensity of these two components must be equal when the whole aggregation of atoms is considered, because as the field goes to zero the light is unpolarized. When we observe the light at right angles to the field, we are viewing the circular components edge-on, so these yield two different frequencies of plane-polarized light in which the vibrations are perpendicular to the field direction. Each of them has only half the intensity of the above-mentioned circularly polarized beams. In addition, the linear z motions emit light in the transverse direction. This light has the original frequency ν_0, vibrates parallel to the field, and has an intensity equal to the sum of the other two. The mean amplitude of the z components for all atoms is therefore $\sqrt{2}$ times as great as that of the x or y components.

Now let us calculate the change of frequency to be expected for the circular components. In the absence of the field the centripetal force on the electron in its circular orbit is furnished by the elastic force, so that by Eq. $29c$ we have

$$F = -kr = -m\omega_0{}^2 r \tag{29e}$$

m being the mass of the electron and ω_0 its angular velocity. After the field is applied, there is a new angular velocity ω, and the new centripetal force must be the sum of the elastic force and the force due to the field (Eq. $29d$). Thus

$$F' = -m\omega^2 r = F \mp F_H = -kr \mp \frac{evH}{c}$$

The positive sign corresponds to a clockwise rotation in the x, y plane and the negative sign to a counterclockwise one. Substituting for $-kr$ its value from Eq. 29e, we then obtain

$$-m\omega^2 r = -m\omega_0^2 r \mp \frac{evH}{c}$$

or, since $v/r = \omega$,

$$\omega^2 - \omega_0^2 = \pm \frac{evH}{mcr} = \pm \frac{e\omega H}{mc} \tag{29f}$$

In order to get a simple expression for the change of frequency, it is necessary to assume that the difference in the ω's is small compared to either ω. This is always justified in practice since it means that the Zeeman shifts are small compared to the frequency of the lines themselves. Then we may put

$$(\omega + \omega_0)(\omega - \omega_0) \simeq 2\omega(\omega - \omega_0)$$

and, from Eq. 29f,

$$\omega - \omega_0 = \pm \frac{eH}{2mc}$$

Since $\nu = \omega/2\pi$, the change in frequency becomes

$$\Delta\nu = \pm \frac{eH}{4\pi mc} \tag{29g}$$

in agreement with Eq. 29a.

In this derivation it has been tacitly assumed that the radius of the circular motion remains unchanged during the application of the magnetic field. The speeding up or slowing down of the electron in its orbit occurs only while the field is changing and is due to the changing number of lines of force threading the orbit. By Faraday's law of induction this change produces an emf just as it would in a circular loop of wire. The resulting increase or decrease of velocity might be expected to change the radius, but the fact is that there is a corresponding alteration in the centripetal force which is just sufficient to maintain the radius constant. The additional force is that represented by Eq. 29d, which has the same origin as the perpendicular force on a wire carrying a current in a magnetic field.

Let us now summarize what should be the observed effect of a magnetic field on a spectrum line. The result will depend on the direction, with respect to that of the magnetic field, in which the source is viewed. When the source is viewed in the direction of the field, along the z axis, we have what is called the longitudinal Zeeman effect. From this direction only the frequencies $\nu_0 + \Delta\nu$ and $\nu_0 - \Delta\nu$ should appear, and this light should be right- or left-handed circularly polarized* [Fig. 29C(a)]. Since light is a transverse wave motion, the z vibrations will not emit light of frequency ν_0 in the z direction.

Viewed perpendicular to the field, the z motions should be observed to give plane-polarized light with the electric vector parallel to the field (p components), and the circular motions, seen edge-on, should give plane-polarized light with the electric vector perpendicular to the field (s components). A spectrum line viewed normal to H should therefore reveal three plane-polarized components [Fig. 29C(b)]—a center unshifted line, and two other lines symmetrically located as shown. This is called

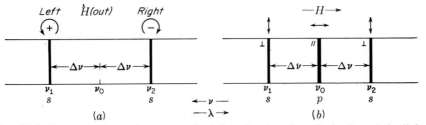

FIG. 29C. Zeeman patterns for a normal triplet, showing the polarization of the light.

a *normal triplet* and is observed for some spectrum lines, though by no means the majority of them.

Since the direction of rotation of the circularly polarized light depends on whether one assumes positive or negative charges as the emitters of light, it is possible to distinguish between these alternatives by using a quarter-wave plate and nicol. Figure 29C(a), where the positive rotation has the higher frequency, was drawn according to our assumption of negative electrons as the emitters.

In Zeeman's early investigations he was not able to split any spectrum lines into doublets or triplets, but he did observe that they were broadened and that the outside edges were polarized, as predicted by Lorentz. The polarization corresponded to emission by negative particles. He was later able to photograph the two outer components of lines arising from the elements zinc, copper, cadmium, and tin, by cutting out the p components with a nicol prism. Preston, using greater dispersion and resolving power, was able to show not only that certain lines were split

---

* Using the right-hand rule with the thumb pointing in the direction of the field, the fingers point in the direction of the + rotations which have the higher frequency designated by ν_1. The opposite direction gives the − rotations with the lower frequency ν_2. Looking against the light, clockwise rotations give rise to right-handed polarized light and counterclockwise rotations give rise to left-handed circularly polarized light. This latter is in agreement with the definitions used in treating optically active substances.

up into triplets when viewed perpendicularly to the field, but that others were split into as many as four, five, or even a much larger number of components. Such patterns of lines, shown in Fig. 29D, are called anomalous Zeeman patterns, and the phenomenon is called the *anomalous Zeeman effect.* The normal triplet separation $2\Delta\nu$ as given by the classical theory is shown by the bracket below each pattern. From Eq. 29a it

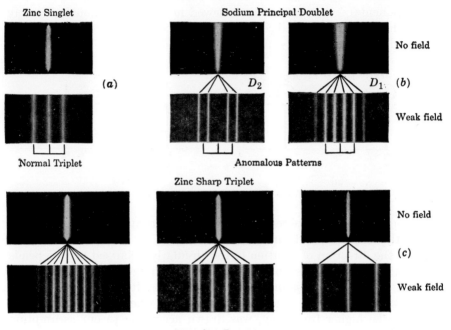

FIG. 29D. Photographs illustrating the normal and anomalous Zeeman effects.

is seen that each of the outer component lines should shift out by an amount proportional to the field strength, thus keeping the pattern symmetrical. In very strong magnetic fields, however, asymmetries are observed in many Zeeman patterns. This phenomenon is known as the quadratic Zeeman effect, although it may also be the beginning of a transition called the *Paschen-Back effect* according to which all anomalous patterns become normal triplets in the limit of very strong fields.

Only the normal triplet can be explained by the classical theory. The more complex patterns are now understood and are in complete agreement with the quantum theory of atomic structure and radiation.*

* For a treatment of the anomalous Zeeman effect, see H. E. White, "Introduction to Atomic Spectra," chaps. 10, 13, and 15, McGraw-Hill Book Company, Inc., New York, 1934.

Each line of an anomalous pattern, when viewed perpendicular to the magnetic field, is found to be plane-polarized.   Usually the center lines of a pattern are p components with their vibrations parallel to the field H, and those symmetrically placed on either side are s components with vibrations perpendicular to the field.   In the longitudinal effect only frequencies corresponding to the s components are observed, and these are circularly polarized.

The quantum theory has developed to such an extent that one can now predict with the greatest certainty the complete Zeeman pattern for any identified spectrum line in a field of any strength.   Conversely, the study of these patterns has become a potent tool in the analysis of complex spectra.

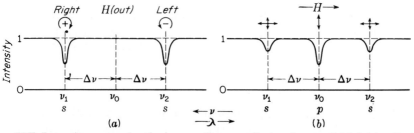

Fig. 29E. Intensity curves for the inverse Zeeman effect.   A normal triplet in absorption.

29.2. Inverse Zeeman Effect.   The Zeeman effect obtained in absorption is called the *inverse Zeeman effect*.   The phenomenon is observed by sending white light through an absorbing vapor when the latter is subjected to a uniform magnetic field.   In considering the longitudinal effect, analogous to Fig. 29$C(a)$, unpolarized light of any particular frequency may be imagined as consisting of right and left circularly polarized components with all possible phase relations.   If now ν_0 represents a natural resonance frequency of the vapor in the absence of a field, the plus circular components (see footnote, page 593) of frequency ν_1 will be strongly absorbed in the presence of a field.   The corresponding minus circular components of frequency ν_1 pass on through with little decrease in intensity, since to be absorbed these must have the frequency ν_2. Hence at frequency ν_1, looking against the field direction as in Fig. 29$C(a)$, right circularly polarized light is transmitted, and for a thick absorbing layer this is one-half as intense as the background of continuous light [Fig. 29$E(a)$].   A similar argument may be given for ν_2.

The Zeeman components of any spectrum line obtained in absorption along the field direction are therefore not completely absorbed, and the light that does get through is found to be circularly polarized in directions opposite to those of the corresponding components obtained in emission.

This is verified by experiment even in anomalous patterns of many components.

Viewed perpendicular to the field [Fig. 29$E(b)$], the p and s components are polarized at right angles to the corresponding components in emission. For ν_0, the parallel components of all incident light vibrations are absorbed and the perpendicular components are transmitted. For ν_1, the parallel components are all transmitted. The perpendicular components, moving across the field, are absorbed by only half the oscillators (the ones having positive rotation, frequency ν_1), giving an absorption line only half as intense as that at ν_0. The result is partially polarized light with a maximum intensity for vibrations parallel to the field H. The same is true for the component ν_2. The absorption of the parallel component for ν_0 is analogous to the selective absorption in crystals like tourmaline (Sec. 24.6), where one component vibration is completely absorbed and the other transmitted. The frequencies of the lines observed in the inverse Zeeman effect are also given by Eqs. 29a and 29b.

29.3. Faraday Effect. In 1845 Michael Faraday discovered that when a block of glass is subjected to a strong magnetic field, it becomes optically active. When plane-polarized light is sent through glass in a direction parallel to the applied magnetic field, the plane of vibration is rotated. Since Faraday's early discovery the phenomenon has been observed in many solids, liquids, and gases. The amount of rotation observed for any given substance is found by experiment to be proportional to the field strength H and to the distance the light travels through the medium. This rotation may be expressed by the relation

$$\theta = VHl \tag{29h}$$

where l is the thickness in cm, θ is the angle of rotation, and V a constant to be associated with each substance. This constant, called the *Verdet constant*, is defined as the rotation per unit path, per unit field strength. In gases the density must also be specified. A few values of the Verdet constant are given in Table 29-I.

TABLE 29-I. VALUES OF THE VERDET CONSTANT IN MINUTES OF ARC PER OERSTED PER CENTIMETER FOR λ5893

Substance	t, °C	V
Water	20	0.0131
Glass (phosphate crown)	18	0.0161
Glass (light flint)	18	0.0317
Carbon disulfide, CS_2	20	0.0423
Phosphorus, P	33	0.1326
Quartz (perpendicular to axis)	20	0.0166

The Faraday effect is so closely associated with the direct and inverse Zeeman effects, presented in the two preceding sections, that its explanation follows directly from the principles given there.   Because the phenomenon is best observed in vapors at wavelengths near an absorption line, the explanation given here will be confined to substances in the gaseous state.   Consider the passage of light through a vapor like sodium where in the absence of a field there are certain resonance frequencies ν_0 at each of which absorption takes place.   When the magnetic field is introduced, there will be for each ν_0, according to the classical theory of the Zeeman effect, two resonance frequencies, one ν_1 for left circularly polarized light and the other ν_2 for right circularly polarized light traveling along the field.   For each of these directions of rotation an absorption curve and a dispersion curve [Fig. 23H(b)] may be drawn as shown in Fig. 29F(a) and (b).

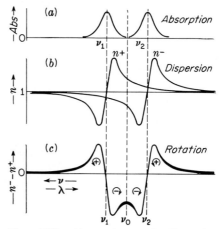

Referring to Fig. 29F(b), it is observed that outside the region ν_1 to ν_2 the value of n^- is greater than n^+.   Therefore positive rotations travel faster than negative, and the plane of the incident polarized light is rotated in the positive direction (see Sec. 28.3).   The difference between the two dispersion curves, as given in Fig. 29F(c), shows that for

Fig. 29F. Absorption and dispersion curves used in explaining the Faraday effect.   These curves refer to the magnetic splitting of a single absorption line.

frequencies between ν_1 and ν_2 the rotation is in the negative direction.

If plane-polarized light is reflected back and forth through the same magnetically activated vapor, the plane of vibration is found to rotate farther with each traversal.   This is not the case for naturally optically active substances like quartz, where upon one reflection the light emerges vibrating in the same plane in which it entered.   It should be noted that when the field direction is reversed, the direction of rotation of the plane of the incident light vibrations is also reversed.   Therefore the sense of the rotation is defined in terms of the direction of the field, positive rotation being that of a right-handed screw advancing in the direction of the field, or that of the *positive* current in the coil which produces the field.

The rotation in the Faraday effect is given by Eq. 29h, which shows that the angle of rotation is proportional to the field strength.   This follows from Eq. 29a for the Zeeman effect.   As the two dispersion curves separate with an increasing field, the differences in index (bottom curve) increase to a first approximation by an amount which is proportional to $\Delta\nu$ and hence to H. This is most accurately true at frequencies far from ν_1 or ν_2, where the dispersion curves over a short frequency interval may be considered as straight lines.

One of the most interesting methods developed for observing the Faraday effect is that shown in Fig. 29G. Without the right- and left-handed quartz prisms or the vapor, no light would be transmitted by the analyzer when crossed by the polarizer as shown. With the insertion of the double quartz prism the light vibrations are rotated by different amounts according to the portion of the prisms (in the plane of the

FIG. 29G. Experimental arrangement for observing the Faraday effect.

figure) through which they have passed. Hence varying amounts of light will now get through the various portions of the analyzer. When this light is focused on the slit of a spectroscope, alternate dark and light bands are formed as shown in Fig. 29$G(b)$. If white light is used as a source in front of the polarizer, the spectrum as observed in the spectroscope will be crossed by a number of approximately horizontal dark and light bands. If now the vapor is introduced into the light path, absorption lines will be observed at all resonance frequencies ν_0. When the magnetic field is turned on, rotation takes place within the vapor according to Fig. 29$F(c)$, thus shifting the bright bands accordingly. Close to the absorption lines the rotation is large, causing greater shifts of the bands. Since this rotation changes continuously with λ, the bands are observed to curve up or down, taking the same general form as shown in the theoretical curve of Fig. 29$F(c)$. Figure 29$H(a)$ is a photograph of these bands for the D lines of sodium taken under high dispersion and resolving power. They show not only the rapid increase in the positive rotation on each side of the absorption frequencies but the opposite rotation between the two. It should be noted that both these sodium lines give anomalous Zeeman patterns [Fig. 29$D(b)$]. The longitudinal effect for $\lambda5896$, D_1, however, is a doublet leading to the same kind of curves as those described above for a normal triplet. Theoretical curves for the D_2 line are left as an exercise for the student.

29.4. Voigt Effect, or Magnetic Double Refraction. In 1902 Voigt discovered that, when a strong magnetic field is applied to a vapor through which light is passing perpendicular to the field, double refraction takes place.* This phenomenon, now known as the *Voigt effect* or

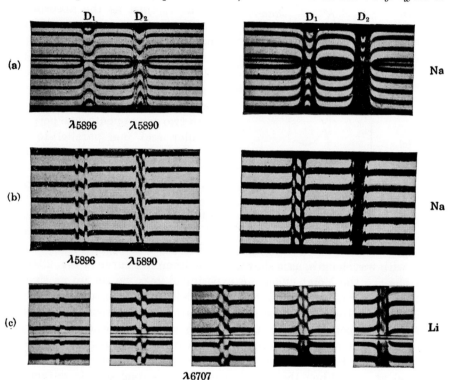

Fig. 29H. Photographs illustrating (a) the Faraday effect near the sodium resonance lines D_1 and D_2, (b) the Voigt effect of the sodium lines, (c) the Voigt effect near the lithium line $\lambda 6707$. (*After Hansen.*)

magnetic double refraction, is related to the transverse Zeeman effect in precisely the same way that the Faraday effect is related to the longitudinal Zeeman effect. In view of this relation the phenomenon is readily explained from absorption and dispersion curves in much the same way as the Faraday effect in the preceding section. Consider a vapor having a resonance frequency ν_0 which in the presence of an external field breaks up into a normal Zeeman triplet [see Fig. 29C(b)]. When white light is sent through this vapor, those light vibrations which have a frequency ν_0 will be in resonance with electrons of the vapor which

* W. Voigt, "Magneto- und Elektro-optik," B. G. Teubner, Leipzig, 1908.

have ν_0 as their frequency and thus be absorbed. This is represented by the central absorption and dispersion curve in Fig. 29$I(a)$ and (b). Other light vibrations, perpendicular to the field, are in resonance with ν_1 and ν_2. These are represented by the $\perp$ absorption and dispersion curves. With unpolarized light incident on the vapor the variations in n near ν_1 and ν_2 are half as great as at ν_0, just as the absorption coefficients at ν_1 and ν_2 are only half as great as at ν_0.

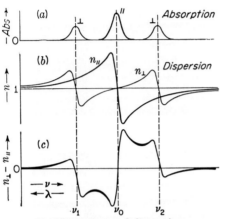

FIG. 29I. Absorption and dispersion curves used in explaining the Voigt effect.

The dispersion curves of Fig. 29$I(b)$ show that if plane-polarized light of any frequency ν is incident on the vapor it will be broken up into two components, one perpendicular and one parallel to H. Since these components have different refractive indices (therefore different velocities), one component gets ahead of the other in phase and elliptically polarized light emerges. The relative magnitude of this phase difference varies with wavelength, as is shown by the difference curve in Fig. 29$I(c)$.

To observe the Voigt effect, an experiment may be set up as shown for the Faraday effect in Fig. 29G. The field should be turned perpendicular to the absorption tube and the quartz double prism replaced by a Babinet compensator (Fig. 27F). Without the absorption tube the spectroscope slit and the photographic plate will be crossed by parallel light and dark bands. When the vapor is introduced, absorption is observed at ν_0. When the field is turned on, strong double refraction close to ν_0, ν_1, and ν_2 causes these bands to curve up or down as shown in the photographs of Fig. 29$H(b)$ and (c). This pattern in (c) is a normal triplet observed in the Zeeman effect of the lithium spectrum.*

The Voigt effect for anomalous Zeeman patterns like those in Fig. 29$H(b)$ has been studied by Zeeman, Geest, Voigt, Landenberg, Hansen,† and others. These results are readily predicted by drawing dispersion curves similar to those shown in Fig. 29I. In any Zeeman pattern the s components form one continuous dispersion curve and the p com-

---

* The lithium line $\lambda6707$ is in reality a doublet, each component of which in a weak magnetic field gives an anomalous Zeeman pattern. In the strong field used to observe the Voigt effect the two have coalesced (the Paschen-Back effect) to form a normal triplet for which the above discussion has been given.

† H. M. Hansen, *Ann. Physik*, **43**, 205, 1914.

ponents another. Their difference represents a plot of the double refraction as a function of the frequency. Its magnitude is proportional to the square of the field strength H.

29.5. Cotton-Mouton Effect. This effect, which was discovered in 1907 by Cotton and Mouton, has to do with the double refraction of light in a liquid when placed in a transverse magnetic field. In pure liquids like nitrobenzene very strong double refraction is observed, the effect being some thousand times as great as the Voigt effect treated in the last section. This double refraction is attributed to a lining up of the magnetically and optically anisotropic molecules in the applied field direction. This lining up would result whether the magnetic dipole moments of the molecules were permanent or whether they were induced by the field. Such an effect should be by theory, and is found to be by experiment, proportional to the square of the field strength. The effect is dependent upon temperature, decreasing rapidly with a rise in temperature. The Cotton-Mouton effect is the magnetic analogue of the electro-optic Kerr effect to be discussed in Sec. 29.10 and is not related to the Zeeman effect.

29.6. Kerr Magneto-optic Effect. In 1888 Kerr* made the discovery that when plane-polarized light is reflected at normal incidence from the polished pole of an electromagnet, it becomes elliptically polarized to a slight degree, with the major axis of the ellipse rotated with respect to the incident vibrations. At other angles of incidence the effect is observable if one avoids the ordinary effect of elliptical polarization obtained by reflection of plane-polarized light from metals at $\phi \neq 0$ by having the electric vector of the incident light either parallel or perpendicular to the plane of incidence. Under these conditions, and without the field, the reflected beam may be extinguished by a nicol prism. Upon turning on the magnetic field the light instantly appears, and cannot be extinguished by a rotation of the nicol. The introduction of a quarter-wave plate suitably oriented will now enable the light to be again extinguished, showing the reflected light to be elliptically polarized. The magnetic field has thus given rise to a vibration component called the *Kerr component* perpendicular to the incident light vibration. This is the Kerr magneto-optic effect and should be distinguished from the Kerr electro-optic effect considered in Sec. 29.10.

29.7. Stark Effect. In the few years following Zeeman's discovery of the splitting up of spectral lines in a magnetic field, many attempts were made to observe an analogous effect due to an external electric field. In 1913 Stark observed that when the hydrogen spectrum is

---

* John Kerr (1824–1907). Scottish physicist, inspired to investigate electricity and magnetism by his association with William Thomson (Lord Kelvin). His name is pronounced like the word "car."

excited in a strong electric field of 100,000 volts/cm, each line split into a symmetrical pattern. A photograph of the effect in the first line of the Balmer series of hydrogen is shown in Fig. 29*J*. When viewed perpendicular to the electric field, some of the components of each line pattern are observed to be plane-polarized with the electric vector parallel to the field (*p* components) and the others plane-polarized with the electric vector normal to the field (*s* components). This is the transverse Stark effect. When viewed parallel to the field, only the *s* components appear, but as ordinary unpolarized light. This is the longitudinal Stark effect.

The theory of the Stark effect has been developed only in terms of the quantum theory and will not be given here.*

FIG. 29*J*. Photograph of the Stark effect of *Hα*, λ6563, in hydrogen. (*After Wierl.*)

The method used for producing strong electric fields of 100,000 volts/cm or more, in which the light source will operate, is based upon the characteristics of the ordinary discharge of electric currents through gases at low pressures. In a discharge of the type shown in Fig. 21*D*, the major part of the potential drop from one electrode to the other occurs across a relatively dark region near the cathode. This region of a specially designed discharge tube, when focused on the slit of a spectrograph, may be made to give photographs of the type shown in Fig. 29*K*. Since the Stark effect is proportional to the field *F*, the pattern of λ3819, for example, may be taken to represent the field strength which is small at the top and increases toward the bottom, nearer the cathode.

The widest Stark patterns are observed in the hydrogen and helium spectra. In the case of all other spectra one seldom observes anything but a slight shift of the line, usually toward longer wavelengths. This effect is called the quadratic Stark effect, to distinguish it from the linear effect observed in hydrogen and helium. In the former case the shifts are proportional to the square of the electric field strength, while in the latter the splittings depend on the first power of this field. Characteristic of the Stark effect, as shown in Fig. 29*K* for the helium spectrum,

---

* For a more extended treatment of the Stark effect and other references to the subject see White, *op. cit.*, p. 401.

is the appearance of new spectrum lines (marked with crosses) where the field strength is high.

29.8. Inverse Stark Effect. The Stark effect with the lines appearing in absorption is called the inverse Stark effect. The phenomenon has been investigated by Grotrian and Ramsauer, using a long tube containing potassium vapor at low pressure and two long parallel metal plates only 1.5 mm apart. With a potential of 14,000 volts on the plates, the absorption lines λ4044, λ4047, and λ3447 were found to be shifted from

FIG. 29K. Photograph of the Stark effect in helium. (*After Foster.*)

the field-free position toward longer wavelength. This shift, although only a few hundredths of an angstrom unit in magnitude, was found to be proportional to the square of the field strength. This is therefore a case of a quadratic Stark effect.

29.9. Electric Double Refraction. Electric double refraction is related to the transverse Stark effect and is analogous to magnetic double refraction, or the Voigt effect, discussed in Sec. 29.4. In 1924 Ladenberg observed the absorption of the sodium resonance lines when produced with and without a strong transverse electric field applied to the vapor. Although the shift of the lines predicted by the quadratic Stark effect was too small to observe even with very high resolving power, double refraction was observed at frequencies close to the absorption lines. This double refraction is attributed to the very small difference in the frequency of the absorption line for light polarized parallel and perpendicular to the electric lines of force. The explanation is therefore analogous to that given for magnetic fields in Sec. 29.4 (see Fig. 29*I*).

29.10. Kerr Electro-optic Effect. In 1875 Kerr discovered that when a plate of glass is subjected to a strong electric field, it becomes doubly refracting. That this effect is not due to the strains that such a field sets up in the glass is shown by the fact that the phenomenon also appears in many liquids and may even be observed in gases. When a liquid is placed in an electric field, it behaves optically like a uniaxial crystal with the optic axis parallel to the field direction, and when viewed from the perpendicular direction, it gives rise to all the phenomena of interference considered in Chap. 27.

It is convenient experimentally to observe the effect by passing light between two parallel oppositely charged plates inserted in a glass cell

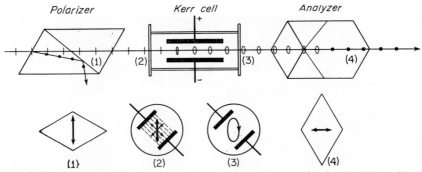

FIG. 29L. Arrangement for the electro-optic shutter, operating by the Kerr effect.

containing the liquid. Such a device, known as a Kerr cell, is shown at the center in Fig. 29L. Such a cell inserted between crossed polarizer and analyzer constitutes a very useful optical device known as the "electro-optic shutter."* One of these uses was described in Sec. 19.7. When the electric field is off, no light is transmitted by the analyzer. When the electric field is on, the liquid becomes doubly refracting and the light is restored. With the cell oriented at 45°, the incident plane vibrations from the polarizer are broken up into two equal components parallel and perpendicular to the field, as shown at the bottom in Fig. 29L. These travel with different speeds and hence a phase difference is introduced and the light emerges as elliptically polarized light. The horizontal component of the vibrations is transmitted by the analyzer.

The change in phase of the two vibrations in a Kerr cell is found to be proportional to the path length, i.e., the length of the electrodes l and to the square of the field strength F. The magnitude of the effect is determined by the Kerr constant j, defined by the relation

$$\Delta = jlF^2\lambda = j\,\frac{lE^2\lambda}{d^2}$$

* For the theory and technique of the Kerr cell see F. G. Dunnington, *Phys. Rev.*, **38**, 1506, 1931.

where E is the potential difference on the plates, in esu (1 esu $=$ 300 volts), Δ the optical path difference for the two components, and λ the wavelength in the medium. The separation d between the plates, and also l, are measured in centimeters. One of the substances most suitable for use in a Kerr cell is nitrobenzene, because of its relatively large Kerr constant. This is shown by the values given for a few liquids in Table 29-II.

TABLE 29-II. VALUES OF THE KERR CONSTANT

Substance	j
Benzene	0.6×10^{-7}
Carbon disulfide	3.21
Water	4.7
Nitrotoluene	123
Nitrobenzene	220

It should be pointed out that electric double refraction for gases discussed in the last section and the Kerr electro-optic effect are not the same phenomenon. In a gas the effect is due to changes inside the atom (Stark effect). In the Kerr effect it is usually due to natural or induced anisotropy of the molecule and a lining up of such molecules in the field. This alignment causes the medium as a whole to be optically anisotropic. As in the Cotton-Mouton effect (Sec. 29.5), the Kerr effect is dependent on temperature. In fact, the Kerr electro-optic effect is the exact electric analogue of that magnetic effect.

PROBLEMS

1. Calculate the Zeeman splitting $\Delta\sigma$ of a singlet line of zinc, the wavelength of which is 4700 Å. Express this splitting in angstroms.

2. The photograph of the normal Zeeman effect shown in Fig. 29D(a) was enlarged 20 times from the original negative. The plate factor of the spectrograph used was 2.3Å/mm at the wavelength of the line, 4700 Å. What was the value of the magnetic field? *Ans.* 43,000 oersteds.

3. Using the value of the constant given in Eq. 29a for the normal Zeeman effect, evaluate e/m for the electron, expressing the result in emu per gram. Compare with the value of this ratio given in the tables of the general constants.

4. In the central Zeeman pattern of the zinc sharp triplet shown in Fig. 29D(c) the two inner components are polarized parallel to the field and the four outer ones perpendicular to it. What must be the relative intensities of the components to yield unpolarized light as the field goes to zero? Sketch a curve for the Faraday effect of this line similar to the one in Fig. 29F(c).

Ans. Inner components twice as strong. Only the four outer ones contribute to the Faraday effect.

5. For the first line of the Brackett series of hydrogen, the wavelength of which is 4.05 μ, it can be assumed that the frequency of revolution of the electron in its orbit equals the frequency of the emitted light. Calculate the Zeeman shifts in a magnetic field of 40,000 oersteds according to the approximate equation 29g, and according to the exact equation **29f**. The difference between these results represents the quadratic Zeeman effect mentioned in Sec. 29.1.

6. By considering the action of an electric field on a vibrating electron, explain why there is no electro-optic effect analogous to the Faraday effect.   (HINT: It would be related to the longitudinal Stark effect.)

7. A grating has a resolving power of 60,000 in the first order.   What field strength would be required to be applied to the source in order that this grating be able to resolve a normal Zeeman triplet (a) in the violet at 4000 Å; (b) in the red at 7000 Å?

8. What angle of rotation in the Faraday effect would be produced by a single traversal of a block of phosphate crown glass 12 cm long situated in a magnetic field of 8000 oersteds?   *Ans.* 25°46′.

9. Plane-polarized light is sent through a 5-cm length of a certain liquid to which a magnetic field of 20,000 oersteds is applied parallel to the direction of the light. If the plane of polarization is found to be rotated by 36°, find the Verdet constant of the liquid.

10. What magnetic rotation by the vapor in the apparatus of Fig. 29G is required to displace the bands upward by one whole band in the focal plane of the lens?   Is the rotation right-handed or left-handed, as viewed against the light?
                                                        Ans. 180°.   Left-handed.

11. Assume that at a frequency much lower than the absorption frequency the dispersion curve is a straight line over a small range.   Assume also that the curves for n^+ and n^- are relatively displaced by a frequency difference corresponding to the normal Zeeman splitting.   Find how the magnetic rotation due to the Faraday effect should depend (a) on the field strength (H); (b) on the dispersion $dn/d\lambda$.

12. Under the assumptions of Prob. 11, Becquerel showed that the rotation $\theta = (1/n) \sum_i B\lambda_i^2/(\lambda_i^2 - \lambda_i^2)^2$, where the B_i's are proportional to the absorption coefficients of the various lines.   If for a given sample of sodium vapor the rotation is 6° at a wavelength of 5900 Å, what will it be at 5910 Å?   The wavelengths of the sodium lines are 5890 and 5896 Å, and the former line is twice as strong as the latter.   The refractive index n may be taken as unity.   *Ans.* 0.74°.

13. Using a system involving a Faraday rotation of 45°, it is possible to devise a system which will transmit light in one direction but not in the other.   Describe such a system.   Does it violate the second law of thermodynamics, and if not, why not?

14. In a Kerr cell filled with nitrobenzene the length of the electrodes is 16 mm and their separation 5 mm.   What phase difference is produced when a field of 10,000 volts/cm is applied?   At this field strength, what fraction of the incident unpolarized light will get through the system when the cell is placed between crossed nicols?   *Ans.* 0.111.

15. Find the strength of the electric field required for a Kerr cell to produce circularly polarized sodium light.   The electrodes of the cell are 5 cm long and 6 mm apart, and the cell is filled with nitrobenzene.

PART III

QUANTUM OPTICS

CHAPTER 30

PHOTONS

In this concluding chapter we shall give a brief account of the way in which the more recently discovered corpuscular properties of light have been reconciled with the wave theory. It will not be possible to recount in any systematic way the steps which have led to our present view of the nature of light nor to discuss its broad implications. This subject forms an important part of a whole field of study, that of atomic or modern physics.* Furthermore, the discussion of one part of this field presents difficulties in view of the essentially mathematical character of the quantum theory, which was first developed as a formalized set of equations and only later expressed in terms of visualizable physical concepts. Nevertheless the student who has not already been introduced to these concepts will, of course, have heard of the particles of light called photons and will naturally be curious as to how such a radically different model can be consistent with such a typical wave phenomenon as interference. It is with the hope of at least partially satisfying this curiosity that the following discussion, brief and incomplete as it is, has been included.

30.1. Shortcomings of the Wave Theory. As long as one is dealing with questions of the interaction of light with light, such as occurs in interference and diffraction, the electromagnetic theory, and in fact any wave theory, gives a complete account of the facts. When one attempts to treat the interactions of light with matter, however, as in the emission and absorption of light and in dispersion, serious difficulties at once present themselves. In many of these it is not merely a matter of slight deviations between experiment and theory, detectable only by quantitative measurements; on the contrary, the theory predicts results that are radically different from those observed. Historically the first case of this kind was encountered in the attempt to explain the distribu-

---

* See, for example, H. Semat, "Introduction to Atomic and Nuclear Physics," 3d ed., Rinehart & Company, Inc., New York, 1954; F. K. Richtmyer, E. H. Kennard, and T. Lauritsen, "Introduction to Modern Physics," 5th ed., McGraw-Hill Book Company, Inc., New York, 1955; Max Born, "Atomic Physics," 5th ed., Hafner Publishing Company, New York, 1951; and L. I. Schiff, "Quantum Mechanics," 2d ed., McGraw-Hill Book Company, Inc., New York, 1955.

tion of energy in the spectrum of a black body (Secs. 21.9 and 21.14). Here the electromagnetic theory was used in conjunction with the classical theory of equipartition of energy, which had been so successful in explaining the specific heats of gases. The predicted curve was nearly correct at long wavelengths, but its course towards shorter wavelengths, instead of passing through a maximum and falling to zero (Fig. 21F), continued to increase indefinitely. It was only by assuming that the oscillators in the radiating source could not exist in states having all possible energies and amplitudes, but only in certain definite ones for which the energy was a whole multiple of some particular value (quantum) that Planck in 1900 was able to derive the exact radiation formula (Eq. 21e).

Other shortcomings of the older theory soon became evident. In the photoelectric effect, the measured energies of the photoelectrons ejected from metal surfaces by light were in marked disagreement with the predictions of electromagnetic theory (see the following section). The amount of energy in the waves falling on a single atom in the case of weak illumination was very much smaller than that observed in the photoelectron, and this led Einstein in 1905 to postulate the existence of photons. In the explanation of the line series observed in the atomic spectrum of hydrogen (Sec. 21.12), Bohr in 1913 had to assume that the electron revolved in a stable orbit without radiating, whereas a charge with strong centripetal acceleration should, according to the electromagnetic theory, rapidly lose energy as radiation (Sec. 20.8). This would cause the frequency to change rapidly and would make it impossible to explain the existence of sharp spectrum lines. The explanation of X rays according to the electromagnetic theory as very short pulses of radiation, caused by the sudden deceleration of electrons as they strike the target, was inconsistent with the observed continuous X-ray spectrum. As was shown by Duane and Hunt in 1917, this spectrum exhibits a sharp cut-off on the short-wavelength side, whereas the Fourier analysis of a pulse yields a continuous spectrum falling off smoothly (Sec. 12.6). The discovery in 1922 of the Compton effect, which is a shift toward lower frequency of scattered monochromatic X rays, was a striking demonstration of the inadequacy of the wave theory, since to explain it one had to postulate that photons collided with electrons in atoms and rebounded like elastic billiard balls (see below).

These constitute a few of the simpler phenomena in which the wave theory failed completely. In many of the more complex interactions between matter and radiation the theory, although giving the rough features correctly, ran into insuperable difficulties when attempts were made to give a complete quantitative account of the facts. One of the earliest phenomena in this class was the anomalous Zeeman effect (Sec.

29.1), and one of the more recent ones the Raman effect (Sec. 22.11). Others could be cited, but the list has now grown so long that it is no longer a question of introducing refinements in the wave theory to obtain agreement. Quantum theory, of which the wave theory is now recognized as an integral part, must be used in dealing with such effects.

30.2. Evidence for Light Quanta. In reaching conclusions about the nature of a phenomenon like light we must rely upon observation of the effects it produces. An individual wave or a particle of light cannot be seen and photographed as can large-scale waves and particles of matter. We can conclude with certainty, however, that light has a wave character from the study of interference and diffraction patterns, of its velocity, of the Doppler effect, etc. Evidence just as convincing exists that light consists of small packets of energy which are highly localized, and any one of which can communicate all its energy to a single atom or molecule. These "particles" are known as light quanta or *photons*. It will be worth while to consider briefly

Fig. 30A. Experimental arrangement for studying the photoelectric effect.

three pieces of experimental evidence of this type, those selected being ones that will be useful in our further discussion of the subject.

In the *photoelectric effect* (Fig. 30A) light enters through the quartz window W and strikes the cathode C, which is a clean metal plate. A current of negative charge is observed by the galvanometer G to flow from C through the evacuated tube to the plate P, which is at some positive potential with respect to C. This shows that electrons of charge $-e$ are being ejected from the surface of the metal cathode. Their velocities and energies as they leave the surface can be studied by varying the voltage V applied to the plate. It is found that the energy is independent of the intensity of the light and is determined by the frequency of the light according to Einstein's photoelectric equation,

$$E = h\nu - p \qquad \text{ENERGY OF PHOTOELECTRONS} \qquad (30a)$$

Here h is the universal constant 6.6254×10^{-27} erg sec, known as *Planck's constant*, ν is the frequency c/λ, and p is a constant characteristic of the kind of metal in the cathode. For most metals p is large enough so that light of fairly high frequency (ultraviolet light) must be used to produce the photoelectrons. The quantum character of light appears in this experiment through the fact that each electron has evidently taken on the same amount of energy $h\nu$ and emerges with the difference between this and the amount p required to get it through the surface. (This interpretation of p is verified in other ways, notably in thermionic emission.)   Furthermore a very faint beam of light still causes some photoelectrons to be emitted instantaneously, and they have the full energy.   Under these circumstances it is apparent that there are very few photons in the beam, each of energy $h\nu$.   On the wave theory the small amount of electromagnetic energy would be spread over the whole surface, and the amount available to any one electron would be insufficient to produce the effect.

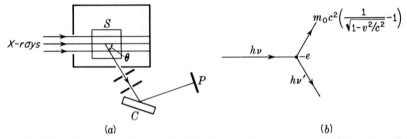

(a)   (b)

FIG. 30B. The Compton effect.   (a) Method of observation.   (b) Energies of the incident photon, scattered photon, and recoil electron.

The *Compton effect* is observed in X rays that are scattered at an angle θ from a scatterer S consisting of some light element like carbon [see Fig. 30B(a)].   A narrow beam is defined by two lead slits and caused to fall on a crystal C.   This diffracts the X rays to the photographic plate P, and by suitably turning the crystal about an axis perpendicular to the plane of the figure, a spectrum may be photographed.   For each monochromatic line present in the original X rays, the spectrum of the scattered rays shows a line shifted to longer wavelengths, the shift increasing with the scattering angle θ according to the equation

$$\Delta\lambda = \frac{c}{\nu'} - \frac{c}{\nu} = \frac{h}{m_0 c}(1 - \cos\theta) \qquad \text{COMPTON SHIFT} \qquad (30b)$$

where m_0 is the mass of an electron at rest.   This equation may be easily derived by applying the laws of conservation of energy and momentum to the collision of a photon and an electron [Fig. 30B (b)].   The electron in question is one that is knocked out of an atom in the scatterer, and its kinetic energy must be represented by the relativity formula given in the figure.   Similarly its momentum, and also that of the photon, must be expressed in terms of relativistic equations, as will be explained below in Sec. 30.3.   But the picture here presented of an elastic collision of particles is clearly foreign to any wave model of light. It has even been possible to detect the scattered photon and the recoil electron simultaneously in the two directions predicted by theory, using a Wilson cloud chamber or Geiger counter.

As a third example of the corpuscular behavior of light we may mention the recently developed *scintillation counter*, which has become a valuable instrument for measuring hard X rays and γ rays. The principle of the instrument is similar to that of the scintillation method which was employed to count α particles in the early studies of radioactivity. As is shown in Fig. 30C, photons in a beam of γ rays enter through a hole in the mirror M and traverse a crystal C, which may be an organic substance like anthracene or one of the inorganic phosphors like caesium iodide containing a small impurity of thallium. Tiny flashes of light occur in the interior of the crystal as a result of the passage of the γ-ray

FIG. 30C. A scintillation counter.

photons. These can be counted electrically by allowing the light to fall on the sensitive surface of a commercial photomultiplier tube T. Nearly all the light can be utilized if the concave mirror M is properly adjusted. In this device the effects of individual photons are observed in a manner just as direct as that used for atomic particles of matter, and it leaves no doubt as to the corpuscular behavior of light when observed under these conditions.

30.3. Energy, Momentum, and Velocity of Photons. In all experiments which reveal the existence of photons, and notably in the photoelectric effect, their energy is found to be determined only by the frequency ν. The latter quantity must of course be measured independently by observing interference, a typical wave property. The constant of proportionality between energy and frequency is Planck's constant h, so we have as an experimental result that

$$E = h\nu \qquad \text{ENERGY OF A PHOTON} \qquad (30c)$$

To obtain an expression for the momentum, we make use of Einstein's equation for the equivalence of mass and energy, according to which

$$E = mc^2 \qquad (30d)$$

This equation has been experimentally verified for matter in studies of nuclear disintegration, and it has been shown to hold in the conversion of radiation into matter that occurs in the creation of electron-positron pairs by γ rays. Combining Eqs. 30c and 30d, one finds that

$$h\nu = h\frac{c}{\lambda} = mc^2$$

and therefore, since the momentum p is the product of mass and velocity,

$$p = mc = \frac{h\nu}{c} = \frac{h}{\lambda} \qquad \text{MOMENTUM OF A PHOTON} \qquad (30e)$$

This result is firmly established by the experimental evidence that in order to obtain Eq. 30b for the Compton effect the momenta of the photons must be taken as $h\nu/c$.

It is assumed in Eq. 30e that photons always travel with the speed c, and in fact it is true without exception that

$$\text{Velocity of a photon} = c \qquad (30f)$$

In this respect photons differ from particles of matter, which can have any velocity less than c. At first sight, Eq. 30f seems to be in contradiction to the observed fact that the measured velocity of light in matter is less than c. But this is the velocity of a group of waves (Sec. 19.10) and not that of the individual photons. As was explained in the chapter on dispersion, light waves traversing matter are retarded by the alteration of their phase through interference with the scattered waves. In the case of photons we may, at least in dilute matter like a gas, picture the photons as traveling with the velocity c in the empty space between molecules, but as having their average rate of progress retarded by the finite time consumed during the process of absorption and reemission by the molecules they encounter. In any experiment where the photon could be expected to be slowed down, for example in an encounter with an electron in the Compton effect, it is found that the energy and frequency are decreased, not the velocity. The only slowing-down that a photon can suffer is its complete annihilation, as happens in the photoelectric effect.

30.4. Development of Quantum Mechanics. The apparently irreconcilable contradiction between the corpuscular and wave pictures of light has been clarified on the basis of a new system of mechanics initiated by Heisenberg and Schrödinger in 1926. This *quantum mechanics* is essential for the treatment of all atomic processes. It also holds for ordinary large-scale processes, although in this case the deviations from Newtonian mechanics are negligible. In quantum mechanics the behavior of the electrons in an atom, for example, is calculated by the use of wave theory, and the solutions of wave equations yield the allowed energy states. Any material particle has associated with it a group of waves, and in the case of a free particle their wavelength is inversely proportional to the momentum p of the particle. This is the celebrated de Broglie relation, which represents an extension of Eq. 30e to matter:

$$\lambda = \frac{h}{mv} = \frac{h}{p} \qquad \text{WAVELENGTH OF A FREE PARTICLE} \qquad (30g)$$

This equation was experimentally verified by Davisson and Germer in the United States and by G. P. Thomson in England. They showed that a beam of electrons may be made to exhibit diffraction and that the pattern corresponded to that produced with X rays by the regular arrangement of atoms in a crystal lattice. Diffraction of a beam of atoms or molecules was subsequently demonstrated by Stern. The analogous behavior of electrons and light is most beautifully demonstrated in the electron microscope (Sec. 15.11). The existence both for matter and for electromagnetic radiation of the two types of behavior, as waves and as particles, was the most significant fact that was interpreted by the quantum mechanics.

The physical significance of the waves that pertain to a given material particle is that the square of their amplitude at any point in space represents the probability of finding the particle at that point. The theory therefore yields the statistical distribution of the particles, and as we shall see, it denies the possibility of going any further than this. Similarly for light the wave theory gives us the statistical or average distribution of photons as the square of the amplitude of the electromagnetic wave. If we postpone for the moment the question of which model, wave or corpuscle, is the real one, and look at the achievements of quantum mechanical theory, we find an extensive array of these, which prove beyond question the soundness of the basic assumptions of the theory. Not only are the many complex features of atomic and molecular spectra accounted for in detail, but also any process involving the extranuclear electrons and their interaction with electromagnetic radiation. Only when attempts are made to apply it to regions as small as atomic nuclei, or in general smaller than the classical radius of the electron e^2/m_0c^2, are there indications that the theory breaks down.

30.5. Principle of Indeterminacy. The possibility of characterizing light as discrete packages of energy called photons would seem to rest upon our ability to determine for a given photon both the position and the momentum that it possesses at a given instant. These are usually thought of as measurable properties of a material particle. It was shown by Heisenberg, however, that for particles of atomic magnitude it is in principle impossible to determine both position and momentum simultaneously with perfect accuracy. If an experiment is designed to measure one of them exactly, the other will become completely uncertain, and vice versa. An experiment can measure both, but only within certain limits of accuracy. These limits are specified by the principle of indeterminacy (often called the *uncertainty principle*), according to which

$$\Delta p_y \Delta y \gtrsim \frac{h}{2\pi} \tag{30h}$$

Here Δy and Δp_y represent the variations of the value of the coordinate and of the corresponding component of momentum of a particle which

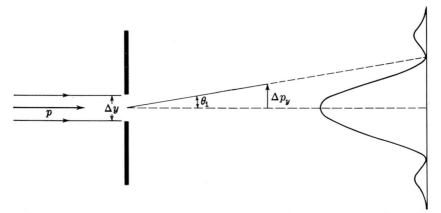

Fig. 30D. Uncertainty in the momentum of a photon when it is diffracted by a single slit.

must be expected if we try to measure both at once, i.e., the uncertainties in these quantities. The symbol $\gtrsim$ means "is of the order of, or greater than." The reason for this semiquantitative way of stating the law will become clear through the example to be given in the following section.

The principle of indeterminacy is applicable to photons, as well as to all material particles from electrons up to the sizeable bodies dealt with in ordinary mechanics. For the latter, the very small magnitude of h renders the Δp_y and Δy entirely negligible compared to the ordinary experimental errors encountered in measuring the large p_y and its corresponding y. When p_y is very small, however, as for an electron or a photon, the uncertainty may become an appreciable fraction of the momentum itself, or else the uncertainty in the position must be relatively large.

30.6. Diffraction by a Slit. Suppose that we undertake to find the position of a photon by passing it through a narrow slit. This will specify its coordinate y in the plane of the screen to within an uncertainty Δy equal to the slit width (Fig. 30D). In doing so the momentum in the

y direction, initially zero in this experiment, is rendered uncertain by an amount Δp_y given by the relation 30h, as we shall now show.

Passage of the light through the slit causes a diffraction pattern to be produced on the screen. We shall assume the screen to be far enough away relative to the width of the slit so that Fraunhofer diffraction obtains. Nearly all the photons will be found within the angle θ_1, corresponding to the first zero of the pattern. We have seen in Sec. 15.3 that this angle is given by

$$\sin \theta_1 = \frac{\lambda}{\Delta y} \tag{30i}$$

The corresponding uncertainty in the momentum is

$$\Delta p_y = p \sin \theta_1 = \frac{p\lambda}{\Delta y} \tag{30j}$$

Introducing the value for the momentum p given by the de Broglie relation, Eq. 30e, we find

$$\Delta p_y = \frac{h}{\lambda} \cdot \frac{\lambda}{\Delta y} = \frac{h}{\Delta y} \tag{30k}$$

This gives $\Delta p_y\, \Delta y = h$, but it will be seen that, since the probability of the photon striking the center of the pattern is greatest, the uncertainty in p_y is not so large as is indicated by Eq. 30k, and hence that our result is consistent with the principle of indeterminacy

$$\Delta p_y\, \Delta y \gtrsim \frac{h}{2\pi} \tag{30h}$$

No doubt this derivation will raise some important questions in the mind of the reader. How does the photon acquire this sideways momentum? How is it possible that the width of the slit should affect a photon which passes through at one place in the slit? The answers to these questions will be postponed until we have given further consideration to the consequences of the principle of indeterminacy.

30.7. Complementarity. We owe to Bohr the interpretation of Heisenberg's principle in such a way as to make clear the fundamental limitations on the accuracy of measurement and their bearing on our views as to the nature of light and matter. According to the principle of complementarity stated by Bohr in 1928, the wave and corpuscular descriptions are merely complementary ways of regarding the same phenomenon. That is, to obtain the complete picture we need both these properties, but because of the principle of indeterminacy it is impossible to design an experiment which will show both of them in all detail at the same time. Any experiment will reveal the details of either the wave or the corpuscular character, according to the purpose for which the experiment is designed.

It further appears that, if one attempts to push the accuracy of measurement to the point where the experiment might be expected to reveal both aspects, there is an unavoidable interaction between the measuring apparatus and the thing measured which frustrates the attempt.   This happens even in a hypothetical experiment which we imagine to be performed by an experimenter endowed with infinite skill and resource.   It is therefore not a question of the usual disturbances caused by large-scale measuring instruments; these can be calculated and allowed for.   The uncertainties we are concerned with here are by their very nature impossible to evaluate without spoiling the experiment in some other way.   If this were not so, we would be able to overstep the boundaries prescribed by the complementarity principle.   To see how these interactions occur, and that they occur just to the degree required by the principle of indeterminacy, we now describe two celebrated experiments which for technical reasons have never been performed exactly as they are here outlined, but for which the results can be confidently predicted on the basis of other actual experiments not quite as simple.

30.8. Double Slit.   The interference fringes in Young's experiment (Sec. 13.3) constitute one of the simplest manifestations of the wave character of light.   Yet it should be possible to reveal the presence of photons by a suitable modification of the experiment.   Such a modification would be the replacement of the observing screen by a photoelectric surface so subdivided that the individual photoelectrons from different parts of the surface could be counted.   If this were done, the largest concentration of photons would be found to occur at the maxima of the interference pattern, and none at all at the minima.   It is impossible to conceive of the interference between different photons going through the two slits as being responsible for such a pattern.   It is even more difficult to understand how a single photon could be constrained to seek the maxima and avoid the minima, since it presumably passed through only one of the slits.   The presence of the other slit should be immaterial, whereas actually it makes possible the interference pattern and its position determines the dimensions of that pattern.   Nevertheless, according to quantum mechanics, the latter interpretation is correct.   The fringes could be produced by single photons, going one by one through the slits.   We know that reducing the intensity of the light does not destroy the interference.   The pattern is therefore a characteristic of each photon, and represents the probability of its arriving at various points on the screen.   This probability must however be calculated by wave theory and is measured by the square of the amplitude. The experiment is one designed to show the properties of waves.

Now let us attempt to refine this experiment with the purpose of finding out through which slit any given photon passed. This might be done by putting two scintillation counters C_1 and C_2 behind the slits, as shown in Fig. 30E. With light of sufficiently high frequency, these would register each photon as it goes through one slit or the other. But

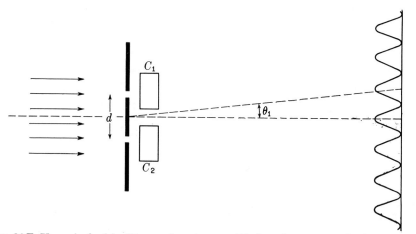

FIG. 30E. Young's double-slit experiment as modified to demonstrate both wave and corpuscular properties of light.

in so doing we have spoiled the interference pattern because of the deflections suffered by the photons in producing the scintillations. For the fringes to be clearly visible it is necessary that these deflections be less than one-quarter of a fringe width, according to the criterion mentioned in Sec. 16.7. Thus

$$\frac{\Delta p_y}{p} < \frac{\theta_1}{4} = \frac{\lambda}{4d} \tag{30l}$$

where θ_1 is the angular separation of adjacent fringes and d the slit separation. Since the counters tell us through which slit the photon passes, they specify the y coordinate to within a distance of at most $d/2$. Hence we may write for the uncertainty in this coordinate

$$\Delta y = \frac{d}{2} \tag{30m}$$

Combination of Eqs. 30l and 30m then yields

$$\Delta p_y \, \Delta y < \frac{p\lambda}{4d} \cdot \frac{d}{2} = \frac{p\lambda}{8} \tag{30n}$$

Upon insertion of the de Broglie value for λ, the requirement that the interference pattern shall not be spoiled becomes

$$\Delta p_y \, \Delta y < \frac{h}{8} \qquad (30o)$$

This violates the principle of indeterminacy according to which $\Delta p_y \, \Delta y \gtrsim h/2\pi$. Hence we see that it is impossible to localize individual photons and at the same time measure their wavelength. This would mean that we had simultaneously determined both position and momentum. It is possible to measure only one of these with precision, according to whether the experiment is designed for photons or waves.

30.9. Determination of Position with a Microscope. Another idealized experiment, first discussed by Heisenberg, is that usually referred to as the "γ-ray microscope." If it is desired to find the position of a particle as accurately as possible, the particle must be illuminated by light of the smallest possible wavelength, since the resolving power is given, according to Eq. 15*l*, by

$$s = \frac{\lambda}{2 \sin i} \qquad (30p)$$

FIG. 30*F*. Measurement of position with a microscope.

We can imagine, in principle at least, a microscope using γ rays which is capable of yielding an extremely small uncertainty $\Delta x \simeq s$ in the position of the particle. If then the particle is at rest, its momentum p_x is exactly zero, and this simultaneous knowledge of both position and momentum would appear to violate the principle of indeterminacy. One factor has been neglected, however; namely, the recoil of the particle when it is hit by a photon of high energy and momentum, which is demonstrated in the Compton effect. This recoil will introduce a relatively large uncertainty in the momentum, just as the principle would predict.

To find the magnitude of the uncertainty, note that in Fig. 30*F* the *x* component of the momentum of the scattered photon can lie anywhere between $+(h/\lambda) \sin i$ and $-(h/\lambda) \sin i$, since it could have entered any part of the objective lens. The *x* component of the momentum of the recoiling particle is rendered uncertain by the same amount, since momentum is conserved in the collision and the momentum of the incident photons can be exactly calculated from the wavelength. Hence for the particle

$$\Delta p_x \simeq \frac{2h}{\lambda} \sin i \qquad (30q)$$

Multiplying by the Δx from Eq. 30p, we find

$$\Delta p_x \, \Delta x \simeq h \qquad (30r)$$

as required. This is an example of the application of the principle of indeterminacy to a material particle. Complementarity is well illustrated in the experiment by the fact that when one uses a very short wavelength, x is found with good precision but Δp_x is made large, while the use of a longer wavelength will allow p_x to be better known at a sacrifice of the accuracy Δx in the measurement of position.

(a)   (b)

Fɪɢ. 30G. (a) Idealized shutter experiment. (b) Result of Fourier analysis of a train of N waves.

30.10. Use of a Shutter. It is also instructive to consider the result of trying to localize a photon by passing light through a very rapidly acting shutter, such as that utilizing the Kerr electro-optic effect (Sec. 29.10). In Fig. 30G(a) let S represent schematically such a shutter, which has been opened only long enough to allow a train of N waves of uniform amplitude to pass through. The experiment could be performed with light so faint that only one photon would pass through in this time. This photon lies somewhere in the *wave packet* (Sec. 11.7) of N waves, and its probability of being found anywhere in the packet is measured by the square of the amplitude. This is uniform along the length

$$\Delta x = N\lambda_0 = N \frac{c}{\nu_0} \qquad (30s)$$

The Fourier integral analysis of a finite train of N waves of equal amplitude yields a certain distribution of frequencies, and when the intensities in various frequencies are plotted, as in Fig. 30G(b), the resulting curve is to a very close approximation the same as that for the Fraunhofer diffraction pattern due to a single slit. The half width of the central maximum is just ν_0/N. Now such a spread of frequency corresponds, according to Eq. 30e, to an uncertainty in the momentum of the photon amounting to

$$\Delta p_x = \frac{h}{\Delta\lambda} = \frac{h\,\Delta\nu}{c} = \frac{h(\nu_0/N)}{c} \tag{30t}$$

Localization of the photon to within a distance Δx has therefore rendered its momentum indeterminate, and as is expected, the product of the two indeterminacies given by Eqs. 30s and 30t is again

$$\Delta p_x\,\Delta x \simeq h \tag{30u}$$

It is to be noted that the wave packet is not the photon, nor can we speak of the photon itself as having any dimensions. The packet is merely a description of the probability of finding the photon in any given position. When one measures the length of a wave train with the Michelson interferometer (Sec. 13.12), he is not finding the length of a photon. The length he is measuring is merely that of the region in which the photon must somewhere lie.

30.11. Interpretation of the Dual Character. Granted the truth of these principles of indeterminacy and complementarity, what can be said about the nature of light? First, it is important to realize that light (as well as the elementary particles of matter: electrons, protons, etc.) is essentially more primitive and subtle than those mechanical phenomena which we can observe on a large scale. All our information about it must be obtained indirectly. The possibility is therefore opened that it might not be feasible to describe light in the terms which we are accustomed to use for everyday things. All our experience since childhood would indicate that it should be possible to say, "Light is like a flight of bullets from a machine gun," or "Light is like a train of water waves." But such a specific statement cannot be made about light, and the complementarity principle indicates that we shall never be able to make it. We can say, "In this experiment light behaves as though it were composed of photons," and, "In that experiment it behaves as though it were waves." Since complementarity rules out any experiment in which one can measure both properties at once, the conclusion is inevitable that the concepts of photons and waves are equally justified and that each is applicable in its own sphere.

The point of view adopted in quantum mechanics with regard to such a dilemma as is presented by the double-slit experiment is simply that a classical description of the motion of a single photon has meaning only within the limits set by the principle of indeterminacy. When the interference pattern is being observed, there is no significance to the statement that the photon went through one slit or the other, i.e., to a statement about its position. When the scintillations are being counted we can specify the position, but then the momentum has lost its meaning. The latter quantity depends on the wavelength, which in turn requires the dimensions of the now nonexistent interference pattern for its determination. Similarly, in the diffraction by a single slit, one may not specify the momentum of a single photon unless the experiment is altered to include a momentum measurement. Conservation of momentum could then be verified, but as long as the diffraction pattern exists this principle can only be applied statistically to describe the average behavior of the photons.

30.12. Realms of Applicability of Waves and Photons. The emphasis which has in this book been placed upon the wave properties of light has a certain justification as long as one does not extend the meaning of the term light to include the very short-wavelength region of X rays and γ rays. The relative prominence of the wave and corpuscular properties changes steadily in favor of the latter as one proceeds through the electromagnetic spectrum in the direction of increasing frequency. Thus radio waves behave in all important respects like classical electromagnetic radiation. This is related to the fact that the photons are extremely small in their energy $h\nu$ and therefore usually very numerous. Similarly visible light of ordinary intensities contains so many photons that their average behavior is accurately given by the wave theory provided that the interactions with the individual atoms of matter do not involve the quantized energy states of the latter. This accounts for the fact that the corpuscular properties of light remained undiscovered for so many years.

The connecting link between the wave and quantum aspects of light (or of matter) is furnished by Planck's constant h. As has been emphasized by Bohr, h is the product of two variables, one characteristic of a wave, the other of a particle. Thus if we designate by T the period, or reciprocal of the frequency ν, the quantum relation may be put in the symmetrical form

$$h = ET = p\lambda \tag{30v}$$

Now E and p are attributes of particles, while T and λ are attributes of waves. If, for example, the magnitudes of the former are large, the latter must be correspondingly small. Hence X rays and γ rays behave in most respects like photons, and their wave character is even difficult to demonstrate. The region of frequencies where particlelike properties begin to become prominent is of course determined by the magnitude of h, and its actual value, 6.625×10^{-27} erg sec, is so small that very high frequencies are required before the wave character begins to be lost. Visible light lies well below this region, and its wave properties may therefore be said to be the most important. If h were much smaller than it is, the quantum theory would never have been required and classical electromagnetic theory would have sufficed to explain all experiments. It is a curious coincidence that the actual size of h, which of course is still unexplained, is such that the nature of light seems to run the whole gamut, from obvious waves at one end to obvious photons at the other, in the observed range of the electromagnetic spectrum.

PROBLEMS

1. Using the de Broglie relation, find the wavelength associated with (*a*) an electron moving at one-third the speed of light; (*b*) an oxygen molecule with its mean thermal velocity of 483 m/sec; (*c*) a rifle bullet of mass 20 g and velocity 300 m/sec.

2. In the shutter experiment of Sec. 30.10 prove that if the shutter is open for a time Δt, representing the uncertainty in the time when the photon goes through, there is a corresponding uncertainty ΔE in the energy of the photon such that $\Delta E \cdot \Delta t \simeq h$. (HINT: Energy and momentum of a photon are related by the de Broglie equation.)

3. An electro-optic shutter chops a monochromatic beam of wavelength 5461 Å at a frequency of 600 Mc. Calculate the approximate width in angstroms of the resulting spectrum line.

4. Look up the equations for the radii and velocities of the electron in the Bohr orbits of the hydrogen atom, and calculate the number of wavelengths included in the circumference of the orbit for which $n = 3$. What can one say as to the position in the orbit that the electron occupies at any given instant?

Ans. 3 wavelengths. Completely indeterminate.

5. Find the number of photons per cubic centimeter in a monochromatic beam of radiation of intensity 10^{-5} watts/cm². Take the wavelength to be (*a*) 0.1 Å; (*b*) 60,000 Å.

6. For light of wavelength 5000 Å, calculate the magnitude of the four quantities appearing in Bohr's complementarity relation (Eq. 30*v*).

Ans. 3.972×10^{-12} erg. 1.668×10^{-15} sec. 1.325×10^{-22} g cm/sec. 5×10^{-5} cm.

7. A microscope of numerical aperture 1.2 is focused on a particle of mass 0.01 mg. If the illuminating light has a wavelength of 4500 Å, what are the values of Δp_x and Δx predicted by Heisenberg's principle of indeterminacy?

8. When a 100-volt electron is passed through a hole 0.02 mm in diameter, what uncertainty in the angle of emergence is introduced? Make a similar calculation for a 200-g baseball thrown with a velocity of 20 m/sec through a hole 50 cm in diameter.

Ans. 1.3 seconds of arc. 6.8×10^{-29} sec.

9. The faintest star that the eye can see is one of sixth magnitude. The energy flux from such a star is 1.15×10^{-15} erg/cm² sec. Taking the effective wavelength of the starlight to be 5600 Å, find how many photons enter the pupil of the eye, of diameter 7 mm, under these conditions.

10. X rays of wavelength 0.72 Å are scattered from a solid at an angle of 60° to the direction of the incident beam. Calculate the change of wavelength due to the Compton effect. *Ans.* 0.0121 Å.

INDEX

Main references are given in **boldface** type